ROBERT C. STEBBINS

Amphibians of Western

Berkeley and Los Angeles 1962
UNIVERSITY OF CALIFORNIA PRESS

North America

UNIVERSITY OF CALIFORNIA PRESS, BERKELEY AND LOS ANGELES, CALIFORNIA
CAMBRIDGE UNIVERSITY PRESS, LONDON, ENGLAND

SECOND PRINTING, 1962
MANUFACTURED IN THE UNITED STATES OF AMERICA

To Cyril and Louise Stebbins

PREFACE

This book provides information on the external form and coloration, habits, and distribution of the species of amphibians inhabiting western North America. It includes a comprehensive coverage of the pertinent literature, unpublished data in field notebooks in the University of California Museum of Vertebrate Zoölogy, and the author's personal observations. The bibliography consists only of literature cited and hence represents but a portion of the total writings relating to western amphibians. Distributional lists, for example, although used in the preparation of the maps, have often been omitted. Several summarizations of literature are available (Bishop, 1943, for the salamanders and Wright and Wright, 1949, for the anurans), hence I have not thought it essential to present a complete bibliography.

The book includes all the known species of amphibians in an area delimited as follows: North America north of the Mexican border and west of a line formed by the eastern boundaries of New Mexico, Colorado, Wyoming, Montana, projected northward along the eastern border of Saskatchewan, Canada (see map, page 2).

All species, and some subspecies, where differences are marked, have been illustrated. To facilitate identification and comparisons, the animals of each major group (salamanders and anurans) are similarly posed. Similarities and differences in size, form, and pigmentation hence may be quickly noted. Tentative identification of species may be made by reference to the illustrations. Keys are provided for more precise determinations. With few exceptions, salamanders are shown in dorsal and ventral views, frogs and toads in three-quarter view.

The drawings are based on representative animals, but some have been modified to emphasize diagnostic features or when in some respect the subject was atypical.

I have put into the volume what I have wanted to know about our western amphibians and hope in so doing to have anticipated questions of persons using the book. Much remains to be learned, as is readily seen from even a casual inspection of the following pages. Some suggestions of problems and questions may be found at the end of the accounts of genera and species.

Many persons have aided in the preparation of the book and to them I wish to extend my sincere appreciation. Dr. Jean M. Linsdale of the Hastings Natural History Reservation of the University of California read most of the accounts of species. Those who have read parts or all of the manuscript at one stage or another in its development are: Charles M. Bogert of the American Museum of Natural History; Dr. Raymond Cowles, Professor of Zoölogy at the University of California, Los Angeles; Dr. Richard Eakin, Professor of Zoölogy at the University of California, Berkeley; Dr. Laurence Klauber of the San Diego Museum of Natural History; Dr. Charles H. Lowe, Jr., University of Arizona; Dr. Alden H. Miller, Director of the Museum of Vertebrate Zoölogy; C. B. Perkins, in charge of amphibians and reptiles at the San Diego Zoo; and William Riemer, assistant in herpetology at the Museum of Vertebrate Zoölogy. Dr. Victor Twitty of Stanford University has given me information on newts. On a number of occasions I have had the advice and counsel of Dr. Seth Benson, Curator of Mammals at the Museum of Vertebrate Zoology. Dr. Robert Usinger, Associate Professor of Entomology at the University of California, checked accuracy of nomenclature in the lists of insects fed upon by amphibians. John Hendrickson of the University of California, and Dr. Robert Storm of Oregon State College have provided information on several species.

The following individuals and institutions have loaned specimens for study and illustration: Mr. Bogert; Dr. Arthur Bragg, University of Oklahoma; Dr. Walter Breckenridge, Curator, Minnesota Museum of Natural History; Dr. Doris Cochran, United States National Museum; Dr. Ian McTaggart Cowan, University of British Columbia; Dr. George Myers, Stanford University Museum of Natural History; Dr. James Slater, College of Puget Sound, Washington; and Joseph Slevin, Herpetologist, California Academy of Sciences. My brother, Ernest Stebbins, and Mr. Riemer assisted me with field work.

The following persons have given me information and advice in the preparation of the distribution maps: Mr. Bogert (southwestern United States and Mexico), Dr. Cowan (Canada), Dr. Ira LaRivers and Benjamin Banta (Nevada), Dr. Lowe, Jr. (Arizona and New Mexico), Dr. T. Paul

Maslin (Colorado), Kenneth Norris (New Mexico), Dr. Slater (Washington), Dr. Storm (Oregon), Dr. Angus Woodbury (Utah), and Richard Zweifel (southern California, New Mexico, and Sonora, Mexico).

Dr. Breckenridge, Dr. Robert Livezey, University of Notre Dame, and Mr. Clifford Pope, Chicago Natural History Museum, have permitted me to draw upon materials published by them. To these and many others to whose writings I have referred, I recognize my indebtedness. Dr. Albert Wright, Professor of Zoölogy (emeritus), Cornell University, and his wife, Anna Wright; Dr. Sherman Bishop, University of Rochester; Dr. Emmett R. Dunn, Haverford College; and Dr. Tracy I. Storer, Professor of Zoölogy, University of California, Davis, are outstanding among those whose published works have been a constant source of inspiration and assistance.

Doubleday, Page and Company and the Comstock Publishing Company permitted me to quote, respectively, from Mary Dickerson's *The Frog Book* and Albert and Anna Wright's *Handbook of Frogs and Toads.*

Miss Marian John and Miss Adele Zimmerman typed most of the manuscript and Mrs. Lois Taylor aided with the lettering of plates. Miss Susan Chattin and my wife helped in many ways in bringing the book to final form.

Dr. Storer generously permitted extensive use of notes that he had accumulated in contemplation of a revision of his *Amphibia of California.* Information abstracted from these notes appears in the text as Storer (MS).

This volume to a considerable extent has been fostered by a John Simon Guggenheim Memorial Fellowship, whose financial support has greatly facilitated its preparation.

Illustrations were prepared by me, unless otherwise credited.

R. C. S.

University of California, Berkeley,
July, 1951.

Salamanders

CONTENTS

Salamanders

Frogs and Toads

Frogs and Toads

Eggs and Larvae

Habitats

INTRODUCTION

Among the major groups of vertebrates, amphibians constitute a small and generally inconspicuous class, although some species are abundant as individuals. The small size of many, their secretive habits, and in some areas their short periods of activity, often render them difficult to observe. With knowledge of the time of activity and manner of occurrence of species, however, one can be relatively sure of finding them. Many are sedentary, moving but short distances in a lifetime, and most are sharply limited in their tolerance of extremes in environmental factors such as humidity and temperature. They commonly require water for breeding and all must live in an environment that provides sufficient moisture to prevent excessive dehydration. Some resemble plants in their sedentary nature and dependence on soil moisture. Under terrestrial conditions, one might designate a "wilting point" (Lowe, 1950:96) for these animals, reached when the absorption of water, obtained through the skin and from food, fails to keep pace with evaporation from the surfaces of the body.

Standing as they do between the aquatic and terrestrial modes of existence among vertebrates, amphibians present a profitable field for investigations bearing on the evolution of land life. Further, the occurrence of many species in small, weakly connected, or separate populations in suit-

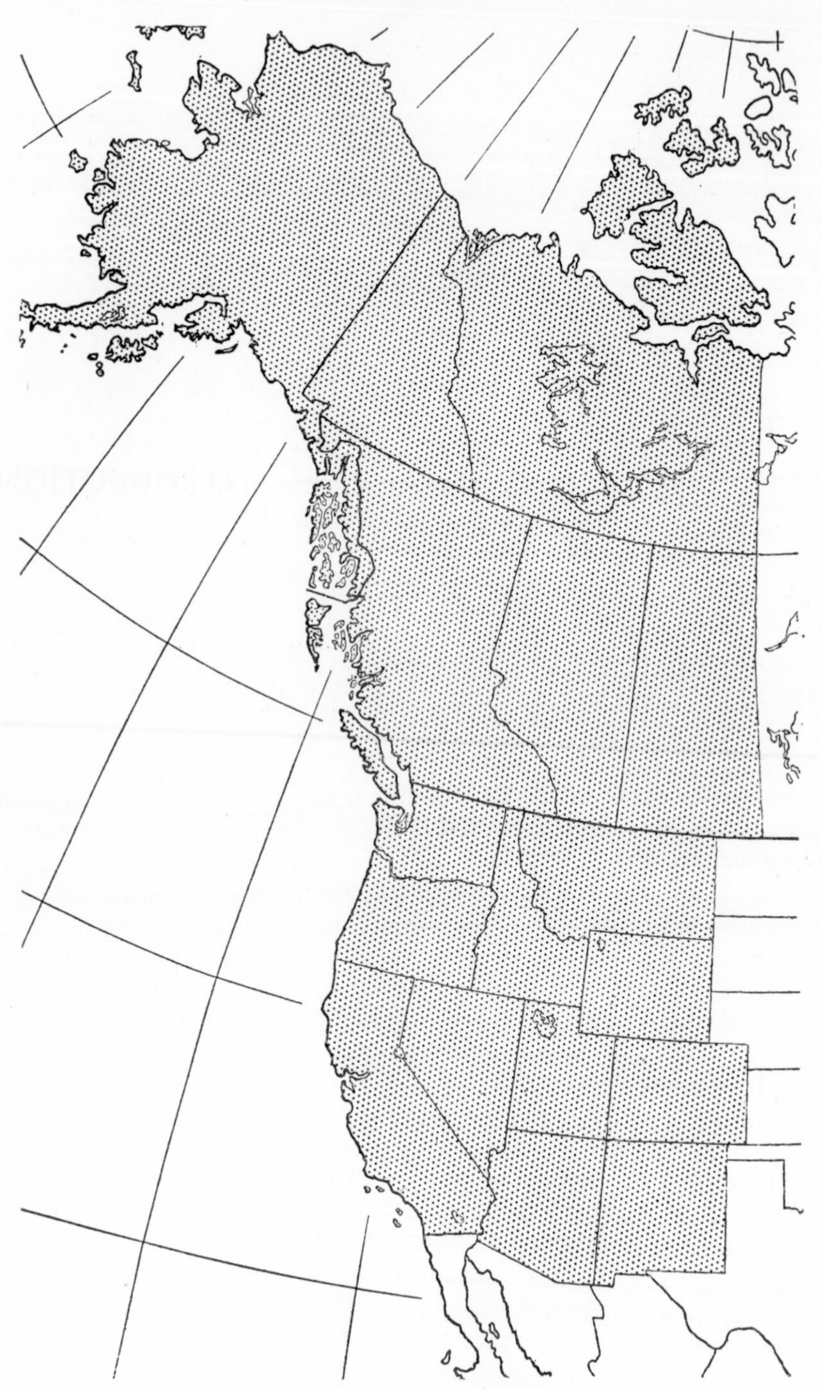

The area covered by this book.

able areas in otherwise generally unfavorable habitats, provides a favorable situation for the study of environmental effects on the structure and dynamics of populations.

There are a number of publications that provide information of a general sort on the natural history of amphibians (Noble, 1931; Holmes, 1927; introductory sections of Bishop, 1943; Dickerson, 1920; Wright and Wright, 1949, and others). I have confined myself principally to assembling facts on species. Such information is gathered under species accounts that form the bulk of the book. Some explanatory remarks regarding these accounts are required.

I have selected, on the basis of popularity and appropriateness, a single common name for each species. I favor the trend that prevails among ornithologists toward standardization of common names. It is, however, probably too early in the development of herpetological nomenclature to press for such standardization.

The type locality is given for each species, principally for its historical interest. The author of the species is indicated following the type locality. The locality is not always stated as in the original description since sometimes a clearer or more precise localization can be made. In a few species, rare or difficult to find, other localities have been listed.

Descriptions of species give estimates of range in size of adults and are not to be considered as precise determinations. Measurements are of total length for salamanders, snout-vent length for anurans, unless otherwise indicated. Emphasis has been placed on colors in life and descriptions are to be so viewed unless otherwise stated. Ridgway (1912) references have seldom been employed since much of the color terminology is meaningless in the absence of the Ridgway charts. When used, however, they are capitalized to distinguish them from less precise color references. Colors generally are given in conventional terms which, although less objective, are, I believe, more useful to the average reader. Usually following the general account of pigmentation are descriptions, in small type, of one or more specific individuals from selected localities. Such descriptions are considered desirable in view of the scant information on life colors of amphibians. Colors change markedly with preservation.

Under the section "Habitat," often a summarization of information on occurrence of the species is given. This summary is commonly followed by one or more descriptions of specific situations under which animals were found. These samples are largely selected from personal field notes and are presented with the thought that such detail may aid in finding animals and in gaining an impression of their habitat requirements.

Under the section "Reproduction" in the accounts of species, "Season" refers to the span of breeding activity. In some species this may represent essentially the total period of surface activity but in others, nonbreeding individuals may be found before and after this period.

The keys have been fully illustrated because of the subtle nature of many of the characters. The longer keys have references facilitating working backward, a procedure sometimes desired. Thus, if one is at category 7b.(2a), (2a) refers to the category that directed the reader to 7b. Descriptions of subspecies are arranged in key form, although for some the characters are rather vague and of dubious diagnostic value. Characters, such as proportional differences, although ordinarily not very useful as key characters, do, at least, indicate trends of variation, knowledge of which may be of value.

CLASS AMPHIBIA

Characterization.—Vertebrates with moist glandular skin, devoid of dermal appendages such as scales, feathers, and hair that characterize, respectively, the fishes and reptiles, birds, and mammals; limbs commonly 4, but sirenids with only anterior pair, and limbs absent in caecilians; toes commonly 4 on forefoot and 5 on hind foot, sometimes 4-4 or fewer (3-3 or 2-2), typically without claws, although some species with horny tips on digits; tail present (salamanders and caecilians) or absent (frogs and toads); when present, rounded or compressed (aquatic species); eyes commonly with movable lids, upper one usually depressed by retraction of eyeball; lower lid in anurans typically with thin transparent portion (nictitating membrane) retractable behind inert lower lid; salamanders without nictitating membrane; some amphibians with nonmovable transparent covering over eyes (larvae, pipid toads, and some aquatic salamanders); nostrils paired, often valvular; external ears (ear drum) absent (salamanders) or present (many anurans); mouth with fine, somewhat conical teeth in both upper and lower jaws (salamanders, some anurans), teeth absent in lower jaw (ranids and others) or wholly lacking (toads); vomerine teeth in salamanders and most anurans and parasphenoid teeth in some salamanders (plethodontids); tongue commonly present (absent in pipid toads) and protrusible (*Ascaphus* and others excepted), in some, extensively so (to about ⅓ length of body in some salamanders); heart 2- or 3-chambered, single ventricle; 1 to 3 pairs of aortic arches; red blood cells typically oval and nucleated (largely without nuclei in *Batrachoseps*).

Respiration by gills, lungs, buccopharynx, skin, separately or in combination; lungs may be reduced in stream-dwelling types and are absent in plethodontid salamanders; gills typically present at some stage of life history; voice generally absent in salamanders (*Dicamptodon* and a few others excepted) but many anurans have vocal cords and resonating pouch (or pouches) in throat region; voice best developed in male anurans; ectothermic (poikilothermic), deriving body temperature from surroundings (air, water, substratum, etc.).

Fertilization external (majority of anurans and some salamanders) or internal (many salamanders); most species oviparous; eggs with varying amounts of yolk (particularly abundant in plethodontid salamanders and some anurans); ova pigmented or not, covered with one or more gelatinous envelopes, commonly deposited in water but sometimes in damp places on land; cleavage commonly holoblastic but meroblastic in some plethodontid salamanders; most with an aquatic larval stage with transformation to adult form.

Salamanders

SALAMANDERS

Order Urodela

Characterization.—Body elongate, with distinct head, trunk, and tail; costal grooves present or not; tail round or compressed, sometimes with well-developed fins; limbs typically 4 (only anterior pair present in sirenids), about equal in size; toes 2-2 to 4-5; eyes with or without movable lids; no nictitating membrane; no external ear; teeth in both jaws; vomerine and sometimes parasphenoid teeth present; tongue commonly protrusible, broadly attached, attached medially and in front, or free all around (pedicelled); voiceless (few exceptions); larva terrestrial or aquatic; aquatic larva with teeth in both jaws, eyes without movable lids, tail compressed and finned; forelimbs and hind limbs grow more or less together, balancer present or absent; aquatic larva generally classified as either pond or brook type; fertilization internal except in Hynobiidae, Cryptobranchidae, and probably Sirenidae; about 150 species (Storer 1943:605).

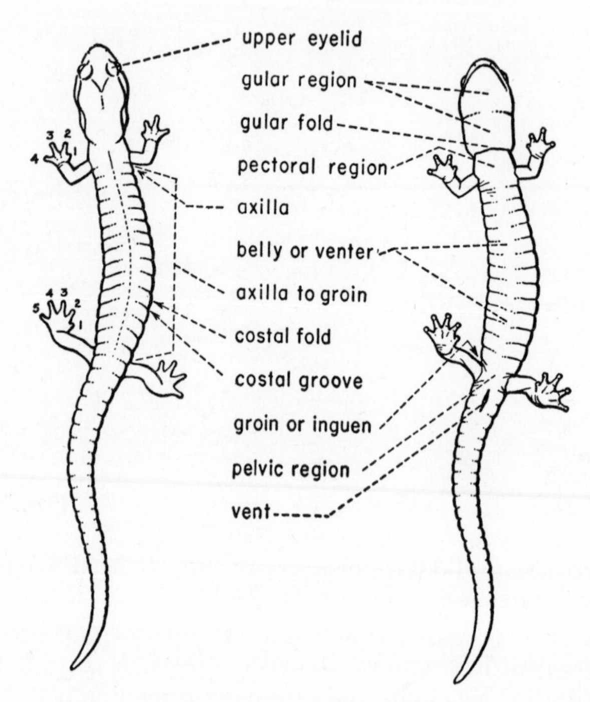

Fig. 1. External characteristics of a salamander (*Aneides flavipunctatus*).

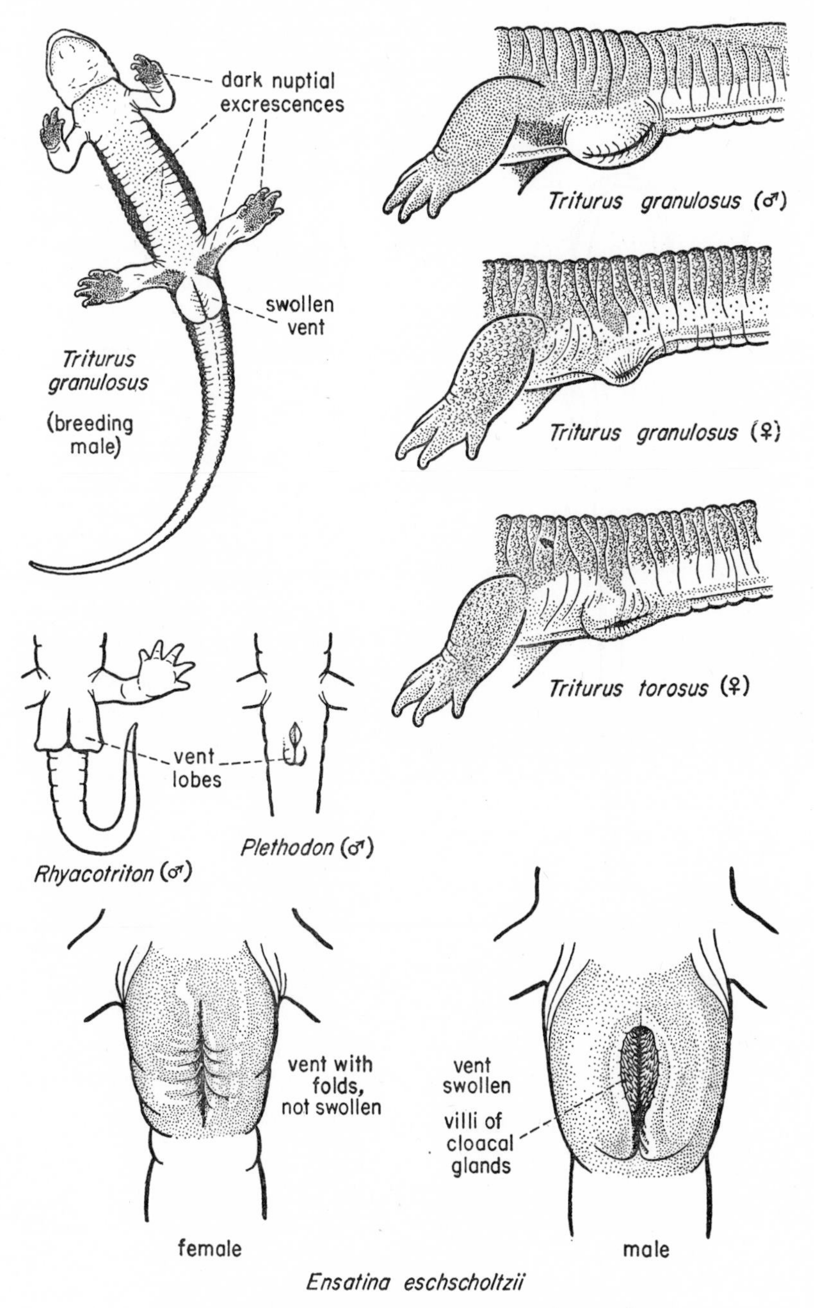

Fig. 2. Sexual characteristics of salamanders.

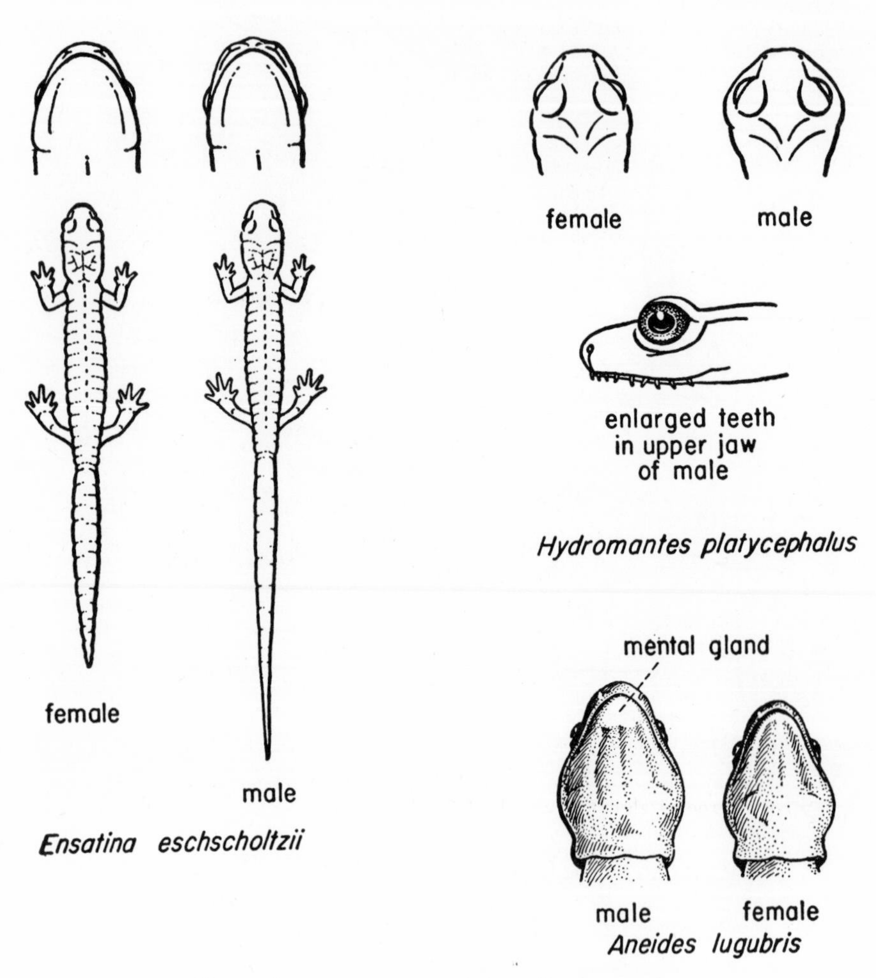

Fig. 3. Sexual characteristics of salamanders.

ACCOUNTS OF SPECIES

KEY TO FAMILIES
Figure 4

1*a*. Groove (nasolabial) (1) extending from nostril to edge of upper lip (magnification may be required for determination); vomerine and parasphenoid teeth present (2); no lungs .... PLETHODONTIDAE, p. 61

1*b*. No groove connecting nostril and upper lip; vomerine teeth present (3 and 4), no parasphenoid teeth; lungs present 2

2*a*. Vomerine teeth in two longitudinal rows, diverging posteriorly between orbits (4); costal grooves absent or poorly defined except in adult males in smooth-skin breeding condition: skin often rough with numerous tubercules .... SALAMANDRIDAE (genus *Triturus*), p. 14

2*b*. Vomerine teeth in transverse series, or sometimes converging slightly posteriorly but not extending between orbits (3); costal grooves present; skin smooth .... AMBYSTOMIDAE, p. 29

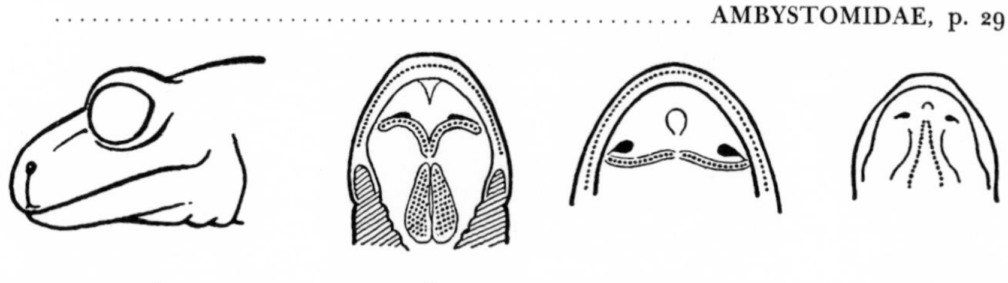

Fig. 4. 1, 2, *Ensatina eschscholtzii;* 3, *Ambystoma tigrinum;* 4, *Triturus granulosus.*

NEWTS

Family Salamandridae

Structure.—Adults range from 5 to 8 inches in total length; eyelids present; tail compressed, with varied development of dorsal and ventral fins when animals are aquatic; tail fins of males become enlarged during breeding season; costal grooves of adults are poorly defined or absent in species in North America; limbs well developed; palmar and plantar tubercles absent or weakly developed; toes 4-5; skin thick, rough when animals are in terrestrial stage, smooth and succulent in adult males during breeding period, when they are aquatic; vomerine teeth distinctive, arranged in an elongate row, one on either side of parasphenoid; tongue small, fleshy, attached along midline, with edges free laterally and posteriorly; lungs but no gills in adults; ypsiloid cartilage present; vertebrae opisthocoelous. *Color.* General coloration in our species as follows: In life uniformly yellowish brown to black above; below pale lemon yellow, orange, or tomato red; iris uniformly dark brown or black or with extensive patches of silver to lemon yellow in upper and lower portions.

Habits.—Newts are largely terrestrial except during the breeding season when they enter ponds and streams to spawn. During this period the males deposit spermatophores which are picked up by the females. The spermatophore consists of a conical mass of gelatinous material capped by a capsule of sperm and is normally deposited in the water. The jelly is produced by glands in the walls of the cloaca. The sperm capsule consists of spermatozoa associated with a prostate-like secretion from pelvic glands in the roof of the cloaca. The head of the spermatophore, including the sperm capsule, is taken into the vent of the female by means of her cloacal lips. Fertilization is internal. The eggs are laid in the water, usually in firm-jellied clumps, but singly in *Triturus granulosus.* The egg proper, or ovum, is situated in a fluid-filled chamber, the capsular cavity, which allows it considerable movement. The fluid zone is surrounded by a firm, two-layered, gelatinous capsule. The larva is of the pond type with the exception of *T. rivularis* whose larva exhibits some characteristics of the mountain brook type (p. 436).

Range.—North America, Europe, Asia, and North Africa.

Remarks.—Variation in *Triturus granulosus* needs study, particularly in California north of San Francisco Bay. An investigation of isolating mechanisms and differences in ecology could profitably be made in the vicinity of Ukiah, Mendocino County, where three species—*granulosus, rivularis,* and *torosus*—occur in the same general area, *granulosus* being associated with *rivularis* in streams immediately west and southwest of Ukiah and with *torosus* on the eastern side of the Ukiah Valley. *Sierrae* and *granulosus* coexist at Chico, California, according to Twitty (1942: 71). This would constitute another area for studies of this type.

The great similarity between *torosus* and *sierrae* and their distribution in relation to the topography and biotic features of California suggest that these forms possibly may be connected and that *sierrae* may properly be considered a race of *T. torosus.*

Geographic variation in *T. torosus* should be investigated. Twitty (1942:73), principally on the basis of larvae studied from near Los Angeles and from Monterey County, believes the *torosus* of southern California are genetically distinct from those farther north. The grotesquely warty form *klauberi* needs to be investigated by means of breeding experiments and by study of its ecology to determine the nature of the warty condition.

Key to Species of *Triturus*

Figure 5

1*a*. Eyes large and protuberant, uniformly brownish black (1 and 5); above black or dark brown, dark color extending well onto undersides of limbs (9 and 13); usually a broad transverse band of dark color crosses vent; below tomato red (in life) with reddish color extending onto upper surfaces of digits; side of upper jaw and lower half or all lower eyelid light-colored (17); snout elongate (1), usually with well-defined light area between nostrils .... *T. rivularis,* p. 21

1*b*. Eyes smaller, with yellow or silvery patches filling out most of iris above and below pupil, but light color may be dull in preserved specimens (2, 3, 6, and 19); above brown or yellowish brown as well as dark brown or black; dark color not extending as far onto undersides of limbs (10 and 14), *T. granulosus mazamae* excepted; vent less often crossed by dark stripe; below yellowish to orange, rarely tomato red (in life), without or with less noticeable reddish color on upper surfaces of digits; side of upper jaw dark-colored or if light-colored then lower eyelid usually dark (15 and 16) (juvenal *T. torosus* excepted); snout shorter; usually with less well-defined light area between nostrils (*T. t. sierrae* excepted) 2

2*a*. Eyes relatively small, when viewed from above corneal surface usually not extending to contour of upper jaw (3); vomerine teeth diverge gradually posteriorly between orbits, forming V-shaped pattern (7); dark dorsal color usually ends abruptly along sides, contrasting with light color of venter (11). . *T. granulosus,* p. 17

2*b*. Eyes larger, when viewed from above corneal surface usually extends to contour of upper jaw (4); vomerine teeth in two parallel rows anteriorly, diverging abruptly posteriorly between orbits, forming Y-shaped pattern (8); edge of upper jaw or nearly entire upper jaw light-colored (16); dark dorsal color usually gives way gradually to light color of venter (12) .... *T. torosus,* p. 23

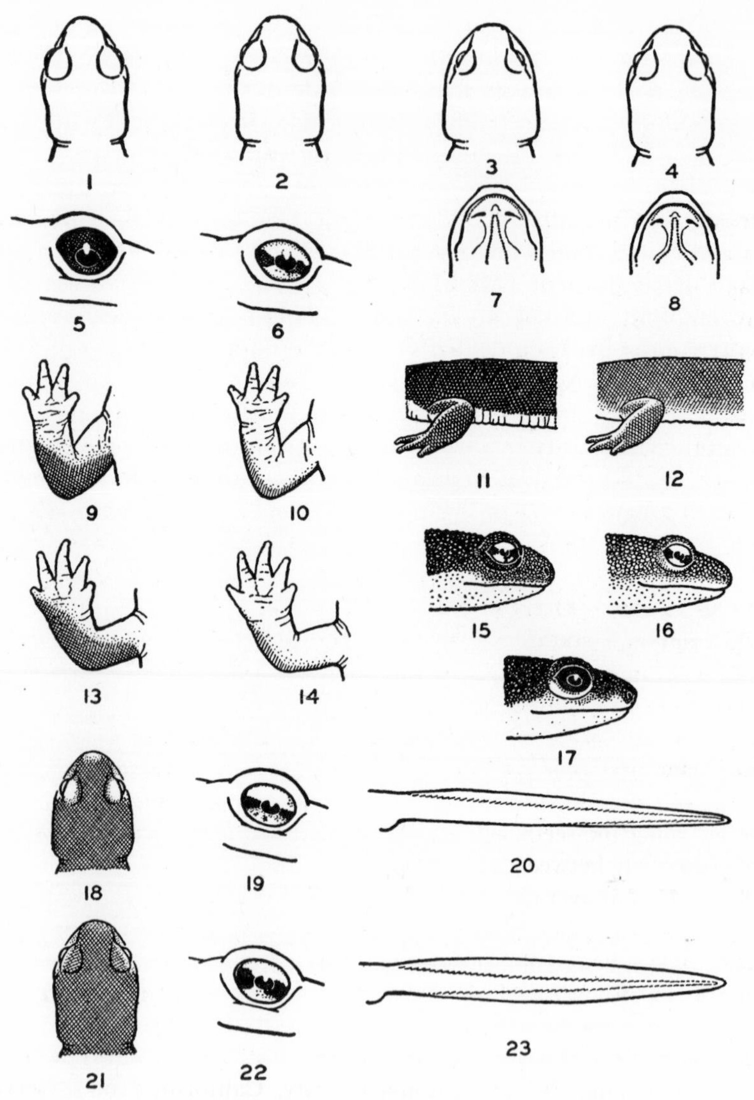

Fig. 5. 1, 5, 9, 13, 17, *Triturus rivularis;* 2, 4, 6, 8, 10, 12, 14, 16, 21, 22, 23, *T. torosus torosus;* 18, 19, 20, *T. torosus sierrae;* 3, 7, 11, 15, *T. granulosus.*

ROUGH-SKIN NEWT

Triturus granulosus (Skilton)

Range.—Principally the humid, coniferous forest area of the Pacific Coast of North America, from Admiralty Island in the Alexander Archipelago of southeastern Alaska, to Santa Cruz and central Santa Clara counties, south of San Francisco Bay, California. The species occurs principally west of the Cascade Mountains in Oregon and Washington but is known (at least two records) from lakes on the east slope in Oregon (Storm, *in litt.*), from two localities in Washington (in Kittitas and Klickitat counties, Slater, *in litt.*) and from the vicinity of Moscow, Latah County, Idaho, where it may have been introduced. In northern California, it ranges inland in the Siskiyou Mountains and southward on the western slope of the Sierra Nevada to the vicinity of Chico, Butte County. (Pl. 48.)

Type locality.—Oregon (Skilton, 1849:202).

Description.—STRUCTURE. Adult approximately 4½ to 7½ inches; resembles *T. torosus* but can be distinguished from it and other *Triturus* by the following rather distinctive characteristics: eyes relatively small, corneal surface when viewed from above usually not extending to edge of upper jaw; iris pale yellow to whitish, usually lighter than in *T. t. torosus* but similar in color to *T. t. sierrae;* snout blunter than in other species; vomerine teeth usually arranged in two rows that diverge gradually posteriorly between orbits, approximately in relationship of two arms of letter **V**; skin averages somewhat rougher and tail fin of breeding male broader than in other species although *torosus* has nearly as large tail fins. COLOR. Above brown to almost black, with darker color apparently more common in individuals from south-central part of range (living animals I have examined from Washington were yellowish brown or tan); below yellow to orange, sometimes near tomato red (individuals observed at mouth of Gualala River, Sonoma County, California); in preservative, ventral color may be buff, whitish, pale yellow, or orange; as in *rivularis,* dark dorsal color may be sharply delimited from lighter ventral color along sides, particularly in animals from southern part of range (transition from dark to light color on sides of body is usually gradual in *torosus*). SEXUAL DIFFERENCES. Lips of cloaca in female form somewhat laterally compressed cone with small vent situated near apex (in other western newts, cloacal aperture is longer, lying in depression between prominent lateral lips) (Fig. 2); tail fins are less prominent and skin is rougher and less succulent in breeding female than in male.

Habitat.—Frequents streams, lakes, ponds, and roadside ditches, principally during the breeding season. Usually found in permanent water. In the range of *T. t. torosus,* streams are, in general, less permanent, are subject to greater fluctuations in flow, are more exposed, and are warmer. Terrestrial individuals are found beneath logs, bark, boards, and other surface objects or crawling in the open. Individuals may be observed in spring, crawling toward breeding sites. On November 25, 1945, at 9:00 A.M. in Napa County, California, I found 5 individuals in the space of 10 feet, all moving in the same direction toward a small stream. One of these was a female heavy with eggs, another was a rough-skin male, and the remainder were immatures. During drier parts of the year and in cold weather the species lives underground, beneath surface objects, or in rotting logs and is seldom seen.

Behavior.—In general, this newt resembles *torosus* (p. 24). It appears to be the most aquatic of our western species, spending more time in the water than the others. A defensive posture may be assumed when an individual is molested. An animal picked up on the highway near Crescent City, California, depressed its back, bending its head and tail upward until they nearly touched one another. The tip of the tail was curled into a tight coil with the orange ventral surface turned uppermost. The limbs were extended stiffly from the sides and the eyes were depressed in their sockets, the lids closed. The gular area was contracted.

Chandler (1918:6) says of the species *Notophthalmus torosus* (*T. granulosus*), in the vicinity of Corvallis, Oregon, "During the greater part of the year the adults are entirely aquatic and live in lakes, reservoirs, slow-flowing streams or sloughs, or almost any other quiet body of water of sufficient size. In the autumn, October and November . . . they leave the water and wander about on land, being commonly found crawling about in dead leaves in patches of woods. A little later, November or December, they retreat to cavities under stumps, logs, or stones where they curl up to spend the cold portion of the winter, sometimes a dozen or more together. On warm days, however, they come forth and wander about in search of food." Chandler suggests that the return to land in winter may be to escape being frozen in the small pools in which they live during the greater part of the year. "The males . . . are more strictly aquatic than the females, and sometimes remain in water the year round or make only short excursions on land."

Food.—The following items have been recorded for metamorphosed individuals: fresh-water sponges; mollusks—snails (*Goniobasis* and *Physa*); earthworms; blood worms; crustaceans—a daphnid (*Cladocera*), ostracods, copepods, amphipods (*Hyalella*); a spider; insects—stoneflies (plecopterans), dragonfly eggs and adults (coenagrionids), Mayfly nymphs (baetids and heptageniids), hemipterans (corixids [waterboatmen] and notonectids [back swimmers]), raphidians, trichopterans (caddis worms—hydropsychids and limnophilids), dipterans (crane flies [tipulids], sand flies [*Culicoides*], *Eucorethra,* chironomids, and chaoborids), beetles (carabids and others), hymenopterans (chalcids, a sawfly); amphibian eggs (*Triturus* and *Rana boylii*); algae and other plant material. (Chandler, 1918:12-14; Schonberger, 1944:257; Farner, 1947:260-61; and Evenden, 1948.)

Schonberger (1944) and Farner (1947) found the species at Crater Lake, Oregon, primarily predaceous but a few dead arthropods were taken indicating a scavenging tendency. Evenden (1948), in western Oregon, found that animal food was taken about 88 per cent of the time, insects predominating. Mayflies were the most important food item. He believed there was competition with trout for the trout's preferred foods.

Reproduction.—The general pattern is apparently similar to that of *torosus* but spawning, considering the species as a whole, extends over a greater period. *Granulosus* may spawn from late December to May, June, or July; most activity in the southern part of the range (Mendocino County, California), seems to be in March or April.

According to Chandler (1918:6), the males return to water and assume breeding characteristics as early as the first of January, whereas the females can seldom be found in water before February. He says (1918:7), "In the vicinity of Corvallis mating does not begin until the latter part of winter, usually in February, and continues well into summer, copulating pairs being found as late as July 14. . . . Eggs have been found by the middle of April, and continue to be deposited until the middle of July." A female with large ovarian eggs, taken in the Cascade Mountains on August 10, suggested to Chandler that in the mountains where the season is late and it is cool, laying may sometimes be delayed until the fall, in which case the eggs may lie over winter before hatching.

EGGS. Usually laid singly, attached to vegetation and other objects in the water. They are smaller than those of our other western newts. Eggs from California obtained by Twitty (1935:79) measured about 1.8 mm. (morula stage), excluding the jelly envelopes. Measurements of a fresh egg, among several from California given to me by Professor Twitty, May 9, 1949, were as follows: diameter to outer surface of jelly envelope 3.63 mm.; ovum 2.16 mm.; inner portion of gelatinous envelope appeared differentiated into possible second layer, about 0.1 mm. in thickness, but this may have been an optical effect; layers combined, approximately 0.7 mm.; ovum moved freely within capsular chamber.

LARVA. Pond type. No persistent distinct longitudinal dorsolateral dark stripes on body as in *torosus* although at time of hatching poorly defined dorsal pigment stripe may be present on either side near base of dorsal fin; fins dark-mottled; trunk with two longitudinal rows of light spots which in older individuals may join to form a single light stripe. At hatching the larvae are smaller than those of the other species, measuring about 12 mm. in length at the time of independent feeding, but they may metamorphose at larger size, at approximately 75 mm. in total length. On June 5, 1949, I received larvae of this species from David Strack. They had been collected a few days earlier in a reservoir in the Moscow Mountains, 7 miles northeast of Moscow, Latah County, Idaho. Thirty adults were obtained in 1948, 4 of which are now in the Museum of Vertebrate Zoölogy. In life they were olive above with cream or pale yellow spots along sides; belly pinkish orange; iris pale yellow or cream.

Chandler (1918:8-9, vicinity of Corvallis, Oregon) describes full-grown larvae, 40 to 50 mm. in length: ground color a mosaic of yellowish and pale gray, peppered all over with black pigment cells; sides with two distinct rows of light spots where black pigment is missing, being replaced by splotch of creamy white pigment; under surface behind gills has reddish tinge due to liver showing through transparent body wall.

Transformation occurred during the month of August. Three to 4 weeks were required for its completion. The smallest sexually mature specimens were from 105 to 110 mm. in length. These were probably developed from eggs laid 4 years before (Chandler, 1918:9).

Key to Subspecies

1a. Dark dorsal pigment extends scarcely below midline of sides; light color on underside of tail usually reaches tip; size larger than *granulosus* and *mazamae* but possibly somewhat smaller than *similans;* males during breeding season generally differ from *similans* males in lighter, more brownish dorsal coloration and in having a less spongy skin, lower caudal fins, and less brilliant ventral color (occasional males, however, approach *similans* in dull Oxford gray or blackish of dorsum and in notably smooth spongy skin). *Range.* Santa Cruz and central Santa Clara counties, north to Napa, Marin, and southern Mendocino counties, California .... *T. g. twittyi* Bishop

1b. Dark dorsal pigment extends considerably below midline of sides, usually crowding out light ventral color toward tip of tail; size smaller (*similans* excepted); in breeding season generally darker above 2

2a. Size larger, males averaging 174 mm. in total length (as based on 44 individuals from two localities—vicinity of Ukiah, Mendocino County, and Chico, Butte County —that ranged from 163 to 206 mm.); border between dorsal and ventral colors well defined; skin of breeding males smooth and spongy, essentially as in race *granulosus;* above slate gray to Oxford gray to almost black; caudal fin of breeding males broader; venter of breeding individuals more brilliant and more opaque yellow, varying from near canary to orange yellow. *Range.* Known from good breeding examples only from vicinity of Ukiah, Mendocino County, and Chico, Butte County, California. Other material from California suggests subspecies extends in coast ranges and Sierra, north of area of intergradation with *twittyi,* at least to the Klamath River and Siskiyou Mountains, California .... *T. g. similans* Twitty

2*b*. Size smaller, males averaging 155 mm. in length (as based on 11 adults from near Tacoma, Washington, that ranged from 146 to 168 mm.); usually no sharp border between dorsal and ventral colors; caudal fin of breeding males narrower; venter in life less brilliant 3

3*a*. Above brownish; ventral surfaces usually heavily suffused with blackish (recently transformed or half-grown individuals show little trace of dark ventral color); dark pigment most often occurs on under surfaces of forelimbs (which are usually almost or entirely dark colored) and sides of breast, just before arms; most individuals have entire pectoral area black or black-spotted as well as black or nearly black under surfaces of hind limbs; most have black stripe across vent; black of pectoral region usually invades throat and belly. *Range*. Known only from type locality, slopes of Crater Lake, Crater Lake National Park, Oregon, but possibly present at higher elevations in other parts of the Cascade Range .... *T. g. mazamae* Myers

3*b*. Above blackish to brown; ventral surfaces largely without blackish suffusion; black stripe less often present across vent. *Range*. Probably from near northern boundary of California northward in western Oregon, Washington, and British Columbia to Admiralty Island, Alaska .... *T. g. granulosus* (Skilton)

The characters and ranges of the foregoing races are given essentially as delineated by Myers (1942a). As pointed out by him much work remains to be done before really adequate systematic treatment of western *Triturus* can be given. I suspect that a careful analysis of variation in size and pigmentation will reveal gradual clines coastally, along the north-south axis of the range. Until such a study is made I hold in question the desirability of giving nomenclatural recognition to *similans,* and possibly *twittyi,* although on biogeographical grounds there seems to me greater chance that the latter may be sufficiently distinct to warrant recognition.

Remarks.—Twitty (1942:69) thinks this species represents the primitive or original form of Californian *Triturus.*

WESTERN RED-BELLIED NEWT

Triturus rivularis Twitty

Plate 2

Range.—Known from Sonoma, Mendocino, and Humboldt counties, and expected in Del Norte County, California. It is apparently restricted to coastal California north of San Francisco Bay where its range coincides closely with the region of optimal development of the coast redwood. (Pl. 48.)

Type locality.—Gibson Creek, about one mile west of Ukiah, Mendocino County, California (Twitty, 1935:73).

Description.—STRUCTURE. Adult approximately 6 to 7 inches; head narrower, nose more pointed, and eyes larger and more protuberant than in other western newts; vomerine teeth as in *torosus;* breeding male with less fully developed dorsal tail fin and less protuberant cloaca than in other species. COLOR. Iris uniformly dark brown (black on casual inspection) in contrast to eyes of others which, in life, possess extensive yellow or pale yellow to silvery markings; above black to brownish (latter in breeding males); light area usually present on snout between nostrils; reddish color like that of ventral surfaces extends onto upper surface of digits; below tomato red (in life) in contrast to yellow and orange of other forms except for some individuals of *T. granulosus;* extensive dark areas on undersides of limbs, not usually as well developed in other species. SEXUAL DIFFERENCES. Cloaca protuberant and crossed by dark stripe in male; occurrence of this marking variable in female.

Habitat.—Frequents fairly rapid streams, of mountain brook type. This choice of habitat is the basis for the name *rivularis.* The species usually breeds where the substratum is clean and rocky.

Reproduction.—The tendency for the male to saddle the dorsal base of the tail of the female with his cloacal lips as occurs in *torosus* and *granulosus* seems not so pronounced. Twitty (1935:74) reports that males deposited spermatophores in captivity and Smith (1941b) has described the spermatophore. On the basis of the material examined by him and information given by Twitty, it appears that the spermatophores of *T. rivularis* may be more firmly attached to the substratum than are those of *T. torosus.* This may in some degree facilitate mating in rapidly flowing rocky streams.

Twitty (*in litt.*) says that *rivularis* begins to spawn when the streams first recede from flood conditions in the spring. In his experience the heaviest spawning is usually between the middle of March and the middle of April, but he has found them spawning as late as the first of May and in dry years he believes they may begin spawning as early as the first of March.

EGGS. Clusters are attached to the under surfaces of stones, frequently in relatively swift water. Eggs are often deposited in large aggregations. In one instance where a count was made, approximately 70 masses were found on the underside of a single stone, in an area 12 by 8½ inches (Twitty, 1935:76). Occasionally the eggs are laid at the margin of a stream, attached to vegetation as in *torosus.* The clusters are commonly flattened instead of rounded, with the eggs often forming only one layer. Twenty clutches averaged 9 eggs (range 5 to 15); ovum about 2.75 mm. (blastula stage), about same size as that of *sierrae* but larger than that of *torosus* and *granulosus* (Twitty, 1935:74); diameter of jelly envelope to outer surface in egg measured by me, 8.56 mm.; diameter of capsular chamber, 5.5 mm. Nine clusters examined by me were a single egg thick except one that had an egg above the general level. These clusters averaged 10 eggs (range 9 to 12). The firm gelatinous capsule, as in *granulosus,* has a thin inner layer. Eggs are often deposited in April.

LARVA. Tends toward mountain brook type; balancer (always present in other species) absent or rudimentary and dorsal fin less prominent, not extending as far anteriorly on body; head flatter and longer than in *torosus;* no dorsolateral dark bands, pigment uniformly distributed over back and sides; eye with yellow pigment, differing from that of adult. Loss of the balancer and reduction of the tail fin are interpreted as adaptations to the mountain brook habitat of this species. Larvae metamorphose at about 45 to 55 mm., as based on the few measurements available.

Remarks.—*Rivularis* is the most distinct and specialized species of the genus in western North America. Adaptations, related to its habit of breeding in streams, are: reduction of the tail fin of the male; firm anchorage of the spermatophore to the substratum; flattened egg clusters; loss of the balancer and reduction of the dorsal fin of the larva.

CALIFORNIA NEWT

Triturus torosus (Rathke)
Plate 1

Range.—The subspecies *torosus* occurs in the coast ranges of California from middle Mendocino County, north of San Francisco Bay, south to the vicinity of San Diego. Slevin's (1928:25) records for Lower California (San Andreas and Keller) are in error. The form *sierrae* occurs at middle and lower elevations of the Sierra Nevada from the vicinity of Chico, Butte County, south through Placer, Eldorado, Tuolumne, Mariposa, Madera, and Fresno counties to Sequoia National Park and vicinity, Tulare County, California. Record of a specimen in the files of the Museum of Vertebrate Zoölogy from Tule River, Tulare County, indicates the range may extend still farther south. Unfortunately this specimen has disappeared, hence its identity cannot be checked.

What may be an isolated northern population of *sierrae* was discovered by Joe Gorman on June 12 and 13, 1950, near the Squaw Creek headwaters of Shasta Reservoir, in the vicinity of Squaw Creek, at an elevation of about 1,400 feet. The locality is about 1¼ miles south of Squaw Creek Camp, Shasta County, California (Gorman, 1951). (Pl. 48.)

Type locality.—Vicinity of the Bay of San Francisco, California (Rathke in Eschscholtz, 1833).

Description.—STRUCTURE. Adult 6 to 8 inches; skin tuberculate except in males in breeding condition; vomerine teeth typically in two rows that parallel one another anteriorly but diverge rather abruptly posteriorly, forming Y-shaped pattern; eyes intermediate in size between *granulosus* and *rivularis;* surface of cornea, as viewed from above, usually extends to or beyond contour of upper jaw. COLOR. Above yellowish brown, reddish brown, light chocolate to dark brown; below pale yellow to orange, never to my knowledge tomato red; in most individuals dorsal and ventral colors grade along sides but in some, rather sharp break occurs between them; upper eyelids and tip of snout may be lighter than rest of head (most commonly in Sierran form); minute brown-tipped tubercles, possibly of seasonal occurrence and related to breeding activities, irregularly present ventrally on lower jaw and ventrolaterally on abdomen; iris with extensive cream, silvery, to lemon-yellow patches above and below pupil; upper iris patch may be best developed. SEXUAL DIFFERENCES. Papillae of skin of breeding male practically disappear and skin becomes smooth and often lighter in color dorsally and less bright yellow ventrally; tail becomes broadened by enlargement of dorsal and ventral fins; limbs increase in bulk; tips of toes (sometimes entire ventral surface of foot) and area at base of hind limbs (sometimes forelimbs) become roughened with numerous minute dark-colored papillae; cloacal region becomes swollen; female does not undergo such changes; posterior portion of vent of male usually marked by transverse dark band; less well-defined marking sometimes present in female. It is difficult to determine sex after the males leave the water and lose their well-defined secondary sexual characters.

Habitat.—The California newt is commonly found in the vicinity of, or within, bodies of water such as ponds, streams, and reservoirs. Permanent water, however, is not necessary. In many areas where the species occurs, the streams and pools dry up during the summer. Although much time is spent on land in moist situations beneath boards, logs, rocks, and in rodent burrows, the adults must return to water to breed. Summer retreats may be sought considerable distances from the breeding area. I have found individuals over 200 feet from the nearest water.

Behavior.—Terrestrial individuals are often active in the daytime, especially during wet weather. Newts are more tolerant of light than most salamanders. Frequently considerable numbers are found when they are seeking breeding ponds, or upon their first emergence in the fall or winter with the first soaking rains. On the night of October 10, 1947, after the first fall rains, I counted 49 individuals, mostly adults, on a 3/4-mile stretch of road at Canyon, Contra Costa County, California.

These salamanders are rather awkward when crawling on land, but they swim with facility by means of lateral undulations of their flattened tails. When swimming, the limbs are commonly extended posteriorly. When in the water, the animals rise to the surface periodically, there releasing gas bubbles.

When handled roughly or otherwise molested this species commonly assumes the following characteristic pose: the head is held nearly vertical, the body is flattened, the legs are extended stiffly laterally, the eyes are depressed into their sockets, and the tail is elevated and arched, sometimes well over the back; sometimes the tip of the tail may be curled and the ventral surface may be turned uppermost revealing its bright orange color; the tail may actively secrete a milky substance from the poison glands.

Thermal data.—On June 28, 1950, at Millard Canyon, Los Angeles County, California, 14 adults were removed from their site of aestivation in a hole partly filled with slightly damp, coarse sand beneath a large boulder, 4 or 5 feet from a stream. Temperatures recorded by Charles Lowe, Jr. were as follows: cloacal temperatures 18.3°, 17.9°, 18.1°, 18.0°, 16.5°; soil 18.1°C.; air outside burrow in shade 19.8°C.; time 8:00 A.M. Two adults found in the open, under a ledge, 2 feet from the stream, at 8:15 A.M., had cloacal temperatures of 16.5° and 16.1°C., respectively; stream 16.1°, air 16.7°C. Another adult, found crawling through the shallow water of the stream at 8:30 A.M., possessed a body temperature of 15.8°C.; stream 16.1°, air in the shade above the water, 17.5°C.

Food.—According to Ritter (1897:84) metamorphosed individuals feed on earthworms, small snails, slugs, sowbugs, and larvae and adults of many species of insects. Larvae eat small aquatic organisms (including mosquito larvae) and decomposing organic matter that collects on stones, sticks, and weeds in the water.

Reproduction.—Smith (1941a) has described breeding in this species. The following account is largely based on his observations. Near the beginning of the mating season males congregate at breeding ponds and assume concurrently a smooth skin, broadened tail, and an enlarged cloaca. In the vicinity of Berkeley, California, they may begin going to water as early as December, but the time varies. Females come later when about ready to spawn. They retain their granular skin and finless tail. When the females first arrive at the breeding ponds, many males may gather around a single female forming a ball of writhing salamanders. In courtship the male straddles the female, clasping his forelegs just behind hers. His hind legs hang free or may clasp her pelvic region. He carries her about in this position as he swims by means of his broad tail. The lips of the cloaca of the male become distended to form a saddle over the dorsum of the female. The male rubs his cloaca over the sacral area of the female, at the same time stroking her vent or tibiofibular region with his feet. The male periodically rubs the snout of the female with his chin. He accomplishes this by shifting forward, bending his head downward, and opening his mouth. His lower jaw is thereby brought into contact with her nose, whereupon he wags his head from side to side rubbing her snout with his intermandibular gland. The male then leaves the female and crawls forward in front of her. He flattens his cloaca against the substratum and vibrates his tail and hind limbs, accompanying this with a general shuddering of his pelvic and thoracolumbar region. The female stands motionless with her snout near the cloaca of the male. The male deposits a spermatophore and crawls forward followed by the female who holds her nose close to his vent. She picks up the spermatophore with the lips of her cloaca. The male continues his spasmodic vibratory movements. He turns suddenly, seizes the female and goes into amplexus again. The secretion from the abdominal glands seems to attract the female to the cloaca of the male, and the hedonic glands on his chin, in the intermandibular area, inhibit her struggles to free herself during amplexus.

In the vicinity of Berkeley, California, breeding activities may begin in autumn. Ritter (1897:93) observed a pair in amplexus in late September. However, successful breeding probably does not occur until later. The breeding season varies greatly in different parts of the range. Storer (1925:52) found eggs near Berkeley as early as December 25, 1922, but in southern California spawning has occurred as late as May 7 (1918). A second period of breeding activity, probably involving another group of adults, usually occurs in March and April. After depositing their eggs, the females leave the water, but the males may remain aquatic for a considerable time.

Observations of Thane Riney in the Sierra Nevada indicate that the species there may be found moving toward water in January and February. On January 9, 1948, between 4:00 and 4:30 P.M., 6 individuals were seen on the road between Jawbone Guard Station and Lumsden Bridge in the Tuolumne drainage. On January 11, 1948, at 4:45 P.M., one individual was obtained at 5,800 feet, on the slope above Lake Eleanor. It was crawling across the Kibbie Ridge trail. Several others were seen crawling on the damp ground. On July 29, 1948, at Kibbie Lake, 6,400 feet elevation, in a shallow pool near the western edge of the lake, at least 20 newts were seen on the mud bottom in water 2 to 3 feet deep. On February 25,

1949, the first newt of the season was seen. It was crawling over a slightly damp surface in a large meadow below Goat Camp near Jawbone Station, in the vicinity of the Tuolumne River, Tuolumne County. On the 26th, 8 others were seen within 100 yards of the river, 7 of them crawling toward the water and the eighth moving along the trail parallel to the river.

Breeding in the Sierra may occur in March and April. Dixon Clarke found an adult male in what appeared to be postbreeding condition at Wood's Creek, Sawmill Flat, Tuolumne County, California, on May 14, 1949. The animal was found in a pool where there had been breeding activity some weeks earlier. Clarke said breeding appeared to be over although he believed there might still have been activity at higher altitudes. The Sierra newt may spawn in relatively swift water, but near Chico adults were found depositing eggs on roots in a small artificial ditch that was almost devoid of current (Twitty, 1942:66).

EGGS. Usually in firm-jellied clumps attached to sticks, the under surfaces of stones, or vegetation in the water, often at depths shallower than 6 inches; outside diameter of the clumps, about 15 mm. Twenty-four egg clusters from a pond near Berkeley, studied by Storer (1925:54) averaged 16.6 to a cluster (range 7 to 29); rarely, a few eggs were attached singly. Ovum 1.88 to 2.80 mm., pale brown to dark brown above, cream-colored or yellowish below, enclosed in a large round or oval fluid-filled capsular chamber, about 5.0 mm. to 6.0 mm. in diameter, surrounded by a firm gelatinous capsule about 0.5 to 1.5 mm. in thickness. This capsule has a thin inner and thick outer layer. Storer (1925:55) found that at Thornhill Pond, in the vicinity of Berkeley, eggs hatched about 52 days after laying but the time required for prelarval development is quite variable.

LARVA. Pond type; recently hatched larvae of coastal form may measure about 11 or 12 mm. and are usually under 60 mm. at metamorphosis; Ritter (1897:76-77) gives average length of 9 individuals, just metamorphosed, as 48 mm.; 7 or 8 gill rakers on anterior face of third arch (6 larvae from Happy Valley, near Lafayette, Contra Costa County, California); general coloration above yellowish usually with two conspicuous longitudinal stripes of black, one along either side of the dorsal fin; dorsal and ventral fins and sides with black spots; below yellow or white, unspotted; occasionally larval striping may persist for a short time. In larvae from Sierra Nevada, dorsal stripes less even and more melanophores present on sides; older larvae tend to become dark-spotted laterally; much more yellow pigment in young larva than in coastal form. Recently transformed and subadult individuals are the most terrestrial members of the species. Recently metamorphosed newts drown if forced to stay in the water. It is presumed that some larvae do not transform until the second summer but in some parts of the range of the species, where breeding sites seldom persist, transformation must occur during the first summer or else there must be an exceedingly high larval mortality. Sexual maturity is not attained until the third year, according to McCurdy (1931:398).

Remarks.—Grotesquely warty newts from several localities in San Diego County, California, have been described as a subspecies (*klauberi*) of *Taricha torosa* (=*Triturus torosus*) by Wolterstorff (1938) and subsequently have been treated as a species, *Triturus klauberi,* by Bishop (1943:80-82). I agree with Twitty (1942:73) and Myers (1942a:82) in questioning the desirability of giving taxonomic recognition to this form. They believe that the warts may be due to a pathogenic agent, although sections of this tissue made by Twitty revealed no parasites. (Pl. 1.) Among the following facts are reasons for doubting the validity of *klauberi:*

(1) The presence of warts is the principal basis for the recognition of *klauberi*. Several specimens from San Luis Obispo County in the Museum of Vertebrate Zoölogy rival in wartiness animals from San Diego County. Other individuals from this county lack warts. Twitty (1942:73) reports warty individuals from near Palo Alto, California. Both warty and nonwarty individuals thus have been found together at widely separated localities with nonwarty animals in intervening areas.

(2) The character of the warts, especially around the eyes and nostrils, strongly suggests an abnormal condition. The eyes and nasal openings of many individuals are nearly closed by the swellings. Some juveniles, however, almost completely lack warts. In general there is an increase in wartiness with increase in size.

(3) In other respects, nontuberculate individuals from San Diego County are indistinguishable from the tuberculate form. The type locality of *klauberi* at Boulder Creek, from which many specimens have been taken, lies only 4 miles above the juncture of this stream with the San Diego River in which typical *torosus* occurs.

Newts from the vicinity of Berkeley (Wildcat Creek) show merging of characters of *T. torosus* and *T. granulosus.* Hybridization may occur between these species in this area. There has been artificial introduction of *Triturus* from various localities. It is unknown whether *granulosus* occurs naturally in the East Bay area, but its coexistence with *torosus* coastally north of the Salinas Valley makes such occurrence likely.

The Sierra newt, described as a species, *Triturus sierrae,* by Twitty (1942) is treated here as a subspecies of *Triturus torosus.* I merely render a taxonomic judgment and in no way discredit the excellence of Twitty's work.

SUBSPECIES

1*a*. Above yellowish brown to dark brown; below pale yellow to orange; eyelids and snout less commonly so extensively light-colored; iris generally deeper yellow and less filled out with light color (22);* tail fins of breeding male well developed (23). *Range.* As given on page 23, except for the Sierra Nevada of California. .... *T. t. torosus* (Rathke)

1*b*. Above generally reddish brown to near chocolate brown; below burnt orange (sometimes yellowish in breeding individuals); upper eyelids and tip of snout generally lighter than rest of head (18) (some animals from Butte County, however, have dark lids); iris (19) silvery to pale yellow above and below pupil; tail fins of breeding male distinctly less well developed (20). *Range.* The foothills of the Sierra Nevada to an altitude of about 7,000 feet .... *T. t. sierrae* Twitty

AMBYSTOMIDS

Family Ambystomidae

Structure.—Adults from approximately 3 inches in *Rhyacotriton* to over 11 inches in *Dicamptodon;* eyelids present; tail more or less compressed; costal grooves usually well defined; limbs well developed; toes 4-5; skin smooth; no teeth extending posteriorly between orbits; vomerine teeth in transverse series, sometimes interrupted; tongue broad, edges free except posteriorly; lungs and ypsiloid cartilage present; adults normally without gills; vertebrae amphicoelous.

Habits.—The adults are largely terrestrial, except in the breeding season. At this time the male deposits spermatophores which are picked up by the female with the lips of her cloaca. Fertilization is internal. The eggs are laid singly or in clumps, attached to objects in the water. Both pond and stream type larvae occur within the family. The larvae are sometimes paedogenic.

Range.—The family is confined to North America. There are three genera in the United States—*Ambystoma, Dicamptodon,* and *Rhyacotriton,* with *Ambystoma* ranging into Mexico. *Dicamptodon* and *Rhyacotriton* are monotypic. Three species of *Ambystoma* occur in our area.

* See Fig. 5, p. 16, for illustrations referred to by parenthetical numbers.

Key to Genera and Species
Figure 6

1*a*. Eye large, horizontal dimension equal to or greater than distance from anterior eye corner to tip of snout (1); costal grooves 14 (sometimes 15), counting one each in axilla and groin; above uniformly brown or variegated, with small whitish flecks; flecks most numerous on sides of head and body (often not discernible in preserved specimens); below orange to greenish yellow in life (cream-colored or whitish when preserved); vomerine teeth typically in two short curved series commonly separated at midline (4); vent of male with prominent rectilinear lobes (6); size of adult small, seldom over 4 inches .... *Rhyacotriton olympicus*, p. 55

1*b*. Eye smaller, horizontal dimension less than distance from anterior eye corner to tip of snout (2); costal grooves usually 12 or 13 (sometimes 11 or rarely 14), counting one each in axilla and groin; not colored as above; vomerine teeth in long continuous curved series or broken into shorter, slightly curved series (3, 5, 7); vent of male without rectilinear lobes; size of adults (except for some individuals of *Ambystoma macrodactylum*) larger 2

2*a*. Vomerine teeth in two essentially straight transverse rows separated by rather wide interspace (3); costal grooves indistinct; above brownish with black marblings (8); adult to over 11 inches .... *Dicamptodon ensatus*, p. 49

2*b*. Vomerine teeth usually in transverse row, straight or angulate, sometimes interrupted narrowly at midline or laterally (5, 7); costal grooves usually distinct; without distinctive pattern of *Dicamptodon* .... AMBYSTOMA, p. 31

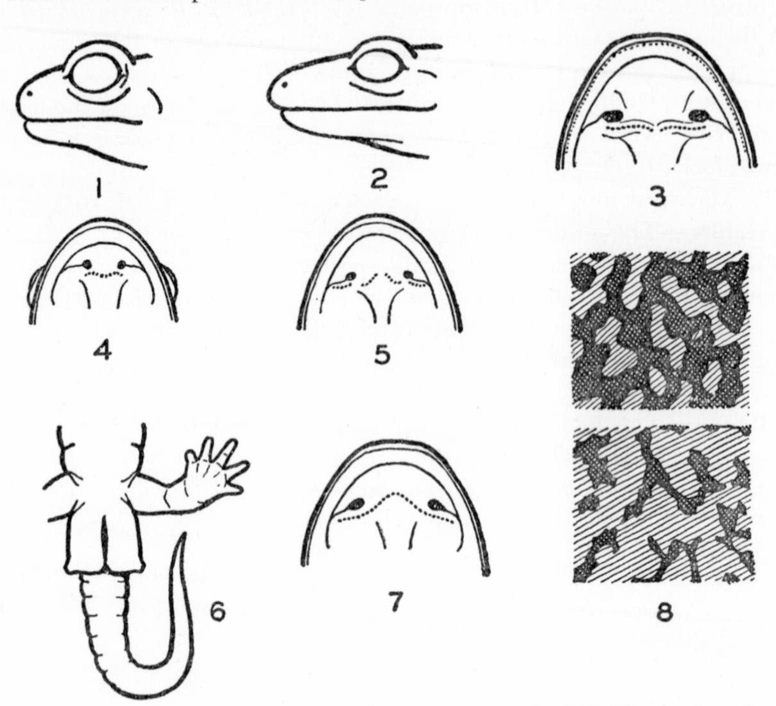

Fig. 6. 1, 4, 6, *Rhyacotriton olympicus;* 2, 5, *Ambystoma macrodactylum;* 3, 8, *Dicamptodon ensatus;* 7, *Ambystoma tigrinum* (*californiense*).

Genus *Ambystoma*

Structure.—Adults from 3½ to 13 inches; body rounded; head broad, depressed, U-shaped in dorsal aspect; eyes of most species relatively small but protuberant; limbs sturdy, with elongate, depressed, tapered toes; palmar and plantar tubercles in *A. tigrinum;* costal grooves well defined with similar, less marked furrows on sides of tail; no conspicuous guanophore-marked sensory pits on sides of head, body, and tail in adults as in *Rhyacotriton;* vent of male without rectilinear lobes; tail oval in cross section basally, becoming laterally flattened distally, weakly keeled dorsally, and unconstricted basally, adapted as a sculling organ.

Range.—From extreme southeastern Alaska and southern Labrador to the edge of the central plateau in Mexico; apparently not in Lower California.

Key to Species
Figure 7

1a. Parotoid glands present, in preserved specimens identified by enlarged openings of glands in parotoid region and sometimes by adhering whitish secretion (1); glandular ridge along upper margin of tail with similar characteristics of enlarged glandular openings and occasional adherent secretion (2); uniformly brown to blackish brown above (except for lightening in parotoid areas and along upper edge of tail) or with small irregular dull whitish or yellowish spots scattered over uniformly brown ground color; no palmar or plantar tubercles; 3 or 4 phalanges in fourth toe (4, 8); premaxillary fontanelle present (3) .... *A. gracile,* p. 32

1b. Parotoid glands absent (5); no well-marked glandular thickening along dorsal edge of tail (6); not uniformly brown above and markings not as above; palmar and plantar tubercles present (13) but sometimes poorly defined; usually 4 phalanges in fourth toe (8); premaxillary fontanelle reduced or absent (7) 2

2a. Broad light-colored stripe (usually yellowish to greenish yellow or tan in life) on dark brown to blackish ground color, extending from head onto tail (9); stripe sometimes broken into irregular patches (10); margins usually irregular; vomerine teeth in 3 or 4 series (11); palmar and plantar tubercles present but sometimes poorly defined .... *A. macrodactylum,* p. 36

2b. No dorsal light stripe or grouping of light markings centrally along back; vomerine teeth in more or less straight line, extending across roof of mouth, sometimes with slight interspaces (12); palmar and plantar tubercles present (13).......... *A. tigrinum,* p. 40

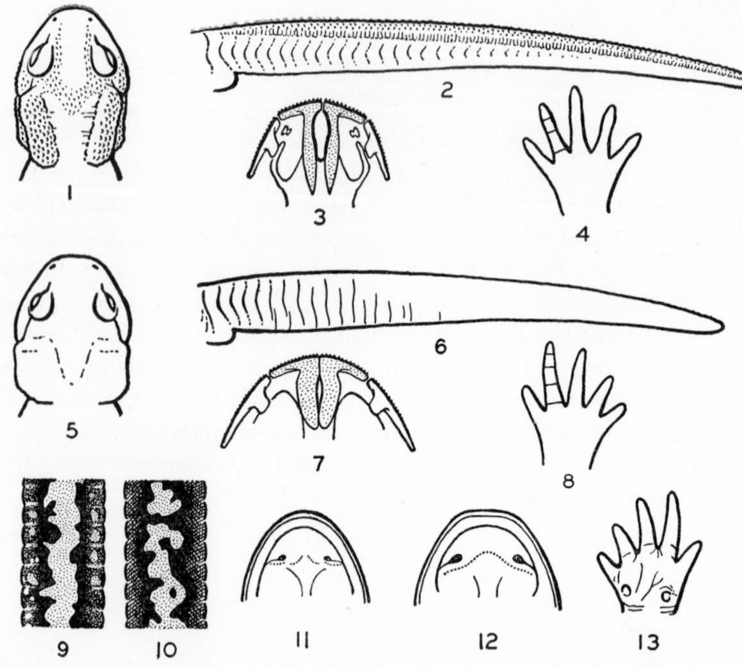

Fig. 7. 1, 2, 3, 4, *Ambystoma gracile;* 5, 6, 7, 8, 12, 13, *A. tigrinum* (*californiense*); 9, 10, 11, *A. macrodactylum.*

NORTHWESTERN SALAMANDER

Ambystoma gracile (Baird)
Plate 3

Range.—Principally the humid coastal forest of the Pacific Northwest from southeastern Alaska, south to the mouth of the Gualala River in northern Sonoma County, California. Professor Slater informs me (*in litt.*) that he has specimens from just east of the Cascade Divide in Washington. (Pl. 49.)

Type locality.—Cascade Mountains, Oregon, near latitude 44° N. (Baird, 1859b:13).

Description.—STRUCTURE. Adult 6 to somewhat over 8 inches in length; varied development of large oval glandular area behind each eye (parotoid glands); eyes prominent; vomerine teeth in nearly straight transverse series, continuous or separated at midline (or elsewhere), to form 2 to

4 groups of teeth; costal grooves 11 or 12, sometimes 10, counting one each in axilla and groin; rounded glandular ridge running length of upper edge of tail; feet without plantar and palmar tubercles, differing in this regard from *A. tigrinum*. COLOR. Ground color uniformly brown to blackish brown above, often lighter on glandular areas mentioned; above with small irregular whitish, bronze, or yellowish markings of varying size (*decorticatum*) or without such marks (*gracile*); below lighter brown to slate; iris dark brown with varied development of silvery guanophores or uniformly blackish. SEXUAL DIFFERENCES. Vent of male more swollen and lined with villose papillae, lacking in female. Margin of vent of female pleated, pleats intersecting vent opening. Male lacks pleated vent margins. Female probably averages shorter tail than male. Of 6 adults in the Museum of Vertebrate Zoölogy, 2 males have tails ½ and 1 inch longer than the snout-vent measurement. Of 4 females, two have tails 3/16 and ¼ inch shorter than the body, one a tail the same length as the body, and one a tail ¼ inch longer than the snout-vent measurement.

Adult female, obtained February 15, 1947, 4 miles north of Orick, 100 feet elevation, Humboldt County, California: Above uniformly dark brown (Clove Brown); glandular area below parotoids tan or light yellowish brown dorsally; dorsal surface of tail toward its base slightly lighter than remainder of dorsal ground color; below grayish purple; iris uniformly blackish.

Habitat.—Found from sea level to 8,000 feet on Mount Rainier, Pierce County, Washington (Slevin, 1928:27). Frequents damp places beneath bark, logs, and other objects in humid coastal areas. Breeds in quiet or slowly flowing permanent water. In the Vancouver region, British Columbia, the species frequents ponds with mud bottoms and with quantities of decaying vegetation or, as at Alta Lake, may inhabit ponds with boulder bottoms, largely without plant growth.

Behavior.—Scarcity of adults of this species in the Museum of Vertebrate Zoölogy suggests that, at least in California, metamorphosed individuals are rare or their habits are such that they are seldom encountered.

Four miles north of Orick, elevation about 100 feet, Humboldt County, California, February 14, 1947, Alden H. Miller and I found 2 adult males and a female. A pair was discovered beneath boards a few feet from a stream in an open area in a forest consisting principally of redwood and Port Orford cedar. The area appeared to have been subjected recently to high water. On November 17, 1948, 8.9 miles northwest of Navarro, Mendocino County, California, I found an adult 50 feet from a stream in an area that gave evidence of having been recently inundated.

Reproduction.—On February 23, 1931, Slater (1936:234, Washington) and H. Hubbel were observing amphibians in a small pond near a street that crosses South Tacoma swamp. The water temperature was 60°F. At this time the salamanders were migrating up the stream. Nearly all the *Ambystoma gracile* appeared to be gravid females, although only one in ten were transformed adults. No courtship activities were observed. Nearly a hundred bunches of eggs of this species were fastened to the vegetation at the edge of the pond.

EGGS. Slater (1936:234-35) in the vicinity of Tacoma, Washington, found egg masses fastened to sticks, such as willow branches or small limbs of fallen trees, from 6 to 24 inches under water in ponds, usually in shallow water near the edges. If firm supports are not available, heavier grasses and herbs are used for attachment. Egg clusters measure from 2 to 6 inches by 2 to 3 inches and contain approximately 30 to as many as 270 eggs; ovum 2 to 3 mm., situated in viscous jelly measuring 6.0 to 7.5 mm. to inner surface of outer capsule; animal pole brown to black, vegetal pole creamy gray to white; outer capsule of clear firm jelly about 2.5 mm. thick (or greater, depending on stage of development); diameter of egg to outer capsule approximately 11 to 15 mm.; outer layer resembles in consistency that of egg masses of *Triturus torosus*. Some eggs of this species may possess a green alga that lines the inner surface of the capsule. This layer of small round nonmotile algal cells appears in older eggs. Method of entrance and possible function of the algal cells is not known, although it may be the same as has been suggested for the wood frog (p. 378).

The time of deposition of the eggs varies with season, altitude, and latitude. In Pierce County, Washington, eggs are laid from January to July 20, and hatch in from 2 to 4 weeks (Slater, 1936:235). Carl and Cowan (1945a:43) found eggs in the Jordan River, British Columbia, on April 20, 1941, and Carl (1943:28) states that at sea level in British Columbia eggs are laid from February to May. Older eggs possessed green algae. Patch (1922:76) reports eggs "possibly of this species" on June 27, at Bella Coola, British Columbia, "in a cold, seeping glacial stream." These masses, about 60 mm. in diameter and one of which contained 87 eggs, "were attached to submerged weed stems and distributed over an area of about a square yard." The eggs had a pale greenish tint, while the surrounding gelatinous mass was clear. Watney (1941:14) has observed egg masses in March, April, and May in different years at Beaver Lake, Vancouver, British Columbia. Hatching occurred in May with about one month required for the development of the eggs.

LARVA. Pond type; 9, occasionally 7, 8, or 10 (counting smallest nubbins) gill rakers on anterior face of third arch; when recently hatched, head and sides of body essentially uniformly colored but pigment may be concentrated along upper sides to form longitudinal stripe on either side near juncture of dorsal fin with body; stripe may be interrupted by whitish or yellowish patches. Older larva deep brown to olive green, with tinges of lighter color on head; many small irregular dark spots may be scattered over dorsum and upper sides (in some individuals from Vancouver [Watney, 1941:15], distinct yellow spots are present on sides of trunk and tail); below cream to pale gray. Larvae 52.0 to 72.5 mm. in length, from Brent's Lake near Summerland, British Columbia, are described by Logier (1932:316) as having light yellow ground color with brown mottlings which showed vertical arrangement on body and were scattered on tail and fins; yellow line, practically free from mottling, extended along side of body and tail. In older larvae, tail fins are reduced, a tendency accompanying increase in size; a roughened strip is present at juncture of tail fin with fleshy portion of tail, representing glandular area of adult; preserved specimens (especially large larvae) may possess a milky exudate in this zone and in the parotoid regions.

Larvae were 14 to 15 mm. in length at hatching at Vancouver, British Columbia (Watney, 1941). Some do not metamorphose until the second spring (or summer), when they are 75 to 90 mm. in length, while others remain as pedogenics for an unknown length of time. John Davis obtained larvae of two sizes at Old Fort Clatsop, Clatsop County, Oregon, August 24, 1940. The larger ones were very nearly ready to metamorphose. They were approximately 4¾ to 6¼ inches in length. The smaller larvae were about 2 to 3 inches in length. On February 23, 1931, Slater (1936:234) observed a paedogenic larva, 140 mm. long, clasp a plant stem and, in 62 minutes, deposit 45 eggs. The eggs developed normally. Carl (1944:34) states that the main food of larvae in Croteau Lake, Vancouver Island, British Columbia, appears to be small clams (*Pisidium*).

Subspecies

(Characters from Dunn, 1944:129-30)

1*a*. Three phalanges in fourth toe; parotoid glands well developed; vomerine teeth usually in four groups, two as in *decorticatum* (see below) and two posterior to and beyond choanae; uniformly dark brown to blackish above except sometimes for lightening in parotoid areas and along upper edge of tail. *Range*. From southern British Columbia on mainland and Vancouver Island, south, west of the crest of the Cascades, into California; in California in coastal mountains to mouth of the Gualala River, northern Sonoma County. Also at Brent's Lake, British Columbia . . . *A. g. gracile* (Baird)

1*b*. Four phalanges in fourth toe; parotoid glands less well developed; vomerine teeth usually in two groups, behind and between choanae; above with pepper-and-salt coloration of light dots (yellowish, bronze, or whitish in life) on dark background. *Range*. Coastal region of southeastern Alaska and British Columbia to about latitude 51°N. (immediately north of northern end of Vancouver Island) . . . . *A. g. decorticatum* Cope

Remarks.—Dunn (1944) has called attention to light-spotted individuals in the Olympic Mountains of Washington which in other respects resemble the race *gracile.* He has suggested the possibility of an undescribed race in the Olympic Mountains. Carl (1944:34) mentions bronze spotting in adults from near Croteau Lake, Forbidden Plateau, Vancouver Island, yet Dunn lists *gracile* as occurring on Vancouver Island. Study should be made of variation in the species in northern Washington and southern British Columbia to determine the nature of the zone of intergradation.

LONG-TOED SALAMANDER

Ambystoma macrodactylum Baird
Plate 3

Range.—From Calaveras and Alpine counties, California, north in the Sierra Nevada into the mountains of northern California, thence through Oregon (except southeastern part) and Washington to northern British Columbia; eastward through central and northern Idaho into western Montana. (Pl. 49.)

In California the species ranges to an elevation of 8,800 feet. At the opposite extreme, a single adult (UCDDZ 3091) was found near Stockton, 1/4 mile from the San Joaquin River, San Joaquin County, on the floor of the Great Valley, at a few feet above sea level. This is the only specimen known from the valley and probably was an escaped animal or one carried there by stream action from the high country of the Sierra Nevada. The date of collection, May 22, 1927, may be significant in the latter regard. This is near the time of high water from melting snows and not long after the usual breeding time of these salamanders.

Ruthven's (1912:517) *Ambystoma stejnegeri* (=*macrodactylum*) described from a small number of specimens taken at Bloomfield, Davis County, Iowa, is apparently the only record east of the Rocky Mountains. This occurrence needs confirmation.

Type locality.—Astoria, Oregon (Baird, 1850:292).

Description.—STRUCTURE. Adult 3 1/2 to over 5 inches; eyes prominent, proportionately somewhat larger than in *A. tigrinum;* costal grooves 12 to 13 (sometimes 14), counting one each in axilla and groin; palmar and plantar tubercles present but sometimes not well defined; vomerine teeth usually in four series arranged in transverse row. COLOR. Ground color above dark brown to black with broad, median longitudinal light stripe of tan to yellow or yellowish green to dark olive green (often slaty in preservative); stripe sometimes rather even-edged but more often with undulating borders; stripe may be interrupted by circular or oval areas of ground color and in some individuals may be broken into irregular patches; stripe extends well toward tip of tail; sides of head and body with varying numbers of white flecks (guanophores) which may extend onto sides of tail; below dark brown or sooty, speckled with white guanophores; preserved specimens may be sooty, pale brown, or dull yellowish below, depending largely on state of dispersion or concentration of pigment of ventral melanophores; ventral color usually somewhat lighter along margin of gular fold and about vent; iris dark brown with scattering of golden flecks. SEXUAL DIFFERENCES. Male with proportionately longer vent opening than female, with vertical rows of papillae on closely set folds that extend from margin interiorly; vent region of breeding male bulbous. Female with shorter cloacal aperture and vent folds without papillae; small rosette of folds, situated anteriorly (evident without spreading vent), set off from posterior, more concealed folds (observation based on preserved specimens); vent region of female not swollen. Head of male appears proportionately less broad in region of eyes than in female.

Adult, obtained on April 30, 1949, 4 miles southwest of Chester, Plumas County, California: Dorsal stripe greenish yellow (Yellow Ocher), brightest on basal half of tail, composed of metallic-appearing cells, greenish gold in color and closely set about glands; melanic network seems to be absent in area of stripe; stripe margined with solid black, lightening laterally; few spots, colored like dorsal stripe, situated lateral to it on upper sides of body and head, and on upper surfaces of limbs; below sooty with purplish tinge (between Deep Quaker Drab and Quaker Drab), darkest on undersides of hind limbs, lightest in gular area; melanophores of venter form weakly connected network; moderately abundant and regular ventral stippling of white, generally single, guanophores over all ventral surfaces; ground color darkens laterally from ventral to dorsal surfaces; guanophores of sides like those ventrally, although many slightly larger and more widely spaced, absent in zone of black pigment (about half width of dorsal stripe) that margins stripe; iris blackish with gold patch in upper part, overlaid by network of blood vessels just above pupil; flecks of dull orange-brown pigment in lower iris.

Habitat.—Adults may be found in the vicinity of ponds or lakes beneath rocks, logs, or other objects. At Crater Lake, Oregon, Schonberger (1944:-257), in the summer of 1935, found adults under rocks near water, and larvae under rocks overlying water connected with the lake. During most of the year transformed individuals are subterranean, at least at lower elevations. Evermann (1897:235) in August, 1896, found many individuals on the shore of Crater Lake under Red Cloud Cliff, in Eagle Cove, and a few about Wizard Island. The salamanders were found under the rocks, just above the edge of the water of the lake. Sometimes as many as a dozen or 15 were found under a single flat stone. Individuals have been taken beneath loose bark of fallen trees and inside rotten logs. Adults enter ponds and lakes to breed.

Four adults were found by Lee Talbot, July 15, 1945, near the Highland Pacific Gas and Electric Reservoir, at 6,820 feet, on the Ebbetts Pass Road, Alpine County, California. One was under the bark of a dead fir tree which lay across a creek that was largely dry except for scattered small pools; two others were found under damp logs along the creek and the fourth under water in leaf litter on the creek bottom. Talbot also collected an adult at Lake Alpine, Alpine County, California, on June 28, 1946. According to his field notes, it was " . . . crawling over the damp ground in a hollow stump early in the morning." Two others were taken at Union Reservoir, 7 miles south of Lake Alpine, " . . . inside rotten, damp logs. They were very sluggish when first found." The dorsal stripe of one was greenish yellow, of the others pale yellowish with a slightly reddish-brown tinge, " . . . almost exactly the color of rotten wood."

Two adults were collected by John Davis and his wife on April 30, 1949, 4 miles southwest of Chester, Plumas County, California. They were found on damp soil beneath logs in a relatively dry portion of a meadow about 100 feet from the nearest water. The meadow was fringed by lodgepole pines.

In July, 1930, larvae were found in numbers in two small unnamed "lakes" on the Alpine County Highway, California. These pools were shallow-margined and clear of aquatic vegetation. The water may have had an acid reaction because of the pine and hemlock needles constantly falling into it. The larvae were seen on the bottom about the margins of the pools, in the shallower water, 12 inches or less in depth. They were dark-colored, closely resembling the fine dark brown to blackish, peaty bottom material. They were exceedingly wary, like those of the lowland California tiger salamander, and had to be scooped out individually. (From Storer, MS.)

Food.—Primarily a scavenger, eating pieces of ants, beetles, and flies, but takes a few live aquatic insect larvae such as those of coleopterous, dipterous, and trichopterous insects (Farner, 1947:259). Food of 10 adults from Crater Lake, Oregon, examined by Schonberger (1944:257) consisted of spiders and insects, including larvae of stoneflies, crane flies, and dragonflies, and adults of beetles, crane flies, mosquitoes, house flies, and camel crickets. Five larvae had eaten mainly larvae and adults of *Chironomus,* a few amphipods (*Hyalella*), *Cyclops,* and odonate larvae.

Reproduction.—Professor James Slater informs me that in Washington the adults go to the breeding ponds shortly after the snow melts and the ponds become free of ice. During courtship the male clasps the female just back of her forelegs and gives short shakes.

EGGS. Laid singly or in small groups of 8 or 10. If the pond is shallow they may be deposited on the bottom, but if deep, with no shallow places, they are usually attached to grasses at the edges. Fitch (1936:636) found eggs and larvae in creeks that dry up completely in summer in the Rogue River Basin, Oregon. From a female 127 mm. in length, 184 mature eggs were taken (Slater, 1936:236). Carl (1942:56) found freshly spawned eggs near Langford Station, 8 miles northwest of Victoria, Vancouver Island, on March 9, 1941, and advanced larvae in May and July. Fitch (1936:636) found freshly spawned eggs in mid-February and mid-March in the Rogue River Basin, Oregon. Ovum 2.5 mm., black at animal pole with lower 2/5 at vegetal pole light gray; 2 jelly envelopes with line of demarcation between them indistinct; inner envelope 6 to 7 mm. in diameter, outer 12 to 17 mm. in diameter, depending on age of egg (Slater, 1936:235).

LARVA. Pond type, in form resembling other ambystomid larvae; 7 larvae, 2 from British Columbia and remainder from Shasta County, California, examined by me, possessed from 9 to 13 gill rakers on anterior face of third arch; general coloration light olive gray to brownish gray, mottled with brownish and black; below whitish. In the region of the Olympic Mountains of Washington, Slater (1936:235) found that eggs hatched in 5 to 15 days. He states that at sea level larvae may transform in July while in the high mountains most do not metamorphose until the beginning of their second year. The size at metamorphosis is about 60 to 75 mm. (Slater, 1936:236).

In the vicinity of Lake Alpine, in the Sierra Nevada of California, above 7,000 feet, H. J. Snook on September 7, 1936, found larvae of two lengths suggesting that they overwinter before metamorphosis, transforming in their second season. The two size groups were individuals 1¾ to 2 inches and 3½ to 4 inches in length.

Remarks.—Breeding adults can be obtained if a net is dragged along the bottoms of shallow ponds where the salamanders lie concealed in mud or under masses of algae, or they may be found together in numbers under boards in slimy mud at edges of ponds and ditches (Fitch, 1936, Rogue River Basin, Oregon).

Mittleman (1948) has recently proposed two races of this species, *A. m. macrodactylum* Baird—in the Columbia Plateau province and northern Basin and Range province in Washington and Oregon, through the Cascade-Sierra province and Pacific Border province from Calaveras County, California, to southeastern British Columbia; the other, *A. m. krausei* Peters—known definitely from the northern Rocky Mountains province in Idaho and Montana, and from southwestern Alberta and British Columbia as far west as Kamloops, and probably north to latitude 58°N.; recorded also from Iowa. These races are differentiated on differences in vomerine teeth counts, relative head width in relation to head length and body length, and coloration. According to Mittleman, the subspecies *macrodactylum* averages a greater number of vomerine teeth, broader head, and less often has a greenish dorsal band than *krausei*.

In my opinion there is too great overlap in the characters submitted as criteria for recognition of these races. The color differences presented are unconvincing.

TIGER SALAMANDER

Ambystoma tigrinum (Green)
Plate 5

Range.—Widely distributed throughout the United States. Not found in New England and the Appalachian uplands, central and southern Florida, Nevada, California except the Central Valley and central coast, and Oregon and western Washington. Barely enters Ontario and is not known in Quebec but is otherwise present in southern Canada. Occurs pretty well over the whole of the Mexican Plateau and onto the coastal plain in Vera Cruz, but apparently does not enter Baja California. (Principally from Dunn, 1940.) Found at over 10,000 feet in Colorado. (Pl. 52.)

Smith and Taylor (1948) hold the view that *A. tigrinum*, with the exception of *A. t. proserpine* in the vicinity of southern Texas, does not occur in Mexico but is replaced by many species.

Oregon records for this species (Slevin, 1928), with the dubious exception of The Dalles, are evidently all erroneous. Storer (MS) has examined the USNM specimens upon which the following locality records are based: Portland, Astoria, Hood River, and Cascade Mountains. The first three are based on *Dicamptodon;* the last on *Ambystoma gracile* (the type).

Reed (1951) has reported larval ambystomid salamanders [probably of this species], in Parker Canyon, at an elevation of 5,000 feet, in the Huachuca Mountains of southern Arizona and in the area of the El Tigre and Santa Maria mines (approximately latitude 30°-31° and longitude 109°-110°), Sonora, Mexico.

Type locality.—Near Moorestown, New Jersey (Green, 1825).

Description.—STRUCTURE. Adult 6 to slightly over 13 inches (Smith, 1949:71); eyes small, interorbital distance 1½ to 2 times their width; vomerine teeth in more or less straight line or arched somewhat anteriorly, sometimes separated by one or more slight interspaces; costal grooves 11 to 13, counting one each in axilla and groin; ventral surfaces of forefoot and hind foot with an inner and outer tubercle. Subspecies structurally closely similar but coloration differs and shows considerable uniformity in various geographic areas. COLOR. Dorsal surface ranges from uniformly yellowish to vaguely dark-spotted on yellowish in individuals of race *diaboli* to the reverse, yellow bars and spots on dark ground color in *mavortium;* below generally gray to flesh-colored with subdued yellowish markings sometimes present, particularly ventrolaterally. SEXUAL DIFFERENCES. Cloacal region of breeding male strongly protuberant. In animals from Chicago area, Pope (1944:46) notes that vent is longer in male, and males average larger and generally have longer tails (longer than body) than females.

Habitat.—The adults spend considerable time in seclusion in the dry season, in burrows of other animals (such as ground squirrels, marmots, prairie dogs, and badgers) and in decayed stumps, but during rainy weather they may be found on the surface beneath bark, logs, rocks, and other objects. The use of underground retreats probably has been important in making it possible for this species to inhabit semiarid regions. This salamander requires fresh-water pools, ponds, slowly flowing streams, and lakes for breeding.

Individuals of the race *mavortium,* taken by Hamilton (1946:51), illustrate summer occurrence in the southern part of the range. Four specimens, ranging from 122 to 150 mm., were obtained on June 14, 1943, in arid country, miles from any stream, on the Mesa Del Oro Plateau, at approximately 6,000 feet, 50 miles southwest of Albuquerque. They were in ground squirrel burrows (*Citellus spilosoma*) at depths of 14 to 20 inches where the sand was slightly damp. Their stomachs were empty.

At the northern extreme of the range, the species exhibits similar habits during summer. Breckenridge (1944:51, Minnesota) tells of a farmer who found more than a score of these salamanders about 4 feet below the ground in a grass-lined burrow (probably a deserted ground squirrel den).

The race *californiense,* like *mavortium,* lives in regions that are dry during a large part of the year, hence individuals spend much time beneath the ground, probably often in burrows of ground squirrels and other animals. The salamanders may be found on the surface during the rainy season after the appearance of rain pools which provide breeding places. Many such ponds are transient, drying up in summer. Individuals have been found in damp cellars, in ditching operations, and beneath surface objects in damp situations.

Taylor (1929:65, Kansas) reports that "Adults were found about midnight coming to the surface of the ground out of prairie dog holes in a prairie dog town about 300 yards north of the river and about 200 yards from a reservoir. Only a single salamander was found in each hole."

At Pinetop (7,315 feet), Arizona, on July 29, 1949, I observed many larvae, probably over 100, in a pond 15 by 75 yards and possibly 1 to 1½ feet deep. The water was held in check by an earthen dam at the end of a gradually sloping grassy field. There were many masses of pale yellow-green algae in the water, especially at the edges of the pond. The larvae were found in shallow water near shore. Many were lurking under the algal mats which their color matched closely. When disturbed, they swam rapidly to deeper water, usually stirring up a cloud of sediment as they went. Water at the edge of the pond at a depth of 2 inches was 28.2°C. at about 4:00 P.M. *Thamnophis elegans vagrans* and *Bufo woodhousii* were present. The surrounding country consisted of grassy open meadows among yellow pines and oaks.

Behavior.—Active on the surface of the ground for only a short period during the year. Individuals may emerge from summer retreats in some parts of the range in late fall (Minnesota), upon the advent of rainy or foggy weather. In other, drier regions, particularly during dry years, aestivation may merge with hibernation and surface activity is restricted to the short breeding period of winter or early spring. At such times surface activity usually occurs at night, many individuals appearing for a few days at breeding ponds and then disappearing until the following year.

Prosser (1911) observed the behavior of larvae at Park Lake, Tolland, Colorado in the summer of 1909. If the salamanders were to be active, the water had to be close to 70°F. During the day they chose shallow water close by deep water where the temperature was near 70°F. At night the larvae went out to deep water probably because it did not cool to so low a point as did the shallow water. They returned in the morning from the deep water to the shallow water only when the temperature of the latter had risen above that of the former. Larvae seemed to favor the parts of the lake where there were rocks for concealment and extensive growth of *Spirogyra*.

Food.—The following items have been recorded: ADULTS (in captivity). Earthworms, mollusks, insects, fish, other salamanders, frogs, a small snake (*Thamnophis s. sirtalis*), and baby mice (Pope, 1944:51; Duellman, 1948:164).

LARVAE. Small worms; small mussels and snails; crustaceans—entomostraca; insects, both aquatic and nonaquatic; small fish—trout; amphibians—spadefoot tadpoles, and larval members of own species (Little and Keller, 1937; Smith, 1934:404; Rahn, 1941).

Sixteen individuals examined by Tanner (1931:169), presumably larvae, had eaten the following: Five specimens from Salamander Lake, Mount

Timpanogos, Utah, elevation 7,500 feet—mollusks (*Stagnicola palustris* [75 per cent] and *Pisidium abditium* [10 per cent]) and insects (caddisfly larvae in cases of *Lemna minor* [15 per cent]); and 11 specimens from San Juan and Iron counties—7 with stomachs empty, the remainder with *Pisidium variabile* and larval and adult beetles (*Dytiscus*), corixids, chironomid larvae, 2 muscoid flies, and detritus.

Reproduction.—In early spring, March in northern areas and middle December through February farther south or in drier regions (in range of *californiense*), the adults leave their subterranean retreats and enter ponds to breed. The first individuals in northern areas may arrive before the ice has disappeared. In at least some parts of the range, breeding seems to depend on rainfall. This is true of *californiense* which may congregate several times in winter during periods of rain. Large adults in New Mexico have been found in what appeared to be breeding condition in summer, following heavy summer rains.

Twitty (1941:1) has described the movement of individuals of the race *californiense* to breeding territory. During the first heavy rain of the season, on January 1, 1940, following a dry summer, Professor W. H. Rich obtained approximately 45 adults between 10 and 11 P.M. on the highway bordering Lake Lagunita near the Stanford golf course, Palo Alto, California. Many of these were males, found crawling in the direction of the lake, which had not yet begun to fill. The lake fills with the onset of winter rains. A few nights later, after another rain, Twitty visited the same half-mile stretch of road and in three excursions between 7:30 and 10 P.M. obtained 15 females and 8 males. In addition, 5 or 6 injured or killed animals were seen. The predominance of females on this trip suggests a differential in the onset of migration of the sexes.

Other observations of mass movements, probably to breeding sites, are those of Bauman (1950:4-5) and Pierson (1950:23-24). On June 18, 1949, at about 8:10 A.M., Bauman and an associate observed a migration of salamanders across the highway about 1.2 miles northeast of Tower Junction in Yellowstone National Park. Their number was estimated at about 100 or more and it required about 15 minutes for the animals to complete the crossing. They ranged from 3 to 8 inches in length. The salamanders may have been headed for a small lake south of the highway. Pierson saw a similar migration in the same area, presumably in 1935. The animals were crossing the highway in great numbers headed, however, in the opposite direction from those observed by Bauman.

Kumpf (1934) has described the courtship of transformed *Ambystoma tigrinum* as observed in the laboratory. The male noses other individuals indiscriminately but ultimately concentrates on females, nudging them in the midventral region and along the sides, sometimes balancing the nosed animal on his head for several moments, or pushing her to the surface. Following this activity, he crawls ahead of the female, rubbing his cloaca against the substratum, while the female walks behind him, her nose at the angle between his hind leg and tail. The tails of both animals are held at a right angle to the substratum and are waved in an undulatory fashion. The male extends his legs sideways, elevating them from ground, then deposits the spermatophore. The female assumes a similar pose and picks up the sperm capsule with the lips of her cloaca. Secretions from the cloaca and skin probably play an important part in arousing the interest of the female, since she will not pick up an isolated spermatophore unrelated to male activity.

Gasco (1881) observed the courtship of larvae. This takes place under water. It consists of rubbing of bodies, varied with short nips at each other and an occasional trip by the male about the immediate vicinity. There is much lashing of bodies and tails. After both individuals are aroused by this "play," the male moves off in front of the female who normally follows with her snout in contact with his cloacal region. The male then deposits a spermatophore but not unless the female has responded in the above manner. Three to 7 spermatophores may be deposited. The female may stop over one of these picking up the sperm capsule with her cloacal lips. She may use her hind legs to push the spermatophore into place. If the female does not follow the male at his first invitation, he returns to continue his "play" until she is sufficiently aroused to do so.

Hamilton (1948a:212-13) describes the egg-laying of this species (subspecies *nebulosum*) in Colorado. "Five female adults collected from Muskee Lake, located 15 miles west of Boulder, Colorado, at an altitude of 8,300 ft., were observed to lay eggs over a two-hour period, immediately after transfer from their natural environment (59°F.) to the laboratory (70°F.) in Boulder (5,300 ft.). The total length of time required for any one female to deposit all of her eggs was not determined.

"The anal sphincter was contracted along the anterior-posterior axis in such a fashion that the mucous membranes of the cloaca were readily visible through the anus. These membranes were quite red and indicated considerable congestion of the smaller blood-vessels. The cloacal glands are always enlarged and the mucous membranes somewhat congested during the breeding season, and this congested condition was greatly increased by the irritation due to rubbing. The animals moved quite rapidly over the bottom of the aquarium and an effort was made to keep the anal region in contact with the coarse gravel bottom as much as possible. Pebbles of a diameter of 0.5 of a centimeter or more, twigs, and aquarium plants were selected as surfaces for deposition of the eggs.

"The egg-laying was continuous except for short interruptions when the salamander rose to the surface for air. The female was in constant motion over the bottom and paused only to deposit the eggs. Eggs were laid in any position that afforded contact of the anus to the surface upon which they were placed. Quite often the animal was suspended beneath the stem upon which the eggs were to be laid with the fore part of the body floating free and the posterior region tightly clasped to the stem. The eggs were deposited singly and the female gradually moved along the object as the eggs were laid. The largest number of eggs deposited in a single operation, that is, touching one another, were seven, although egg masses up to forty had been collected in the various lakes. The number of eggs per egg-mass in nature is extremely variable, with occasional single eggs.

"When a small rock, twig, or other surface was selected for depositing the egg, the object was tightly clasped between the hind limbs, and the anus was rubbed vigorously in a lateral plane against the surface of the object. The tail was elevated in a vertical plane, and moved from side to side quite rapidly. At other times the tail moved rather slowly. The tail and body movements suddenly ceased and the animal remained quite motionless with its anal opening tightly pressed against the surface for from one to three seconds as the egg was laid.

"The vigorous rubbing of the anus upon objects upon which eggs were deposited seemed to be a preliminary step necessary for the actual deposition of the egg. This rubbing movement appeared to act as a stimulus for the extrusion of the egg or eggs although rubbing frequently occurred without deposition of an egg.

"During the egg-laying process the female's body was arched upward between the fore and hind limbs. The head was lowered somewhat, but the tail was noticeably elevated, sometimes as much as thirty degrees, and reached its greatest elevation at the end of the egg deposition. Muscular contractions that began about one centimeter anterior to the hind limbs and traveled posteriorly to the anal region along the body wall, were observed occasionally during the deposition of the egg. Other muscular contractions had their beginning immediately back of the forelimbs and passed posteriorly to the region of the hind limbs along the sides. The contractions arising in the region of the lower abdomen seemed to be for the purpose of passing the egg along the lower part of the oviduct, while those contractions arising in the more anterior region of the body might help in the movement of eggs within the body cavity and with their entrance into the ostium.

"Male salamanders present in the aquarium paid no attention to the egg-laying although two nonlaying females were observed eating eggs."

EGGS. Laid singly or in small clusters as in *californiense, melanostictum,* and *mavortium,* or in larger globular or oblong masses (2¼ inches by 2¾ inches) consisting of from 23 to 110 eggs, averaging 52 (Bishop, 1943:162), as in *tigrinum*. Gasco (1881:332-33) records 1,047 eggs as the full complement of a single female. These were laid in groups of 12 to 20. Eggs are attached to twigs, weeds, and other objects in relatively quiet water, usually at rather shallow depths. They are usually deposited late in winter in the southern part of the range and early in spring farther north. Ovum 1.9 to 4.0 mm., light to dark brown above, pale cream to buff below, surrounded by 3 jelly envelopes consisting of 2 somewhat denser inner coats with thicker soft outer coat; egg with membranes measures 4.5 to 10.0 mm. in diameter. Eggs hatch in about 14 (Ruthven, Thompson, and Gaige, 1928:26) to 18 or 20 days (Smith, 1911).

LARVA. Pond type but lacks balancers; 17 to 22 gill rakers on anterior face of third arch; vomerine teeth in U-shaped pattern with arms of U directed posteriorly; dorsal fin extending anteriorly to region above axillae; above mottled dark brown to black and yellow; below commonly yellowish, unmarked; iris golden yellow surrounded by black in race *californiense*. Mosauer (1932:4) describes living larvae found July 23, 1930, in a shallow isolated pond in Dark Canyon, Guadalupe Mountains, New Mexico, as light greenish; Smith (1934:402) young larvae of race *mavortium* in Kansas as greenish, with no or but 3 to 4 very indistinct, broad blotches across back, and larger larvae as uniform grayish above, lighter below, with no markings; and Breckenridge (1944:50, in Minnesota) as yellowish green, with series of dark spots and a light lateral stripe; large larvae as pale dingy yellow, finely peppered with dark spots tending to clump into blotches.

Larvae 2½ inches in total length, obtained June 25, 1949, on the south side of the University of Utah campus, Salt Lake City, Salt Lake County, Utah: Greenish yellow or light greenish olive above, including dorsal fin; whitish below; orange-yellow area on sides between limbs; light blotches on tail and body greenish yellow; gill filaments buff with greenish tinge; iris copper.

Larva about 3 inches in length, obtained 8 miles south-southwest of Flagstaff, Coconino County, Arizona: Above olive green, spotted with sooty; lemon-yellow spots in row on upper sides; tail membranes light brownish olive with sooty variegations; below gold, reduced in gular area which tends toward whitish; underside of limbs and tail grayish olive; gill filaments light brown; iris dull copper with narrow, pale gold pupillary ring.

At hatching larvae may be about 10 to 15 mm. in length. Metamorphosis occurs in approximately 2 to 4 months, late in summer, according to Cope (1889). Larvae of *californiense* transform at about 3 inches in length while those of *tigrinum* may reach 4⅞ inches. Other races as axolotls may reach 7 to 10 inches but may transform at smaller size. In the race *tigrinum*, according to Pope (1944:50), sexual maturity may be reached in the spring following transformation.

In some areas larvae may be exceedingly abundant. At Medical Lake, Spokane County, Washington, they are seined locally at night for fish bait. As many as 159 individuals have been taken in a single drag of the net and 209 dozen animals in one evening. These larvae were sold at 50 cents per dozen. They were 3 to 7 inches long (Slater, 1934b:190).

Slater (1937:82) records egg-laying by larvae from 10 miles north of Chelan, Chelan County, Washington. In addition to *melanostictum*—*diaboli, mavortium,* and probably also *nebulosum* are sometimes pedogenic. Pedogenesis appears impossible for *californiense* in most areas where it occurs, because of the ephemeral character of the breeding ponds.

An individual hatched in captivity lived 11 years after transformation (Blanchard, 1932:99). One in the Philadelphia Zoölogical Garden lived 10 years, 4 months (Conant and Hudson, 1949:2). Flower (1925:284) says there are many records in the London Zoölogical Gardens of axolotls living for 4, 5, and 6 years and there is a record of one living 9 years, 4 months, and 20 days.

Remarks.—Some individuals fail to metamorphose. Rahn (1941), writing about the species in Wyoming, notes the following: An active thyroid is necessary for transformation. If the gland is removed, no transformation occurs but thyroid feeding will cause metamorphosis in these operated animals. Perhaps failure to metamorphose in nature is due to an underfunctioning of the thyroid. Wyoming and most of the Rocky Mountain area are in the so-called "goiter belt" (where both humans and livestock suffer from goiter). The cause of this condition is related to insufficient iodine in the diet. It is possible certain lakes are deficient in iodine. In eastern United States, the species invariably transforms, while in such western regions as Colorado, Wyoming, and southward to Mexico, this process is much delayed or never occurs.

Failure to metamorphose can have disastrous results. Rahn (1941:14) tells of finding some 1,200 10- and 12-inch axolotls dead in a dried-up pond in the Red Desert region of Wyoming. On the other hand, in a permanent body of water there is an ample food supply for a larval form throughout the warm season and no danger of desiccation, in contrast to an adult existence along the arid shore lines.

Key to Subspecies

Figure 8

1a. Above with dark spots and blotches on yellowish, gray-green, to dark gray ground color or uniformly dark-colored (1, 2); ventral surfaces lighter, sometimes with spots and blotches of dusky 2

1b. Above with whitish to yellow markings on dark ground color (3, 4, 5) 3

2*a*. (1*a*) Adult to slightly over 12 inches; ground color light olive with markings on dorsum and sides consisting of scattered circular black spots (1). *Range.* North Dakota (north and east of Altamount Moraine) into Alberta and Saskatchewan .... *A. t. diaboli* Dunn

2*b*. Adult to somewhat over 9 inches; without definite markings in adult, dark gray or blackish (2) (young with circular yellow spots). *Range.* Interior Basin and Colorado Plateau in Utah, western Colorado, northwestern New Mexico, and northern Arizona .... *A. t. nebulosum* Hallowell

3*a*. (1*b*) Above brown to black with large even-edged markings of yellow (cream in preservative) (4, 5) 4

3*b*. Above with dark ground color forming network, setting off whitish light-colored areas with indefinite borders (3); adult to about 8½ inches. *Range.* Southwestern Canada in British Columbia and Alberta; the United States in Washington, Oregon, Idaho, Montana, Wyoming, North and South Dakota, and Nebraska .... *A. t. melanostictum* (Baird)

4*a*. (3*a*) Markings of spots and bars (4); some bars may extend across body, others from mid-dorsal line to ventral surface; below with dark and light mottling; adult to 10 inches. *Range.* Kansas, Oklahoma, central and western Texas, eastern Colorado, central and eastern New Mexico .... *A. t. mavortium* Baird

4*b*. Markings of spots, largely concentrated on sides (5); adult to 8 inches. *Range.* Confined to California from Sonoma and Sacramento counties, respectively, north and northeast of San Francisco Bay, south in the Central Valley to Kern County and coastwise into Monterey County. .... *A. t. californiense* Gray

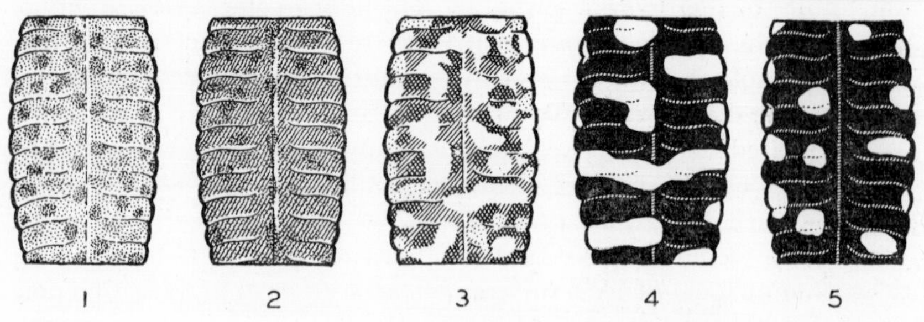

Fig. 8. 1, *Ambystoma tigrinum diaboli;* 2, *A. t. nebulosum;* 3, *A. t. melanostictum;* 4, *A. t. mavortium;* 5, *A. t. californiense.*

Remarks.—Dunn (1940:162) points out that the Mexican form *velasci* and the California form *californiense* are so similar to *tigrinum* that their separation is questionable. Should the distinction be dropped, the whole lot could be called *A. t. tigrinum.* The other races, however, are considerably different.

Factors causing neoteny and pedogenesis in the species should be investigated as also many phases of the life history, particularly of *californiense, mavortium,* and other less well-known races.

The status of the *Ambystoma* in extreme western New Mexico and central and southeastern Arizona should be determined. Franklin (1915) comments on animals observed at Flagstaff, Arizona. *Ambystoma* were found at 7,000 feet in a small stream that flowed through an area of red rock. Both gilled and air-breathing forms were found together in the water. The larvae were olive brown with dark irregular spots on back, sides, belly, and on the tail fin. The air breathers were darker and less spotted. The animals lightened as the water warmed. Boys in the area found eggs in June, and immature gilled individuals gotten by them were about 2 inches long.

PACIFIC GIANT SALAMANDER

Dicamptodon ensatus (Eschscholtz)
Plate 3

Range.—Principally the humid coastal forest from Santa Cruz and western Santa Clara counties through San Mateo County, California, north, in the coastal mountains, to the southwestern mainland of British Columbia; inland through the Siskiyou Mountains into the Cascade Range and probably the northern Sierra Nevada in northern California; occurs west of the crest of the Cascade Mountains in Oregon and Washington. Also recorded from northern Idaho and the Rocky Mountains of western Montana. (Pl. 49.)

Type locality.—California in the vicinity of San Francisco Bay (Eschscholtz, 1833:6).

Description.—STRUCTURE. Adult to 12 inches; stout-bodied with sturdy limbs; skin smooth; tail compressed, rounded below, particularly basally, narrow above; costal grooves indistinct, usually 12 (sometimes 11 or 13), counting one each in axilla and groin; toes 4-5; fourth toe with 3 phalanges, differing in this regard from most *Ambystoma;* undersides of feet nontuberculate; tongue broad, only slightly free laterally; vomerine teeth usually in relatively straight transverse series, rather widely separated at midline; premaxillary fontanelle and lacrimals present as in *Rhyacotriton* but differing in this regard from most *Ambystoma;* nasals present. COLOR. Ground color above light reddish brown, purplish brown, brown, to grayish brown with well-defined irregular marblings of dark brown to black; below light-colored, light brown to yellowish white, usually unmarked except for dark blotches anteriorly in gular area; sides with sparse scattering of white guanophores; iris dark brown with indistinct, diffuse scattering of small golden to coppery flecks, discernible under magnification.

Individual 4¾ inches in snout-vent length, obtained 4½ miles north and 1½ miles east of Orick, Humboldt County, California: Above with marblings of blackish brown and gray, latter rendered so in part by presence of numerous, minute, metallic-appearing pigment flecks; sides of body slate gray with clusters of guanophores (?) forming whitish spots, largest slightly under 1 mm.; below purplish gray, lightening in gular area to gray with still more purple; chest lighter than remaining underparts; margin of vent cream; melanophores form network ventrally; iris dark brown with minute flecks of dull buffy bronze forming vague patches above and below pupil.

Habitat.—In California this species is largely restricted to the coastal redwood belt where the humidity is sufficiently high to permit diurnal as well as nocturnal surface activity. Fitch (1936) however reported larvae in the Rogue River Basin, Oregon, in interior creeks in dry open woods or in areas of chaparral. Adults are found under logs, bark, rocks, and other objects, usually in damp situations not far from a permanent stream or in the water.

Graf (1949:79) believes that if collectors work the heads of the very small mountain streams in the big timber areas during the dry months when the streamlets are reduced to a trickle, more of the seemingly rare mature individuals would come to light. He turned up 2 animals in such a situation, both buried under the coarse gravel at the foot of a small pool of a small stream. The larval specimens in this pool and others nearby were all in the last stages of transformation to the terrestrial form. The locality was on the west side of Grass Mountain, Lincoln County, Oregon.

Near Orick, Humboldt County, California, on February 14, 1947, I found an individual, about 2½ to 3 inches in snout-vent length, with contrasting ashy gray and dark brown marblings, beneath a piece of wood at the base of a 3-foot bank along a logging road. The surrounding rolling hills were covered with a heavy growth of bushes and sword fern, much of this vegetation overgrowing old logs and other refuse from logging operations. There was only a sparse growth of redwoods and Port Orford cedar, due to lumbering operations. There was a small stream 150 feet away. The ground was wet from recent rains.

Near Middletown, Napa County, California, on November 17, 1947, I obtained a recently metamorphosed individual under a large rock 40 feet from a permanent stream, a tributary of Saint Helena Creek. The animal was marbled on the head but the pattern had not developed posteriorly. The stream was moderately swift, its bed rocky. Plants were growing to the water's edge, hence its flow had probably been stable. Douglas fir, bay, and maple grew along the canyon bottom.

Behavior.—The species is nocturnal and sometimes diurnal. On February 15, 1947 (10:10 A.M.), near Orick, Humboldt County, California, I found an adult crouching in a niche 5 feet from the ground on the side of the steeply sloping base of a Port Orford cedar. The salamander was in bright sunlight. On an overcast rainy day, a few days later, one was found by Alden Miller several feet from the ground in a bush. Climbing ability is indicated. This species may emit a screaming sound when molested. Professor Theodor Hoover of Rancho del Oso, Santa Cruz County, California, says this salamander utters a noise or "bark" and that he has had his attention called to an individual in this way. I have heard these animals give a low-pitched rattling sound when irritated. *Aneides lugubris* and *Ensatina eschscholtzii* are other western urodeles capable of vocal sounds. Maslin (1950) has studied sound production in *Dicamptodon* and other urodeles.

Food.—Adults feed on land snails and slugs; insects such as beetles, caddisfly larvae, moths, and flies; small mammals such as shrews and white-footed mice; and other amphibians. In a fecal mass from a large adult obtained by me were the remains of 4 beetles, one apparently a carabid, a snail shell, and some fine fur, possibly of a shrew. Five larvae from Del Norte County, California, examined by Schonberger (1944:257) had fed on amphipods (*Hyalella*), a sowbug, and caddisflies (*Setodes* type). Larvae from the Siskiyou Mountains, California, and Rogue River, Oregon, examined by Fitch (1936:637), contained water beetles, other beetles and beetle larvae, a wasp, caddisfly larvae, a moth, a fly, a bug, a spider, and water snails. Crayfish have also been reported.

The larvae are tenacious in retaining food. Ward Russell (field notes of Alden Miller, September 28, 1942) took 4 on a hook in a hole 3 feet deep in a small, cold stream 8 miles northeast of Hyampom, Trinity County, California. The animals stayed back in the dark or under a riffle so that they could not be seen, but took the bait left on the bottom. Bird breasts and mouse livers, by-products of skinning, were used as bait. The salamanders made no effort to resist being pulled from the water. Twice the hook apparently had not caught; they merely held on to the food and did not let go until swung onto the bank.

Diller (1907:907-8) in Douglas County, Oregon, observed an 8-inch *Dicamptodon* with a 2-foot garter snake in its jaws, held by its head and neck. The salamander was turned over and over and dragged about, in the snake's effort to free itself. Graf (1949:80) on July 3, 1941, at Cape Lookout, Oregon, had a similar experience, finding a 7-inch terrestrial individual gripping a 25-inch *Thamnophis sirtalis* just behind its eyes. The snake was moving feebly, suggesting that the struggle had been going on for some time. The lower jaw of the snake was folded back beneath the head, suggesting that the snake may have struck first, being met head on by the jaws of the salamander. Unfortunately in neither case was it possible to see the undisturbed outcome of the struggles.

Reproduction.—EGGS. About 70 eggs, presumably of this species, were collected by Henry and Twitty (1940:248) at the ranch of H. L. Brubaker in the Santa Cruz Mountains in San Mateo County, California, on June 19, 1937. The eggs were identified on the basis of the appearance later of mountain brook characteristics in the developing larvae and the presence of a large adult female near the clutch. They were laid singly, fastened by short peduncles to the surface of a timber which was probably partly submerged in a rapidly flowing stream. The eggs had a single jelly coat and were without pigment, in the "tail bud" stage of development. I calculate egg size in the tail bud stage from the figure published by Henry and Twitty (1940) as approximately 6.4 mm. Storer's account (1925:81-83) seems to relate to eggs of *Ambystoma gracile* rather than *Dicamptodon.* Kessel and Kessel (1943a:111), on the basis of developmental rates give November and December as the probable hatching period at Corte Madera Creek, Marin County, California.

Dethlefson (1948:81-84) reports that "On March 20, 1948, near Ben Lomond, Santa Cruz County, California, Mr. Dan Coon, while drilling into sandstone and mud on a hillside to make an outlet for a spring, had penetrated with the drilling rod to a distance of about twenty feet when he felt an obstruction of some soft, tough substance. After forcing the narrow steel rod through the obstruction, he noticed small, white eggs being carried out of the drill hole by the water. They were washed out singly, or in clumps of about a dozen to thirty; they numbered approximately one hundred in all. Accompanying the eggs were the dismembered parts of two full-grown adults of *Dicamptodon.* . . . After an interval of about an hour he returned to the spring and discovered in the pool at its outlet a third adult specimen, measuring 243 mm., which had apparently been forced out by the water from the same hole. . . . The salamander was large and fat, and showed very weak pigmentation in comparison with three other captive adults. Such lack of coloration suggests that it had been underground for some time, perhaps since the preceding winter.

"Upon examination of nineteen egg capsules which were salvaged a few days later [the eggs had been buried], it was noted that they were completely devoid of pigment, quite round, and lacked the covering of jelly noted by Storer (1925), although they tended to be in clumps, each egg having a barely recognizable pedicel of jelly. The embryos contained within the capsules were at a very early stage of development. The average diameter of the capsules was 5.5 mm. [The apparent absence of the jelly capsule may have been due to dehydration when the eggs were buried (RCS)].

"Three weeks subsequent to the finding of the first nest, Mr. Coon, while drilling another nearby spring, found five more adult salamanders under practically the same conditions. No eggs were noted at the time, but upon dissection of one of the salamanders approximately eighty eggs were removed in large clumps. They were very nearly the same size as the eggs from the first spring. . . .

"The adults in this case also were weakly pigmented in comparison with specimens held captive over a long period. . . ."

LARVA. Mountain brook type; gill slits and filaments reduced but not as greatly as in *Rhyacotriton* (p. 60); 5 to 7 gill rakers (based on 9 animals from Marin County, California) on anterior face of third arch. Dorsal fin with prominent, irregular, smoky, light and dark marbling, not found in *Rhyacotriton* larva, with which this species, in its earlier stages, might be confused; above brownish with numerous minute specks of whitish which may unite to form small blotches; blotches along middle of back may form more or less well-defined longitudinal stripe; poorly defined whitish streak usually extends diagonally ventroposteriorly from the eye; below whitish, typically unmarked; dorsal tail fin arises just anterior to region of attachment of hind limbs or farther posteriorly; no balancers; gills short, bushy, and dull red in color in life. Absence of the body fin and balancers and the simultaneous appearance of both forelimbs and hind limbs in development are considered adaptations to the mountain brook habitat. Kessel and Kessel (1943a:111), in Mill Valley, Marin County, California, found that recently hatched larvae grew fastest in May and June; by late September, they averaged about 95 mm. in length, and slightly over 100 mm. when one year old. Growth was slow during fall and winter. By April of the second year, the larvae had attained an average length of 118.2 mm. Full larval growth, at around 135 mm., was reached by June (Kessel and Kessel, 1943b:142). Storer (1925:87) states that the majority of larvae probably do not metamorphose until the second summer when they may be about 200 mm. in length. Metamorphosis at large size seems to be characteristic of this species.

Reed (1949:81), however, found a small metamorphosed individual near sea level on the bank of a small branch of Fogarty Creek, 3/4 mile south of the Lincoln Beach Post Office, Lincoln County, Oregon, on April 13, 1946. It measured 96.5 mm. in total length of which 39.0 mm. was tail. Further, Dr. L. Griffen, who has collected many specimens of *Dicamptodon,* informed Reed that in the middle part of the Oregon coastal mountains he has never found an individual, either larval or adult, larger than approximately 110 mm.

Kessel and Kessel (1944, Marin County, California) found that metamorphosis of larvae begins in early summer and continues until about the end of September. They found no evidence for metamorphosis the first year of larval life. The average length of 5 individuals at metamorphosis was 134.6 mm. These measured 130, 140, 135, 140, and 128 mm. The last was an individual observed in the field; the others were animals kept for a time in the laboratory. The average length at transformation has been recorded as 150 mm. Large larvae 247 and 286 mm. in length, probably neotenic, have been reported respectively by Storer (1925) from Muir Woods, Marin County, California, and Bishop (1943:176) from Oak Grove, Clackamas County, Oregon. Kessel and Kessel (1944) observed that aquarium larvae shed at the time of metamorphosis. They noted that transformation was delayed when larvae were kept in deep water where they could not reach land. May neoteny be common in areas where streams are high and steep-sided?

In summary I quote Dethlefsen (1948:83-84), "With the information now at hand the following is suggested as a probable life history for *Dicamptodon ensatus*. With the arrival of autumn rains, adult salamanders, after feeding, begin to burrow at the base of a spring emptying into a stream as here described. By early March they have established a subterranean nest on the course of the spring and there proceed to mate and lay eggs. The larvae become recognizable during late April or early May, but remain within the egg capsules, depending upon the remainder of the yolk for food. They remain in the underground pool, developing in this manner throughout the summer, until the first of the following autumn when they hatch out and wriggle down through the mud. They emerge finally, as first-year larvae, into the open streams where the rest of their metamorphosis takes place. The emerged first-year larvae have thus spent five to eight months underground since beginning their development.

"The foregoing is borne out by various . . . facts as follows:

"(1) *Dicamptodon* adults are seldom encountered except during the rainy season. Some individuals have been found on hillsides, apparently at quite a distance from water, although possibly about to burrow into a spring. Dr. E. L. Kessel reports that they are good burrowers, captive specimens having kept him awake at night by digging and attempting to bury themselves in the gravel of their terraria. His captive specimens have also shown an ability to live for many months without eating.

"(2) During several consecutive years of exhaustive collecting, Kessel and Kessel (1943a) found neither eggs nor newly hatched larvae; the smallest larval specimen which they discovered measured 37 mm. in length. . . . Moreover, all of the first-year larvae collected by Kessel and Kessel were found following the autumn rains, none whatever being found during the summer, although second-year larvae were abundant. The first-year larvae were collected in the early spring, the water being too turbid during the winter for the observance of newly hatched larvae. The collectors assumed from their results that the larvae are hatched in November.

"(3) Henry and Twitty (1940) reported that the embryos required five months or more to consume the yolk to the point where it is necessary to seek other food.

"(4) No evidence has been reported of prefeeding larvae of *Dicamptodon* being collected in open waters."

Remarks.—Much remains to be learned of the life history and habits. Comparison of individuals from the extremes of the range should be made to discover if differences between populations can be detected. Search should be made for the species in the area between coastal Washington and British Columbia and in the area of the interior occurrence in northern Idaho and western Montana to determine whether or not the range is actually discontinuous (see map, Pl. 49).

OLYMPIC SALAMANDER

Rhyacotriton olympicus (Gaige)
Plates 3 and 4

Range.—Coastal humid coniferous forests of western Washington southward through Oregon into northwestern California; in California as far south as the region west of Dyerville in southwestern Humboldt County. Not known east of the Cascade Mountains. (Pl. 49.)

Type locality.—Lake Cushman, Washington (Gaige, 1917:2).

Description.—STRUCTURE. Adult 3 to 4 inches; eyes proportionately larger than in other members of family, horizontal dimension equal to or greater than distance from anterior eye corner to tip of snout; snout short and rounded; tongue oval, broadly attached along midline, lateral margins slightly free; vomerine teeth in transverse series usually separated medially and arching anteriorly on either side of midline; premaxillary fontanelle present (differing in this regard from most *Ambystoma*); nasals lacking; tail relatively short, rounded below, narrow above, oval at base but flattened distally; sensory pits arranged in fairly well-defined rows on head, body and tail—pits often marked with white guanophores; pits constitute lateral line system commonly found in aquatic adult and larval salamanders; costal grooves 14 (sometimes 15), counting one each in axilla and groin; limbs short; toes 4-5, slightly webbed at base; fourth toe usually with 3 phalanges instead of 4 as in most *Ambystoma;* no palmar or plantar tubercles. Adult possesses minute lungs, 5 to 7 mm. in length which, although small, are highly vascular and filled with air. Lung reduction probably accompanied the adoption of the brook-dwelling habitat. COLOR. Above uniformly chocolate brown or, south of Columbia River, flecked and variegated in varying degrees with small, irregular dark markings which become more sparsely distributed laterally; dark markings are on an olivaceous ground color; below greenish yellow (in California) to yellowish orange (Washington), unmarked or with varied development of dark blotches; scattering of white guanophores on sides of head, neck, and body, scarce on tail; guanophores associated with pit organs but also found elsewhere; iris dark brown to blackish, flecked with white to pale yellow pigment; light-colored iridic markings sometimes form network of varying continuity, best developed above and below pupil. SEXUAL DIFFERENCES. Rectilinear lobes present on either side of vent in male, best developed in adult (p. 11).

Adult female obtained on February 13, 1947 at Boise Creek, at about 800 feet, near Willow Creek Post Office, Humboldt County, California: Above coarse, broken network of dark brownish olive on olive ground color; guanophores scarce on dorsal surfaces, half dozen or so on body, none on tail; guanophores abundant on sides of body and neck, few on tail, considerable numbers in gular area and on chest, scarce on lower abdomen. absent on underside of tail; few guanophores on undersides of limbs, but dorsal surfaces without them; guanophores white, not greatly branched; ventral surfaces greenish yellow, lighter on undersides of limbs, spotted and blotched with blackish; iris dark brown with scattered metallic flecks and spots of golden above and below pupil.

Adult, obtained on April 27, 1948 at Lake Crescent, 4.9 miles southeast of Fairholm, Clallam County, Washington: Above uniformly chocolate brown; scattering of white guanophores over dorsal surfaces, scarce toward midline and on tail; ventral surfaces uniformly orange yellow; scattering of guanophores in gular area and in ventrolateral areas of body and tail; guanophores concentrated on sides of head, neck, body, and tail base; scarce distally on tail; dark ventral markings, forming spots and blotches, confined to gular area and chest.

Habitat.—In and near small, rapidly flowing, well-shaded, permanent streams. (Pl. 35, fig. 1.) I have obtained this species where the water has been clear, cold (commonly 6° to 10°C.), and moving and have collected this salamander by turning stones at the edges of small cascading streams and in seepage areas draining into such streams. Individuals may be found in wet situations within a few inches of water or resting in shallow trickles. Individuals may be found lying on a rock surface in a thin film of moving water. When collecting is done along streams, the species must be seized quickly or it may plunge into the water and be lost. Fitch (1936:637) found 5 young individuals in rock slides in a deep, heavily shaded ravine in saturated basal layers of pebbles and rocks, through which water was seeping slowly (Rogue River Basin, Oregon).

Myers (1943:125) reports finding larvae in a tributary of Willow Creek near U.S. Highway 299, 1.2 miles by road west of the boundary sign of Trinity National Forest, in east-central Humboldt County, California. They were found in cold water that cascaded downward over boulders covered with thick moss, kept green and dripping from the spray. They were discovered through the gentle shifting of small stones (3 or 4 inches in diameter) in the quietest part of the stream close to the road. Here they were found hiding under the stones in 2 to 4 inches of water. I have found larvae in thin films of water in seepage areas.

In one section of Madeline Creek near Lake Cushman, Washington, about ½ mile above the trail junction, the creek passes through a broken gorge with perpendicular walls up to 30 feet in height. Here, little sunlight filters through and the spray from numerous waterfalls gives the effect of a constant drizzle. In this area, on June 24, 1930, Phillips G. Putnam found *Rhyacotriton* numerous, especially in the cavelike recesses beneath large rocks. Sometimes as many as 8 would be seen together on a single mossy stone. They were very alert and most of them would plunge into the foaming water to escape. (From Noble and Richards, 1932:19.)

Along the Hoh River in western Washington, on April 13, 1948, I found this species in an old rock slide in a seepage area that drained into a small cascading stream, 15 feet away. The rocks were covered by a nearly continuous mat of moss. The salamanders were found in cold trickles among the rocks. Alders, maples, and Douglas fir grew along the stream. Clumps of sword fern were present nearby.

On February 13, 1947, I searched the rocky margins of a cascading stream, a tributary of Willow Creek, near the Boise Creek Public Camp Ground. The stream tumbled down a steep, north-facing slope that was heavily covered with Douglas fir and maple. There was abundant growth of moss over the logs and rocks along the stream. *Rhyacotriton* were sought under rocks at the water's edge where they are known to come to shore to rest and feed within easy reach of the protection of the stream. Under a rock 15 by 8 by 5 inches, about 10 inches above the stream, I found an adult female. She rested on a damp, almost soggy area of fine grayish sediment. Two routes of escape into the stream were available to her: one would have taken her into turbulent water, the other into a relatively quiet pool.

Behavior.—Adults are found both in water and on land. On several occasions I have obtained them by turning stones near water, finding animals that had evidently come ashore to rest and forage. When first exposed, an individual may remain quiet for an instant but it soon wriggles away into the stream which is often only a few inches away. Charles Lowe, Jr. observed an adult crawling, exposed in the open, in a well-shaded, spray-drenched area several feet from a stream. I have found most adults beneath rocks in seepage areas or in shallow creeks. They are active, efficient swimmers, moving quickly through the water by rapid lateral undulations of the body and tail. The limbs do not appear to be used in swimming but are extended posteriorly along the sides.

THERMAL DATA

Locality	Date	Time	Temperature, °C. Body	Water	Air
CALIFORNIA					
Hennessy Creek, 1.3 mi. W of Burnt Ranch P.O., along U.S. Highway 299, Trinity Co.	April 23, 1948	6:00 P.M.	9.2	9.5	
			9.3	9.5	
	November 19, 1948	5:30 P.M.		7.5	
	March 24, 1949	8:30 to	8.5	8.8	9.3
		9:00 A.M.	8.4	8.8	9.4
3.1 mi. E of Blue Lake, along U.S. Highway 299, Humboldt Co.	April 24, 1948	12:00 M.	9.6	9.6	9.9
			9.4	9.6	9.9
	November 20, 1948	11:00 to	7.5	7.7	7.1
		11:30 A.M.	7.6	7.7	7.2
			7.6	7.7	7.2
	March 23, 1949	3:00 P.M.	8.8	9.1	10.4
			8.9	9.1	10.7
10.6 mi. W of Dyerville, along road to Honeydew, Humboldt Co.	April 24, 1948	1:30 to		9.7	9.9
		2:00 P.M.		10.9	10.0
	November 21, 1948	9:00 to	7.3	7.6	7.3
		9:15 A.M.	7.5	7.6	7.2
			7.6	7.6	7.3
			7.4	7.6	7.3
OREGON					
Perham Creek, Wygant State Park, Hood River Co.	April 21, 1948	12:30 P.M.	7.9	8.0	12.0-12.2*
			7.8	8.0	12.0-12.2
			8.0	8.0	12.0-12.2
			8.0	8.0	12.0-12.2
WASHINGTON					
6.3 mi. SE of Cathlamet, along U.S. Highway 30, Wahkiakum Co.	April 11, 1948	6:30 P.M.	6.8	7.0	6.1
8 mi. SE of Cathlamet, along U.S. Highway 30, Wahkiakum Co.	April 11, 1948			8.0	7.2
Quinault, Grays Harbor Co.	April 12, 1948	4:00 P.M.		7.8	
Hoh River (tributary stream), 4.0 mi. ESE of junction U.S. Highway 101, Jefferson Co.	April 13, 1948	12:00 M.		7.4	
Lake Crescent, 4.9 mi. SE of Fairholm, along U.S. Highway 101, Clallam Co.	April 13, 1948	4:00 P.M.	5.8	5.9	6.6
			5.9	5.9	6.7
			5.9	5.9	6.6
			6.0	5.9	6.6
South end of Lake Cushman, Mason Co.	April 17, 1948	4:30 P.M.	7.6		8.6

* Air temperature not taken directly at site of capture of salamanders.

Reproduction.—Phillips G. Putnam on June 5, 1930, in one of the small streams near Lake Cushman, Washington, found *Rhyacotriton* apparently paired. At least individuals of opposite sex were found together and the ovaries and testes appeared to be in breeding condition. On June 7, in Elk Creek, a single egg was found attached to a tendril on the underside of a stone, and it was assumed to have been laid by *Rhyacotriton*. Another pair were found together June 11 in Triple Trip Creek where the water temperature was 10°C. and the air temperature 14°C. Paired individuals were found in Madeline Creek on June 24 and on July 6, and after considerable search on the latter date a single egg was found, again assumed to have been laid by *Rhyacotriton*. Dissection of gravid females had led Putnam to conclude that a single individual must lay very few eggs and he writes in the field: "The *Rhyacotriton* eggs are apparently deposited singly beneath stones and are without conspicuous gelatinous capsules. An adult *Rhyacotriton* deposits approximately only twelve eggs which are naturally difficult to find." (From Noble and Richards, 1932:19.)

Noble and Richards (1932:20) induced females to lay by means of pituitary implants. The eggs were attached to the sides and upper surfaces of the rocks placed in their containers. The average number laid by 5 females was 5, the maximum 8, and the minimum 3.

EGGS. The eggs are large and pigmentless. In formalin they average 4.5 mm. exclusive of the capsules. In the living egg there appear to be 3 capsules: a soft, gelatinous inner one, a firmer, more opaque middle one, and a thick, transparent outer capsule. In the fresh egg the middle capsule was so thin that it might be considered merely a membrane covering the inner capsule. In the preserved egg the middle capsule is very distinct. For a few hours after laying, the outer capsule exhibited a series of fine ridges. By the time the two-cell stage was reached, these ridges had entirely disappeared. (Noble and Richards, 1932:20.)

Seventeen adult females examined by me from California to Washington, obtained at different times of the year, averaged 9.2 ova (range 7 to 15) per female. Counts were made only in individuals possessing ova 2 mm. or more in diameter. The largest eggs were found in a female, 55.8 mm. in snout-vent length, collected April 13, 1948, near Forks on the Calawah River, Clallam County, Washington. They measured about 3.9 mm. In my material from Washington, large ova were found in females in mid-April through early July, suggesting a spring or early summer laying period. Ovarian eggs were generally considerably smaller in individuals taken in August and November. Several of these fall individuals possessed large eggs, however. Two adult females, obtained October 1, 1932, had respectively, 7 and 10 ovarian eggs about 3.4 mm. in diameter. Increase in diameter of the oviducts was correlated with increase in size of ova. Animals obtained in California suggest that oviposition may occur earlier in the southern part of the range. Five females collected in mid-February possessed ovarian eggs approximately 3 mm. in diameter.

Males from Washington largely lacked spermatozoa in the sperm ducts in September. Several taken in mid-April and in early July had ducts well laden with sperm. Four adult males obtained in mid-February, 1942, in California and a single one found November 16, 1947, had the sperm ducts filled with spermatozoa.

LARVA. Mountain brook type. Gill slits reduced; no gill rakers or only few low nubbins; gill filaments short, rather broad, somewhat flattened, few per arch. Myers (1943:125) gives the following distinguishing characteristics between larval *Rhyacotriton* and small larval *Dicamptodon*. In *Rhyacotriton* the snout is shorter and much rounder and less bluntly shovel-shaped from above, but blunter and more bulldog-like in side view than in *Dicamptodon;* eyes directed more dorsally with peculiar configuration of snout making them seem to be pointed more anteriorly; eyes appear round and staring and somewhat "crossed" when viewed from the front; a shallow groove runs upward and backward from each nostril, not evident in *Dicamptodon;* color consists of speckling of irregular black dots on olivaceous or brown ground color of dorsum; *Dicamptodon* has bold, irregular, smoky-dark-and-light mottling or marbling on dorsal-caudal fin, not present in *Rhyacotriton;* variegation of duller, more grayish dorsum of *Dicamptodon* is caused entirely by irregular, small, light areas; under surface yellow, frequently sprinkled with at least a few dark flecks (in individuals south of the Columbia River) whereas *Dicamptodon* commonly lacks markings on its clear whitish venter. I may add that *Rhyacotriton* exhibits greater gill reduction than *Dicamptodon*. The filaments are broader, fewer, and shorter, the gill slits smaller, and the gill rakers are absent or vestigial.

SUBSPECIES
Figure 9

1*a*. Above uniformly dark chocolate brown with numerous fine whitish specks (4); dark dorsal pigmentation ends abruptly along sides; extensive suffusion of fine speckling of whitish along sides; below unmarked orange yellow or with mottlings of brownish in gular area and few well-defined dark spots or blotches on underside of body (2) and tail; some individuals have dark markings only in gular area. *Range*. West of the crest of the Cascades in Washington from the Olympic Peninsula south to the Columbia River and probably coastally in Oregon to Cape Lookout, Tillamook County. In the north, ranges interiorly at least to near Shelton, Mason County, and to the south to Oak Point, Cowlitz County, Washington .... *R. o. olympicus* (Gaige)

1*b*. Above with pale olive or olive ground color largely obscured by numerous spots, blotches, and reticulations of blackish to blackish brown (3); whitish speckling, although usually present, not conspicuous; dark markings on sides grade into similar markings on venter; below generally greenish yellow, commonly heavily flecked and spotted with dark melanic blotches (1); dark markings seldom concentrated in gular area; gular area commonly marked like remaining underparts. *Range*. Coastally in northwestern California and southwestern Oregon, from southern Humboldt County, California, north at least to the Rogue River Valley, Curry County, Oregon. Ranges inland in California to vicinity of Willow Creek, in extreme eastern Humboldt County .... *R. o. variegatus* Stebbins and Lowe

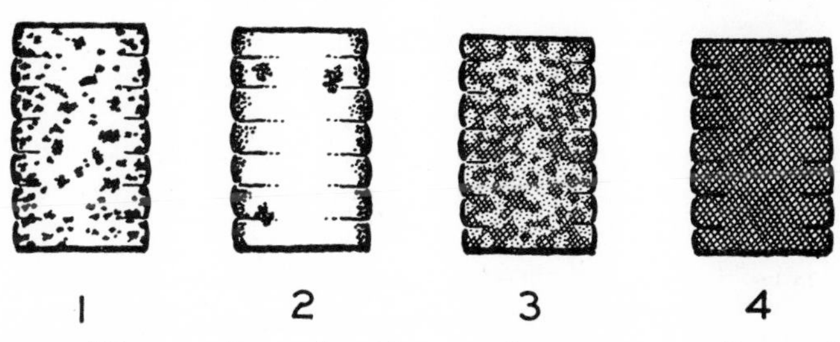

Fig. 9. 1, 3, *Rhyacotriton olympicus variegatus;* 2, 4, *R. o. olympicus.*

LUNGLESS SALAMANDERS

Family Plethodontidae

Our species range in size from approximately 3 inches (*Batrachoseps* and others) to somewhat over 6 inches (*Aneides lugubris*); eyelids present; tail rounded or oval in cross section; costal grooves well defined; limbs well developed; toes 4-4 or 4-5; palmar and plantar tubercles in some (*Ensatina*); skin smooth; vomerine teeth usually in two arched series, approaching and sometimes meeting one another at midline; parasphenoid teeth forming single, elongate oval patch or in varying degrees divided along midline; tongue free all around or attached anteriorly; lungless—respiration buccopharyngeal and dermal; ypsiloid apparatus reduced or absent; nasolabial groove present, a distinctive characteristic; vertebrae amphicoelous or opisthocoelous.

Loss of lungs may be related to a brook-dwelling ancestry. Elimination of the lungs, of hydrostatic function in salamanders, increased the specific gravity thereby probably facilitating locomotion in moving water. The greater oxygen content of such water may have made their respiratory function less important. Dermal and buccopharyngeal respiration then assumed a dominant role.

The nasolabial grooves are thought by Whipple (1906:25) to function in clearing the nostrils of water that collects there when the head has been flooded. Such flooding may occur through encounters with wet vegetation or other wet objects. The excess fluid is carried by capillary action away from the nasal openings.

Habits.—Terrestrial or brook-dwelling. Males deposit spermatophores. The sperm capsule of the spermatophore is picked up by the female with the lips of her cloaca. Fertilization is internal. Sperm is stored in the spermatheca in the roof of the cloaca of the female. Such sperm may be used in some species to fertilize eggs laid months after insemination. These salamanders lay eggs with the dubious exception of *Hydromantes* of Europe which has been thought to be viviparous. The adults of some species brood the eggs. The young generally resemble the adults except for different proportions and sometimes color and pattern differences. All species considered here are terrestrial and none possesses an aquatic larval stage. Certain eastern forms, however, such as *Desmognathus, Eurycea, Hemidactylium,* and others, have gilled aquatic larvae.

The family is confined to the New World except for *Hydromantes* of Sardinia, northeastern Italy (the Udine country), northwest Italy, and adjacent southeastern France, and possibly Corsica. Plethodontids are distributed over most of North America but are largely absent from the central part. They occur in Central and South America.

In South America they are present in the high Andes in all three ranges in Colombia to the vicinity of Merida in Venezuela and Quito in Ecuador. Lowland or foothill species are known from: wet, west coast Ecuador and Colombia, into the middle Magdalena forest; coastal slopes of middle Venezuela back of Puerto Cabello; the Amazon valley from Pará to eastern Peru and northern Bolivia. The Plata plethodontid, *Ensatina platensis,* said to be from the vicinity of Montevideo, Uruguay, is here considered as based on a specimen from the Sierra Nevada of California (p. 92).

Remarks.—Soler (1950) has reëxamined the anatomical features of the salamanders of the genera *Desmognathus* and *Leurognathus,* concluding on the basis of vertebral and other differences that they should be removed from the family Plethodontidae and reinstated as the family Desmognathidae. In view of the anatomical variety embraced by other amphibian families, I would be inclined, at present, to regard the desmognathids as warranting no greater than subfamilial rank.

KEY TO GENERA
Figure 10

1*a*. Toes 4 on both fore and hind feet (1) .... BATRACHOSEPS, p. 105

1*b*. Toes 4 on forefeet and 5 on hind feet (including first digit even though reduced) (2) 2

2*a*. (1*b*) Tongue pedicelled, margin free all around (3); head and body flattened; tail relatively short and blunt-tipped; toes with fleshy web at base (4) .... *Hydromantes platycephalus,* p. 146

2*b*. Tongue attached anteriorly (5); head and body not notably flattened; tail longer and often with finely tapered tip; toes not strongly webbed 3

3*a*. (2*b*) Tail with pronounced constriction at base (7) (constriction usually not well developed in young animals (8)), in cross section rounded above, narrowing ventrally (as examined near base of tail) (7); palmar tubercles present (18); costal grooves 12, counting one each in axilla and groin; no dorsal light-colored stripe extending from head onto tail .... ENSATINA, p. 87

3*b*. Tail without basal constriction, not narrowed ventrally, in cross section circular or nearly so (9); no palmar tubercles (19); costal grooves usually 13 or more, counting one each in axilla and groin 4

4*a*. (3*b*) Posterior part of maxillary bone with teeth (13); premaxillary teeth usually not notably enlarged (except in breeding males), rarely detectable by stroking tip of snout (with mouth closed) (14); tips of toes not expanded (2); **T**-shaped terminal phalanges; premaxillary bones separate (15); posterior portion of mouth less markedly curved upward (17); broad, light-colored longitudinal dorsal stripe often present .... PLETHODON, p. 63

4*b*. Posterior part of maxillary bone without teeth (10), sharp edged; premaxillary teeth usually considerably enlarged, frequently detectable by stroking tip of snout (11); tips of toes expanded (6) (*Aneides flavipunctatus* excepted); **Y**-shaped terminal phalanges; fused premaxillary bones (12); posterior portion of mouth usually curved upward giving animal "smiling" expression (16); no broad light-colored dorsal stripe except in young *A. hardii* and *ferreus* ...... ANEIDES, p. 125

Genus *Plethodon*

Structure.—Adults from 3½ to nearly 6 inches; body and tail rounded, long, and slender; limbs relatively small but considerably longer than width of body; toes 4-5, tips not enlarged; **T**-shaped terminal phalanges; palmar and plantar tubercles absent; costal grooves well defined with similar furrows on tail; tail without basal constriction; tongue attached anteriorly and along midline, edges free; posterior portion of maxillary bone with teeth; separate premaxillary bones; premaxillary teeth usually not notably enlarged, often not detectable by stroking of snout (projecting teeth have been noted, however, in *Plethodon elongatus*); vomerine teeth

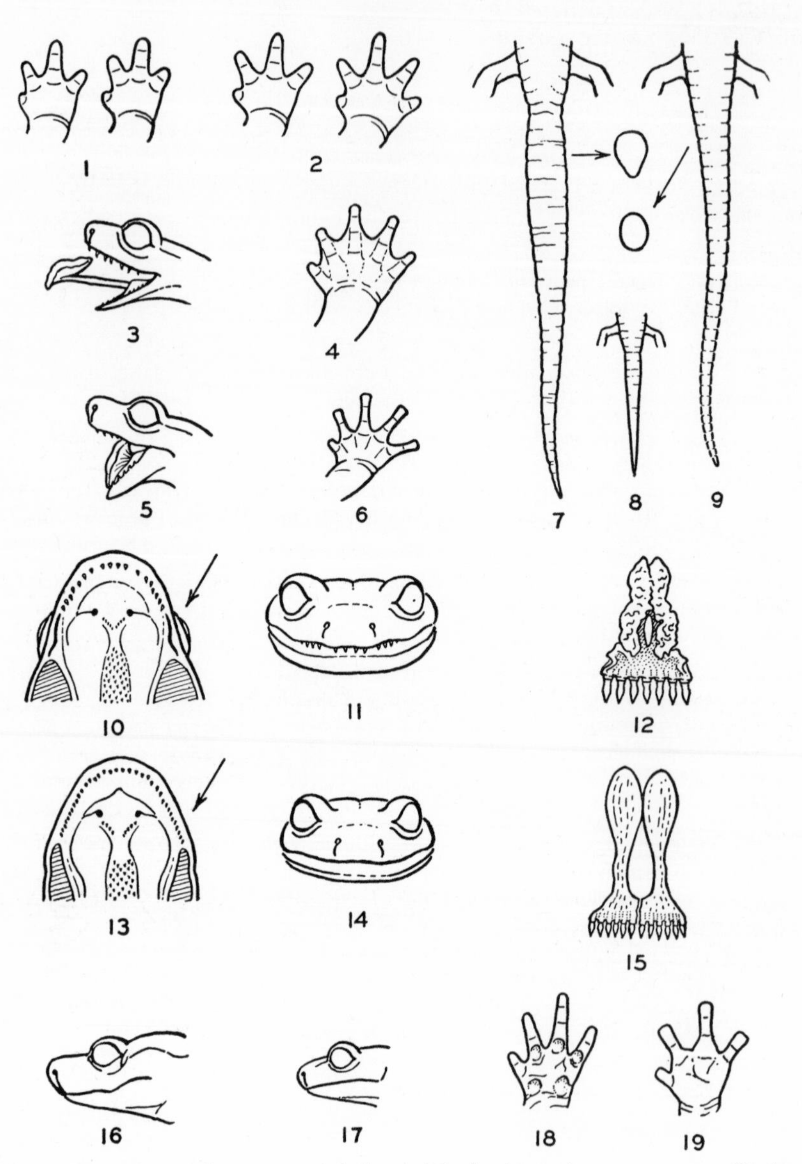

Fig. 10. 1, *Batrachoseps wrighti;* 2, *Plethodon cinereus;* 3, 4, *Hydromantes platycephalus;* 5, 6, 9, 10, 11, 12, 16, 19, *Aneides lugubris;* 7, 8, 18, *Ensatina eschscholtzii;* 13, 15, *Plethodon elongatus;* 14, 17, *Plethodon dunni.*

in two series behind nares; series extend diagonally posteriorly approaching and sometimes connecting with one another at midline in V-shaped arrangement; vomerine teeth 4 to 12 per series in our species; parasphenoid teeth in elongate ovoid patch usually separated short distance from vomerine teeth but sometimes connected with vomerine series as in some *P. vandykei;* parasphenoid teeth often reduced in number or absent along midline, in effect forming two separate or variously connected parasphenoid patches; patches often connected anteriorly.

COLOR.—Generally dark brown above with broad longitudinal stripe of yellow, cream, reddish brown, or orange brown extending from snout to tip of tail; stripe often obscured with dark color on head and toward end of tail; stripe commonly absent in adult *P. neomexicanus* and occasionally not evident in other species; below cream-colored, slaty to black; when dark-colored ventrally, sometimes with light-colored breaks in ground color, particularly in gular area; whitish to golden pigment (guanophores?) scattered over venter, sides, and sometimes in dorsal stripe; iris dark brown with varied development of silvery to golden pigment flecks.

Remarks.—In view of the widespread general distribution of members of this genus, it seems anomalous that it is so poorly represented in the Rocky Mountains. The presence of the species *P. vandykei* (*idahoensis*) and *P. neomexicanus* at the northern and southern extremes of this mountain range in the United States, suggests the desirability of a thorough search of the intervening area. It seems plausible that species (or subspecies of currently recognized forms) of this genus may eventually be discovered in this region. It seems likely that the range of *P. v. idahoensis* will be extended although Charles Lowe, Jr. and I failed to find it in searching in northwestern Washington. The rock rubble niche is scarce along highways in this area. Better success may be had to the southeast.

Much remains to be learned of the natural history of our western members of this genus. For example, the eggs of *P. v. idahoensis* and *P. neomexicanus* have not been described, and there is a question as to the identity of the egg cluster described by Wood (1934:191) for *P. elongatus.*

The sympatric relations of *dunni* and *elongatus, dunni* and *vehiculum,* and *vandykei* and *vehiculum* are worthy of study.

KEY TO SPECIES
Figure 11

1*a*. Costal grooves 18 (occasionally 19) 2

1*b*. Costal grooves 17 or less 3

2*a*. (1*a*) Fifth toe commonly with single phalanx; dorsal stripe absent, vague in young; Jemez Mountains, Sandoval County, New Mexico. . *P. neomexicanus,* p. 76

2*b*. Fifth toe with two phalanges; dorsal stripe present (often dull) (11) except in large individuals; coastal northwestern California and southwestern Oregon .... *P. elongatus,* p. 72

3*a*. (1*b*) Dorsal stripe absent 4

3*b*. Dorsal stripe present (11), lighter than sides 6

4*a*. (3*a*) Dorsal coloration black or blackish brown (1); gular area usually mottled with dark color on light background (15) or dark with few scattered light-colored areas centrally (14); parotoid glands absent (12); costal grooves usually 15 or more 5

4*b*. Dorsal coloration lighter, brownish yellow in life to light brown in preservative (3); gular area extensively light-colored, largely without dark pigment centrally (16, 17); parotoid glands present (13); costal grooves usually 14 or less .... *P. vandykei,* p. 80

5*a*. (4*a*) Toes long (20); costal grooves 15 (rarely 16); ventral surfaces extensively covered with light and dark markings giving salt and pepper style of coloration (6, 7); iris generally light-colored in life—coppery, salmon-colored, or brassy (22) .... *P. vehiculum,* p. 84

5*b*. Toes shorter (21); costal grooves 17 (occasionally 18); light-colored markings on darker venter largely confined to gular area (14) and chest; iris generally dark-colored with spare scattering of brassy (18) .... *P. elongatus,* p. 72

6*a*. (3*b*) Dorsal stripe with well-defined, essentially even edges (5) 10

6*b*. Dorsal stripe with irregular, broken edges that are well or poorly defined (2, 3, 4) 7

7*a*. (6*b*) Dorsal stripe reddish brown or pinkish not commonly yellowish in life; parotoid glands absent 8

7*b*. Dorsal stripe commonly yellow or yellowish tan not reddish brown in life; parotoid glands present (*dunni* excepted) (13) 9

8*a*. (7*a*) Below essentially uniformly colored (although sometimes with small scattered white guanophores), without numerous light and dark markings (due to breaks in melanic ground color), except sometimes in gular area and on chest .... juvenal *P. vandykei,* p. 80

8*b*. Below with numerous light (gaps in melanic ground color) and dark markings commonly over entire ventral surface (6, 7) .... *P. vehiculum,* p. 84

9*a*. (7*b*) Parotoid glands present (13); toes partly webbed (23); costal grooves 13 or 14; dorsal stripe on body essentially without dark markings centrally (3, 4) .... *P. vandykei,* p. 80

9*b*. Parotoid glands absent (12); toes not partly webbed (19); costal grooves commonly 15 (occasionally 14 or 16); dorsal stripe on body commonly with scattered dark markings centrally (2) .... *P. dunni,* p. 68

10*a*. (6*a*) Numerous relatively large dark markings extensively distributed in dorsal stripe (2); rather large, light flecks on sides (10); upper surface of proximal segments of hind limbs with light and dark markings (19); in life, dorsal stripe yellow or yellowish tan .... *P. dunni,* p. 68

10*b*. Fewer, commonly small, centrally situated dark markings in dorsal band (5); markings consisting of diffuse clouding or punctations, with band often largely unmarked laterally; sides unmarked or with small, often closely set, light markings (9); upper surfaces of proximal segments of hind limbs uniformly light-colored (20) or dark-colored (21); in life, dorsal stripe commonly reddish brown, rarely yellow 5

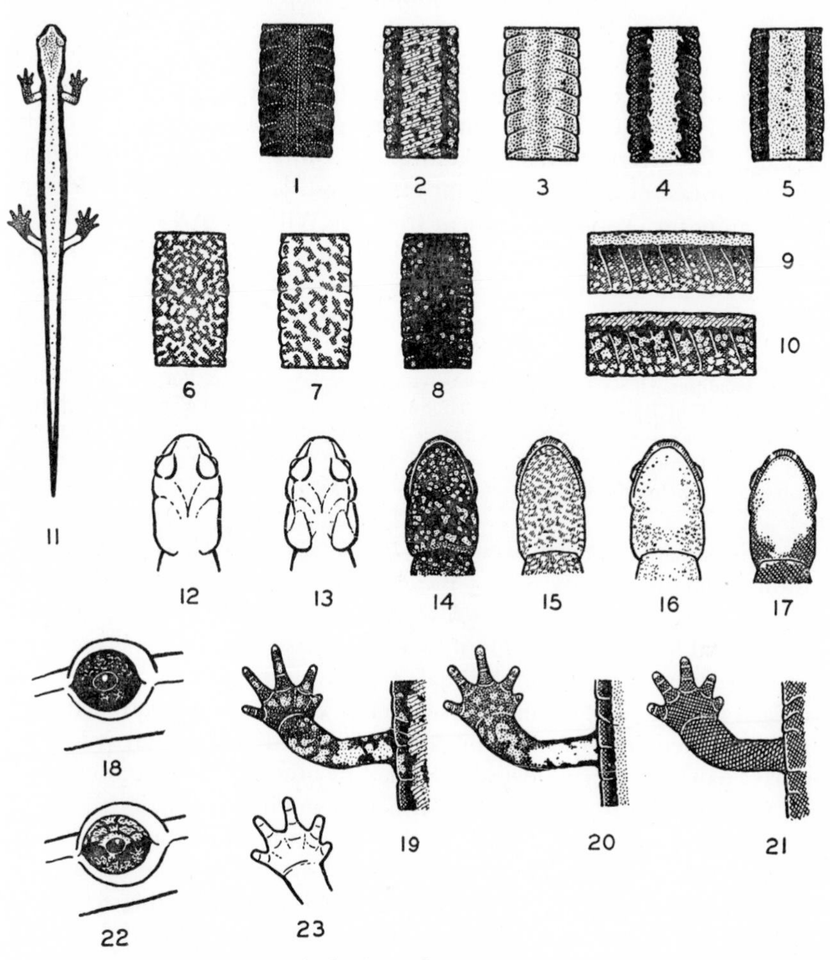

Fig. 11. 1, 14, 18, 21, *Plethodon elongatus;* 2, 10, 12, 19, *P. dunni;* 3, 13, 16, 23, *P. v. vandykei;* 4, 8, 17, *P. v. idahoensis;* 5, 6, 7, 9, 11, 15, 20, 22, *P. vehiculum.*

DUNN SALAMANDER

Plethodon dunni Bishop
Plate 8

Range.—Humid coastal forest of western Oregon from the Rogue River Basin, Curry County, in the southwestern part to immediately north of the Columbia River in Wahkiakum and Cowlitz counties, Washington. Not known east of the Cascades but ranges well onto the western slope of these mountains. Apparently absent from the Willamette Valley. (Pl. 50.)

Type locality.—Just outside the city limits of Portland, Clackamas County, Oregon (Bishop, 1934:171). Some of the specimens came from Eagle Creek, near Portland (Bishop, 1934:169).

Other localities. OREGON. *Columbia Co.*—2.8 mi. S of Scappoose, along U.S. Highway 30; 4.5 mi. SSE of Rainier, along U.S. Highway 30. *Clatsop Co.*—3.2 mi. NW of Clatskanie. *Douglas Co.*—4.8 mi. NW of Umpqua (by road). *Lane Co.*—8.9 mi. SE of Dexter, along State Highway 58. *Linn Co.*—7.9 mi. ESE of Foster, along U.S. Highway 20. WASHINGTON. *Cowlitz Co.*—2 mi. E of Stella. *Wahkiakum Co.*—6.3 mi. SE of Cathlamet.

Description.—STRUCTURE. Resembles *P. vehiculum;* adult averages larger, 4 to occasionally slightly over 5 inches; costal grooves usually 15, sometimes 14 or 16, counting one each in axilla and groin; 2½ to 4 (usually 3) intercostal folds between tips of toes of adpressed limbs; vomerine teeth 5 to 11 per row (in 15 adult animals from various parts of range); rows arranged in form of **V** behind internal nares, sometimes connected at midline; parasphenoid teeth in elongate club-shaped patch, narrowing anteriorly; patch in varying degrees divided by absence of teeth along midline; patches usually connected anteriorly, sometimes posteriorly. COLOR. In life, coloration closely resembles that of *Ambystoma macrodactylum;* dorsal stripe extends from snout and upper eyelids to near tip of tail; stripe tan to dull greenish yellow or olive yellow, brightening to yellow ocher or light tan on tail (dull tan or dirty white in preservative) with flecks of dark brown or black, which in some individuals may almost wholly obscure stripe; stripe commonly obscured with dark markings on head and tip of tail; sides dark brown with spots of whitish (groups of guanophores) and tan or yellowish (lipophore patches occupying breaks in melanic ground color); light markings stop short of dorsal stripe, hence stripe margined with blackish; guanophore patches most abundant on lower sides; proximal segments of limbs with blotches colored like dorsal stripe; below slaty with small pale spots of yellowish or orange (again occupying breaks in melanic network); spots with yellowish to whitish guanophores; light markings largely absent on underside of tail; iris dark brown with scattering of brassy. JUVENILE. Dorsal stripe and proximal segments of limbs above usually less obscured with dusky than in adults; stripe often yellowish green, brightening on tail. SEXUAL DIFFERENCES. Tail longer and head broader behind eyes in male than in female; 15 adult animals (8 males, 7 females) examined by me from north to south in range of species showed no sexual dimorphism in vomerine teeth although a male had the highest count; vomerine teeth counts ranged from 5 to 11 per row with 5, 6, and 7, commonest numbers; jaw and vent differences as mentioned for *P. vehiculum* (p. 85).

Adult female, RCS 2096, obtained on April 7, 1948, ½ mile west of the mouth of Lobster Creek, Rogue River, Curry County, Oregon: Few white punctate or puncto-stellate guanophores on head, most abundant between eyes and snout; few scattered along the back, particularly at edges of dorsal stripe; few on tail; scarce on upper surfaces of limbs, most abundant distally; guanophores present in moderate numbers, tending to clump to form spots and blotches on sides between limbs and on sides of head, particularly behind eyes and on neck; few on sides of tail, particularly basally; those on sides have yellowish cast; guanophores scattered and clustered in small numbers on ventral surfaces; in gular and chest regions present in yellowish gaps in melanic ground color; scarce on underside of tail; melanophores form moderately dense network ventrally; orange-yellow (Ochraceous-Buff) breaks occur in melanic ground color on sides, particularly on sides of head and neck behind eyes and on body between limbs; these gaps stop short of dorsal stripe which is margined with uniform blackish brown; dorsal stripe obscured with dark spots, particularly on head and at tip of tail, both of which are quite dark; stripe brightest (yellowish tan [Buckthorn Brown]) on basal ⅔ of tail; remainder of stripe, where not obscured by dusky markings, olive brown (Dresden Brown); proximal segments of limbs colored like dorsal stripe; underside of body between gular fold and pelvic region, dark purplish gray; underside of tail darker; gular area, particularly anterior ⅔, lighter than body (near Quaker Drab); posterior margin of gular fold pale gray; margins of vent darkly pigmented; undersides of feet slate (Deep Quaker Drab); light flecks in gular area and on chest dull yellowish (Olive-Buff); iris dark brown with silvery patch above and light-colored flecks below pupil.

Dr. Robert Storm has recently informed me of what appears to be a melanistic form of this salamander in Oregon. He describes (*in litt.*) an adult (114 mm. in total length) as follows: Dorsal ground color deep brown, flecked on trunk with not over two dozen light flesh-colored areas, each about 0.5 mm. in diameter; no dorsal stripe evident; tail deep brown with no flecks on distal ⅘; top of head mainly deep brown, with few minute whitish flecks; venter slate, chin paler, both with flesh-colored flecks, but more prominent on chin; no flecks on ventral surface of tail, except immediately posterior to vent; few scattered flesh-colored flecks on deep brown dorsal coloration of limbs. Black plethodons have been found on the east slope of Mary's Peak, Benton County.

Distinguished from *vehiculum* by its larger size, more compressed tail, and more strongly mottled sides; edges of dorsal stripe usually less regular and coloration of stripe differs from *vehiculum;* in latter it is only occasionally yellow and is usually less greenish, brighter than in *dunni;* tan-backed individuals of *dunni* are usually duller than similarly colored individuals of *vehiculum;* dorsal stripe usually does not reach tip of tail, except in juveniles (typically does so in *vehiculum*). Differs from *elongatus* in its lower costal groove count, in bodily proportions, and in having light-colored mottling on upper surfaces of legs, lighter, more yellowish, dorsal stripe and in usually possessing numerous light markings ventrally on body and in gular area (involving breaks in melanic ground color).

Habitat.—Fitch (1936:637) collected at least 20 specimens along with several *P. elongatus,* mostly in rock slides in a ravine on the north side of the Rogue River, 11 miles above its mouth, Curry County, Oregon. This species occurs along the same kinds of streams as *Rhyacotriton olympicus* but is less aquatic. I have found many individuals beneath moss-covered rocks in and near permanent seepage areas and persistent small streams. Individuals have been found almost invariably on soaked surfaces. On several occasions, upon turning a rock near a stream, one of these salamanders has taken to the water, swimming against the current to a place of concealment beneath a rock. Temperatures of water-soaked soil at a number of collection sites, taken in April, 1948, ranged from 7° to 11°C. *Dunni,* with the possible exceptions of *P. vandykei* (which I do not know well in the field) and *Aneides flavipunctatus niger,* is our most nearly aquatic western plethodontid.

On April 7, 1948, I hunted salamanders near the mouth of Lobster Creek on the Rogue River, Curry County, Oregon. I turned rocks along a cascading stream that flowed south into the Rogue River. The stream was about 2 feet wide near the road but farther up the hillside it was in large part hidden among moss-covered rocks. The angle of the bed was about 35°. *Plethodon dunni* were present in great numbers. Charles Lowe, Jr. and I collected 17; many more might have been taken. Most were found singly under the moss and rocks, sometimes in trickles of water and frequently on water-soaked soil and among thoroughly wetted rocks. Several pairs of adults were found together. One member of one of these pairs had large eggs showing as yellowish masses in her abdomen.

The young animals at Rogue River, with their greenish-yellow dorsal stripe, reminded me of *Aneides flavipunctatus* in the northern part of its range. The dorsal stripe of the adults was obscured in varying degrees by dusky. One pair darted from beneath a moss-covered rock into the stream. Both immediately swam upstream. This positive reotropism may have survival value in tending to prevent the animals from being carried downstream over the rocks where they might be injured. Search was made for eggs. Sheets of moss were torn from the rocks and fine gravelly soil, but no egg clusters were found. All animals collected were obtained along a strip of stream bottom 3 feet wide by about 60 feet long and in a moss-covered rocky seepage area 10 to 15 feet wide and 20 feet long that adjoined the stream. Thermal conditions were uniform, the air 6 inches above the ground in the shade was 10.8°C.; the substratum where the animals were found, 10.8°C.; and the water was 10.9°C.; time 3:30 P.M. The area was well shaded, principally by bay trees which provided a canopy of about 75 per cent. There were scattered clumps of sword fern.

The ecological niche of *dunni* appears similar to that of *Rhyacotriton.* Of their distributional relationship in Oregon, where the two forms have similar ranges, Dr. Storm informs me that *Rhyacotriton* occurs higher in the mountains than *dunni* and that the latter extends to lower elevations than does the ambystomid. There is, however, broad overlap in altitudinal, as well as horizontal range. He states further that *vehiculum* is more tolerant of heat and dryness than *dunni,* which makes *vehiculum* easier to encounter in logged or burned areas.

Reproduction.—Slater (1939b:154) reports a specimen found by Murray Johnson at Portland, Oregon, May 1, 1937, that contained 18 light cream-colored eggs about 2 mm. in diameter, and many smaller ones. The salamander measured 130 mm. in length. Bishop (1943:244) mentions females taken in June, 1936, near Portland, with ovarian eggs about 1.5 mm. in diameter.

An adult female obtained by me April 7, 1948, ½ mile west of Lobster Creek, along the Rogue River, Curry County, Oregon, was brought into the laboratory at Berkeley, heavily laden with eggs. She was induced to lay by pituitary implantation (Noble and Richards, 1930). Laying began May 25 and was completed May 26. Thirteen eggs were deposited. In laying, the salamander rested her foreparts on the bottom of the container with her hindquarters directed upward against the side of the jar. The eggs were broadly attached to the jar by the outer jelly envelope and some of them retained a slender connection with the egg nearby. All were fertile and developed to the gastrula stage before spoiling. Sperm for fertilization must have come from that stored in the spermatheca of the female since an opportunity for breeding in captivity seems remote (19 individuals were kept together in a gallon jar).

EGGS. A representative egg was unpigmented and surrounded by 2 (possibly 3) envelopes of translucent jelly; ovum, 4.5 mm.; inner jelly layer, 0.4 mm.; questionable second layer, 0.08 mm.; outer jelly envelope,

1 mm.; over-all diameter, including jelly envelopes, about 7 mm.; surface of outer gelatinous capsule irregular. The female showed no brooding tendency and was removed when she began consuming her eggs.

DEL NORTE SALAMANDER

Plethodon elongatus Van Denburgh
Plate 7

Range.—A narrow strip of humid coastal forest from central Humboldt County, California, north into southwestern Oregon, along the Rogue River. (Pl. 51.)

Type locality.—Requa, Del Norte County, California (Van Denburgh, 1916:216).

Other localities. CALIFORNIA. *Del Norte Co.*—5 mi. E of Requa; Klamath; 7 mi. S of Crescent City. *Humboldt Co.*—4 mi. N, 1½ mi. E of Orick, about 50 ft. elevation; 5.5 mi. E of Blue Lake, off U.S. Highway 101. *Trinity Co.*—4.2 (by road) ESE of Salyer.

Description.—STRUCTURE. Adult to about 4½ inches; costal grooves usually 17, sometimes 16 or 18, counting one each in axilla and groin; 6 to 8 (often 7) intercostal folds between tips of toes of adpressed limbs; vomerine teeth 4 to 7 per row (based on 7 adults); rows separated at midline; parasphenoid teeth arranged in elongate ovoid patch separated short distance from vomerine teeth; parasphenoid patch divided along midline into two club-shaped groups (2 animals), a single patch (3 individuals), or partly separated at anterior and posterior ends (1 animal). COLOR. Above dark brown to nearly black with broad tan to reddish-brown dorsal stripe originating on head (including eyelids, although color of lids often obscured with dusky) and extending onto tail; in larger individuals stripe usually clouded centrally with dusky or sometimes absent; entire stripe or margins thereof may be reddish or pinkish in young animals; upper surface of limbs, including proximal portion, dusky; below largely uniformly slaty, lightening on undersides of feet and in gular area; whitish guanophores generally scarce dorsally but often moderately abundant on head and limbs; considerable numbers of guanophores on sides of body particularly between limbs but scarce on sides of tail; most individuals with yellowish, pale orange, and light gray breaks in melanic network on chin, throat, and sides of head and neck; iris with brassy marks above and below pupil or uniformly dark brown. JUVENILE. Well-defined dorsal stripe, pinkish in color, characteristically present. SEXUAL DIFFERENCES. Male with slightly more pointed lower jaw, and snout somewhat more truncate than in female but differences do not always hold; vent shorter in male and with a tendency to gape in preserved specimens; vent margin with relatively few pleats, extending toward opening often at nearly a right angle to its long axis; in female, pleats more definite and approach opening diagonally, anteromedially; vent margins of some males extended posteriorly on either side as short free flaps.

Adult female, HR 536, 59 mm. in snout-vent length, obtained on February 14, 1947, near Boise Creek, about 2 miles west of Willow Creek Post Office, at about 800 feet elevation, Humboldt County, California: Dorsal stripe evident but suffused medially throughout its length with dusky brown; lighter marginal areas of stripe and mottlings on dorsum of head orange buff (Ochraceous-Buff); stripe suffused posteriorly with brown (Clove Brown); guanophores absent dorsally except for a few that form whitish stippling on head and eyelids and for somewhat greater numbers on dorsal surfaces of limbs; upper surfaces of limbs colored about like dorsum, exclusive of dorsal stripe; upper surfaces of feet colored like venter but lightening at toe joints and toward tips of toes; pale yellow and white spots and blotches in gular area; under magnification some of these gaps in melanic ground are tinged with yellow, apparently from presence of lipophores, while others are filled with single or clustered guanophores; yellowish (Pale Chalcedony Yellow) markings most abundant on posterior half of gular area; more anterior ones paler yellow (close to Ivory Yellow); underside of tail and body deep slate gray (Blackish Mouse Gray); ground color of gular area brown (close to Clove Brown); ground color of ventral surfaces composed of close network of melanophores that set off minute spherical gray glandular areas; light scattering of whitish guanophores over all ventral surfaces; guanophores largely absent from sides of tail but concentrated in considerable numbers on sides of body between limbs and on sides of neck and head, mostly behind eyes; these cells, in most instances, seem to overlie gaps in melanic ground color; sides of head with pale yellowish-brown (Light Ochraceous-Buff) spots and blotches, occupying gaps in melanic ground color; iris dark brown with half-dozen stellate or punctostellate silvery guanophores above and several below pupil.

Comparisons.—Differs from *dunni* in having (1) relatively shorter limbs (usually 7 costal interspaces between tips of toes of adpressed limbs as opposed to 3 or 4 in *dunni*); (2) greater costal groove count (usually 17 instead of 15); (3) shorter toes; (4) subdued dorsal stripe in large adults; (5) central suffusion of dusky throughout dorsal stripe in contrast to rather uniform blotching or speckling throughout stripe in *dunni;* (6) pinkish-brown rather than dull brown, yellowish-olive, or greenish-yellow dorsal stripe; (7) few or no light-colored (orange-yellow, in life) breaks in melanic ground color along sides and on ventral surfaces.

Differs from *vehiculum* in usually having 17 instead of 16 costal grooves; usually 7 instead of 4½ to 5½ costal interspaces between tip of toes of adpressed limbs; shorter toes; usual loss of dorsal stripe in large adults;

uniformity in color of stripe (pinkish brown) whereas *vehiculum* may have reddish-brown, tan, yellowish-tan, or yellow stripe; more uniform melanic network on venter; *vehiculum* commonly has numerous gaps in this network, or melanophores may be reduced to form spots and blotches on light-colored ground.

Habitat.—Individuals have been found in rock slides, beneath rotting logs, and under slabs of bark in damp situations. Wood (1934:191) reports the species as "not uncommon" in such situations near Requa, California, on a south-facing slope with Sitka spruce, redwood, and madroño. I have found individuals most frequently in talus of road cuts, where growth of moss indicated that the deposit had been in repose for some time. Rock rubble with considerable fine soil seems to be preferred. In soil moisture requirements this species is similar to *P. vehiculum*. It is commonly found on damp soil. I have not found it in saturated situations such as characterize the ecological niche of *P. dunni*.

At the Boise Creek locality (mentioned under "description"), on February 14, 1947, Harold Reynolds found an adult under a rock above a talus slope on the south side of U.S. Highway 299. Alden Miller, Reynolds, and I obtained 8 additional individuals upon digging in the talus. The loose material of the rock slide answered well the description of the "rock rubble" niche given me by Joseph Slevin, who has collected many of these salamanders.

The talus was composed of rocks mostly 2 to 4 or 5 inches in greatest dimension. The rocks had somewhat rounded edges, were dark colored and appeared to have been in repose for some time. They were covered with a light growth of moss and in places were partly amalgamated with soil and were held by rootlets from scattered small ferns. A small maple tree shaded the deposit, and its leaves formed a thin layer over many of the rocks. The slope of the talus was about 45° to the north. The slide material measured about 50 feet along its base and approximately 30 feet at its greatest height. The surrounding forest consisted chiefly of Douglas fir, with scattered bay, madroño, tan oak, and maple. Seepage from a well-forested slope above the talus probably makes possible the occurrence of the salamanders there even in summer. In the loose material they can seek depths at which moisture and temperature conditions are favorable.

Behavior.—Like other species of the genus *Plethodon* this salamander, when uncovered, may attempt to escape by backing into the substratum. It moves with marked lateral undulations of the body.

Food.—Wood (1934:191) found an undigested annelid worm, about 100 mm. in length, in the stomach of one individual.

Reproduction.—Wood (1934:191) on November 4, 1933, near Requa, Del Norte County, California, a few days after the first heavy fall rain, found two small irregular clusters of salamander eggs, about 100 in number, presumably of this species. The eggs were under a piece of fallen redwood bark together with an adult *P. elongatus*. The eggs were closely cemented together by a small quantity of viscous jelly-like material, and were about 3 mm. in diameter, nearly spherical, but attenuated on one side to a noticeable point. Some contained embryos up to nearly 1.5 mm.

I obtained a gravid adult female, 62 mm. in snout-vent length on February 15, 1947, 4 miles north and 1½ miles east of Orick, Humboldt County, California. She possessed 11 eggs, averaging about 3.8 mm. in diameter, 5 in the left and 6 in the right ovary. Another adult, 58.2 mm. in snout-vent length, taken November 16, 1947, 2 miles west of Willow Creek Post Office, Humboldt County, California, possessed 10 eggs, each approximately 3 mm. in diameter, 6 in the left and 4 in the right ovary. From this I suspect that *elongatus,* as appears to be true of our other western species of the genus *Plethodon* for which there is information, normally deposits its eggs in spring or early summer, with hatching occurring in fall or early winter. The small size of the embryos of the eggs found by Wood (if they were truly eggs of this species), however, appears anomalous if this is correct.

Remarks.—Fitch (1936:638) found 2 individuals of this species associated with *P. dunni* in a ravine on the north side of the Rogue River, 11 miles above its mouth, Curry County, Oregon, but in general *dunni* prefers wetter situations than *elongatus.*

Plethodon elongatus and *P. vehiculum* replace each other geographically with no overlap in their ranges so far as is now known (Pl. 51). Their habitat requirements, as far as soil moisture and cover is concerned, appear almost identical. Similarity of their niches may preclude their coexistence. *Plethodon dunni* on the other hand, exists almost wholly within the range of *vehiculum.* They probably do not compete much with one another because they seem to prefer different microenvironments, *dunni* the soaked soil along streams and in seepage areas, and *vehiculum* the damp, less saturated ground generally farther from the stream margins. Although I have collected scores of both of these species, they seldom have been taken under the same cover although they may be found a few feet apart when variation in moisture spans their requirements. A similar relationship seems to exists in Washington between *vehiculum* and *vandykei,* the latter possibly the ecological equivalent of *dunni,* replacing this species to the north. The ranges of *dunni* and *vandykei* may be allopatric for the same reason that those of *dunni* and *elongatus* are mutually exclusive—extensive overlap in niche requirements.

In the Museum of Vertebrate Zoölogy are animals from coastal Humboldt County (Orick, Blue Lake, and Requa) and from Boise Creek in the extreme eastern part of this county. The Boise Creek occurrence (Stebbins and Reynolds, 1947) was, until now, the most interior station reported for the species. Since then an immature animal has been found 4.2 miles east-southeast of Salyer in western Trinity County. From a mixed lot of 23 animals from these localities, I found it possible to segregate individuals into two groups, principally on the basis of the configuration of the head and degree of melanism. The 13 animals from Boise Creek and Salyer differed from the 10 coastal animals as follows: (1) all 6 adults from the coast had obscure dorsal stripes, whereas only 3 of the total of 7 adult animals from the interior were so characterized; (2) there was less tendency in the coastal animals toward light spotting of the gular area and sides of the body than in the interior animals; (3) the furrows on the tail seemed more definite; (4) the snout longer; (5) the head more swollen behind the eyes, perhaps reflecting greater masseter development in the coastal animals. In limb and toe length and costal groove count, no differences were evident.

With collecting at stations interior to the range of this species, as now determined, the differences observed may be found more widespread. It may then be desirable, should such additional material come to hand, to recognize an interior subspecies of this salamander. At the present time insufficient specimens are available for adequate analysis.

JEMEZ MOUNTAINS SALAMANDER

Plethodon neomexicanus Stebbins and Riemer
Plate 6

Range.—Known only from the type locality in the Jemez Mountains, 12 miles west and 4 miles south of Los Alamos, altitude about 8,750 feet, Sandoval County, New Mexico. (Pl. 51.)

Type locality.—See above (Stebbins and Riemer, 1950).

Description.—STRUCTURE. Adult to slightly over 5 inches (5⅜ inches), average about 4½ inches; slender elongate species with short limbs and toes and with tail usually slightly shorter than body, rarely longer; costal grooves well defined, 18 (rarely 19), with similar furrows on tail; limbs relatively short, 7½ to 8½, usually 8, costal interspaces between tips of toes of adpressed limbs; fifth digit on hind foot usually with only one terminal phalanx (3 exceptions in 20 animals studied); other species of the genus *Plethodon* possess 2 phalanges in fifth toe; toes relatively short, about like *P. elongatus,* partly webbed basally; vomerine teeth usually 7 per row (range 5 to 11); parasphenoid teeth separated from vomerine teeth and arranged in single oval patch, broadest posteriorly; this patch usually shows reduction of teeth along midline, resulting in division in varying degrees into two patches. COLOR. Above brown (near Bone Brown) stippled with pale gold (Baryta Yellow) chromatophores, punctostellate in form; dorsal ground color and stippling quite uniform throughout except dorsolaterally where ground color tends to darken slightly and golden flecks less uniformly distributed; sometimes golden flecks clumped here, vaguely outlining an area usually occupied by dorsal stripe in other species; eyelids slightly darker than rest of head, probably due to underlying dark color of eyeballs; without magnification iris appears blackish with pale blue-green (almost silver) patches above and below pupil; gular area and underside of tail buff cream (Drab); body sooty blue (Heliotrope-Slate) with purple patches, resulting from underlying visceral colors; underside of limbs slightly lighter than upper surfaces; ventral surfaces of feet colored about like gular area; light-colored pigment cells on lower sides of body, ash gray (nearly white), sometimes with buffy cast, becoming pale gold on upper sides; melanic network tends to be reduced beneath them; they form fine stippling, spots, and blotches in gular area and on chest and abdomen (mostly lateral in position); they are scarce on underside of tail; upper and lower surfaces of limbs stippled with such cells, pale yellow in color. One individual lacked light-colored chromatophores completely; even light eye color was absent. JUVENILE (MVZ 49022). Resembles adult but possesses dorsal stripe, and color of underside of tail whitish with grayish cast instead of buff cream; close, rather uniform, pale gold stippling (appearing light gray with golden tinge to unaided eye), along back from upper surface of head, including eyelids, well toward tip of tail; stippling broken here and there but generally quite uniform, forming vaguely defined dorsal stripe; light-colored chromatophores form coarse blotches and spots on sides—on side of head behind jaw angle, on neck, between limbs, and at base of tail; they are separated from finer speckling of dorsal stripe by vague zone, dorsolateral in position, where light flecks reduced in abundance; edges of dorsal stripe vaguely indicated by tendency toward clumping of such flecks; few scattered light-colored pigment cells in gular area, mostly lateral in position and also laterally on chest and abdomen where they form pale yellow spots and blotches. SEXUAL DIFFERENCES. No external characters for determining sex evident. Examination of vent required for determination.

Habitat.—The Jemez Mountains in western north-central New Mexico lie approximately 30 miles west-northwest of Santa Fe. This essentially volcanic range rises to 11,500 feet at Santa Clara Peak and supports heavy stands of timber and perennial streams. The body of the range forms an island of Transition-Canadian Life-zone rising out of an Upper Sonoran plain. However, this island is not well separated from similar mountain groups to the north and east. It is essentially the southwestern corner of the main mass of the Rocky Mountains of Colorado. (Pl. 35, fig. 2.)

According to Bailey (1913), the Transition Zone in New Mexico occurs between 7,000 and 9,500 feet elevation; the Canadian occurs from 8,500 to 12,000 feet. The Transition Zone, 10,000 square miles in extent, occurs in the southern portion of the state only as small scattered islands and is characterized by Bailey as being extremely uniform in climate, fauna, and flora throughout New Mexico. Furthermore, even the isolated southern mountain regions contain few species which are not common to the main mass of the Rockies. Presumably the same is true of the 2,000 square miles of Canadian Zone which is largely confined to the northern part of the state. Of the Jemez Range, Bailey specifically states: "The plant and animal life is mainly that of the southern Colorado mountains. . . ."

Because of the scattered nature of these mountain areas and the manner in which they rise out of the arid and relatively level Upper Sonoran plains, Bailey feels they are able to precipitate the maximum amount of rain and snow. Heavy snows occur in winter; some banks often last into late spring in the Canadian Zone. During midsummer there are frequent, often daily, showers of rain or hail.

August 14, 1949. The type locality, 12 miles west and 4 miles south of Los Alamos, at 8,750 feet elevation, Sandoval County, New Mexico, is an area with a slight to moderate (10° to 35°) slope facing west to northwest covered with a good stand of timber; it is 150 yards from a large open meadow used as summer range for sheep. No stream and almost no exposed rocks are in the immediate vicinity.

At the collection site the principal trees are *Abies concolor, Acer glabrum neomexicanum, Picea pungens, Populus tremuloides,* and *Pseudotsuga mucronata* of which *Pseudotsuga* is by far the most abundant. Beneath the trees an understory of herbaceous plants, 2 to 6 inches high and uniformly spaced, provides a rather continuous cover over the ground. Occasional shrubs rise to 1½ feet. Grass in thin, small clumps rises to 18 inches in the level areas where herbaceous plants are shorter and more sparsely distributed. The smaller plants associated with the salamanders include: *Actaea viridiflora, Artemisia franserioides, Fragaria mexicana, Galium* sp., *Geranium eremophilium, Osmorrhiza obtusa, Oxalis metcalfei, Rubus parviflorus, Salix* sp., *Thalictrum cheilanthoides, Trautvetteri grandis* (?), *Trisetum montanum, Vaccinium scoparium* and *Viola* sp.

A 1- to 1½-inch mat of dead needles and leaves, sooty brown in color, covers the soil. This mat is made up mostly of *Pseudotsuga* needles but the leaves of the broad-leafed plants are most conspicuous. Rotting and already well-rotted logs are abundant, particularly on the sloping ground. The majority of such logs are well rotted throughout, saturated with water and well covered with lichens and mosses. It is in association with such logs, especially those of the *Pseudotsuga,* that the salamanders are found. They were taken under the bark, in fissures in the center of decomposed logs and also beneath logs where they were in contact with the soil.

The following animals were observed to share the logs with the salamanders: centipedes (several kinds, all small), spiders, earthworms, camel crickets, carabid beetles, wireworms and snails. The less well-rotted logs often housed ant colonies—such logs did not yield salamanders.

Search for specimens was made in spots other than the type locality but no salamanders were found. Hence, it is not known whether the animal occurs at higher or lower elevations, whether it is restricted to the relatively shaded northwest-facing slopes or whether it prefers forests predominantly of *Pseudotsuga.*

The following is a description of a typical collection site.

Time, 5:15 P.M. An adult taken in the middle of a log which is 6 inches in diameter, 7 feet long, and well covered with mosses. Water is easily squeezed from the decayed wood. Leaf litter is thick and dry on top but wet just beneath the surface. Slope, 30° to NNW. Site, 40 feet upslope from previous capture. *Acer* and *Pseudotsuga* overhead, the herbaceous cover thick, 4 inches high. This spot is the most shaded of all so far, with a canopy of 60 to 70 per cent; reduced when maples lose their leaves. When first exposed the animal started quickly down a crevice in the rotten wood. Camel crickets and carabid beetles present. Temperature of wood where salamander taken 12.8°C., surface of leaf mat 14.8°C., air 3 inches above log 16.2°C. Clouds breaking up after releasing only a few small drops.

All of the 18 specimens taken at the type locality were captured within an area of 75 by 200 yards. Considerable time was spent searching in an ideal-looking, but slightly drier, area immediately adjacent to the type locality. No salamanders were found here.

Charles Lowe, Jr. visited the type locality on August 30. He searched for 3 hours but found no salamanders. He reported conditions too dry.

In view of the snow blanket in the winter and the rains in the summer it is supposed that this species is active on the surface during the summer months. In this respect it would be more like the eastern plethodontids in habit than the western forms. (Habitat notes from Stebbins and Riemer, 1950.)

VAN DYKE SALAMANDER

Plethodon vandykei Van Denburgh
Plate 9

Range.—The Coast, Olympic, and Cascade mountains of western Washington and the mountains of northern Idaho. The subspecies *idahoensis* is known only from the type locality, the northeastern corner of Coeur d'Alene Lake, on the south shore of Wolf Lodge Bay, opposite Wolf Bay Lodge, at 2,160 feet, Kootenai County, Idaho. (Pl. 50.)

Type locality.—Paradise Valley, Mount Rainier Park, Washington (Van Denburgh, 1906:61).

Other localities. WASHINGTON. *Clallam Co.*—Forks (CPS). *Grays Harbor*—Ox Bow Station, 3 mi. SE on Ox Bow Creek (CPS); Lake Quinault, 10 mi. up Col. Bob trail (CPS). *Jefferson Co.*—N of Hoh River Bridge (CPS). *Lewis Co.*—Tilton River, W Fork (CPS); 2 mi. from Highway up W Fork of Tilton (CPS); Paradise Valley (CAS). *Mason Co.*—Skokomish River Valley; 6 mi. above S end of Lake Cushman (AMNH); Skokomish River at Devil's Staircase (CAS); Olympic Mts. (CPS); Triple Trip (CPS); Hoodsport (AMNH). *Pacific Co.*—Falls, 6 mi. SW of South Bend. *Pierce Co.*—Carbon River near Carbon Glacier.

Description.—STRUCTURE. Adult approximately 3½ to 4½ inches; parotoid glands present; costal grooves 14, sometimes 13, counting one each in axilla and groin; 2 to 3 intercostal folds between tips of toes of adpressed limbs; toes relatively short with skin connecting bases of digits farther toward tips of toes than in *vehiculum* and *dunni* but similar in this characteristic to *elongatus* and *neomexicanus;* vomerine teeth 4 to 12 per row (10 adults, 7 of them *idahoensis*); rows usually narrowly separated at midline; vomerine teeth separated or occasionally connected to parasphenoid teeth; parasphenoid teeth in ovoid patch, narrowing anteriorly and with teeth sometimes reduced or absent along midline, particularly posteriorly. COLOR. Yellowish or tan stripe extending from snout and including upper eyelids to tip of tail, brightest on tail (stripe sometimes dark clay-colored in alcohol [Van Denburgh, 1906:62], often yellow ocher in life); edges of dorsal stripe may be somewhat irregular particularly in *idahoensis;* sides of head, body, tail, and upper surfaces of legs uniformly brown or yellowish brown to black, in some individuals of subspecies *vandykei,* so nearly color of dorsal stripe as to blend with it; some individuals with considerable number of small gaps in melanic ground color of upper surfaces of limbs, particularly basally; these may unite in *vandykei* to form extensive patches of light color; light limb color like dorsal stripe; belly light yellow or flesh-colored, sometimes mottled with light brown (in light phase *vandykei*) or generally dusky to black (*idahoensis*), except for gular area; throat and sometimes distal portion of ventral surface of tail yellow in life; throat patch when present usually of variable size; patch involves disruption of melanic ground color; in dark animals tips of toes lighter than general ground color; belly and sides with scattered gray flecks (guanophores); guanophores largest and closely set along lower sides, largely stopping short of dorsal stripe resulting in stripe being margined with black or brown; few whitish guanophores scattered laterally along dorsal stripe and on head; iris blackish with silvery, pale gold, or brassy metallic markings. Some individuals of *vandykei* are as dark-sided as *idahoensis* but differ in having a wider, more even-edged dorsal stripe, less clouding of stripe on head; more light color (like color of stripe) on upper surfaces of limbs; more light flecking of ventral surface of body and somewhat more light color in gular area. Such melanistic *vandykei* may be collected along with lighter-colored animals. JUVENILE. Colored like adult except dorsal stripe often brighter and more yellowish; guanophores on sides fewer and relatively larger; ventral surfaces darker, and yellowish gular area better defined. Juveniles of the subspecies *vandykei* closely parallel young *idahoensis* in coloration but dorsal stripe warmer yellow and dark color of sides less intense black, more brownish than black. Like *idahoensis* gular area usually light colored, yellowish in life. SEXUAL DIFFERENCES. In fullest expression of external sexual differences, male has more truncate snout and somewhat more prominent upper lip than female; nasolabial groove terminates in tubercular projection from edge of upper lip; lower jaw is more pointed; and vent margins extend posteriorly as blunt finger-like lobes on either side of posterior margin of vent. Female lacks or has but weak development of lip tubercle, has rounded lower jaw, and vent is simple slit (based on subspecies *idahoensis*).

Adult female, RCS 2227, 61.7 mm. in snout-vent length, obtained April 17, 1948, on the West Fork of the Tilton River, 1 mile northwest of State Highway 5, Lewis County, Washington: Light phase—Sparse scattering of white, nearly punctate guanophores over all dorsal surfaces, most abundant on tail and snout, few on dorsal surfaces of limbs; guanophores larger and more numerous, of variable size and irregular distribution, on lower sides between limbs and low on sides of head; few basally on sides of tail, largely absent distally; few laterally in gular region, especially posterolaterally; few on undersides of limbs and laterally on body; few scattered about vent and base of tail; absent elsewhere on underside of tail; upper surface of body olivaceous (Medal Bronze or between Isabella Color and Dresden Brown), darkening to brown (Snuff Brown) on head; limbs colored about like head, perhaps slightly lighter (slightly duller than Raw

Sienna); eyelids slightly darker than rest of head due to dark pigmentation of eyeballs; ventral surfaces with network of pale lipophores and scattering of melanophores, irregular in arrangement; underside of body light purplish brown (between Avellaneous and Wood Brown); gular area old gold (near Chamois); undersides of limbs and tail yellow (near Honey Yellow); iris dark brown with silvery guanophores forming half-crescent at upper margin of pupil and second irregular crescent-shaped network well above pupil margin; scattered stellate guanophores in lower iris.

Adult female, RCS 2231, 53 mm. in snout-vent length obtained April 19, 1948, on the south shore of Wolf Bay, opposite Wolf Bay Lodge, 2,160 feet, Kootenai County, Idaho: Dorsal stripe from head to base of tail, yellow olive (Orange-Citrine) grading to old gold (Yellow Ocher) on tail; stripe obscured on head by suffusion of melanophores and guanophores; ground color dorsally on body and limbs, exclusive of stripe, black with hoary suffusion of numerous closely set, whitish, punctostellate guanophores; these guanophores generally not connected with one another; hoary suffusion over all dorsal surfaces except for most of dorsal stripe and narrow margin on either side of it; pigment cells metallic golden in color, present in dorsal stripe along narrow zone at its margins; these cells become reduced and finally disappear toward tip of tail; guanophores clumped on lower sides to form large whitish spots of irregular outline and distribution; guanophores occur as flecks of gray (Pallid Mouse Gray) over ventral surfaces, including undersides of limbs, are scarce toward tip of tail and posteriorly in gular area, are absent from undersides of feet except for few deeply situated single cells, and are most abundant on sides; few small pale yellow (near Colonial Buff) breaks in melanic ground color ventrally on body, particularly in gular area; ventral surfaces blackish brown (Blackish Brown [3]); gular area and feet lighter, former purplish brown (near Dusky Drab) and latter purplish gray (near Light Drab); iris dark brown with upper edge of pupil margined with gold (Baryta Yellow) and with network of similar color above pupil; few flecks of pale yellow in lower iris.

Habitat.—Found in damp places beneath stones, bark, and other surface objects, usually, but not necessarily, near running water. Slevin (1928:59) reports that individuals were collected under stones along the upper edge of the bed of the Calawah River near Forks, Clallam County, Washington. They were found where small seepages from the banks kept the soil wet. On June 21, 1936, Bishop (1943:275) found the animals in similar places along this river, " . . . among the small stones and gravel washed clean by the waters of the springs." I found 2 individuals on April 17, 1948, among moss-covered rocks on the steep well-shaded, south bank of the West Fork of the Tilton River, 1 mile northwest of State Highway 5, Lewis County, Washington. Most of the rocks were waterworn and were of considerable size. The salamanders were found where there was but little soil mixed with the rocks. The surfaces of the rocks were damp, but not wet. Both individuals, a juvenile and an adult, were found a foot or so from the edge of the river. The area would have been well shaded in summer by maples, which at the time of my visit were leafless. There were several seepages into the stream 30 to 40 feet away but none where the salamanders were found.

Individuals upon which the name *idahoensis* was based were taken by Slater and Slipp (1940:42) at the foot of a high-cut bank above the road which follows the edge of Coeur d'Alene Lake—2 adults from rock and earth talus and 3 juveniles from the gravel floor at the entrance of a very wet mine 0.6 of a mile distant. The forest in the vicinity consisted of much Douglas fir and dwarf maple but yellow pine and open areas of arid Transition predominated a few miles to the westward.

Charles Lowe, Jr. and I collected 28 individuals of the form *idahoensis* on April 22, 1948, at the type locality. Most of them were found under rocks of a north-facing talus above the highway. The rocks were mostly under 5 inches in diameter and there was considerable soil mixed with them. The rocks were moss-covered and a scattering of broad-leaf alder-like seedlings were growing on the slope, indicating the talus was not freshly formed. The soil was damp but not wet, resembling soil moisture conditions under which we found *P. elongatus*. Temperature of the soil at the collection site was 6°C.; air temperature, 6 inches above the ground in the shade at 2:45 P.M. was 10°C. Individuals ranging in size from what appeared to be recently hatched young to adults were found. The animals behaved in characteristic plethodon manner, wriggling backward into the loose rock when they were exposed. The color of the dorsal stripe was noted as closely matching the color of the moss on the rocks. Several individuals were found beneath moss-covered rocks on a ridge above the highway in an area unmodified by man. (Pl. 36, figs. 1 and 2.)

Reproduction.—Noble (1925:6) mentions a clutch of eggs of *P. vandykei* (subspecies *vandykei*) that was obtained by Phillips Putnam. Putnam, as quoted by Noble, said the eggs were "fastened together in a grapelike mass and attached to the stone by a string of elastic material." The stone was in a damp situation and was covered by moss.

I collected a gravid female, 61.7 mm. in snout-vent length, along the West Fork of the Tilton River, 1 mile northwest of State Highway 5, Lewis County, Washington, on April 17, 1948. She contained 14 eggs, 2.6 mm. in diameter, 8 in the left, 6 in the right ovary. When preserved, the eggs appeared orange yellow.

An adult female received from James R. Slater, collected July 1, 1949, at "Cataract Creek, where it flows into Carbon River, Rainier National Park, Pierce County, Washington," contained 11 eggs. These were 2.4 mm. in diameter, 6 in the left and 5 in the right ovary.

Noble (1931:49) has figured the larva. The gills at a well-advanced stage of development are shown as composed of 3 elongate primary lobes, each lobe possessing a number of finger-like subsidiary projections (5 or 6?).

Remarks.—In Washington this species resembles *Ensatina eschscholtzii* in general form and some individuals also resemble the latter in coloration, but the body is less flattened, the tail less compressed toward its ventral surface, the limbs are shorter and stouter, the toes webbed basally, and the eyes are relatively smaller. The presence of a dorsal stripe further distinguishes most individuals from *E. eschscholtzii*. The young look much like *P. vehiculum* but usually can be distinguished by an extensive light-colored patch in the gular area, and the irregular, often almost scalloped margins of the dorsal stripe.

SUBSPECIES
Plate 9

1*a*. Dorsal stripe broader; sides black or brown, sometimes so nearly color of stripe as to blend with it; proximal segments of limbs with light color like dorsal stripe; gular area more extensively light colored. *Range*. As given for species exclusive of range of *idahoensis* .... *P. v. vandykei* Van Denburgh

1*b*. Dorsal stripe narrower; sides black, contrasting with dorsal stripe; proximal segments of limbs blackish or nearly so; gular area with less light color. *Range*. Northeastern corner of Coeur d'Alene Lake, on the south shore of Wolf Lodge Bay, 2,160 feet, Kootenai County, Idaho .... *P. v. idahoensis* Slater and Slipp

WESTERN RED-BACKED SALAMANDER

Plethodon vehiculum (Cooper)
Plate 8

Range.—Southwestern British Columbia including Vancouver Island, south and west of the crest of the Cascades, through Washington into western Oregon, at least as far south as Coquille, Coos County. (Pl. 51.)

Type locality.—Astoria, Oregon (Cooper, 1860).

Description.—STRUCTURE. Adult 3 to about 4 inches; costal grooves 16, sometimes 15, counting one each in axilla and groin; 4½ to 5½ intercostal folds between tips of toes of adpressed limbs; vomerine teeth 4 to 7 per row (6 adult animals from various parts of range); vomerine rows closely approach but usually do not meet one another at midline; parasphenoid tooth patch oval in shape, broadened slightly posteriorly, generally separated from vomerine tooth rows; parasphenoid patch often with teeth reduced in number along midline, resulting in division of patch, in varying degrees, into two tooth-bearing areas; patches commonly connected anteriorly (4 of 10 animals), connected both posteriorly and anteriorly (1), separated anteriorly (1), completely divided (2), and undivided (2); vomerine and parasphenoid tooth arrangement essentially as in *P. dunni*.

COLOR. Dorsal longitudinal stripe usually clearly defined, sometimes with few black specks which may somewhat obscure central portion, leaving narrow margin of light color on either side or, occasionally, animal may be completely dark above; margins of stripe usually regular; stripe variable in color from light reddish tan to yellow; in 34 individuals from various parts of range, frequency of colors of dorsal stripe were: blackish 5, reddish brown 15, tan 7, yellowish tan 3, and yellow 4; dorsal surface of proximal segments of limbs usually colored like dorsal stripe; dorsal surfaces stippled with fine white guanophores, most abundant on head; guanophores usually present on head when largely absent elsewhere; upper sides next to stripe deep blackish brown to black, lightening to sooty toward ventral surface; scattering of white guanophores on lower sides; ground color of ventral surface of body darkest between limbs, bluish sooty in life; gular area light gray; undersides of tail and limbs intermediate in color between those of body and gular area; most individuals with many small gaps in melanic ground color over all ventral surfaces; these gaps may be light gray or pale yellow to pale orange yellow in life; lipoid colors may give gular area, chest, and underside of tail of some animals orange or yellowish cast; some individuals have small gaps in melanic ground much reduced; others have melanic pigment reduced to scattering of irregular spots and blotches; pale grayish-white guanophores scattered over all ventral surfaces, becoming somewhat reduced in number on underside of tail; distribution of ventral guanophores is independent of breaks in melanic ground color, light yellow and orange gaps in ground color encroach on lower sides of body, head, and tail and in many individuals approach dorsal stripe, particularly anteriorly; some individuals have much reduced melanic color (3 in above lot of 34 animals); they are generally yellowish or orange throughout although they may exhibit slight darkening on upper sides next to dorsal stripe; iris with golden, salmon, to coppery markings, often considerably obscuring dark brown ground color. JUVENILE. Colored essentially like adult except dorsal stripe often lighter, less obscured with dusky, and more sharply set off from lateral dark pigmentation. SEXUAL DIFFERENCES. Adult male tends to have slightly more pointed lower jaw and margins of vent slightly raised and extended behind into short rounded free flaps; female tends to have more rounded lower jaw and possesses pleated vent margin.

Adult, RCS 2173, 50 mm. in snout-vent length, obtained April 12, 1948, 3.6 miles south-southwest of Quinault, U.S. Highway 101, Grays Harbor County, Washington: Dorsal stripe yellow (basal 1/3 of tail and edges of stripe anteriorly, Deep Chrome, remainder obscured by melanophores), on close inspection observed to consist of scattering of guanophores, extending posteriorly at least to sacral area, overlaid by lipophore network; in few places guanophores appear silvery, evidently where they show through gaps in apparently more superficial yellow lipophore network and capillary bed; upper sides blackish brown, without guanophores; spots and blotches of clustered white guanophores concentrated ventrolaterally; guanophores extend over ventral surfaces of body, chest, gular area, region of vent, and on undersides of limbs; those ventrally and laterally situated lie principally in small gaps in melanic ground color; gaps may also bear lipoid color and may extend toward dorsal stripe as yellowish spotting beyond guanophore zone of sides; distal two-thirds of tail stippled with white guanophores except ventrally; underside of tail with yellow spots, lipoid colored gaps in melanic ground; sides of face and neck marked like sides of body; proximal segments of hind limbs colored above like dorsal stripe, including its underlying guanistic color; less definite yellow color similarly situated on forelimbs; whitish guanophores scattered over dorsal surfaces of distal segments of limbs; yellow color of gular area, chest, underside of tail, and in gaps in melanic ground of venter, dull Naples Yellow; iris dark brown with coppery to pale gold guanophores forming well-developed patch in upper and smaller, less well-defined patch in lower portion.

Habitat.—Found beneath logs, bark, stones, moss, and leaves in damp situations. Individuals have been discovered in considerable numbers in cleavage planes among dead leaves. Watney (1938:89) reported the species at Vancouver, British Columbia, in a forest of Douglas fir and alder. Dr. Robert Storm of Corvallis, Oregon, informs me that when he wishes to obtain *vehiculum* he goes to the old logging roads in the Coast Range and digs into shaded outcrops, since these are the most unfailing source. I have found this salamander beneath moss and bark of logs and in fissures of decayed logs. The species is commonly found on damp soil, less commonly in wet situations.

Food.—Termites and other soft-bodied insects appear to be the main food (Carl, 1943:33).

Reproduction.—A female collected near the Hoh River, Jefferson County, Washington, September 20, 1919, contained eggs about 2.5 mm. in diameter (Slevin, 1928:55). Bishop (1943:281) found a few eggs 2 mm. in diameter and many small ones in large females collected on June 20, 1936, near Shelton, Washington. Individuals taken in February at Portland, Oregon, had only small ova. Carl (1943:33, British Columbia) gives the following information on reproduction. "The eggs are as large as peas and are laid in grapelike clusters attached to the sides or roof of a hollow space in a moist location. It is likely that the female remains with the eggs during the period of incubation. The developing young pass through a gilled larval stage within the egg and hatch in the adult form."

A female obtained by me, 6.3 miles southeast of Cathlamet, Wahkiakum County, Washington, on April 11, 1948, was induced to lay by pituitary implantation (Noble and Richards, 1930). Oviposition began May 31, 1948, and 9 eggs were laid by June 2. A tenth egg was retained. The manner of laying and the appearance of the eggs were as in *P. dunni* (p. 71).

The following description of the eggs of this species is based on this clutch.

EGGS. Two transparent jelly envelopes, an inner firm one and outer softer one; these measured respectively 0.2 to 0.45 mm. and 0.8 to 1.0 mm.; there appeared to be a thin layer between them when the capsules were swollen with water (measurements made after eggs had been on wet surface for 2 hours); ovum 4.5 mm.; to surface of outer jelly capsule, about 5.8 to 6.0 mm.; surface of outer jelly envelope irregular; eggs attached by broad flaring base composed of jelly continuous with outer capsule. As with *P. dunni,* fertilization had occurred, presumably from stored sperm. By July 19, 1948, several embryos had reached the head fold stage of development but shortly thereafter died. The female was not solicitous as to the eggs, although for several days after laying she lay by them without moving, appearing dead, but she could be roused by shaking of the container. After this she wandered about the jar, seldom going near the eggs. Once, possibly by coincidence, she lay curled against them.

ESCHSCHOLTZ SALAMANDER

Ensatina eschscholtzii Gray
Plates 10 and 11

Range.—Mountains of the Pacific Coast from the southwestern mainland and Vancouver Island, British Columbia, south to extreme southern San Diego County, California. Ranges inland in California through the Siskiyou and southern Cascade mountains, thence southward through the Sierra Nevada into the mountains of southern California. Ranges of the races *klauberi* and *eschscholtzii,* the terminal races, respectively, of the interior and coastal series of subspecies, overlap in southern California and although there is zonal confluence, interbreeding is unknown. The race *xanthoptica,* common in the vicinity of San Francisco Bay, California, also occurs opposite the Bay in the foothills of the Sierra Nevada with the Sierran form, *platensis.* A hybrid between these two races was found April 30, 1948, on Jawbone Ridge, at 3,100 feet, about 8 miles east of Groveland, Tuolumne County, California. (Pl. 52.)

Type locality.—California (Gray, 1850:48), later amended to Monterey, California (Boulenger, 1882:54).

Description.—STRUCTURE. Adult 3 to 6 inches; tail rounded above, somewhat compressed ventrally, constricted at base; toes 4-5; palmar but no plantar tubercles; eyes large and protuberant; 12 costal grooves, counting one each in axilla and groin; vomerine teeth 12 to 32 (average 24) per row, arranged in 2 arcs that curve anteriorly and that approach but rarely meet one another at midline; parasphenoid teeth in two elongate wedge-shaped patches between eyes, converging but rarely meeting anteriorly. COLOR. Coloration highly variable ranging from uniformly brown to reddish brown above to dark brown or black, spotted and blotched with orange, yellow, or cream (see key to subspecies). JUVENILE. Head larger, body and tail relatively shorter, and basal constriction of tail not as pronounced as in adult. In coloration resembles adult in races *klauberi, croceater, xanthoptica,* and *eschscholtzii* but young *platensis* usually lacks orange spotting and juvenal *oregonensis* has dark blotches like adult of race *picta.* Young of all races but *croceater, klauberi,* and *eschscholtzii* have considerable numbers of white to pale blue guanophores on dorsal surfaces; guanophores of skin reduced in number or absent in races mentioned. SEXUAL DIFFERENCES (figs. 2 and 3). Adult male readily distinguished from female by long slender tail (when unregenerated, usually as long or longer than body whereas in female it is shorter than body), longer and more truncate snout (rounded in female), more extensive bifurcation of nasolabial groove and swollen cloacal region.

In view of the marked color differences among the subspecies of this salamander, descriptions follow:

Oregonensis.—Light to dark brown above, often uniformly colored, but sometimes minutely flecked with light color (in life, pale yellow to orange) due to irregular distribution of melanophores and lipophores; eyelids dark, like skin of head; sides usually mottled due to irregular distribution of lipophores and melanophores, with light-colored markings concentrated in costal grooves; light color along sides pale orange or yellowish orange; basal half or less of upper surface of proximal segments of limbs yellowish to yellowish orange; distal segments colored like upper surfaces of body, although usually somewhat lighter; feet light-colored, particularly on toes, stippled with melanophores; ventral surfaces of limbs and tail usually light orange or yellowish due to presence of lipophores, but occasionally whitish; remaining ventral surfaces whitish or variously spotted and blotched with clusters of pale orange to yellowish lipophores; ventral surfaces with fine, usually evenly spaced, ventral stippling of melanophores; pleuroperitoneum similarly marked; guanophores usually present in considerable numbers along sides of neck and body, less common on sides of tail, although usually present basally; guanophores may be present dorsally in varying numbers but they are often scarce and sometimes are absent except for concentration at upper base of each limb, forming patch of irregular shape beneath lipophore network; iris with varying numbers of guanophores forming patch of whitish, yellowish, bronze, or copper in upper part and sometimes smaller patch in lower part; iridic guanophores sometimes absent.

Color changes with growth.—Juvenile resembles *picta* (Pl. 10, figs. 4, 14) in dark blotching of body and tail; ground color brown above, grading into reddish brown on tail; proximal segments of limbs, yellowish to yellowish orange; distal segments like body, but somewhat lighter; below gray, resulting from closely set melanophores on whitish, lipophore-free or weakly marked venter; dorsal surfaces sprinkled with guanophores except for proximal segments of limbs where they are scarce or absent, except for patches at upper bases of limbs beneath lipophore network; guanophores usually heaviest on head, lightening posteriorly on body and on distal segments of limbs, sometimes sparingly present on ventral surfaces.

With growth, major changes are obscuring of juvenal blotching, reduction in conspicuousness of guanophores, lightening of ventral surfaces, and dulling of color of tail.

Xanthoptica.—Above orange brown (Seal Brown to Blackish Brown (2)), extending on sides to or a little below a line connecting upper surfaces of limbs; lower limits of dark dorsal coloration, particularly on sides between limbs, irregular and somewhat mottled; ground color of eyelids yellowish orange (Salmon Orange); below orange (Apricot Orange) except on abdomen and lower thoracic region where orange tan (Ferruginous); ventral orange color brighter where it approaches dark dorsal coloration—bright orange (Flame Scarlet) on sides of head and reddish orange (Grenadine Red) on sides of body and tail; a few melanophores on chin and melanic patches on soles of hind feet and sometimes ventral surfaces; proximal segments of limbs reddish orange (Grenadine Red) above; distal segments similar in ground color to proximal segments but with mottling of melanophores on forelimbs and rather extensive network on hind limbs, obscuring lipochrome ground color; orange color lightens on toes to yellowish orange (Salmon Orange); guanophores present but indistinct, situated on dorsal and lateral surfaces of body and head, including eyelids; usually few observed on tail, limbs, or ventral surfaces; guanophore patch present beneath lipophore network at base of upper side of limbs as in *oregonensis;* iris with most of upper half light yellow (Picric Yellow); few or no guanophores in lower part.

Color changes with growth.—Juveniles uniformly orange brown above lightening to orange or reddish orange toward tip of tail, probably partly due to thinning of melanophores distally; upper eyelids usually lighter than head, often with yellowish cast; ventral surfaces buff to whitish but close examination reveals presence of lipophores in varying numbers; some juveniles have continuous lipophore network over all ventral surfaces, others may have central longitudinal region on body and narrow margin about vent without them; areas of loosely arranged lipophores may appear whitish on casual examination; undersides of proximal segments of limbs usually yellowish; ventral surfaces essentially without melanophores, but occasionally some may be present, usually on tip of chin, in gular area, and a few in scattered clusters on body; proximal segments of limbs orange or yellowish orange above; distal segments colored like upper surface of body; feet orange above, buffy below; guanophores pale blue to silvery, numerous on eyelids, head, and body, thinning on tail and largely absent from proximal segments of limbs; present on distal segments of limbs and sides of body and neck, seldom present ventrally; iris with well-developed yellow patch occupying most of upper part and with or without a small patch in lower part.

With growth, melanin becomes more pronounced, darkening dorsum of body and distal segments of limbs; buff or whitish coloration of ventral surfaces changes to uniform orange as lipophores become more abundant and more deeply pigmented; coloration shifts from yellowish orange to orange or even reddish orange, most noticeably on proximal segments of limbs; guanophores become obscure.

Eschscholtzii.—Adult uniformly reddish brown to brown above, without pattern or with vague light or dark blotching;[1] upper eyelids pinkish, orange, buff, or less commonly brownish, usually lighter than dorsal ground color, with few or no melanophores; tail often with irregular distribution of melanophores dorsally, particularly toward tip, resulting in varying degrees of vague orange blotching; dorsal melanism ends in rather abrupt irregular line alongside of head, body, and tail, about on a level with dorsal surfaces of basal portions of limbs; lipophores extend somewhat farther ventrally forming fringe of pale orange red beyond darker coloration; ventral surfaces of head, body, and tail usually whitish, in some individuals entirely without lipophores or melanophores; when melanophores are present, they usually occur sparingly on chin, in postgular region, and about vent; pleuroperitoneum without melanophores except at base of mesenteries and in vicinity of large blood vessels; lipophores sometimes present ventrally, coloring under surfaces of limbs and tail pale orange red, but never covering body and gular region; proximal segments of limbs above usually uniformly orange or reddish orange to elbow and knee but about one of three individuals with some melanism of distal portions; distal segments usually with mottling of melanophores on reddish orange background but in some individuals melanism more uniform, resembling that of upper surfaces of body although usually somewhat lighter; under surfaces of limbs pinkish or white, particularly on proximal segments; feet whitish, with speckling of melanophores, least abundant on toes; iris uniformly dark brown; usually no guanophores in skin.

Color changes with growth.—Juvenile uniformly reddish orange above with weak development of melanin; orange coloration most intense on tail, in part due to re-

[1] Some individuals from the San Gabriel and San Bernardino mountains of southern California are dark blotched, in a manner suggestive of the race *picta,* while animals farther south and at lower elevations may exhibit a reversal of this condition, having breaks in the melanic ground color.

duced melanism; upper eyelids usually lighter than head; below white with pale pinkish-orange color often present on underside of tail and limbs; a few melanophores usually present on tip of chin; proximal segments of limbs reddish orange above; distal segments mottled with melanophores on orange ground color; feet whitish; whitish guanophores on head (including upper eyelids), usually along sides of head from jaw angle on to neck, and on sides of body; also usually present, but somewhat less abundantly, on upper surface of body.

With growth, melanin becomes more pronounced, accompanied by darkening of upper surfaces of body and distal segments of limbs; pale orange coloration of ventral surface of tail and limbs may fade to whitish; guanophores become obscure.

Picta.—Adult female, MVZ 44034, 55.5 mm. in snout-vent length, obtained 3 miles north of Klamath, Del Norte County, California, December 12, 1946, by W. F. Wood and J. Slevin. Ground color above between dark tan (Amber Brown) and brown (Argus Brown); dark dorsolateral blotches of blackish brown; sides of body mottled with light orange (Capucine Yellow); light-colored area on snout yellowish orange (Salmon-Orange); ground color of tail light yellow (Buff-Yellow), marked with dark brown (Clove Brown); sides of tail light yellow (Light Orange-Yellow); proximal segments of limbs above orange yellow (Deep Chrome) basally, lightening to pale yellow (Light Orange-Yellow) distally; ventral surfaces light orange (pale Orange-Buff) with pinkish cast, resulting from presence of pale orange-yellow lipophores, scattered and somewhat irregular in arrangement in gular area but forming a rather uniform network elsewhere; melanophores distributed as a fine, rather uniform stippling over ventral surfaces; guanophores present in considerable numbers in breaks in melanic ground color dorsally and laterally—golden in color, probably due to overlying lipophores; guanophores scattered over all ventral surfaces except underside of tail, reduced on under surfaces of limbs; eye patch diffuse, orange yellow (Light Cadmium) to lemon yellow (Empire Yellow), occupying upper quarter of total area of iris; small patch in lower iris.

Lipophores, as in other coastal races, are important in the production of the tones of color of the dorsal and lateral surfaces of the body and limbs, particularly the proximal segments. Several color phases, resulting primarily from the color of the pigment of these cells, are observed. For example, near Orick, Humboldt County, where I recently obtained a series of these animals, of 20 adults, 7 tended toward orange, 8 toward buff yellow, and 5 were lemon yellow. Such variability is seen in *oregonensis,* in areas approaching the zone of *picta,* although apparently on a smaller scale.

I cannot comment on color changes with growth as I have not seen living young. Preserved specimens have markings similar to those of adults.

Platensis.—Adult with variable number of reddish-orange spots on dorsum and sides of head, body, and tail; spots with irregular borders and of variable size, ranging from flecks which are scarcely visible to marks 3 mm. or more in diameter; upper eyelids spotted, often yellowish rather than orange; ground color dark brown dorsally, blending laterally with pale gray to whitish of ventral surface; ventral surfaces with stippling of melanophores; proximal segments of limbs above yellowish orange to orange red, lighter below; distal segments of limbs spotted like body but on a somewhat lighter ground color; toes and ventral surfaces of feet lighter than remainder of distal segments of limbs; digits faintly crossbanded with light color at joints; guanophores scattered, usually singly, over most of dorsal and lateral surfaces and sometimes sparingly on ventral surfaces; concentration of these cells usually present at base of each limb on upper side, forming patch of irregular shape beneath lipophore network as in *oregonensis, xanthoptica,* and *picta;* iris dark brown with or without silvery to gold guanophores in upper part; when present these cells occur in variable numbers from 2 (as based on present material) to network which fills most of upper iris; guanophores less common in lower iris.

Color changes with growth.—Juvenile nearly black above with obscure orange spotting or spotting absent; proximal segments of limbs yellow to yellowish orange; ventral surfaces dusky except for under surfaces of proximal segments of limbs which may be pinkish orange; dorsal and ventral colors grade gradually along sides of head, body, and tail; guanophores numerous on dorsal surfaces, particularly on head and body, less so on tail.

With growth, ground color becomes less intense black and may eventually assume a brownish cast; dorsal light spotting becomes more intense and reddish-orange color of adult appears; all spots, including those on eyelids become better defined; more orange or reddish appears in color of proximal segments of limbs; ventral surfaces become lighter; guanophores become less apparent.

Croceater.—Adult with dorsal pattern of irregularly outlined, lemon-yellow to yellowish-cream spots of variable size and shape; spots generally larger than in *platensis* and smaller than in *klauberi,* ranging from less than 1 mm. to 7 mm. in greatest linear dimension, averaging 3 to 4 mm. in width; large spot regularly present in each parotoid region; parotoid spots broadly separated at midline; upper eyelids commonly without pattern; ground color above solid black to deep blackish brown, blending laterally with pale gray of venter; ventral surfaces with stippling of melanophores; proximal segments of limbs yellow above, lighter below; distal segments of limbs usually unspotted, slightly lighter than ground color of upper surface of body; toe joints lighter than remainder of foot, giving toes faintly crossbanded appearance; iris dark brown, sometimes with several silvery to bronze guanophores (3 to 10 in animals studied) in upper part and none or 1 or 2 in lower part; guanophores may appear in small numbers on upper surface of head and sometimes elsewhere, as on tail.

Color changes with growth.—On the basis of 13 individuals of varying size from juvenile to adult, the following changes appear to occur: juvenile with uniformly black ground color above, broken by blotches of bright lemon yellow; proximal segments of limbs above similar in color to dorsal blotches; distal segments of limbs somewhat lighter than ground color of body; ventral surfaces gray, except for underside of proximal segments of limbs which may be pale yellow; dorsal and ventral colors grade gradually along sides of head, body, and tail; guanophores concentrated on upper eyelids, interorbital region, and snout, but also sometimes present elsewhere as on upper surface of tail. With growth, dorsal and ventral ground color lightens and in old adults may become deep blackish brown and pale gray, respectively; yellow color in pattern lightens and in old individuals becomes cream colored; guanophores of skin may disappear entirely or become largely confined to head.

Klauberi.—Adult with dorsal surfaces of body and tail with large, usually rectilinear, orange blotches, often 5 or 6 mm. or more in greatest linear dimension; blotches variable in size and arrangement, sometimes distributed in checkerboard fashion, often connected to form diagonal or transverse bands, or in varying combinations of spots and bands; markings tend to be distributed in row on either side of midline of body, and when bands are present they seem to be composed of a pair of blotches joined medially; outlines of blotches usually regular; marks on tail often form bands; head marks consist of blotch in each parotoid area, extending a variable distance anteriorly on to upper eyelids and laterally on sides of head behind eyes; parotoid blotches may or may not be connected at midline; when connected, a **U**-shaped mark is formed with arms of **U** extending anteriorly on to eyelids; ground color deep blackish brown to black above, grading along sides into deep gray (often with purplish tinge) ventrally; melanophores present in considerable numbers on ventral surfaces; distal segments of limbs unpatterned, colored like ground color of body but somewhat lighter; joints of toes lighter than remainder of foot giving toes crossbanded appearance; light orange patch on metacarpal and metatarsal region; proximal segments of limbs orange above—lighter, sometimes yellowish, below; orange color of proximal segments usually extends beyond elbow and knee; iris dark brown, apparently without guanophores; guanophores not apparent on body.

Color changes with growth.—Juvenile black on head, body, and tail with sharply contrasting orange to reddish-orange dorsal blotches; proximal segments of limbs above also orange to reddish orange, although slightly lighter than body blotches, below yellowish orange; distal segments of limbs somewhat less intensely black than body;

ventral surfaces deep gray; feet dusky with toes crossbanded with light and dark marks; guanophores, if present, few in number.

With growth, black coloration becomes somewhat less intense; dorsal blotches become somewhat lighter orange, becoming yellowish cream in occasional older individuals; ventral surfaces and distal segments of limbs lighten to sooty; guanophores become obscure; light areas, on upper surface of metatarsal and metacarpal regions, become more pronounced.

Habitat.—*Ensatina eschscholtzii* occurs in the Transition and Upper Sonoran life-zones. The light-blotched subspecies, *platensis* and *klauberi,* and the unblotched subspecies *oregonensis* may range into the lower Boreal Zone. In California, in the southern part of the state, the species seems to be largely a canyon dweller. In drier regions, the animals tend to select north-facing slopes and deep canyons where temperatures and conditions of humidity are favorable. Greatest concentrations of individuals are likely to occur on flat or gently sloping benches, above flood level, rather than on steep slopes. A perennial stream is often present although it is not a necessity, since individuals have been found miles from water. In northerly areas, the species is more widely distributed, frequently occurring on ridges as well as in the canyons. (Pl. 37.)

Ensatina frequents areas where there is considerable leaf litter. A leaf mat acts as an insulating blanket helping to conserve the moisture of the substratum and buffering temperature fluctuations. It is sought not only as a place of refuge but also for the insects, spiders, crustaceans, and earthworms that occur in or beneath it and that serve as food. These salamanders are capable of digging only to a limited extent by wriggling into leaf litter or loose soil. They cannot burrow into firmly packed ground. During dry weather, they may be forced to retreat to considerable depths. Thus they tend to frequent areas where there are holes in the ground such as rodent burrows, rotted-out root channels, and openings among rocks.

When the surface is damp and temperatures not too high, considerable time is spent above ground where most feeding probably occurs. The presence of surface objects under which insects, spiders, and other prey may hide is a common feature of the habitat. The salamanders may be found under boards, logs, rocks, in refuse heaps, leaf litter, under bark, and inside logs.

The species occurs in association with a variety of plants, but some kinds are more often present than others. In Transition areas, common species are the coast redwood, Big Tree, incense cedar, canyon live oak, black oak, Douglas fir, white fir, and yellow pine. In the Upper Sonoran Zone, coast live oak, bay, madroño, wild black walnut, and Digger pine are often found. In both zones the trees mentioned may be present in pure stands or in varying combinations.

Understory vegetation is often scarce, particularly in more northerly areas where the animals occur in dense forests. Such growth may interfere with surface movements and thermal requirements for feeding and other activities. Colonies seem best developed in marginal belts between dense and sparse vegetation, in "edge" situations. Thus, in redwood stands, they may occur in areas of interdigitation with coast live oak, bay, and madroño, or in patches of tan oak, of local occurrence within the redwood forest. Advantages can be seen for such selection. The dense growth and continual shade of the conifers permits prolongation of activity with the passing of the rainy season and the approach of summer, and the deciduous vegetation allows greater insolation in winter and hence more favorable temperatures for surface activity at this season.

Behavior.—Most often found singly, but adults, during the breeding period, may be encountered in pairs; subadults and juveniles occasionally are found in groups of 2 or 3. This salamander usually lies quietly when first exposed but after a few moments, if not torpid it may lunge forward, crawling with considerable speed. When quiet, the tail may be curled. The tail is capable of some prehension, particularly in the male. When molested, an *Ensatina* may stand stiff-legged, well up on its toes, with the body arched downward, the tail elevated and arched upward, the neck erect, and the head held horizontally or directed somewhat downward; the tail may actively secrete a milky, sticky, astringent fluid; it may be swung in the direction of the disturbance; the salamander may rock slowly back and forth on stiff legs; a squeaking sound may be produced by forcing air through the nares or past the lips by gular contractions. The tail may be shed but usually only under stress, commonly breaking at the basal constriction.

The annual cycle of activity of an *Ensatina* colony in California may be sketched as follows:

With the first soaking rains in the fall or winter, animals of all sizes, including newly hatched young, emerge from their summer retreats. In some areas, considerable dehydration may have occurred during the dry period and feeding may have been limited. The movement to the surface makes possible replenishing of water by dermal absorption and resumption or increase in feeding. Surface activity continues while temperatures and moisture conditions are favorable, which may last until late spring or early summer, even in southern areas. At high elevations and in the north there may be considerable depression or complete cessation of activity in winter, the animals being driven underground by freezing temperatures. Winter decline is, of course, less marked to the south.

Most breeding appears to occur in early spring, in February and March. At this time adults are commonly found in pairs. After a period of a few weeks, numbers of adults drop off rapidly. Their disappearance is probably related to reproductive activities—selection of a nesting site, egg laying, and attendance[2] upon eggs. The young remain longest on the surface. Perhaps their growth requirements impel them to prolong feeding.

The eggs are laid sometime in spring or early summer, with incubation taking place during the dry period. Probably temperatures for development are most favorable at this time. Moisture conditions are met by selection of the nesting site and possibly by discharges from the bladder and skin of the adults. The time of hatching is not known. The smallest young, however, appear with the first rains in the fall or winter.

Ensatina seems to be colonial in habit, particularly in the south, where conditions of temperature, humidity, and vegetational features are quite variable. Some of the smaller colonies seem to be almost wholly panmictic, a reproductively active male having an equal chance of meeting any breeding female. There is no indication of territorial behavior. Several males may occur together, and their relative positions within the population may shift. That home areas exist, at least for some individuals, has been shown by repeated captures of the same individuals, in restricted areas, over a period of 3 years.

With respect to movements of individuals, an important agency of dispersal should be pointed out. The tendency for the animals to congregate in the bottoms of canyons, particularly during dry weather, places them in a position to be transported by stream action during storms. I have repeatedly observed individuals under water-borne debris along roads at the mouths of canyons. *Ensatina* can tolerate complete submergence for several hours and some individuals may survive in water for considerably longer periods. Upon removal from water, if still alive, they usually revive in a few minutes. Thus, conceivably an individual could be carried many miles and then be cast ashore to become established in an area far removed from its homesite.

Body temperatures for this species, as based on a field study of the race *xanthoptica* over a period of 3 years, were found to range from 1.6°C. to 18.4°C. (mean 11.6°C.).

Food.—The following items have been recorded: earthworms; sowbugs; millipedes; centipedes; arachnids—spiders, pseudoscorpions, ticks, and mites; insects—springtails (collembolans—entomobryids and sminthurids), a thysanuran, earwigs, termites, camel crickets, aphids, caterpillars (noctuids), flies, beetles (bruchids, ptinids, and carabids) and beetle

[2] The few egg clusters that have been found (5) were attended by the female and in one instance a young male was present also.

larvae, and ants. Small snails and slugs probably also are taken. (Partly from Zweifel, 1949.)

Reproduction.—I have observed courtship (figs. 12, 13) in the subspecies *xanthoptica* (Stebbins, 1949b). The male creeps to the side of the female with his body usually carried close to the ground (fig. 12, 1). As he approaches her head, his forward movement slows and his progress may become almost imperceptible. He noses the side of her neck and head. Ultimately he concentrates on her throat and face, rubbing her with the side of his head and neck (2). She may respond by tilting her head upward at an angle of about 45°. He then slides his body past her (3), moving beneath and against her gular area until his sacral region is against her throat (4). He begins to massage her throat by swaying his body, executing a rotary movement of his hindquarters. If she has become sufficiently interested in him she rests her throat against his lower back and follows him as he slowly moves forward with his back arched sharply upward. His tail trails between her legs. The "tail walk" (Noble, 1931:389) may last for several hours (5). Finally the male stops, extends his legs laterally and brings his vent against the substratum (6). He then rocks laterally on his hind legs and the female moves her head in a counter fashion stroking his sacral area with her throat (7). Her movements may continue after his cease. After stroking him a minute or so she lifts her head (8). The male crawls forward. As he moves she reapplies her throat to his lower back and they move forward in the "tail walk" until her vent is over the spermatophore (9). The sexual act is consummated when the female squats on the spermatophore, taking it into her cloaca by means of her cloacal lips. At the same time the male lurches backward, frees his long whiplike tail, and throws it over her lower back. The distal portion of the tail is writhed violently and is moved in a stroking fashion over the back and tail base of the female (10). Following this the animals separate but after a few moments they may court again.

Six adult females from a marked population of the race *xanthoptica* in the Berkeley Hills, Contra Costa County, California, have been found, each with a sperm capsule protruding from her vent, on the following dates: November 13 and December 4, 1948, and January 22, February 5 and 12, and March 12, 1949. Adult males possess active sperm in their sperm ducts from the time of their emergence, usually early in October with the first rains, to late March when most adults disappear. Presumably breeding may occur at any time during this period. The reproductive cycle appears to be similar to that described for *Eurycea bislineata* by Weichert (1945).

Observation of the race *eschscholtzii* in the Santa Monica Mountains of southern California indicates a close correspondence to *xanthoptica* in breeding habits although emergence, on the average, occurs later, in November or December. Adult *platensis* from the Sierra Nevada of California were found active in considerable numbers in late April and early May, 1948. Males possessed sperm in the vasa deferentia. This suggests that breeding may occur later in the interior mountains than coastally. Gnae-

Fig. 12. Courtship in *Ensatina eschscholtzii*. Stages 1-10 explained in the text.

Fig. 13. Courtship in *Ensatina eschscholtzii* (continued).

dinger and Reed's (1948:195) observations on the species in Oregon suggest that breeding activity there resembles that of *platensis*.

EGGS. Laid in terrestrial situations usually in spring and early summer, probably often in burrows of other animals. A clutch of 12 to 14 is common.

Van Denburgh (1898:140-41) reported an adult female with 3 eggs from Mill Valley, Marin County, California, found April 19, 1896, under a decaying log in the redwoods. The eggs measured 6 mm. and were "almost or quite" without pigment. They were covered with a thin gelatinous coating which caused them to stick together. When placed in a container the female took charge of the eggs, holding and later moving them about in a crook in her tail.

Two individuals, one an adult female, the other a young male 43 mm. in snout-vent length with 13 "white" eggs were found in a nest chamber, at a depth of nearly 2 feet below the surface of the ground, during the excavation of a tunnel system of the rodent *Aplodontia rufa phaea* in the hills 3 miles west of Inverness, Marin County, California, on June 4, 1913 (field notebook of C. L. Camp in the Museum of Vertebrate Zoölogy). After preservation in alcohol, the eggs measured 5.5 to 5.75 mm. in diameter and to the outer jelly coat, 5.9 to 7.5 mm. The eggs were in the head fold stage of development.

Joseph Grinnell found 2 clusters of eggs, each with an adult in attendance, at Carlotta, Humboldt County, California, on July 26, 1923. The salamanders with their eggs were found in chambers in dampish soil beneath slabs of redwood. The eggs measured 5.0 to 5.5 mm. in diameter across the yolk mass and to the outside of the jelly coat, 7.6 to 7.8 mm. The position of the embryos suggested cleavage of a meroblastic type. When found, the eggs were nearly transparent but with preservation they become opaque (Storer, 1925:112). I have been able to locate only one of these clutches consisting of 16 eggs. The eggs were in a receptacle with the adult, a female. The embryos of this lot possess limbs at the toe bud stage of differentiation.

Gnaedinger and Reed (1948) have made observations on the subspecies *oregonensis* in northwestern Oregon. They believe that egg laying occurs later in northwestern Oregon than in California. When this view was expressed the species *eschscholtzii* was not considered as including the *Ensatina* of the interior mountains of California. The first young were collected on November 1, 1945. Females with large eggs in the ovaries were found as follows: December 15, one with 16 eggs—diameter of the large eggs, 4.74 mm; January 11, one with 15 eggs, 4.12 mm; May 15, one with 14 eggs, 4.0 to 4.5 mm. and one with 15 eggs, 4.6 to 4.8 mm. Twice opposite-sexed pairs were found in nature, March 1 and April 21.

An adult female obtained on April 8, 1948, 3.6 miles southwest of Coquille, near U.S. Highway 101, Coos County, Oregon, deposited 16 eggs in captivity on May 8. She was solicitous of her eggs. Occasionally she left the clutch but invariably returned. She frequently rested beside or over the eggs with her gular area in contact with them. The eggs tended to adhere loosely to one another and to the substratum but there were no peduncles. A representative egg was unpigmented, measuring 4.35 mm. across the whitish yolk mass; 2 transparent jelly envelopes were present, an inner firm one measuring approximately 1.0 mm. in width and an outer loose layer about 0.8 mm. in thickness. All the eggs were fertile, fecundated by sperm stored in the spermatheca of the female; a male was not present during the female's period of captivity. Development of the eggs had proceeded to the limb bud, gilled stage by late July (25-29), when they spoiled. The gills at this time, after approximately 2 months of development were well vascularized, triparted, and leaflike.

Keith Murray found 2 egg masses at Big Lagoon, Humboldt County, California, August 9, 1949. In a large, rotted spruce log, about 3 feet in diameter, he found 3 adult salamanders of the subspecies *picta*. The log was covered with thick mossy growth and a layer of decayed leaves and soil. The salamanders were in cracks in the wood, beneath this layer. Two had egg masses and were curled up against but not around them. The wood was soft and only a trifle damp. The area was well shaded by large spruce and alders, with a dense undergrowth of salmonberry, thimbleberry, and blackberry. There was a green grassy patch around the log.

I examined the eggs November 10, 1949, after about 3 months' preservation. They measured approximately 7.5 mm. to their outer jelly coats. The clusters contained, respectively, 19 and 25 eggs held together loosely by adherence of their jellies, like a bunch of grapes. No peduncles were evident. The embryos were well developed, the digits well formed, but there was still a large yolk mass and the triparted leaflike gills were extensive. In one embryo the spread of the central gill lobe on one side was from near the tip of the snout to the insertion of the forelimb. The gills were highly vascular.

As regards reproduction in the blotched races of the interior mountains, less is known. An adult female *platensis,* obtained by me at Jawbone Station, 3,500 feet, Tuolumne County, California, on April 30, 1948, was induced to lay eggs by implantation of 2 pituitary glands of the newt *Triturus torosus*. Ten eggs were laid between June 15 and 16. Four were retained. All the eggs spoiled.

Two adult female *platensis,* each with an egg cluster, were found together under a rotten log at Park Creek, about 14 miles east of Placerville, Eldorado County, California, on September 9, 1948, by M. Wixman.

There were 9 eggs in one clutch, 8 in the other. The females were curled about the eggs. They continued to brood their eggs in captivity despite the fact that the embryos were dead. They were probably killed by high temperatures in the process of moving them to a lower elevation. The eggs appeared almost ready to hatch. A representative egg measured 10.5 mm. to the outer surface of the gelatinous capsule. An embryo removed from the egg measured 25.7 mm. in total length.

Howard (1950:236) on August 8, 1949, near Park Creek, 4 miles above Sly Park, Eldorado County, California, found a clutch of 11 eggs and an adult male and female *platensis*. The salamanders and eggs were together under the bark near the upper surface of a Douglas-fir log, about 2 feet above the ground. The tree had been down for about 15 years. The nearest wet soil was at a spring about 100 feet away. Decayed wood near the eggs was nearly dry enough to burn. The eggs measured 10.0 to 11.5 mm. in diameter. Embryos 13 mm. in snout-vent measurement and 21 mm. in total length were present.

Again on May 21, 1950 in the same log, about 10 feet from the site of August 8, 1949, Howard found another female with 12 eggs. The eggs were from 6 to 7 mm. in outer diameter and were composed almost entirely of yolk with no visible embryos. When pieces of the rotten log about the eggs were squeezed between the fingers, drops of water exuded.

Dr. Laurence M. Klauber received an adult *croceater* (=*klauberi*) with a set of 14 eggs on July 25, 1927, found near Julian, San Diego County, California. The eggs were adherent and nonpedunculate, yellowish and opaque, measuring about 8 mm. in diameter.

The average numbers of large ovarian eggs in females of subspecies examined by me were, *oregonensis* 10 (5 to 14); *picta* 11 (7 to 16); *xanthoptica* 14 (13 to 14); *eschscholtzii* 14; and *croceater* 15 (only a single female was available for each of the last 2 subspecies).

Key to Subspecies

Figure 14

1*a*. Above uniformly colored, in life blackish brown, brown, or reddish brown (2, 6, 10) 2

1*b*. Above not uniformly colored, with dark or light-colored blotches (14, 15, 16, 17) 4

2*a*. (1*a*) Iris dark brown, without yellow or brassy coloration in life (such color is often lacking in preserved specimens) (1); toes whitish above; venter white, except usually for underside of tail and limbs, without numerous black stipple marks (magnification usually required) (3); dark pigmentation (melanophores) of sides usually even with or above line connecting bases of upper surfaces of limbs (2). *Range.*—Coastally, from extreme southern San Diego County to central Santa

Barbara County, California, and interiorly at least to Forest Home in the San Bernardino Mountains and Indian Canyon in the San Jacinto Mountains .... *E. e. eschscholtzii* Gray

2*b*. Iris with yellow or brassy color (5, 9); toes orange above; venter with varying amounts of black ventral stippling or blotching (magnification often required) (7, 11); dark pigmentation (melanophores) of sides usually extending below line connecting upper surfaces of bases of limbs (6, 10) 3

3*a*. (2*b*) Venter uniformly orange (in life) with black ventral stippling absent or scanty and tending to be clumped (7); yellow eye patch well developed but often lost with preservation (5); melanophores of sides of body not notably irregular in distribution (6); entire proximal segments of limbs (4) and upper eyelids (18) light-colored in majority of individuals. *Range.*—From central Napa and southern Sonoma counties, north of San Francisco Bay, south, east of the Bay, to central Santa Clara County, California. Also on Jawbone Ridge, Tuolumne County in the Sierra Nevada, California.... .... *E. e. xanthoptica* Stebbins

3*b*. Venter whitish or with faint scattered spots of orange or yellow, occasionally with considerable orange or yellowish suffusion; ventral melanic stippling relatively uniform (11); eye patch less well developed than in *xanthoptica* (9); melanophores of sides of body usually irregular in distribution, producing mottled effect (10); usually only basal ½ or ⅓ of upper surface of proximal segments of limbs light-colored (8); eyelids dark (19). *Range.*—From British Columbia south in coastal mountains to northern Sonoma County, California .... *E. e. oregonensis* (Girard)

4*a*. (1*b*) Above with dark blotches of varying size, shape, and abundance (14) 7

4*b*. Above with light-colored spots or blotches (reddish orange, cream, or yellow in life) on dark brown to black ground color (15, 16, 17); dark blotches absent 5

5*a*. (4*b*) No definite parotoid blotches or U-shaped band on head; distal segments of limbs spotted (12); spots generally average smaller, are usually irregular in outline, and are more numerous (15). *Range.*—The southern Cascades and the Sierra Nevada of California .... *E. e. platensis* (Espada)

5*b*. Definite blotch in each parotoid region or U-shaped band on head (20, 21, 22); distal segments of limbs uniformly dark-colored, rarely spotted (13); spots generally larger, less numerous, and more regular in outline (16, 17) 6

6*a*. (5*b*) Light-colored U-shaped mark on head with arms of U reaching eyelids (20); central portion sometimes interrupted, forming distinct parotoid blotches (21); lateral extension of head-marking passing below postorbital furrow, sometimes to lateral gular area (23); eyelids nearly always with light-colored markings (20, 21); large rectilinear blotches, bars, and bands on body and tail (17); markings usually orange (sometimes cream) in life. *Range.*—Mountains of San Diego and western Riverside counties, California .... *E. e. klauberi* Dunn

6*b*. No U-shaped mark on head; distinct blotch in each parotoid area (22), usually without lateral extension on side of head below postorbital furrow (24); eyelids typically unmarked (22); spots on body smaller, more irregular in outline, and usually not rectilinear (16); markings usually yellow (sometimes cream) in life. *Range.*—Tehachapi Mountains south of Kern River Valley to the vicinity of Mount Pinos, Kern County, California .... *E. e. croceater* (Cope)

7a. (*4a*) Ventral surface of body essentially without stippling of melanophores (3); in life, no light color in eye (1) or orange or yellowish color on underside of body (exclusive of tail and limbs) .... *E. e. eschscholtzii* Gray (Some individuals from the San Gabriel and San Bernardino mountains and possibly other areas in higher mountains of southern California.)

7b. Ventral surface of body with uniform and close melanic stippling (11); in life, yellowish to bronze patch in upper iris (9); varying amounts of orange or yellow coloration widely distributed over all ventral surfaces. *Range.*—Confined to a narrow coastal strip from northern Humboldt County, California to northern Curry County, Oregon .... *E. e. picta* Wood and juvenal *E. e. oregonensis* (see *3b.* for range).

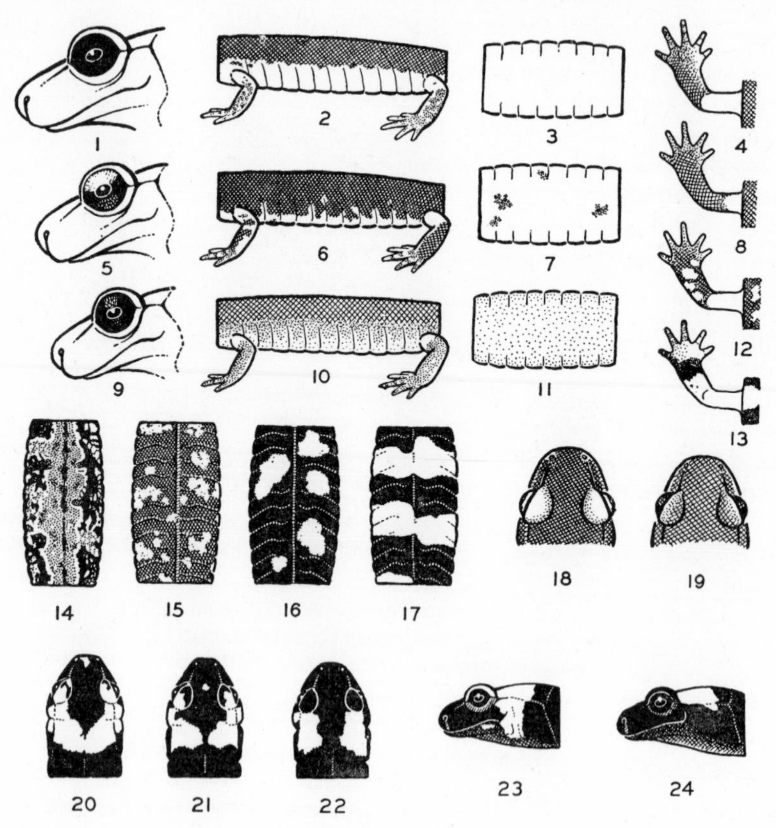

Fig. 14. 1, 2, 3, *Ensatina eschscholtzii eschscholtzii;* 4, 5, 6, 7, 18, *E. e. xanthoptica;* 8, 9, 10, 11, 19, *E. e. oregonensis;* 12, 15, *E. e. platensis;* 14, *E. e. picta;* 16, 22, 24, *E. e. croceater;* 13, 17, 20, 21, 23, *E. e. klauberi.*

Remarks.—The relationships of the subspecies whose ranges overlap should be studied—as between *platensis* and *xanthoptica* in the Sierra Nevada where hybridization occurs and *klauberi* and *eschscholtzii* in the

San Bernardino Mountains and mountains of San Diego County where the animals seem to coexist without interbreeding.

The species should be sought in other Transition and Upper Sonoran areas such as the White Mountains, Telescope Peak, and the Channel Islands of California and the San Pedro Mártir Mountains and Cape region of Lower California.

The range of the subspecies *croceater* needs to be more thoroughly worked out. This form, or intergrades with *klauberi,* may be found at Frazier Mountain, Shake Camp, Big Pines, and in other Transition Zone areas in mountains between Fort Tejon and Crystal Creek. Fort Tejon is the southernmost locality for *croceater*. Crystal Creek in the San Bernardino Mountains, about 100 miles in an air line to the southeast, is the next locality for spotted ensatinas, here occupied by *croceater-klauberi* intergrades.

It would be of interest to determine to what extent, if any, physiological differences correlate with the observed morphological variation in this species. In this regard a comparative study of subspecies with regard to thermal and moisture tolerances and metabolism might be undertaken.

Genus *Batrachoseps*

Structure.—Adults from about 3 to 7 inches; wormlike; head small; body and tail rounded; limbs small in relation to size of body, their length only slightly more than greatest width of body (*B. wrighti* and *B. pacificus pacificus* excepted); toes 4-4, innermost rudimentary, tips not dilated; palmar and plantar tubercles absent; costal grooves well defined with similar furrows on tail; tail without basal constriction; tongue oval, attached along midline and anteriorly, free laterally and behind; vomerine teeth in single row on either side or forming patch on either side behind nares; parasphenoid teeth in single broad patch or in varying degrees separated into 2 patches by toothless zone along midline; patches sometimes elongate and club-shaped; premaxillary bones separate (*B. wrighti*) or fused; erythrocytes nucleated (*B. wrighti*) or largely without nuclei; with or without dorsal longitudinal stripe of reddish, brown, dull yellow, or buff.

Range.—Northwestern and extreme southwestern Oregon southward along the coast of California to the San Pedro Mártir Mountains in northern Lower California. Also in the foothills of the Sierra Nevada of California and on certain of the islands off the southern coast. Reported from Colima, Mexico (Gadow, 1905:204), La Paz, Lower California

(Lockington, 1880:295), and Hassler Harbor, Alaska (Cope, 1889:127) but these records need confirmation.

Remarks.—The relationship between *Batrachoseps pacificus* and *B. attenuatus* in southern California should be investigated through study of the coloration of living animals as well as investigation of possible ecological differences. With respect to the latter, Camp's (1915) observations are suggestive (p. 118). Of particular importance in working out this problem would be a study of *Batrachoseps attenuatus leucopus* from San Diego County, individuals of which approach *B. pacificus* in their punctate arrangement of ventral melanophores, seemingly longer limbs and broader head, and obscuring of the dorsal stripe. Since many individuals from the San Diego area have ventral melanophores arranged as a network, as is true of animals from the San Pedro Mártir Mountains in Lower California, the possibility of correlation of pigmentation with life-zone or that *pacificus* and *attenuatus* coexist in this region as in the Los Angeles area should be investigated.

Batrachoseps from Catalina Island appear to me to be intermediate in some aspects of coloration and in proportions between *B. a. attenuatus* and *B. p. major*. They seem not to differ greatly from some individuals of *B. a. leucopus*. The relationship of *B. p. catalinae* should be reviewed.

Some of the problems of variation and relationships involved in such a study as indicated above are pointed out by Dunn (1926:230-31). The table below provides comparative data on the forms of *Batrachoseps* recognized in this book.

	Costal grooves	*Intercostal folds between tips of toes of adpressed limbs*	*Intercostal folds overlapped by hind leg when adpressed to side*	*Total length* (average in mm.)	*Tail length* (percentage of total length)	*Vomerine teeth per row or patch*
Batrachoseps attenuatus						
attenuatus	18-21(20)	10-12½	3 -3½	89.0(73-114)	53.7-58.1	8-16
leucopus	18-20(19)	8-11	4 -4½	87.0(66-127)	50.0-62.2	5- 8
Batrachoseps pacificus						
pacificus	17-18	9-11	5½-6½	96.5(72-129)	44.0-54.3	7-10
catalinae	20-21	10-13	3½-4½	105.7(79-133)	53.2-60.3	6- 7
major	18-20(19)	9-10	4 -4½	117.0(82.7-162)	52.0-57.0	7-11
Batrachoseps wrighti	16-17	6½- 7	4½-5	91.6(84-97)	51.8 (Average of 3 males and 3 females lumped)	8-15

A comparative study of the ecology of *wrighti* (presumably the most primitive species), *pacificus,* and *attenuatus* would be a valuable adjunct to a study of the systematics of this genus.

Batrachoseps should be sought in the Sierra Madre of Mexico. Gadow (1905:204) states, "Probably it occurs all through the slopes of the western Sierra Madre, which is mostly clad with pine-forest." The specimen obtained by Gadow, a juvenile, was found at about 7,000 feet in the stump of a decayed pine tree. The possible occurrence of the genus at La Paz, Lower California, should also be checked. Habitat conditions in the higher mountains of the Cape appear suitable for its occurrence.

Key to Species
Figure 15

1a. Limbs small, scarcely longer than width of body (2, 3); toes shorter (2, 3); costal interspaces between tips of toes of adpressed limbs, 8 to 13; costal grooves 18 to 21 (occasionally 17 in *B. p. pacificus*); premaxillary bones fused (4); erythrocytes largely without nuclei; preserved individuals with belly covered with rather uniform, moderately heavy, melanic network (7) or minutely speckled with melanophores (6); in life, stippling of fine white guanophores overlies ventral melanic ground color (7); ventral ground color ranges from deep sooty to whitish or yellowish 2

1b. Limbs larger, considerably longer than width of body (1); toes longer (1); costal interspaces between tips of toes of adpressed limbs, 6½ to 7; costal grooves 16 or 17; premaxillary bones separate (8); erythrocytes nucleated; belly with close network of heavily pigmented melanophores (appears black on casual inspection) (5); ventral melanic network weak where guanophore patches appear, resulting in light-colored blotches in preserved specimens even though guanophores may no longer be apparent;

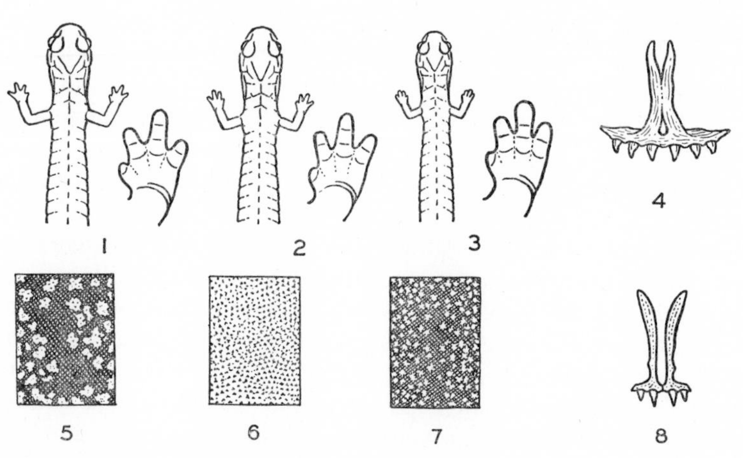

Fig. 15. 1, 5, 8, *Batrachoseps wrighti;* 2, 6, *B. pacificus;* 3, 4, 7, *B. attenuatus.*

in life, ventral surface appears black, with spots and blotches of white formed by closely set groups of guanophores (5) .... *Batrachoseps wrighti,* p. 120

2*a*. Ventral surface of adults light-colored with ventral melanophores (usually at least some of them) occurring as separate black flecks (magnification may be required) (6); dorsal stripe often vague or lacking in adults; limbs and toes relatively longer (2); adult size large, to 7 inches; fringes of, and on, the Los Angeles coastal plain and certain of the Channel Islands off the coast of southern California .... *B. pacificus,* p. 115

2*b*. Ventral surface dark with melanophores forming continuous network (occasionally discontinuous in race *leucopus*) (7); dorsal stripe commonly present in adults; limbs and toes relatively shorter (3); adult size smaller, seldom much over 5 inches; coastally from extreme southwestern Oregon to northern Lower California and the foothills bordering the east side of the Central Valley of California; the floor of the Valley in the vicinity of San Francisco Bay ...... *B. attenuatus,* p. 108

CALIFORNIA SLENDER SALAMANDER

Batrachoseps attenuatus (Eschscholtz)
Plate 12

Range.—Coastal regions from southwestern Oregon (near Gold Beach) into northern Lower California at Ensenada and in the Sierra San Pedro Mártir; in the Sierran foothills from near Chico, Butte County, to White River, Kern County; scattered records for the Central Valley of California in the vicinity of San Francisco Bay; on Santa Cruz Island off the coast of southern California and on Goat Island in San Francisco Bay, California. Gadow (1905:204) mentions occurrence at Colima, Mexico, and specimens in the Museum of Vertebrate Zoölogy are labeled La Paz, Lower California, but this locality needs confirmation. I have seen the specimen (a juvenile) upon which Gadow's record was based and I concur with his identification. (Pl. 53.)

Type locality.—Vicinity of San Francisco Bay, California (Eschscholtz, 1833:1-6).

Description.—STRUCTURE. Adult 3 to approximately 6 inches; costal grooves 18 to 21, usually 19 or 20, counting one each in axilla and groin; vomerine teeth 5 to 16 per patch, in 2 separate groups or connected at midline; patches elongate along axis extending diagonally posteriorly from behind internal naris toward midline; usually 2 to 3 teeth present across greatest width of patch; parasphenoid teeth in broad oval patch separated some distance from vomerine patches; in some animals slight tendency toward reduction of teeth along midline and in occasional individuals parasphenoid patch partly divided; majority (5) with single parasphenoid patch (7 animals examined from Alameda County, California). COLOR. Ground color generally dark brown to blackish, often with dorsal stripe of brownish, pale yellow, or reddish tan which in some animals may possess dark herringbone markings and sometimes a broken dark vertebral line; dorsal stripe sometimes obscure centrally or represented by flecks and mottlings of buff to rusty brown; rusty or buff spot sometimes present centrally on upper surface of neck or on occiput, commonly when dorsal stripe obscure; dorsal stripe often set off laterally by black line or row of black spots; ventral surface of body sooty to blackish, consisting of close network of melanophores (animals south of Los Angeles coastal plain sometimes with punctate and punctostellate melanophores) overlaid with stippling of numerous whitish guanophores; underside of tail, particularly basally, often with yellowish to yellowish-olive cast in vicinity of San Francisco Bay; such color has not been noted south of Salinas Valley, California, although the underside of the tail may be beige or light tan in some animals, particularly those from well south in the range; iris dark brown, usually with flecks of brassy. JUVENILE. Resembles adult except limbs relatively longer, body stouter, and tail shorter. SEXUAL DIFFERENCES. Sexes distinguished with difficulty. In fullest expression of external differences, male has broader, somewhat more truncate, snout than female and vent tends to have slightly raised edges anteriorly. Vents of both sexes have pleated edges but opening is proportionately somewhat shorter in males than females. Vent of male, in preserved specimens, tends to gape more than in female.

Adult female, RCS 1375, 37 mm. in snout-vent length, obtained December 27, 1946, at Madelia Canyon, Sherman Oaks, Santa Monica Mountains, Los Angeles County, California: Dorsal stripe evident but not well defined; ground color of stripe sooty brown overlaid by minute whitish to buffy flecks (guanophores and lipophores [?]); stripe margined on either side with broken black line; narrow irregular zone of buff at edges of stripe; tinges of buff on eyelids; orange-brown nuchal spot present; streaks, spots, and flecks of rusty in sacral area and on tail; ventral surfaces, including the underside of the tail, with deep sooty melanic network overlaid by uniform stippling of ash-white guanophores; sides with similar ground color stippled with pale blue guanophores; iris dark brown with gold chromatophores forming large irregular patch in upper and few scattered flecks in lower portions.

Habitat.—Occurs in the Upper Sonoran and Transition life-zones, in moist situations on the ground, in leaf litter and beneath surface objects of all sorts. In dry weather, retreats underground, probably employing the burrows of other animals such as those of earthworms, arthropods, and rodents, or by using old root channels or other cavities in areas where the soil is firm.

Near White River, at the Kern-Tulare County line, California, on December 11, 1945, I obtained 25 slender salamanders beneath surface litter in a parklike area in the drainage above the small town of White River. The animals were found in a shallow valley with numerous interior live oaks and buckeye. There was a lush growth of grass beneath the trees but little other understory vegetation. Scattered rocks were covered with moss and lichens. The black soil in more open areas was carpeted with rosette plants, principally filaree. There was a small stream about 1 foot deep and about 6 feet wide, flowing to the northwest. Sycamores were present along this watercourse. On the hills surrounding the valley was considerable *Ceanothus*. There was cattle sign but the area did not appear overgrazed. Several wood-rat nests were seen. Such nests have often yielded salamanders in the San Francisco Bay area. Although the soil was damp in many places, where sheltered by surface objects it was dry. There was snow on the hills above and indications that there had been a light fall in the valley.

The salamanders were all adults, among them several gravid females, but they were the smallest I have ever seen.

Behavior.—When inactive, commonly found curled in a tight watch-spring-like coil with head toward the center and resting on a loop of the body, like a small snake. Frequently several individuals may be found beneath the same object. I once found 12 under a log 2 feet long and 10 inches in diameter. May crawl by using diminutive limbs with but slight, if any, lateral undulations of the body. At other times, particularly when actively trying to escape, the species may use sinuous movements in locomotion. When picked up, this salamander may move quickly and haphazardly by lashing its body from side to side in violent contortions. The tail may be shed under stress but is without a fixed breaking point.

Although it is wormlike in form, I have never observed this salamander to burrow. It evidently uses the burrows of other animals (such as earthworms) or cracks in the substratum. It is able to worm its way through loose soil or leaf litter but is unable to penetrate firmly packed soil. Indeed, I know of no western salamander that constructs burrows of its own.

On December 5, 1947 I found 14 slender salamanders beneath pieces of shale, wood, and leaf litter in a deep ravine on the north side of the Santa Monica Mountains, Sherman Oaks, Los Angeles County, California. The salamanders were in an area 2 feet across, in the canyon bottom. The soil at the collection site was 10.2 to 10.5°C.; air temperature 6 inches above the ground in the shade 10.5°C.; the time, about 3:00 P.M. It was sprinkling lightly after a hard rain the night before, one of the first rains following the dry weather of the summer. Four of the animals were adult females with large eggs, apparently ready for laying.

All individuals were disinclined to move. When exposed they lay quietly in whatever position they happened to come to rest. No gular movements could be detected. When placed back down, one animal lay in this position for approximately 2 minutes. It then slowly rolled over and lay still. I snipped off the tip of the tail of another animal. It did not move. Even when a second piece was cut it still lay motionless. Upon removal of a third piece, the animal wriggled away. The characteristic defensive contortions of the species could not be induced, although several individuals flipped from side to side when held by the tail.

The torpid state of these salamanders was probably related to their recent emergence. They appeared considerably dehydrated. After they had been on damp paper towels for several hours in the laboratory, gular movements were evident and the animals no longer looked emaciated.

Food.—Earthworms, small slugs, and many kinds of small terrestrial arthropods such as sowbugs, millipedes, and insects, including collembolans, aphids, caterpillars, small beetles (weevils, etc.), beetle larvae, and ants.

Reproduction.—Maslin (1939:209-12) has discussed reproduction in this species largely as observed in the San Francisco Bay area, California. The following comments are mainly from his paper but are modified to include personal observations. Eggs may begin to develop within females in May, at about the beginning of the dry season and reach their full development in the late fall and winter months—October, November, December, and January. Oviposition commences at the beginning of the rainy season. John Hendrickson and I found gravid females burrowing into loose soil beneath redwood leaf litter on October 16, 1948, in the Berkeley Hills, following the first fall rain. Many of them laid eggs the next day in the laboratory. In the region of San Francisco Bay, egg laying begins in October or November, and by December or probably earlier the eggs are all laid. The time of laying varies geographically and with the season. The time of hatching is also variable but commonly occurs in the spring. Development is slow due to the low temperatures of winter; young of similar size are found over a period of several months in spring.

In the table on page 112, are given records of occurrence of the eggs under natural conditions.

These locations probably do not represent the usual laying sites. The eggs are no doubt more commonly deposited underground. A single female lays about 12 eggs but the number may vary from 4 to 21. Larger clusters of eggs may be found because of the habit of females of laying together. Three adult females examined by me from Madelia Canyon, Santa Monica Mountains, Los Angeles County, California, that were obtained in December, had 9, 6, and 4 large cream-colored ovarian eggs.

Spermatogenesis occurs during the summer. Eisen (1901:3) remarks,

Records of Occurrence of the Eggs of *Batrachoseps attenuatus*

Date	*Locality* (California)	*Collection site*	*Number of eggs*	*Authority*
Jan., 1906	Palo Alto, Santa Clara Co.	Partly buried in depressions under rocks on a moist hillside		Burke, 1911: 414
Jan. 5, 1907	Palo Alto, Santa Clara Co.	Under a log in a moist ravine in small pockets in the ground	35	Burke, 1911: 414
Jan. 8, 1915	Snelling, Merced Co.	In a log lying in river-washed debris	15 (presumably of this species)	Grinnell and Storer, 1924: 654
Mar. 7, 1920	Strawberry Canyon, Berkeley, Alameda Co.	Beneath a plank in a moist springy place near a brush pile	53	Storer, 1925: 94
Mar. 14, 1922	Palo Alto, Santa Clara Co.	In a small pocket beneath the surface of the soil in a garden		Snyder, 1923: 86
Jan. 24, 1925	Berkeley, Alameda Co.	About 1 foot below the surface of the ground under some dense foliage	7 and 12 (in two groups close together)	Myers, 1930a: 58
Nov. 5, 1938	Berkeley, Alameda Co.	Under a piece of tin on the surface of the ground	74(+ ?)	Maslin, 1939: 209

"While these batrachians are very common almost everywhere in California, their testes are only active at a time when it is almost impossible to procure any specimens of the species." June and July is the only time they are "adult" (Eisen).

I have observed that spermatozoa are present in great numbers in the sperm ducts when these animals first appear with the fall and winter rains and sperm continues to be found well into spring, suggesting that the males are capable of spermatophore production throughout most, if not all, the period of surface activity.

EGGS. From 4 to slightly over 6 mm. to outer capsule; ovum 3 or 4 mm. in diameter, unpigmented, white to cream in color, surrounded by 2 jelly layers—thin outer layer, often diagonally furrowed, rather tough but not sticky, and an inner layer of semirigid jelly; an innermost third layer, probably the capsular cavity, is recognized by some. When laid, the eggs are usually connected like a string of beads but they may become separated and individual eggs are commonly found with a peduncle on one side and a fragment of a peduncle persisting on the other side. Eggs may occur in several groups. Adults may remain near the eggs. Whether females ever brood their eggs in the manner of the Eschscholtz salamander (p. 101) is unknown. Individuals in captivity have shown no brooding tendency.

The gills of developing embryos are trilobed, consisting of 3 slender unbranched filaments. A single blood vessel (arteriole) forms an elongate loop in each gill element, coursing near the surface of each. Vessels of capillary size do not appear to be present. Emmel (1924:372) believes that the reduced vascularity of the gills is compensated for by the high percentage of nonnucleated blood cells in this species (90 to 98 per cent). Among amphibians this condition appears to be peculiar to *B. attenuatus* and *B. pacificus*. *Batrachoseps wrighti,* as based on one adult examined by me, has about 95 per cent of the red cells nucleated. This is more nearly the condition generally found among amphibians. The gills are lost before the young abandons the egg. A young individual, measured at hatching, was 16.5 mm. in length (Snyder, 1923:88); one hatched January 28 from eggs found January 5, 1907, by Burke (1911:414) was 17 mm. in length and was dull black in color.

SUBSPECIES

(Characters partly from Dunn, 1926)

1*a*. Dorsal stripe often dark, in life set off by light color of sides consisting of dense stippling of guanophores; sides may appear somewhat darker than dorsal stripe in preserved specimens with fading of guanophores; generally lighter below, melanophores sometimes appearing as punctations; hind limb extending over 4 costal folds when adpressed to side; intercostal folds between tips of toes adpressed limbs, 8 to 11; costal grooves 18 to 20 (19), counting one each in axilla and groin. *Range.*—San Diego County, California; also northwestern Lower California and Los Coronados Islands off the west coast. Animals from the San Pedro Mártir Mountains, Lower California, may belong to this race, although they are considerably darker than individuals from San Diego County. The range perhaps should include also the Nevada de Colima, Mexico .... *B. a. leucopus* Dunn

1*b*. Dorsal light-colored stripe often present—reddish, yellowish, or brown, often well defined; in life, light-colored guanophore stippling of sides contrasts less sharply with dorsal stripe because of its lighter color; generally dark below, melanophores typically forming close network; hind limb extending over 3 to 3½ costal folds when adpressed to side; intercostal folds between tips of toes of adpressed limbs, 10 to 12½; costal grooves 18 to 21 (20). *Range.*—As for species except for the range of *leucopus*—from southwestern Oregon, in the coastal mountains, probably to the Puente Hills, Los Angeles County, California; also in the foothills of the Sierra Nevada and on Santa Cruz Island off the coast of southern California ...... *B. a. attenuatus* (Eschscholtz)

With respect to differentiating these salamanders, Hilton (1945:108) says ". . . teeth cannot be said to be distinctive." My own observations are in accord with this, hence dentitional characters used by Dunn (1926) are omitted.

Remarks.—It is impossible at the present time to present good subspecific characterizations. Extensive field work and a critical analysis of the characters of living animals are required before a clear picture of subspecific variation, if it exists, can be presented.

An analysis of pigmentation in living animals on either side of the Salinas Valley, California, reveals marked differences. These data are presented as indicative of the work that needs to be done on this species (p. 115).

The Alaska slender salamander, B. *caudatus* Cope is an enigma. Cope (1889:127) listed one specimen, the type, received from Henry E. Nichols from Hassler Harbor, Alaska. Dunn (1926:234), treating the form as a subspecies of *attenuatus*, indicates he examined 2 specimens (USNM 17260, 20489), presumably from Yakutat Bay, and the type specimen (USNM 13561) from Hassler Harbor (on Anette Island). Dunn (1926:234) states, "The type is the only specimen in good shape and with authentic provenance. USNM No. 17260 and 20489 are recorded as from Yukatat [Yakutat?] Bay with a query. These two specimens are in very poor condition and cannot be accurately determined." No specimens have been found since. *Caudatus* is said to closely resemble *attenuatus*—parasphenoid teeth in 2 patches; costal grooves 21; tail greatly elongate; color dark brown above, somewhat lighter below.

	Skyline Blvd., 3 mi. N of turn-off to San Francisco Co. Jail, San Mateo Co., Calif.; 58 animals, collected Feb. 13, 1948.	1 mi. S of Monterey, E side of Munras Ave., Monterey Co., Calif.; 55 animals collected Feb. 14, 1948.
Size	Larger	Smaller
Dorsal stripe	Usually well defined; buff markings common; more yellow in red when this color dominant; generally lighter; light and dark elements tend toward longitudinal streaking, often in form of fine tracery, best developed on tail and in sacral area.	Often vague; only one individual had buff markings; reddish color, when present, deeper, more obscured or darkened with melanin; light and dark elements tend to be globular or punctate.
Ventral surfaces	Generally somewhat lighter with yellowish gular area and tail that contrasts with venter; guanophores appear more irregular in distribution, are coarser, particularly in gular area, are more widely spaced and tend to be concentrated in ventrolateral areas; viscera shows as more intense purplish red.	More uniformly dusky; gular area and underside of tail nearly same color as venter or only slightly lighter; ventral stippling of guanophores averages denser and more uniform; viscera does not appear as intense purplish red.
Pigmentation of testis	Weak to great and only 4 of 16 animals classed as lacking melanic pigment.	8 animals studied were classed as lacking melanic pigment, although in this group and San Mateo animals, few scattered melanophores were usually present.

In iris pigmentation and degree of development of a nuchal patch, the two groups were similar.

PACIFIC SLENDER SALAMANDER

Batrachoseps pacificus (Cope)
Plate 12

Range.—Alluvial deposits of the southern California coastal plain and on the nearby Channel Islands. All mainland localities are in the drainages of the Los Angeles, San Gabriel, and Santa Ana rivers in Los Angeles, San Bernardino, Riverside, and Orange counties. The most interior station is near Redlands, San Bernardino County. The animals occur both on the plain (at Los Angeles and near Long Beach) and in low mountain valleys (Santa Ana Mountains). Specimens in the collection of the California Academy of Science, San Francisco, from San Diego and Los Coronados Islands off the coast, suggest that this species may extend farther south than now recognized. Insular records are for Catalina, San Miguel, Santa Rosa, Santa Cruz, and Anacapa islands (Hilton, 1945:113). (Pl. 53.)

Type locality.—Santa Barbara, California (Cope 1865:196). Possibly one of the islands off the coast from Santa Barbara because the species has not since been found at Santa Barbara on the mainland.

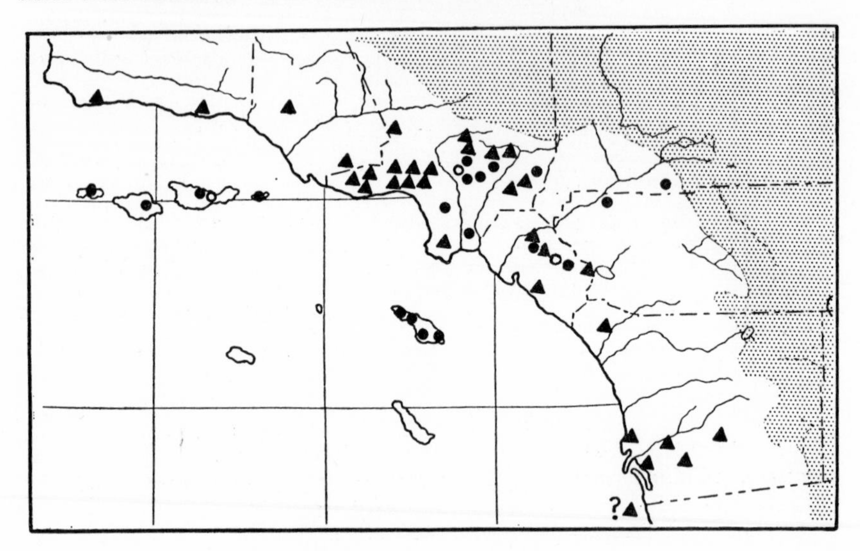

▲ BATRACHOSEPS ATTENUATUS
● BATRACHOSEPS PACIFICUS
○ LOCALITIES WHERE BOTH SPECIES OCCUR TOGETHER

Fig. 16. Localities of occurrence of *Batrachoseps attenuatus* and *B. pacificus* in southern California. The questioned locality at the lower right indicates uncertainty as to the relationship of the *Batrachoseps* population of Los Coronados Islands. (Largely derived from a map prepared by Charles Lowe and Richard Zweifel.)

Description.—STRUCTURE. Resembles *attenuatus* but generally more plethodon-like in habitus; adult larger, to approximately 7 inches; head and body proportionately broader, tail may average shorter, and limbs and toes longer; costal grooves 17 to 21 (mostly 19 and 20), counting 1 each in axilla and groin; vomerine teeth in 2 groups, usually separated at midline; teeth in single row or in patch 2 or 3 teeth across; vomerine teeth tend more toward plethodon-like arrangement, with teeth in a single row, than do those of *attenuatus;* parasphenoid teeth in elongate club-shaped patch, narrowing anteriorly, separated from vomerine teeth; parasphenoid teeth may be reduced in number along midline resulting, in some animals, in formation of 2 separate patches which, however, are often connected anteriorly; parasphenoid tooth patch differs from that of *attenuatus* in being more elongate, narrowing more anteriorly, and tending more often to be divided along midline. COLOR. Dorsal surface brown with varying amounts of pale gold speckling and blotching; in some animals gold color faint, diffuse, discernible only under magnification; in others relatively large blotches present; coarser markings tend to be elongate along long axis of body; metallic gold color tends to be concentrated dorsolaterally and on tail and snout; metallic color sometimes suffused with pink or rust (possibly an overlying lipoid pigment), largely obscuring its gold tint; reddish color tends to be concentrated on tail, snout and neck; lower sides with varying abundance of ash white guanophores forming a salt and pepper effect in association with melanic stippling; ash gray flecking gives way to fine pale gold flecking as generally coarser gold markings of dorsal "stripe" are approached; proximal segments of limbs dorsally with pale gold, rust or pinkish metallic color, like dorsal surface of body; light limb color gives way distally to fine gold and ash white flecking; throat and ventral surface of tail pale, dull yellowish to pinkish beige; abdominal region light slate; ventral surface with few (*B. p. catalinae*) to many (*B. p. major*) whitish guanophores; guanophores most abundant in gular area, on chest, and ventrolaterally on venter, scarce or absent on underside of tail; iris with varying amounts of metallic gold pigment, most abundant in upper part; rust, pink, or ash white are often associated colors. JUVENILE. Similar to adult in form but with relatively longer limbs and shorter tail; greater tendency toward dorsal stripe and ventral coloration sooty to slate, darker than in adult. SEXUAL DIFFERENCES. Similar to those described for *B. attenuatus.*

Subspecies *major* from Altadena, Los Angeles County, California: Coloration generally lighter than in *B. attenuatus,* ventral surface in adults usually with separate melanophores forming minute blackish stippling rather than network although partial network may be present; above light pinkish brown, ash brown, to yellowish brown with scattering of whitish guanophores; dorsal stripe usually obscure in adult; some individuals with reddish-brown tinge on upper surface of snout and edges of upper eyelids and faint suggestion of rust on dorsum of body and tail, becoming more intense on tail; occasionally guanophores may occur in sufficient numbers to impart hoary suffusion to dorsal surfaces; below pinkish or yellowish white to pale slate, usually lightest on underside of tail; ventral surfaces with salt-and-pepper style of markings due to presence of many melanophores and whitish guanophores; guanophores absent along midline of underside of tail but concentrated on sides of neck and body; limbs colored like body; iris dark brown with scattering of brassy. JUVENILE. Dorsal stripe well defined, reddish brown in color; stripe may end immediately anterior to insertion of forelimbs; rusty area on dorsal surface of snout extends onto outer surfaces of upper eyelids; below blackish to slate consisting of network of melanophores and stippling of guanophores, including the underside of the tail.

Half-grown individual, RCS 2556, obtained August 13, 1948, on Santa Cruz Island, Santa Barbara County, California: Vague dorsal stripe of brown, slightly lighter than upper sides; under magnification seen to be margined with broken chain of large, pale bluish-white guanophores and with scattering of such guanophores in stripe; many vague stellate and punctostellate pale gold chromatophores in stripe; few coppery red cells, perhaps lipophores, in stripe, most conspicuous on eyelids and at tip of snout and tail; lipophores (?) also form clusters at upper bases of limbs; white guanophores form stippling over dorsal surfaces of limbs; ventral surfaces rather uniformly deep purplish slate (Dark Quaker Drab), lightening slightly in gular area; melanophores form close network ventrally, tending to break up centrally in gular area; no ventral lipophores; guanophores numerous, white with pale bluish cast, stellate and punctostellate, scattered over all ventral surfaces; lower sides marked like venter but guanophores thin out toward dorsal stripe, resulting in dark margin of ground color next to stripe; iris dark brown with extensive fine tracery of pale gold to silvery around pupil and second circular zone of such pigment some distance peripheral to pupillary ring. This individual resembled *B. attenuatus* more than *B. pacificus pacificus* in coloration; but in its large eyes, relatively long limbs and toes, and 18 costal grooves, it was closer to the latter.

Immature individual, RCS 2555, locality data as above: Vague dorsal band marked with buff, formed by much broken network of pale gold chromatophores (lipophores?); melanic network weakened beneath lipophore (?) network; few reddish-coppery cells (lipophores?) in sacral area and on tail, especially toward tip; separate, numerous, whitish and golden pigment cells on eyelids, snout, and neck; no nuchal patch; stippling of whitish guanophores at upper bases of limbs but no guanistic patches; below pale purplish gray (Pale Ecru-Drab); ventral melanophores unconnected in gular area, on chest, and on proximal segments of limbs; some melanophores partly connected with one another on body and distal segments of limbs; those on posterior half of tail form still more continuous network; considerable numbers of white punctostellate guanophores in gular area and on chest, becoming punctate on body where they are most numerous ventrolaterally but not as abundant as on chest and in gular area; guanophore stippling also present on tail; no lipophores discernible ventrally; melanophores form network on sides where there are white guanophores of variable size; laterally situated guanophores are more conspicuous than those ventrally situated; some guanistic patches large, others punctate and minute; iris dark brown with flecks and tracery of pale gold to brassy in upper part and few scattered flecks of similar color below pupil.

Habitat.—Found under rocks, boards, and other surface litter, commonly beneath coast live oaks (*Quercus agrifolia*). The mainland subspecies, *major,* has been found in such situations on alluvial fans fringing the Lost Angeles coastal plain. At several localities I have noted the substratum as sandy loam. Camp (1915:329) observes that localities where *major* occurs lie in the upper edge of the Lower Sonoran Life-zone (mesa oak association) whereas in the same general areas *B. attenuatus* appears to inhabit the Upper Sonoran Zone (maple-sycamore association in the mountain canyons), possibly getting out into the valleys occasionally along watercourses.

Campbell says that he has found 15 or 20 under a single board in his garden in Monrovia, California, in the spring months. Toward the middle of April they begin to disappear and by the second week in May no more are to be seen (Storer, MS).

Reproduction.—Two adult females, obtained December 17, 1947, at Altadena, Los Angeles County, California, contained 15 and 20 fully developed ova, approximately 3.4 mm. in diameter. The eggs appeared about ready for laying. These individuals were found, along with a number of adult males, subadults, and young, beneath a grass rug that was largely covered with eucalyptus leaves in the bottom of a concrete fish pond. About an inch of water was present in the pond. The salamanders were found principally in folds in the mat (or beneath it) in wet places but not in the water.

Hilton (1945:113) mentions an individual from San Miguel Island, obtained May 20, 1919, that possessed ovarian eggs 2 mm. in diameter.

Three size-groups were evident in a number of animals examined by Campbell, March 16, 1929. They measured 30 mm., 45 to 60 mm., and 90 to 120 mm. (Storer, MS).

Key to Subspecies

(Characters partly from Hilton, 1945)

1a. Eyes larger; habitus more plethodon-like; limbs relatively longer, hind limb of adults overlapping 5½ to 6½ intercostal folds when adpressed to side; 9 to 11 intercostal folds between tips of toes of adpressed limbs; costal grooves 17 to 20 (19), counting 1 each in axilla and groin; vomerine teeth usually in single row, except with larger numbers of teeth when they may be in 2 irregular rows or arranged irregularly; parasphenoid teeth in 2 elongate patches, narrowly separated medially, or in 1 patch deeply notched in front; dorsal stripe obscure or absent. *Range.* Islands off the coast of Santa Barbara County, California—namely San Miguel, Santa Rosa, Santa Cruz, and Anacapa. .... *B. p. pacificus* (Cope)

1b. Eyes smaller; habitus less plethodon-like; limbs relatively shorter, hind limb overlapping 3½ to 4½ intercostal folds when adpressed to side; vomerine teeth usually in short patches consisting of several rows of teeth or teeth irregularly arranged; parasphenoid teeth in single patch or separated in varying degrees into 2 patches; dorsal stripe faintly present or obscure 2

2a. Usually 19 costal grooves (18 to 20), counting 1 each in axilla and groin; hind limb overlapping 4 to 4½ intercostal folds when adpressed to side; 9 to 10 intercostal folds between tips of toes of adpressed limbs; parasphenoid teeth in single broad patch or in varying degrees separated along midline; venter of adults usually with punctate melanophores only; ventral white speckling (guanophores) often dense; vent usually not margined with black. *Range.* Scattered localities in Los Angeles, San Bernardino, Riverside, and Orange counties in southern California. Localities are: Sierra Madre, Arroyo Seco (near Pasadena), Monrovia, and Covina, in Los Angeles County; Redlands, San Bernardino County; and Riverside, Riverside County .... *B. p. major* Camp

2*b*. Usually 20 to 22 costal grooves, counting 1 each in axilla and groin; hind limb overlapping 3½ to 4½ intercostal folds when adpressed to side; 10 to 13 intercostal folds between tips of toes of adpressed limbs; parasphenoid teeth in broad patch with median furrow variously separating two sides; venter of adults usually with melanophores forming network laterally, with punctate melanophores commonly confined to central area; ventral white speckling (guanophores) weak; vent tends to be margined with black. *Range.* Confined to Catalina Island off coast of Los Angeles County, California .... *B. p. catalinae* Dunn

Remarks.—Dunn (1926), Bishop (1943), and Hilton (1945) have treated all the members of the genus *Batrachoseps* as subspecies of a single species *B. attenuatus.* Owing to present lack of what, to me, is convincing evidence for intergradation in the face of evidence for the coexistence of the forms *major* and *attenuatus,* I follow Campbell (1931a:133) in recognizing the larger, lighter-colored form of the islands and mainland of southern California as specifically distinct from *B. attenuatus.* In support of the specific distinctness of these forms, Campbell (1931a:132) has stated that *major* (variously treated: as a species in itself, a race of *attenuatus,* and, recently, as a subspecies of *pacificus*) and *attenuatus* were found together in South Pasadena and that *pacificus* and *attenuatus* are said to coexist on Santa Cruz Island. Recent collecting has confirmed both observations and has brought to light an additional area of overlap. Charles Lowe and Richard Zweifel have found the 2 species under the same pieces of cover near Irvine Park in the Santa Ana Mountains.

Pigmentation of individuals from near Redlands, San Bernardino County, California, suggests a present or previous intermixing of *attenuatus* and *pacificus* stocks. The animals there, however, seem closest to *pacificus.*

Campbell, on morphological grounds, includes *major* with the insular forms, *catalinae* and *pacificus* (both at one time considered species). In the absence of thorough systematic work with living individuals of the forms of this genus and from personal familiarity with the relationship between *major* and *attenuatus* in southern California, I follow the recommendations of Campbell who has had considerable field experience with these animals.

OREGON SLENDER SALAMANDER

Batrachoseps wrighti (Bishop)
Plate 12

Range.—The western slope of the Cascade Mountains of Oregon. Known only from the following localities: 8.7 miles southeast of Sandy,

Clackamas County (type locality); near the mouths of Moose Creek and nearby Trout Creek, tributaries of Quartzville Creek which drains into Middle Santiam River, Linn County; near Cherryville and from 1/2 mile east and 1/4 mile south of Wemme, Clackamas County. Dr. Robert Storm and Donald Dunlap of Oregon State College, Corvallis, Oregon, and John Hendrickson of the University of California found the species at the Trout Creek and Wemme localities. Storm recently found it about 2 miles south of McKenzie Bridge, Lane County. (Pl. 53.)

Type locality.—Woods bordering the Mount Hood Highway, 8.7 miles southeast of Sandy, Clackamas County, Oregon (Bishop, 1937:94).

Description.—STRUCTURE. Adult approximately 3 1/2 to 3 3/4 inches; costal grooves well defined, 16 to 17, counting 1 each in axilla and groin; 6 1/2 to 7 intercostal folds between tips of toes of adpressed limbs; 4 1/2 to 5 intercostal folds overlapped by hind leg when adpressed to side; limbs small and slender, but considerably longer than diameter of body; tail rounded basally, somewhat compressed distally, without basal constriction, with furrows similar to costal grooves; vomerine teeth 10 to 15 per row, usually separated at midline but sometimes connected on one or both sides with parasphenoid teeth; parasphenoid teeth arranged in elongate oval patch, narrowing anteriorly, and often divided along midline; palatine dentition thus more like *pacificus* than *attenuatus*. COLOR. In life dorsal stripe varies from bright chestnut to reddish brown, extending from head to tip of tail, sometimes blotched with black centrally; stripe sometimes dull brownish yellow or grayish brown in large individuals, only slightly different from color of sides; upper sides deep brown or black, below which are many irregular bluish-white spots (clusters of guanophores) on slaty ground color; upper surfaces of legs dark, with small light spots; below dark slate to almost black, with numerous small bluish-white spots (groups of guanophores), becoming scarcer toward midline; throat, ventral surface of tail, and lower surfaces of limbs strongly flecked with light spots (guanophores). SEXUAL DIFFERENCES. Two or 3 enlarged teeth on each premaxillary of male, sometimes perforating upper lip; similar, rather vague snout and jaw differences as described for *B. attenuatus*. Vent of male bordered by narrow depressed area with lips elevated, particularly anteriorly; in female vent is simple slit.

Adult, RCS 2253, 41 mm. in snout-vent length, obtained April 21, 1948, at the type locality: Dorsal stripe reddish brown (near Chestnut on body), brightest on tail (Mahogany Red), broadening on head to include upper eyelids; stripe composed of network of pale gold chromatophores, largely overlaid by suffusion of reddish lipophores (?); ground color of limbs blackish with pale bluish-white spots and blotches composed of guanophores; dorsal surfaces of limbs with stippling of pale gold chromatophores, some of which (particularly on proximal segments of limbs) are overlaid with reddish to form spots and blotches of rusty, like dorsal stripe; ground color of ventral surfaces almost solid black, darker than Blackish Mouse Gray; gular area and undersides of feet slightly lighter, near Blackish Brown (3); ground color deepens to glossy black next to dorsal stripe; ash gray (Pale Gull Gray) spots and blotches ventrally and on sides, composed of clusters of guanophores; ventrally guanistic spots most numerous ventrolaterally on body, less abundant on underside of tail; melanic ground weak or absent beneath guanistic patches; pale gray blotches give way, about one-half distance up sides, to fine golden stippling, near to but paler than Sulphur Yellow; these chromatophores stop short of dorsal stripe, resulting in stripe being margined with black, although on tail guanophores frequently join stripe; iris dark brown with coppery crescent margining upper edge of pupil; 2 flecks of similar color in lower iris.

Habitat.—Bishop (1937:94-95) found this salamander in forests bordering the Mount Hood Highway, where there were mixed soft- and hardwoods on the base of a pastured slope. The first 3 individuals were under the bark of a rotting log, probably fir. Several others were beneath chips and logs on the surface of the ground, but the majority were found lying between pieces of bark piled in a heap at the base of a stump. Some were coiled in a closed spiral with the head held much like a snake. The animals were collected in intermittent showers in small, open, gladelike areas. I have found individuals in termite channels in rotting logs.

On April 21, 1948, Charles Lowe, Jr., and I visited the type locality. An adult female, heavy with eggs, was found in a watchspring-like coil with her head resting on a loop of her body. She was discovered at a depth of approximately 10 inches beneath small fragments of reddish-brown decayed wood at the surface of black soil, rich in humus. A male was found in a similar place 2 feet away and a third individual in a termite channel in a piece of decayed wood. The wood was soft, crumbling readily in one's fingers and moist enough so that water could be squeezed from it. The temperature of the wood was 8°C.; air temperature 6 inches above the ground in the shade, to one side of the wood litter, 12°C. The wood fragments were heaped up about the base of a much-fissured and decayed stump, forming rubble not unlike the rock-rubble talus niche of *Plethodon elongatus*. There were numerous openings among the fragments permitting the salamanders movement within the deposit. The surface of the rubble was covered with a thin mat of dead alder and maple leaves and Douglas fir boughs.

The surrounding level ground was covered with *Oxalis* and a scattering of sword fern. These plants were sufficiently well spaced and the surface layer of alder and maple leaves smooth enough to permit the salamanders nocturnal wandering with little interference with their locomotion. There was considerable moss on logs in the area but only a light growth on the stump. I suspected the leafy canopy would be nearly 100 per cent in summer when the deciduous trees were in leaf. The collection site was about 175 feet east of the Mount Hood Highway in a shallow depression which receives water that drains from the road. The ground was wet. It was raining lightly. There was great range in the amount of moisture available to the salamanders. They could move from damp soil, in openings about the roots, through the wood debris into relatively dry, vertical fissures in the stump, to moderately damp rubble 5 feet above the ground, at the top of the stump.

Behavior.—As with other species of *Batrachoseps,* when slowly crawling forward, the body may be held nearly in a straight line. The relationship of the body and limbs in locomotion of this sort in *Batrachoseps* has been described by Peabody (1941) as two men walking in a line carrying a pole between them. Most other salamanders move the body in marked lateral undulations when crawling. An individual obtained by Charles Lowe, Jr., when first seized, engaged in a violent series of flipping movements that threw it repeatedly into the air. These contortions were followed by a sudden cessation of movement. This behavior is similar to that of *attenuatus.*

Reproduction.—An individual obtained by me on April 21, 1948, at the type locality, possessed 11 fully formed ovarian eggs. Following 2 implantations of whole pituitaries of *Hyla regilla,* on May 25 and 27, 1948, oviposition began at 9:00 A.M. on June 1 and was completed at 7:15 P.M., June 2. The eggs were laid in a rosary-like string and possessed 2 transparent jelly envelopes. Except for somewhat larger size they closely resembled those of *B. attenuatus.* Measurements were as follows: Connecting strand between successive eggs in chain, about 20 mm. by 1 mm.; ovum unpigmented, cream colored, 4 mm.; inner jelly layer, 1 to 2 mm. thick; outer jelly layer, 0.8 to 1.0 mm. in thickness; diameter of egg to outer jelly envelope, 9.7 to 10.0 mm. The surface of the outer jelly envelope was marked with diagonal furrows, probably resulting from rotation of the egg in passing through the oviduct. The eggs were remarkably large for the size of the salamander. The female showed no brooding tendency. All the eggs were fertile, presumably impregnated by sperm stored in the spermatheca of the female. The gill structure of the embryos was different from that of *B. attenuatus.* The gill was triparted with these primary divisions further subdivided. Several major vessels and a number of smaller ones were present in each primary division, a more extensive vascular bed than in *B. attenuatus* (Stebbins, 1949a:165). Seven young hatched on October 13, 133 days (about 4½ months) after laying (fig. 17). During the developmental period, the eggs were kept on a damp paper towel (changed once a week) in a dark room at 12°C. Four of the original 11 eggs were preserved. The young had short tails, relatively long limbs and large heads; they were black above with a scattering of pale gold chromatophores and sooty below with a few pale bluish-white guanophores, largely ventrolaterally situated. For details on laying, development, and hatching of the eggs see Stebbins, 1949a:161-68.

If the female upon which the foregoing observations are based is representative in her reproductive behavior, then *B. wrighti* is more like our species of the genus *Plethodon* than the other species of *Batrachoseps* in time of egg laying and development of the eggs.

Remarks.—This species was originally described by Bishop (1937) as *Plethopsis wrighti* but with procurement of additional specimens and further study it has appeared desirable to me to view this form as *Batrachoseps* (Stebbins and Lowe, 1949:116-29).

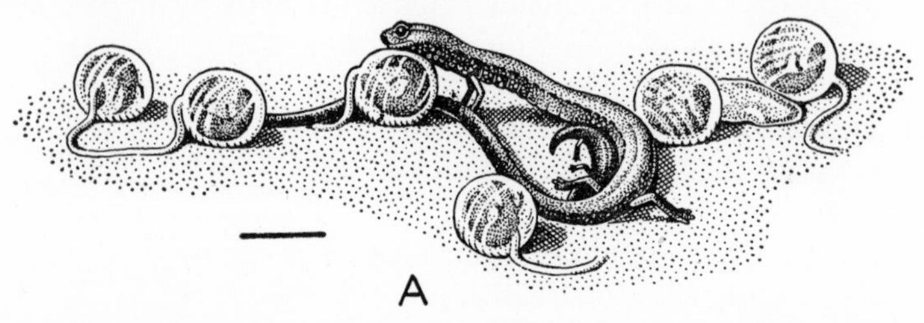

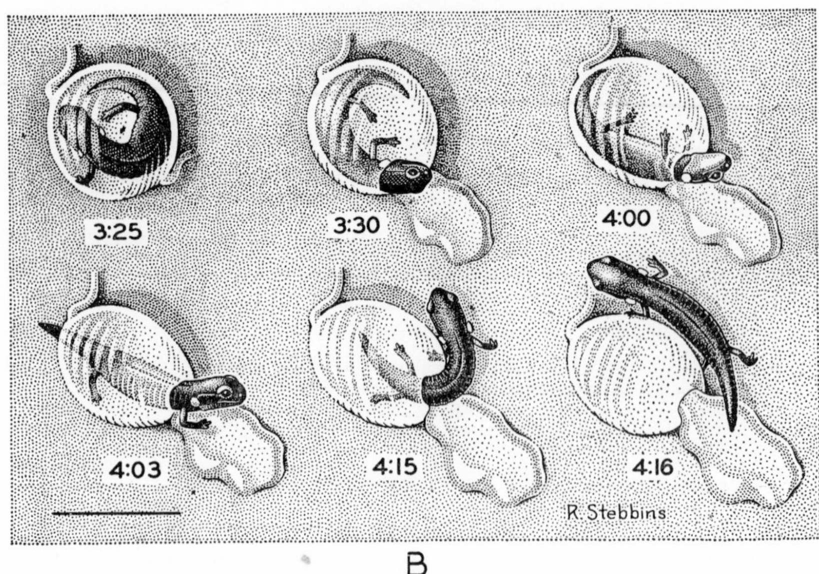

Fig. 17. A. Adult female *Batrachoseps wrighti* with eggs. Hatching had begun. One young was at her side. Several hours later all eggs had hatched.

B. Stages in hatching. Drawings were based on sketches made during hatching of a single individual. The time (P.M.) at each stage is indicated. Note the blob of jelly extruded upon rupture of the egg membranes.

The horizontal line in both sketches represents 10 mm.

Genus *Aneides*

Structure.—Adults 3 to 6 inches; jaw muscles well developed giving head of most adult individuals somewhat triangular shape in dorsal aspect; eyes large and protuberant; costal grooves well defined; tail rounded, unconstricted at base; limbs well developed; toes 4-5, tips enlarged (*A. flavipunctatus* and *A. hardii* excepted); **Y**-shaped terminal phalanges; no palmar or plantar tubercles; tongue attached anteriorly and along midline, free laterally and posteriorly; in many individuals, particularly adult males, projecting premaxillary teeth can be detected by stroking tip of snout with finger; posterior portion of maxillary bone sharp-edged, without teeth; premaxillary bones fused.

Range.—Pacific coast of North America from Vancouver Island to southern California; eastern United States in the Appalachian Mountains (*Aneides aeneus*); Sacramento Mountains, Otero County, New Mexico (*Aneides hardii*).

Key to Species
Figure 18

1*a*. Adult with 3 to 5 intercostal folds between tips of toes of adpressed limbs (1); toes relatively shorter and with less tendency toward expansion of tips than in other species (2); mandibular teeth not markedly flattened (3) 3

1*b*. Adult with 1 to 1½ or less intercostal folds between tips of toes of adpressed limbs or toes touching or overlapping somewhat (4); toes relatively longer, with expanded tips (5); mandibular teeth enlarged and flattened (6) 2

2*a*. With definite light spots (sulphur in life) of varying size and abundance on gray-brown to dark brown ground color (occasional individuals are without spots or have extremely small markings) (9, 10); usually 15 costal grooves (rarely 14 or 16), counting 1 each in axilla and groin; chunkier species—limbs and toes heavier; head averages broader behind eyes .... *A. lugubris,* p. 139

2*b*. Above (in life) with numerous minute whitish and brassy flecks forming large irregular light-grayish blotches, often with brassy tinge (preserved specimens may merely show light and dark mottlings) (11); usually 16 or 17 costal grooves, counting 1 each in axilla and groin; slimmer species—limbs and toes slender; development of jaw muscles usually less pronounced .... *A. ferreus,* p. 126

3*a*. Ground color of venter, black but with scattered gray punctations due to presence of large glands, most pronounced in males (12); melanophores form close, dense network; above solid black to dull greenish (nearly always black in preserved specimens), with or without whitish or yellowish spots (7, 8); no dark-edged dorsal stripe in juvenile. Coastal California in the vicinity of and north of San Francisco Bay ....
.... *A. flavipunctatus,* p. 131

3*b*. Ground color of venter not black, light purplish brown in life, light gray, pale yellow, to soiled white in preservative, with melanophores appearing as separate punctations or forming weak, often irregularly connected network; ground color above brown in life, with (15) or without mottlings of bronze to rust; juvenile with dark-edged dorsal stripe of grayish brown, yellowish brown, to rusty brown. Sacramento Mountains, Otero County, New Mexico .... *A. hardii*, p. 135

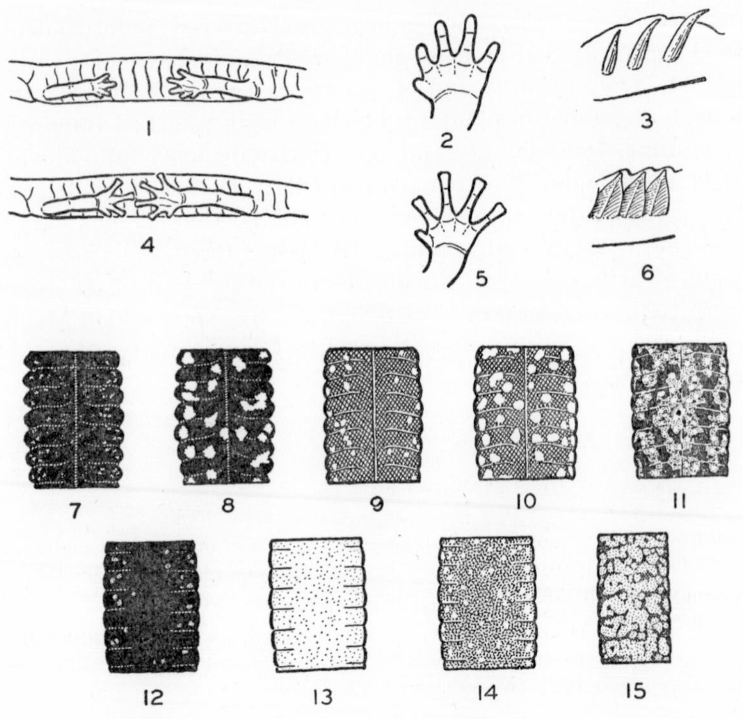

Fig. 18. 1, 2, 3, 7, 8, 12, *Aneides flavipunctatus;* 4, 5, 11, 14, *A. ferreus;* 6, 9, 10, 13, *A. lugubris;* 15, *A. hardii.*

CLOUDED SALAMANDER

Aneides ferreus Cope
Plate 13

Range.—Largely in the humid coastal forest from central Mendocino County, California, northward west of the crest of the Cascades to the Columbia River. On Vancouver and adjacent smaller islands, British Columbia. Apparently absent from Washington, although the species occurs in the vicinity of Portland, Oregon, on the south side of the Columbia River. The record for Gorst Creek, Kitsap County, Washington (Slater, 1939a:4), is based on a specimen of *Plethodon vehiculum* (USNM 62710).

Absence (or rarity?) of the species in Washington may be related to the Pleistocene ice advance that extended to the Columbia River. (Pl. 54.) Island is unglaciated. (Pl. 54.)

Type locality.—Fort Umpqua, Oregon (Cope, 1869:110).

Description.—STRUCTURE. Resembles *A. lugubris* (p. 139) but averages smaller and more slender and has somewhat less pronounced development of jaw muscles; adult 3½ to 5 inches; body elongate and flattened; costal grooves 15 to 17, counting 1 each in axilla and groin; tips of toes of adpressed limbs may overlap to 1½ costal folds or, rarely, may be separated as much as 1½ folds; tail rounded in cross section, somewhat compressed toward tip, with grooves corresponding to costal folds; digits slightly expanded and truncate at tips; innermost toe on forefeet and hind feet slightly more reduced than in *lugubris* (first digit with short phalanx but not as free as in *lugubris*); vomerine teeth 4 to 8 per row (in 6 adult animals from various parts of range); rows closely approximated at midline, perhaps sometimes connected, forming broad **V**; parasphenoid teeth in large, elongate oval patch well separated from vomerine teeth; teeth sometimes reduced in number along midline tending toward bifurcation of patch; patch often single; shape of parasphenoid patch more like *hardii* and *flavipunctatus* than *lugubris* but vomerine rows more like *lugubris*. COLOR. Above, ground color black to dark brown, commonly with irregular marbling or clouding of pale gray to whitish with flecks of brassy or copper (light markings are due to presence of guanophores and xanthophores [?]); below dusky with whitish specks in life but when preserved, cream, buff, or gray, stippled with melanophores or with a melanic network; iris dark brown with flecks of brassy. JUVENILE. Ground color dark brown to blackish, mottled with copper and brassy, light color (coppery or brassy in life) concentrated to form patches in following areas: between eyes to tip of snout, dorsolaterally on either side of neck above forelimbs extending from base of head to level of insertion of limbs, upper surface of basal portions of limbs and on dorsum of tail. Preserved specimens are dark brown to black, usually without mottlings and with above areas buff-colored. Bronze or brassy patches become obscure with increase in size; among preserved animals a juvenile 26 mm. in snout-vent length had them well developed; one 28 mm. had neck markings much reduced, and one 34 mm. had only a faint suggestion of markings, with snout patch absent. Recently hatched young, averaging 25 mm. in length, are described as having a brass-colored dorsal stripe (Storm, 1947:62); stripe extended just back of head to base of tail where it narrowed and intensified in color toward tip of tail; brass-colored triangle with apices at eyes and snout, and brassy areas on proximal segments of limbs were present as in older young. SEXUAL DIFFERENCES. Essentially as in *A. lugubris* (p. 139).

Adult male, RCS 1587, 71 mm. in snout-vent length, obtained on February 15, 1947, 4 miles north of Orick, Humboldt County, California: Ground color above dark brown (Blackish Brown [3]), with pale yellow clouding of guanophores (?), golden under magnification, that form irregular patches over all dorsal surfaces; spots of irregular outline and size on sides of tail, body, and neck, composed of clusters of guanophores (?); tips of toes pinkish; ventral surface of body and tail grayish brown (Hair Brown); gular area, anteriorly, lighter purplish brown (Benzo Brown); melanophores arranged in a network ventrally with numerous small spherical glands appearing as dots of light gray in the reticulum; spots of whitish to pale yellow (guanophore clusters?), of variable size and irregular outline, over all ventral surfaces, although scarce on tail; iris dark brown, with numerous coarse and fine flecks and lines of pale gold to silvery above and below pupil.

Juvenile, RCS 1533, 38 mm. in snout-vent length, obtained February 14, 1947, at Boise Creek, about 800 feet elevation, about 2 miles west of Willow Creek Post Office, Humboldt County, California: Ground color of dorsum blackish brown, composed of close network of melanophores; dark color largely obscured by numerous cream to pale copper chromatophores that form dense stippling and partial network arranged in form of vague stripe full length of body; these chromatophores aggregate to form pale orange-yellow (Capucine Buff) spot on snout, triangular in shape, with apices of triangle extending to anterior surfaces of eyelids and tip of snout; they also form pair of elongate patches on shoulders above forelimbs and stripe nearly full length of tail, pinkish rust (light Ochraceous Salmon) in color; similar color present on upper surfaces of proximal segments of limbs; below dark gray (Mouse Gray), composed of closely set melanophores, not forming network; ventral ground color overlaid with stippling of whitish guanophores; considerable numbers of whitish guanophores on sides, especially between limbs; iris dark brown with golden to bronze patch in upper iris and a few flecks of such color in lower part.

Habitat.—Found in cracks in logs and between the bark and heartwood of standing and downed dead trees. It is occasionally found on the ground beneath surface objects. I have collected numbers of these salamanders beneath leaf mats that form on the top of sawed stumps, principally of Douglas fir, in mixed redwood and Douglas fir stands and beneath the bark of such stumps. Individuals also have been found under the loose bark of dead stream alder and Port Orford cedar. Storm and Aller (1947:60) state that this species ". . . lives primarily in rotting fir logs in open clearings . . ." (Pl. 38, fig. 2.)

Near Orick, Humboldt County, California, on February 15, 1947, I found 11 individuals, all adult but one, beneath loose bark of sawed stumps of Port Orford cedar. Eight or 10 such stumps were investigated along the north side of a tributary of Prairie Creek, between 10:30 and 11:45 A.M. The creek and its logged margins formed a gap in the dense redwood forest. The area was well illuminated. There was a dense growth of sword fern, *Gaultheria,* and sedges about the bases of the stumps. Most of the stumps were 8 or 10 feet high with only patches of bark remaining. Some of them stood with their bases nearly in the stream and all were in areas subject to flooding with a slight rise in stream level. Four adults were found at the first stump investigated. Two were on one side, about 5 feet apart, and 2, about 2 feet apart, on the opposite side. These animals may have represented 2 pairs. The bark peeled off readily in large slabs. The surface under the bark was smooth, hard, and damp. One individual when exposed poised motionless, head downward, with body and tail well off the slippery, nearly vertical, surface. This attests to the adhesiveness of the broad, flat, foot surfaces and the spatulate digits. Other animals observed under the bark were centipedes, millipedes, carabid beetles, camel crickets, slugs, and earthworms.

Behavior.—An agile climber; probably the most arboreal of the western *Aneides.* Van Denburgh (1916:216) records 2 individuals found by Joseph Slevin ". . . taken from the rotten wood of a dead tree in which they were living some 20 feet above the ground."

Capable of marked color change. When kept in a dark, cold room at 12°C., 6 adults were dark-colored, with the dorsal light-colored cloudings obscure. In the laboratory at 21°C., where well illuminated, the light-colored markings of the animals became conspicuous, almost dominating the dark ground color. The changes evidently are achieved principally by changes in the melanic pigmentation.

Food.—Storm and Aller (1947:59-60) have studied feeding habits of this species. They found that the animals apparently feed at random on the smaller arthropods found within the logs in which they dwell. Numbers and availability of food types produce differences in amounts and kinds consumed. In 63 stomachs examined, percentages of food items were: ants, 57 per cent; adult beetles, 29 per cent, larvae, 6.4 per cent; spiders and acarids, each 19 per cent; isopods, 14 per cent; termites, 11 per cent. Other arthropods present in small numbers were: centipedes, millipedes, pseudoscorpions, and insects such as collembolans, cockroaches, hemipterans (tingids and others), homopterans, dermapterans, culicids, and larval dipterans.

Fitch (1936:638) reports the stomach contents of 5 specimens from between Lobster and Silver creeks in the Rogue River Basin, Oregon, collected May 22, 1935: 2 large orange-colored mites, 1 beetle grub (length 12 mm.), a small beetle, a heavily armored kind of weevil, and some unrecognizable fibrous material.

Reproduction.—EGGS. Probably commonly deposited in late spring and early summer, hatching in late summer or fall. A cluster of 9 eggs described by Dunn (1942:52), was found by J. A. G. Rehn and son on August 16, 1941, near Patrick Creek, 2,000 feet, Del Norte County, California. The salamander was found "alongside of eggs under bark of fallen Douglas fir." (J. Rehn quoted by Dunn.) Dunn found 8 of the eggs still attached separately to a bit of the bark after their arrival in Philadelphia. So close together were the attachments that most of the eggs were in contact. The eggs measured approximately 6 mm. in diameter and the pedicles were 4 mm. long. One egg dissected had 2 jelly envelopes and contained a fully formed young with the yolk sac still partly protruding from the stomach. The young animal measured 15 mm. It possessed a single large, flat, leaf-like, allantoic gill on each side. As the animal was coiled, one lobe of the gill extended over the eye, one almost over the hand, and the third part well back over the body. The gills are evidently like those of *A. lugubris*. Fitch (1936:638) reports a female with 12 ova, taken May 22, 1935, in the coastal forest between Lobster and Silver creeks in the Rogue River Basin, Oregon. The eggs measured about 4 mm. in diameter.

Two clusters, apparently recently laid, were found by Storm (1947: 60-61) on July 7, 1946, some 4 miles west of Philomath, Benton County, Oregon. Both were discovered within a rotting Douglas fir log, about 2 feet in diameter, which lay on an exposed southern slope, surrounded for at least 50 yards by low herbaceous growth, largely grasses. The exterior of the log was fire-charred. The eggs were in separate small cavities beneath the exterior about 2 feet apart and near the base of the south side of the log. The eggs numbered 17 and 9 and were arranged in grapelike clusters. The individual eggs were about 5 mm. in diameter each with a milky, yellowish gelatinous covering continued at one end into a strand about 3/4 inch long. The strands were twisted about and adherent to one another toward the point of attachment. Both clusters were attended by a male and female. A third cluster of 8 eggs was found August 20, 1946, in a cavity in the same log. No adults were present. The embryos were nearly full grown. Five of these eggs, turned over to a foster parent, hatched in a terrarium between September 8 and 16, 1946.

A female obtained May 23, 1946, by Storm (1947:61) laid 13 eggs in sphagnum moss in a terrarium on either July 6 or 7, 1946. The eggs were deposited in a gourd-shaped hollow in the moss constructed by the female and were attached to strands of moss, singly and in groups of 2 and 3. The eggs measured 4.5 mm. in diameter and were attended by the female. All but 2 of the eggs spoiled but these, along with the 5 eggs mentioned above, hatched. Three of the young averaged 25 mm. in length.

Eggs laid in captivity by an individual from 8.4 miles southeast of Sandy, Clackamas County, Oregon, in June, 1948, were attached by gelatinous peduncles. Measurements of a representative egg, given me by

Charles Lowe are: peduncle 0.9 mm. in diameter and 9.0 mm. from base to upper surface of egg; 2 transparent jelly envelopes, outer one continuous with outer layer of peduncle, .08 mm. in thickness; outer envelope with small, low, conical projection opposite peduncle; inner envelope 1.0 mm. thick; capsular cavity, 0.1 mm.; ovum whitish, unpigmented, oval, 5.1 by 4.1 mm., with its long axis continuous with axis of peduncle.

BLACK SALAMANDER

Aneides flavipunctatus (Strauch)
Plate 13

Range.—In the coastal mountains of California from Santa Cruz County to northern Humboldt County and interiorly in the Klamath Mountains to the vicinity of Baird (site now under the water of Shasta Dam), Shasta County, California. Not known from the region east of San Francisco Bay. Hilton's (1948) record of an *Aneides* resembling this species, from the Mount Hood region of Oregon, apparently is based on specimens of *Aneides ferreus*. Dr. Hilton has kindly allowed me to examine his material. (Pl. 54.)

Type locality.—New Albion, California (probably the coastal portion of Sonoma County, *fide* Storer, 1925:119) (Strauch, 1870:71-72).

Description.—STRUCTURE. Adult 4 to 6 inches; in form resembles *A. hardii,* more plethodon-like than other species (body long and limbs relatively short); costal grooves 14 or 15, counting 1 each in axilla and groin; 3 to 5 intercostal folds between tips of toes of adpressed limbs; digits, like *hardii,* relatively shorter and with more rounded tips than in *ferreus* and *lugubris;* vomerine teeth 1 to 5 per row (6 adult animals from various parts of range); rows rather widely separated; parasphenoid teeth in elongate ovoid patch well separated from vomerine teeth; patch single or with teeth variously reduced along midline; patches connected anteriorly or posteriorly or at both ends. COLOR. Ground color of ventral surfaces slate to black with numerous small ash-gray spots; under magnification, ventral coloration is seen to consist of melanophores, associated with blood vessels, forming close network that sets off ash-gray glandular areas; ventral color usually lightens on chin, along margin of gular fold, on undersides of limbs and feet, and toward tip of tail; margins of vent pigmented or not; iris dark brown with flecks of silvery to pale gold; dorsal coloration variable, animals south of Golden Gate uniformly black without or with fine white spots; those north of Golden Gate with conspicuous spots of white or pale yellow, of variable size, shape, and abundance; and those toward northern end of range with olive to greenish suffusion due to presence of pale gold pigment cells, or uniformly black with white spotting; individuals with pale gold pigment cells have them especially concentrated along sides; in northern animals spotting is present in varying amounts or is absent. JUVENILE. Dorsal surfaces black, suffused in varying amounts with dull bronze or greenish bronze resulting from presence of fine stippling or network of pale gold; some individuals decidedly green; suffusion of gold flecks may become obscure with increase in size; bases of limbs yellowish above; otherwise juvenile marked like adult. SEXUAL DIFFERENCES. Male with broader, more triangular head due to greater development of jaw muscles; width of snout greater, evidently due to enlarged upper lip; lower jaw more pointed; and glandular spotting of ventral surfaces more pronounced than in female; vent in male tends to gape (in preserved specimens) and is without pleated edges; male with mental gland, usually evident as light-colored, heart-shaped patch situated as in *lugubris* (fig. 3, p. 12).

Adult, RCS 1044, 71 mm. in snout-vent length, obtained September 29, 1946, 1/4 mile northwest of Lucerne, Lake County, California: Ground color above black, lightening dorsally to dusky on outer edges of upper eyelids, snout, tip of tail, and toes; tips of toes pink due to blood of digital sinusoids; marked over all dorsal surfaces with numerous white spots of irregular outline and ranging in size from about 0.4 to 3.7 mm.; below sooty, lightening on anterior 2/3 of gular area, along edge of gular fold, on undersides of limbs and feet, and on underside of tail, particularly distally; margin of vent white, without melanophores; ventral surface of body, posterior part of gular area, vent region, and undersides of limbs, with minute spherical ash-gray glands; large whitish blotches like those dorsally, some 3 mm. in greatest width, on ventral surface of body (particularly laterally) in pelvic region, on chest, and in gular area; markings composed of dense aggregates of white guanophores; under magnification white marks have black stippled appearance where melanic color evident at apertures of glands; melanic network tends to weaken beneath guanistic patches; lighter areas, particularly gular region, have pinkish tinge; tip of tail with pale olive cast; iris dark brown with flecks of pale gold above and below pupil; iridic markings most abundant above pupil.

Juvenile, RCS 713, 34 mm. snout-vent length, obtained February 10, 1946, 8.9 miles south of Piercy, near U.S. Highway 101, near Lane's Redwood Flat, Mendocino County, California: Dorsal surfaces of body and tail metallic olive or bronzy green (Oil Yellow to Olive Yellow), under magnification exhibiting numerous golden chromatophores overlying melanic ground color; proximal segments of limbs above yellow (Pale Greenish Yellow); distal segments of limbs sooty, speckled lightly with white guanophores; ventral surfaces black, consisting of network of melanophores; scattering of white guanophores in gular area, on chest, on lower abdomen, and about vent; iris dark brown with flecks of pale yellow around pupil.

Habitat.—Found upon or in wet soil in rocky situations along streams and in talus where seepages occur or in damp situations not far from water. Profusely white-spotted animals occur near Lucerne, Lake County, California. At one locality they were found beneath talus, 100 feet back in a damp mine shaft. Judged by the range in size of individuals, the colony in the mine must have been resident there. Wood (1936:171) has found the species particularly common in burnt-over areas.

In collecting this salamander in redwood areas, I have had the greatest success in working along small streams and seepages. Like certain of the plethodons, this *Aneides* seems to be particularly abundant in rock slides, especially among rocks that have been in repose long enough to permit growth of moss. In the redwood country, the animals favor wet surroundings, sometimes occurring in thin trickles of water, in situations reminding me of the niche of *Rhyacotriton.* More interiorly, however, as at Clear Lake in Lake County and near Shasta Dam in Shasta County, they are found in less wet situations.

Near Burnt Ranch, Trinity County, California, on July 25, 1945, from 2:30 to 2:55 P.M., I searched a heavily wooded north-facing slope southwest of the highway. The forest was of dogwood, redbud, alder, tan oak, black oak, madroño, and Douglas fir. There were moss-covered rocks and many rotting logs. A barkless longitudinally fissured log 30 feet long by about 1 foot in diameter lay parallel to the 25° slope and was shaded by a madroño tree. It was sufficiently decomposed to make its disruption with a shovel quite easy. An adult *Aneides flavipunctatus* was discovered when a long piece of wood was split off the side of the log. The animal was very active; I had to move quickly to catch it. It was beautifully green (Celandine Green) above and black below; the iris was dark, flecked with pale yellow. Later observations revealed that this coloration was the light phase for individuals of this northern population. Other animals observed in the log were several large slugs, 4 to 6 inches in length, some smaller slugs about 1 inch in length, scorpions, and centipedes. Two juvenal *Aneides ferreus* were found, about 1½ feet apart, on the opposite side of the log.

Twelve miles northwest of Shasta, along U.S. Highway 299, Shasta County, California, on April 23, 1948, I found many young in slumps of soil and rock from the banks of a small creek. These slumps were from banks cut by high water and they were kept wet by capillary water from the nearby stream. The present stream was 3 to 4 feet wide and 3 to 6 inches deep, with a rocky bed. The collecting site was below a 20-foot waterfall in a rocky bowl-shaped area about 25 feet across. The region was well shaded by canyon oaks and alders that grew on the rocky, mossy slopes above the creek. (Pl. 39, fig. 3.)

Behavior.—May use the tail in a prehensile fashion. Capable of jumping forward 4 to 6 inches by raising the tail and striking it forcibly against the ground at the same time employing the hind limbs.

Food.—Stomachs of most individuals obtained 1/4 mile north of Lucerne, Lake County, California, were empty. Spiders and beetles (elaterids) were identified in the stomachs of some of these animals.

Reproduction.—On July 23, 1895, Van Denburgh (1895:777, 778) received a large adult female with 15 eggs (about half the number found) from Los Gatos, Santa Clara County. He wrote: "Each egg was about 6 mm. in diameter, almost spherical, and inclosed in a thin, tough, gelatinous sheath. Each of these sheaths was drawn out, at one place, into a slender peduncle, which was attached to a basal mass of the same gelatinous substance. In this way, each egg was at the end of an individual stalk, and all were fastened to a common base. This base had evidently been anchored to a stone or lump of earth. . . . The salamander and eggs were found under the platform in front of a barn, in dry earth next the foundation wall, and about fifteen inches or more below the surface. The ground had been filled in, and was full of spaces." Some dry, rotten wood was found near the eggs. One of 2 smaller salamanders was nearby.

Van Denburgh (*loc. cit.*) also mentions a large adult female from Los Gatos, examined by him on July 30, 1895, several days after receipt, which had 25 eggs evidently still in the ovaries, 12 in the right and 13 in the left. The eggs were like those described above, except that they lacked the gelatinous covering. Storer (1925:123) reports a female with 7 eggs taken at Laytonville, Mendocino County, on July 1, 1913, in damp earth, 9 inches below the surface of the ground in a cellar. The eggs measured 5.9 to 6.4 mm. (after 11 years in preservative) being slightly elongate in the direction of the peduncles; peduncle 0.5 to 1.0 mm. in diameter and 5.0 mm. in length. Eggs deposited in captivity by females collected by Charles Lowe, Jr., fit the foregoing descriptions. It should be added, however, that 2 jelly envelopes are present: an outer one about 0.2 mm. and an inner one approximately 0.65 mm. in thickness, and that a low nipple-like projection is situated on the outer surface of the egg opposite the peduncle. Numbers of large ova in adult females examined by me were as follows: Santa Cruz County, 24, 20, and Lake County 8, 8, 10, 12, 12, 14, 16.

Subspecies

(Largely from Myers and Maslin, 1948)

1*a*. Adult and half-grown individuals shiny black without light spots or speckling (sometimes with minute white markings); cloacal lips black; 90 per cent of individuals show figure of .80 or less in following proportion: length of forelimb plus length of hind limb divided by distance from armpit to groin (southern form has longer body in relation to limb length); costal grooves 13 (occasionally 14) excluding half groove, dorsal to inguen, and counting one each in axilla and groin; head relatively broader; tail averages somewhat more compressed. *Range.* Delimited by the wooded Santa Cruz Mountains; included almost entirely within western Santa Clara, northern Santa Cruz, and southernmost San Mateo counties. Subspecies is separated from the northern populations by most of San Mateo and all of San Francisco counties south of Golden Gate, and by Marin County on the north, although it is rather expected that *flavipunctatus* will eventually be found in Marin County .... *A. f. niger* Myers and Maslin

1*b*. Adults black or suffused with varying amounts of pale greenish, with or without light spots; cloacal lips white or nearly white; 90 per cent of individuals show figure greater than .80 in following proportion: length of forelimb plus length of hind limb divided by distance from armpit to groin (northern form has shorter body in relation to limb length); costal grooves never more than 13 and frequently 12; head relatively narrower; tail less compressed. *Range.* As for the species, except for range of *niger* .... *A. f. flavipunctatus* (Strauch)

SACRAMENTO MOUNTAINS SALAMANDER

Aneides hardii (Taylor)
Plate 13

Range.—Known only from the region of the type locality, Cloudcroft, approximately 9,000 feet, and from Aqua Chiquite, Sacramento Mountains, Otero County, New Mexico. The tops of these mountains have a coniferous forest and provide cooler and more humid conditions than occur in the surrounding country, most of which is desert. (Pl. 51.)

Type locality.—Cloudcroft, Sacramento Mountains, New Mexico, elevation 9,000 feet (Taylor, 1941:77).

Description.—STRUCTURE. Adult approximately 3 to 4¼ inches; 14 or 15 costal grooves, counting 1 each in axilla and groin; 3 to 4½ intercostal folds between tips of toes of adpressed limbs; digits short and with rounded tips; vomerine teeth 7 to 10 per row (in 3 adult individuals) forming much flatter **V** behind nares than in *lugubris;* vomerine series unconnected (in 4 adults examined); parasphenoid teeth in elongate oval patch, less attenuate anteriorly than in *lugubris* but similarly variously divided along midline. COLOR. Above mottled gray to grayish tan or bronze, light color nearly obscuring dark brown ground color; tail often more uniformly bronze and somewhat lighter than body; some individuals (particularly young) have dorsal color in fairly definite stripe, margined on either side by dark, often broken, line; large adults may lack light-colored dorsal mottling; belly uniformly light purplish brown (in life) to slaty or soiled cream (in preservative); throat whitish to yellowish;

ventral surfaces of limbs and tail light brown sometimes with pinkish tinge; legs above, particularly basally, colored like back; iris dark brown with coppery tinges. JUVENILE. With brown to rusty-bronze dorsal stripe, margined on either side by more or less continuous blackish line; ground color of dorsal and ventral surfaces tends to be darker than in adult, and throat more whitish. SEXUAL DIFFERENCES. Vent of male with transverse furrows; in female vent simple slit; mature male with circular mental gland.

Six individuals (2 adults, 1 subadult, 2 juveniles, and 1 hatchling), obtained August 4, 1949, near the type locality: All individuals with dorsal ground color of dark brown marked with varying amounts of pale gold to pale greenish-gray chromatophores (guanophores?). Largest adult with only sprinkling of golden pigment cells dorsally; these tend to be concentrated dorsolaterally; guanophores most abundant on tail; tail color nearly bronze, pigment disposed in blotches; minute stippling of pale gold to cream guanophores on sides and sprinkling on dorsal surfaces of limbs; ventral surface light purplish brown, darkest on underside of tail; gular area, except posterior margin, almost cream; under magnification melanophores appear as small punctations of black, arranged in rings; scattered flecks of pale yellow pigment on throat; melanophores absent or reduced beneath these markings.

Another adult is almost uniformly light greenish-gray above with dark brown ground color showing through here and there, particularly dorsolaterally and in costal grooves; guanistic (?) suffusion on head and tail extensive, largely unbroken; suffusion less evident on eyelids; under magnification these cells appear stellate or punctostellate and golden in color; limbs with grayish color best developed near upper bases; belly purplish; gular area buff or light orange yellow; underside of tail grayish brown, lighter than belly; undersides of limbs like tail; stippling of pale gold to cream chromatophores on sides; numerous gaps in punctate melanic ground color of gular area, filled with cream chromatophore clusters; iris dark brown with numerous orange chromatophores above and below pupil and forming pupillary ring.

A juvenile has continuous copper to orange dorsal stripe, extending from top of head well toward tip of tail; under magnification stripe observed to be formed of network of orange chromatophores overlying dark brown melanic ground color; stripe margined by narrow zone of ground color, largely free of light-colored chromatophores; below sooty, with few, largely single, cream guanophores ventrolaterally; gular area whitish, sprinkled with whitish to cream guanophores; upper sides stippled mostly with single, pale gold chromatophores that stop short of dorsal stripe and thus set off area of dark ground color that margins stripe; iris orange, under magnification seen to be heavily marked with orange chromatophores.

Habitat.—The type specimen was found on June 29, 1940, beneath the bark of a rotten pine log in a heavy pine forest. Taylor (1941:79) writes, "The type locality of this species is in a region, for the most part, too arid to support plethodont salamanders. However, the higher mountain tops have clouds and fog, as well as more rainfall, and in such a habitat the present species was discovered."

On August 4, 1949, Wm. Riemer and I motored from creosote bush-mesquite desert, in the vicinity of Alamagordo, north and then east into the Sacramento Mountains. We passed through piñon-juniper-covered foothills in reaching the humid coniferous forest of the mountain top. We looked for salamanders in a shady north-south canyon about 1/4 mile northwest of Cloudcroft. I was struck with the similarity between this forest and our northwest coastal Douglas fir forests of California, Oregon, and Washington. The timber was abundant and there were green grass and other herbs as well as abundant damp leaf litter and many rotten logs on the forest floor. (Pl. 38, fig. 1.)

The first salamander was found in a fissure beneath a flake of bark on the north side of a dead Douglas fir. The tree lay uprooted and at right angles to the 30° north-facing slope. The tree was about 75 feet long and 2 1/2 feet thick at its base. The surface of the wood upon which the salamander rested was damp but not wet. There was a colony of ants under the bark on the sunny side of the log, about 3 feet away; a sowbug and spiders were also seen under the bark. A juvenile, about 1 inch in total length, was found in a similar place at the other end of the log. Here, the collecting site was 14.5°C.; the air, 6 inches above the ground, 15°C.; the time 11:15 A.M. The sky was overcast and a light rain was falling. The ground was covered with a rather dense herbaceous growth including grass and columbine. There were many branches and logs lying about, but few rocks. The leafy duff beneath the grass was thick. The area of collection was in a break (about 100 to 125 feet across) in the dense Douglas fir-spruce forest. In the canyon bottom, 75 feet away, were maples.

Along an abandoned oiled road, 300 yards up the canyon, I searched among talus and fissured rock on the upper side of a road cut. An adult female, laden with eggs, was found when fissured rock was pried with a shovel from a nearly vertical bank in a sheltered cove along the road. The salamander was behind cracked rock about 5 feet above the level of the road. Above the exposed rock was considerable soil and overhanging vegetation. There was a scanty growth of moss on the rocks. The hillside above and below the road was heavily forested.

About 1 mile east of Cloudcroft we found a number of individuals beneath some talus that had long been in repose. Douglas fir, spruce, and yellow pine were conspicuous trees in this area. Spanish moss hung from the conifers and there was lush growth of grass and many wild flowers in bloom. Clouds hung low over the forest, hiding the tops of many of the trees. Many logs were investigated by peeling the bark and breaking them open with a shovel, but no salamanders were found in this way. At the time of our visit, the salamanders were apparently just emerging, as several weeks later Kenneth Norris and Charles Lowe, Jr., of the University of California, Los Angeles, obtained about 100 of these animals.

Associated animals noted under objects were camel crickets (2 or more kinds), tenebrionid and carabid beetles, ants (at least 3 kinds), termites, sowbugs, centipedes, millipedes (several kinds), and earthworms. Earthworms were extremely abundant, some being found 3 feet from the ground under bark of rotten logs.

We inquired of a resident of Cloudcroft regarding weather conditions. There is snow in winter which is usually off by about mid-March. Rains commonly begin in mid-July. This year (1949) they started in late July. They had been light but fairly continuous, except for several days, prior to our visit. The Sacramento range was continuously blanketed with clouds during our stay in the area, from the afternoon of August 3 to the 5th.

I visited the vicinity of Cloudcroft again on March 15, 1950. At this time there were still scattered patches of snow on north-facing slopes and in shaded areas. Surface conditions were not favorable for salamander activity. There was ice under the bark of many of the rotting logs and the ground was frozen hard below an inch or so of needle duff. Grass was dead and the moss on rocks and logs was yellow-green, appearing dormant.

Reproduction.—In August, 1949, Lowe and Norris found a cluster of 3 eggs in an advanced stage of development. These have been reported by Lowe (1950). The eggs were found inside a large, moist, decomposing Douglas fir log lying under a canopy of Douglas fir and dwarf maple on a steep north-facing slope. Each egg contained a larva in an advanced stage of development with the yolk sac still protruding from the midgut, and with the usual pair of large, flat, leaflike, trilobed allantoic gills. The outer capsule of the egg, as in other *Aneides,* had a relatively long pedicel; the pedicels were twisted about one another and fused together at a common adhesive base. The cluster was suspended from the roof of a small moist cavity in the rotting wood. An adult female was close by.

Remarks.—*Aneides hardii* is the least specialized member of the genus. Indeed, until recently (Lowe, 1950), it was regarded as a member of the genus *Plethodon.* In habitus and in certain aspects of dentition it is close to *Plethodon,* but its affinity to *Aneides* is evident from (among other things) the lack of teeth on the posterior portion of the maxillary bone and the presence of **Y**- rather than **T**-shaped terminal phalanges. *Hardii* is probably close to the ancestral stock if not actually the ancestor from which the other forms, *aeneus, ferreus, flavipunctatus,* and *lugubris,* were derived.

ARBOREAL SALAMANDER

Aneides lugubris (Hallowell)
Plate 13

Range.—The coastal mountains of California from Humboldt County to San Diego County; also in the foothills of the Sierra Nevada from Calaveras to Madera counties; recorded from Los Coronados Islands, off the northwestern coast of Lower California, Catalina Island off the coast of southern California, Año Nuevo Island in extreme northern part of Monterey Bay, and South Farallon Island off San Francisco Bay, California. (Pl. 54.)

Type locality.—Monterey, California (Hallowell, 1848:126).

Description.—STRUCTURE. Adult around 4 to 7½ inches (190 mm., Storer, MS); head broad, triangular, widened, and deepened behind eyes due to large jaw muscles; eyes protuberant; tail slender, somewhat prehensile; costal grooves usually 15, rarely 14 or 16; tips of toes of adpressed limbs meet, overlap or fail to meet usually up to 1 intercostal fold; toes with enlarged tips; vomerine teeth 4 to 7 per row (5 adults from vicinity of Berkeley) forming V behind nares; vomerine rows connected or not; parasphenoid teeth arranged in much elongate club-shaped patch separated short distance from vomerine teeth; parasphenoid teeth tend to be absent along midline, sometimes giving appearance of 2 parasphenoid patches; patches commonly connected anteriorly. COLOR. Above dark brown with cream to sulphur-yellow spots varying in size and abundance; below whitish with numerous minute melanic stipple marks which in some individuals may give venter grayish cast, depending, in part, on whether pigment of melanophores dispersed or concentrated; underside of tail and feet dull yellowish; iris with variable number of flecks of silver to pale yellow on dark brown ground color; in some individuals light pigment forms patches in upper and lower iris with upper patch usually largest. JUVENILE. Resembles adult but yellow punctations less evident or absent and suffusion of guanophores (?) gives dorsum clouded appearance, suggestive of coloration of adult *A. ferreus.* SEXUAL DIFFERENCES. Not readily apparent—head width, tail length, and shape of lower jaw appear essentially the same in both sexes. Male with mental gland, well defined in some individuals but in others obscure. In preserved animals gland appears as flat, slightly raised, platelike heart-shaped area anteriorly on underside of lower jaw, lobes of heart projecting posteriorly.

In preserved individuals vent tends to gape more in male than in female and villosities of cloacal glands evident just inside vent margin. In female vent lining and sometimes vent margin with smooth diagonal pleats that converge on cloacal aperture. Vent region usually slightly more swollen than in female. Swollen appearance of vent and mental gland probably undergo seasonal change.

Adult female, RCS 1075, 95.3 mm. in snout-vent length, obtained October 6, 1946, on a tributary of the west fork of Chalone Creek, San Benito County, California: Tail, snout, limbs, and feet light pinkish brown (Fawn Color) above; dorsum of head and body dark brown (Bone Brown); below very light bluish gray (Pallid Mouse Gray) on body and in gular area, under magnification seen to be minutely and sparsely stippled with melanophores; under side of tail, especially toward tip, light yellowish tan (Cinnamon-Buff); underside of toes, feet, and limbs purplish pink; numerous yellow (Apricot Yellow) spots on upper surfaces of body, tail, and limbs; those on eyelids and in parotoid areas somewhat lighter yellow (Pinard Yellow); rather sharp break between dorsal and ventral colors along sides; no guanophores evident anywhere on body; iris dark brown with silvery and pale bronze flecks above and below pupil, most abundant in upper iris.

Juvenile, RCS 1916, 24 mm. in snout-vent length, obtained December 15, 1947, in Madelia Canyon, Sherman Oaks, Santa Monica Mountains, Los Angeles County, California: Ground color above deep blackish brown overlaid with blotches of pale blue to whitish and golden to brassy chromatophores; whitish chromatophores larger than golden ones and in close groupings that form blotches of irregular size and shape; golden chromatophores scattered among these whitish blotches but also forming other patches independently; pale buff patch on snout extending posteriorly to include anterior portions of eyelids, composed of light-colored chromatophores; cream-colored patches of similar pigment at upper bases of limbs; distal portion of limbs colored like body but somewhat lighter; ventral surfaces uniformly sooty throughout, composed of closely set melanophores; sparse stippling of white guanophores over ventral surfaces, disappearing toward tip of tail; white guanophores concentrated along sides; iris dark brown with pale gold flecks forming patch in upper part and light flecking below pupil.

Habitat.—Frequents both trees and ground. An individual in Sonoma County, California, was found in a tree at a height of at least 60 feet in the nest of a red tree-mouse (Benson, 1930, MVZ field notes). This salamander has been found in tree cavities, principally in coast live oaks (*Quercus agrifolia*) to a height of 30 feet. As many as 35 individuals have been found in such a cavity during the summer months. The species occurs beneath rocks, boards, logs, and other surface objects when the surface is damp. It also has been discovered inside decayed logs and stumps, in rock walls, mine shafts, damp cellars, rodent burrows, and in wood-rat houses. It may be more terrestrial than arboreal in habit.

Near Garberville, Humboldt County, California, on July 26, 1945, about 1:30 P.M., I investigated what appeared to be a Douglas fir log 12 feet long and about 3 feet in diameter. It was without bark and possessed several longitudinal cracks. It lay parallel to a 30° north-facing slope in the shade of a bay tree. Black oaks and Douglas fir were present. Poison oak was abundant. Despite the dry, warm surroundings, the interior of the log was cool and very moist. A large yellow-spotted adult *Aneides* was found 3 feet from one end of the log, in the damp wood. The log was thoroughly investigated but no other salamanders were found.

The region of the west fork of Chalone Creek, San Benito County, California, is characterized by rocky outcrops, imparting a rugged outline to the surrounding hills. The dominant rocks are volcanic breccias and tuffs, the former rough-surfaced. The region is semiarid, with chaparral the dominant plant cover. The more abundant chaparral species are chamise, *Ceanothus,* and manzanita. The xeric plants, *Selaginella* and a fern (*Pellaea*), occur among the rocks. Common trees are coast live oak, Digger pine, and buckeye. Streams are for the most part intermittent. Surface litter is not abundant. Leaf litter, consisting principally of oak leaves and pine needles, is spotty in occurrence. Near the bottom of a north-south canyon, a south tributary of the west fork of Chalone Creek, on October 6, 1946, Lee Talbot and I came upon a covered, cement-boxed spring. The concrete structure was at the head of a small gully and was well imbedded in the ground. Its interior measured approximately 4½ feet wide, 4½ feet high, and 10 feet long. The walls and ceiling were concrete, but the back of the chamber was earth, from which water seeped. There was about a foot of clear, cold water near the drainage pipe, and standing water extended back toward the seep for a distance of about 5 feet. The bottom near the seep was of reddish-brown mud over which trickled a small stream of water. The concrete walls were damp, and roots projected through crevices, several inches into the tank.

Upon lifting the concrete manhole cover that sealed the only opening, other than the drainpipe, I saw an *Aneides* submerged in 2 or 3 inches of water, near the water's edge toward the back of the spring. The animal was profusely covered with sulphur-yellow spots. A Pacific tree toad was also seen hopping about on the mud at the back of the tank. I crawled inside and collected the salamander and tree toad and then began searching the walls. From nearly every nook and cranny, the peering shoe-button eyes of *Aneides* could be seen in the dim light. I collected about a dozen, mostly adults but in the lot were several subadults and juveniles. In the mud at the back of the spring, I also found 2 *Batrachoseps.* The tank contained the only surface water in the area. There had been no rain for several months. These facts probably account for the concentration of amphibians at the spring.

In Sepulveda Canyon, on the north side of the Santa Monica Mountains, Los Angeles County, California, on December 8, 1947, a nearly adult *Aneides* was found in an oak-filled ravine, about ¼ mile by road from Sepulveda tunnel. The salamander was discovered in damp black soil beneath oak leaf-litter on a steep bank where a lateral gully joined the main ravine. The animal was found about 1½ feet from a coast live-oak tree with a hollow at its base. Acorn shells and small fragments of bone were present near the salamander suggesting that it may have been in a rodent burrow. The soil temperature at the site of collection was 8.6°C.; air 6 inches above the ground in the shade, 10°C. The surrounding hills were covered with chaparral, principally chamise, buckwheat, and *Ceanothus,* with scattered clumps of laurel sumac, and lemonade berry. Wild black walnuts were common, particularly on north-facing slopes and in the gullies. Sycamores grew along the main drainage of the canyon.

Near Groveland, Tuolumne County, California, on April 29, 1948, I found a nearly adult individual in a charred log, approximately 10 feet long and 1½ to 2 feet in diameter. The temperature of the wood at the collection site was 4°C.; air temperature at 4:00 P.M., 3.5°C. The log lay parallel to a 15° to 20° slope that faced to the southwest. One end of the log lay at the margin of a canopy of black oaks, the other end in scattered low-growing *Ceanothus* and manzanita, at one side of a wet meadow. There was a small stream 30 to 40 feet away, largely fed by water from melting patches of snow about the meadow. There were scattered rocks, some moss-covered. Although there was green grass in the meadow, there was little about the log or beneath the oaks. The log was in an "edge" situation between the brush-fringed meadow and a black oak, yellow pine stand. There were also scattered groups of Digger pine in the area.

About 15 to 20 yards away, at the lower edge of the meadow, I broke into a yellow pine log about 70 feet long and approximately 3 feet in diameter. The bark was, for the most part, intact. There were many termites and termite galleries in the log. Two adult salamanders were found, about 20 feet apart. The log lay fully exposed and unshaded in a nearly level area among scattered *Ceanothus* and manzanita.

Behavior.—Nocturnal. An active, agile climber; the expanded digits and prehensile tail are adaptations for climbing. The pose assumed when this salamander is disturbed resembles that of *Ensatina.* It may utter a mouselike squeak, apparently accomplished by forcing air between the jaws or through the nasal passages (or both) by means of gular contractions, since no lungs are present. It breathes as do other plethodontids but the large blood sinuses at the tips of the toes probably make possible somewhat more digital respiration than in most other genera. Ritter and Miller (1899:695) state, "The toes, in fact may be considered to have assumed in a measure the function of external gills." Capable of rather marked color change from pale to dark brown.

THERMAL DATA

Locality	Date	Time	Size	Temperature, °C.			Conditions of occurrence
				Body	Substratum	Air	
California							
Sepulveda Canyon, N side Santa Monica Mts., Los Angeles Co.	Dec. 8, 1947	10:00 A.M.	nearly adult		8.6	10.0	On damp black soil beneath oak leaf-litter; animal may have been in rodent burrow.
Monterey, Monterey Co.	Feb. 14, 1948	4:00 P.M.	adult	9.0	9.2	12.0	Beneath well-imbedded log resting on oak leaf-litter.
Tuolumne Co.							
6 mi. ESE Groveland	Apr. 29, 1948	4:00 P.M.	nearly adult		4.0 (inside rotten log)	3.5	In rotten pine log.
1.1 mi. ESE Groveland	Apr. 30, 1948	10:45 A.M.	large adult	6.1	6.7	8.0	On damp soil under piece of bark.
Jawbone Station	May 1, 1948	9:45 A.M.	subadult	2.8	3.5 (wood under bark)	9.0	Subadult under bark of rotten pine log; female in decayed wood of same log.
			adult ♀	3.0	3.0 (decayed wood)		
Jawbone Station	May 1, 1948	11:00 A.M.	adult ♂	5.2			In rotten log.
			adult ♀	5.5			In rotten log.

Food.—May feed to some extent upon fungus (Miller, 1944:226). The large saber-like teeth (especially of the lower jaw) and the stout jaw muscles may be employed in scraping and biting off such material from the walls of tree cavities. Zweifel (1949:285) reports the following in more than 20 per cent of the stomachs of 13 *Aneides* studied in the Santa Monica Mountains, Los Angeles County, California, obtained during the winter and spring rainy seasons of the years 1948 and 1949: "beetles 77 per cent, phalaenid [noctuid] caterpillars 46 per cent, sow bugs 38 per cent, centipedes 38 per cent, and ants 23 per cent. The ants make up a very small amount of the total bulk. With the exception of earwigs and ticks, all food items listed for *Ensatina* were also found in one or more *Aneides* stomachs. A larger sample would most likely include these missing items." These salamanders also eat slender salamanders (*Batrachoseps*) and spiders.

Miller (1938:123) made the interesting observation that although this species fed readily on isopods of the genus *Ligia,* large specimens of *Armadillidium vulgare* escaped because of their ability to roll up into a ball which the salamanders apparently were unable to swallow. Both isopods occur naturally in the habitat of the salamander.

The strength of their jaws and the efficiency of the dentition is attested by their ability to bite. I have had the palm of my hand deeply lacerated by one of these amphibians.

Reproduction.—EGGS. The eggs are found in July, August, and September beneath objects on the ground, in subterranean niches, or in tree cavities. Twelve to 18 eggs may compose a cluster. Each egg is attached by means of an elongate peduncle, 8 to 20 mm. in length and 1 to 2 mm. in diameter. The peduncles may be twisted about one another and the clusters attached by them to the walls and the roof of the nesting cavities. Two jelly envelopes are present, an outer one, 0.2 mm., and an inner one, about 1.0 mm. in thickness; capsular space, 0.1 mm.; ovum ovoid, unpigmented, whitish to cream, 6.9 by 7.4 mm. The eggs measure from 6 by 7 to 9.5 mm. to the outer envelope—the former are oval, the latter are more rounded and usually advanced in development. There is no scar on the opposite side of the eggs as in *Batrachoseps attenuatus* but a low, rounded nipple-like projection may be present in those freshly laid.

The eggs are tended by the female or perhaps by both sexes. Presumably the adult helps to keep them moist with body fluids, either from skin or bladder (or both). Such attention to the eggs seems necessary, for in captivity removal of the parent usually results in the appearance of mold and spoilage of eggs. The adult may also protect the eggs from predation. The period of incubation may be 3 to 4 months. Hatching may occur in August and September with the young appearing on the surface of the ground sometime after the first fall or winter rains. Individuals at hatching measure about 26 to 32 mm. in total length. The gills of the larva are large, paired, triparted, highly vascular, leaflike structures. They are so situated that their upper surfaces lie close to and concentric with, the inner surface of the egg capsule. In atrophied form they may persist for a brief period after hatching, as based on the observation of hatchlings in the laboratory. When the young appear on the surface in nature, they are without gills. All ages from newly hatched young to adults may be found together in a single tree cavity, indicating the use of the same chamber by successive generations.

Ritter and Miller (1899) report the discovery of a clutch of eggs at Berkeley, California. These were found slightly beneath the surface of the ground in a hole beneath the overhanging base and on the south side of a large palm tree. An adult was present. The hole was discovered as a student was loosening the earth about the roots of the tree. The salamander squeaked when it was exposed. The soil was dry. The eggs hatched in the laboratory on September 13th, about 50 days after they were found. They were discovered attached to a clump of earth by narrow peduncles about 8 mm. long, the adhesive, expanded ends of which were more or less confluent basally.

Seth Benson (1930, MVZ field notes) describes a nesting site, found August 31, 1932, in a coast live oak tree on the campus of the University of California at Berkeley. Cavities in the oak had at one time been coated with tar and closed by a rock wedged into the entrance. The first cavity had rotted in spite of this treatment, only a small amount of tar remaining. It was filled with a damp mass of fungus, rotten wood, and earthy material. This hole contained 2 large salamanders, 3 smaller ones, and a mass of 24 eggs. The second cavity was lined with tar and contained no rotten wood, yet 2 small salamanders inhabited it. This cavity was partly filled with water. The hole leading into it was very small and probably would not have permitted the ingress of a larger animal.

The first cavity was about 6 feet above the ground, was 6 to 8 inches deep, and about 6 inches in diameter. The eggs were about 6 inches from the opening but since workmen had partly opened the chamber, Benson could not be certain that the position of the eggs was the original one.

The eggs were fastened by pedicels to a central mass composed of interwoven strands similar to the pedicels. Living, moving embryos were present. A capsule measured 9 mm. in diameter, and a removed embryo, 25 mm. in length. The adult salamanders measured, respectively, 170 and 150 mm. in length, the 5 smaller animals 100, 75, 75, 70, 70 mm.

Kessel and Kessel (1942:71-72), on September 19, 1942, near the southeast base of Mount Tamalpais, Marin County, California, found a cluster of 17 eggs, attended by a female. The eggs were attached to the underside of a large rock buried about 2 feet below the surface of soil from a house excavation. Fifteen of the eggs had their peduncles twisted together; 2 were attached separately, about 4 mm. from the margin of the cluster and about the same distance from each other. The peduncles were approximately 10 mm. long; the eggs were 8 to 9 mm. in diameter. Embryos about 24 mm. in length were present. They were active and pigmentation was well advanced.

Dr. Loye H. Miller has been successful in hatching this species by suspending the eggs in a cheesecloth bag with a wick attached which touches the water in a jar.

Subspecies

1*a*. Light spots of dorsum and sides generally few, small, and scattered (populations in mountains east of Soledad and Gonzales, in Monterey and San Benito counties, California, however, are as conspicuously spotted as *farallonensis*); averages larger. *Range.*—Same as for species except south Farallon Island .... *A. l. lugubris* (Hallowell)

1*b*. Light spots of dorsum abundant, varying in size from small flecks to spots 3 to 4 mm. in greatest dimension; averages smaller. *Range.*—Apparently confined to south Farallon Island off San Francisco Bay, California ... *A. l. farallonensis* (Van Denburgh)

MOUNT LYELL SALAMANDER

Hydromantes platycephalus (Camp)
Plate 12

Range.—Principally in the Boreal Life-zone (several records from the Transition Zone) of the Sierra Nevada from Alpine County south to northern Tulare County, California. Locality records for this species are: Tenaya Canyon, 5,800 feet; Upper Yosemite Fall, 5,140 feet; Half Dome, 8,850 feet; near Mount Lyell, 10,800 feet; near Triple Divide Peak, 10,700 feet; upper Glacier Point Trail (Ledge Trail), 6,700 and 6,900 feet; Firefall Ledge below Glacier Point, about 6,300 feet—all in Yosemite National Park; Sonora Pass, 8,600 feet, Peeler Lake, Silliman Gap, 10,200 feet, and Twin Peaks, 10,000 feet (at the boundary of Sequoia National Park)—outside Yosemite National Park. Search should be made for the species in the Trinity Alps of northern California, and in the Boreal Zone in the Rocky Mountains, particularly in Canada. (Pl. 51.)

Joe Gorman has recently found *Hydromantes* at an elevation of 1,500 feet, near the Squaw Creek headwaters of Shasta Reservoir, Shasta County, California.

Type locality.—Head of Lyell Canyon, 10,800 feet altitude, Yosemite National Park, California (Camp, 1916b:11).

Description.—STRUCTURE. Adult to slightly over 4 inches; head and body flattened; snout blunt; tongue pedicelled, edges free all around; eyes relatively small; toes 4-5, blunt-tipped, partly webbed; costal grooves usually 13; vomerine teeth 11 to 16 per row (in 6 adult animals), each row slightly arched anteriorly and together forming much broadened V (in some individuals teeth arranged almost in transverse row); parasphenoid teeth in 2 patches well separated from vomerine teeth and from each other; patches elongate ovoid and divergent posteriorly. COLOR. Above dark chocolate to blackish, marked with mottlings of pale gray to pinkish buff composed of numerous whitish flecks (guanophores?) sometimes largely obscuring dark ground color; dorsal coloration resembles granitic rocks common in habitat of this salamander; below sooty to blackish, often with irregular patches (guanophore clusters) of pale gray, particularly laterally on venter, beneath limbs, and in gular region. JUVENILE. Entire body deep blackish brown to black; scattered pale yellow (golden) stippling or groups of pale yellow pigment cells on dorsal surfaces; few silvery guanophores in gular area and on chest but less common elsewhere ventrally; nostrils much larger in relation to size of body than in adult. SEXUAL DIFFERENCES. Male averages longer than female and has wider head; maxillary teeth project below margin of upper lip only in male; in preserved specimens lips of cloaca gape in male but are usually closed in female; male possesses mental gland, obscure in some individuals.

Seven individuals, adults and subadults, observed May 8, 1946, obtained on Half Dome, Yosemite National Park, Mariposa County, California: Above dark brown; metallic golden and pale orange-brown chromatophores irregularly distributed over all dorsal and lateral surfaces, forming diffuse, reticulate pattern of vague, pale yellow blotches; ventral surfaces brownish, somewhat lighter than above; undersides of feet, belly, pelvic area, and tail, largely free of guanophores; gular area, chest, sides, ventrolateral areas on abdomen and undersides of limbs, with rather large, irregular patches of whitish guanophores; iris dark brown with golden, whitish, and orange-brown chromatophores forming extensive broken patches above and below pupil; iris color in harmony with general coloration.

Adult male, 68 mm. in snout-vent length, were obtained on July 30, 1946, 1 mile northeast of Mount Lyell, 10,800 feet elevation, Tuolumne County, California: Ground color dorsally dark brown [Blackish Brown (3)], consisting of heavy network of melanophores; guanophores (?) form extensive patches of ash gray over melanic ground, on all dorsal surfaces and on sides; guanistic patches suffused with brownish centrally on body and head; under magnification guanistic patches seen to be composed of metallic silvery and pale gold cells with pinkish-orange cast, due to presence of capillaries; ground color purplish brown (Deep Brownish Drab) in gular area, on chest and undersides of feet and tail; deep slaty gray (uniformly Dark Quaker Drab) on abdomen;

ventral melanophores on magnification seen to form close stippling which gives way to network posteriorly on abdomen; guanophore patches cream (Light Buff) on casual inspection, white under magnification, most abundant in gular area and scattered ventrolaterally along sides of neck, body, and tail; few guanistic blotches on undersides of limbs; iris dark brown with numerous flecks and lines of silvery with greenish-yellow tinge, surrounding pupil; light iris color obscured by darkly pigmented, superficial blood vessels in narrow zone above and below pupil.

Juvenile, 22.9 mm. in snout-vent length, from the same locality as above: Ground color above solid black with sprinkling of pale greenish-yellow guanophores (?) (Naphthaline Yellow) over all dorsal surfaces; guanophores most plentiful on head from eyelids anteriorly and on tail, not as abundant, however, as in adult; below black, composed of close network of melanophores, with scattering of few single, silvery white guanophores (no clusters as in adult) in gular area, on chest and undersides of limbs; iris well filled out with orange-gold to gold chromatophores forming nearly solid patches above and below pupil; eye marked by horizontal dark stripe through pupil.

Habitat.—The substratum is typically of decomposed granite with little humus. Grass, moss, lichens, heather, alpine willow, white-barked pine, and azalea are plants which may occur in or near areas inhabited by this salamander but vegetation may be almost completely lacking as it is on the top of Half Dome in Yosemite National Park where many individuals have been found. Two low altitude records are Tenaya Canyon at the base of Cloud's Rest (5,800 feet) and the base of Upper Yosemite Fall (5,140 feet). In searching for the Mount Lyell salamander, the collector should turn rocks that rest on silt at the edges of water trickling from melting snow. The animals are usually found on wet bare earth or rock, seldom actually in water. I have not found the animals under rocks situated well out in meadows. Probably the best time to look for this salamander is with the late spring and early summer melting of the high country snowpack.

On July 15 and 16, 1930, Dr. Tracy Storer and Eugene Boone found the species at Deadman Creek Canyon, 8,600 feet, about 2½ miles southwest of Sonora Pass, Tuolumne County, California. Boone had been hunting conies (*Ochotona*) in a mass of granite slide rock and was watching from within the entrance of a small "cave" beneath several large granite slabs when his attention was drawn by one of these salamanders which was walking slowly over the sandy granitic soil on the sloping floor of the cave. The animal was observed on the evening of July 15, at 6:15 P.M.

The next evening Dr. Storer searched several crevices leading outward between and beneath the granite blocks and got a second animal. The salamander was found at 6:10 P.M., during a period of search from 4:30 to 7:10 P.M. Search was made on subsequent evenings but no others were found.

The "cave" was below broken granitic cliffs. It was about 12 feet deep and barely high enough for one to sit in the entrance. The floor was of fine sand and gravel. Various large pieces of granite were wedged in the upper part so as to form a series of angular chambers mostly sloping upward from where they opened into the cave. These too were floored with a fine granitic soil compacted by the spring run-off and were still slightly damp; in a few chambers was a sparse growth of moss.

In and about the rock slide were thickets of *Prunus emarginata, Holodiscus discolor, Quercus vaccinifolia, Chrysothamnus* sp., and *Artemisia.* Red fir (*Abies magnifica*) and lodgepole pine (*Pinus murrayana*) grew on the flatter ground in the floor of the canyon toward the creek, a hundred yards below. Up on the ridges was western juniper (*Juniperus occidentalis*) and on the south wall of the canyon, mountain hemlock (*Tsuga mertensiana*). In the rock slide were evidences of conies, the bushy-tailed wood rat, and the California badger.

The cave is almost opposite "Deadman's Grave" which gives the name to the creek here and which is shown on the Stanislaus National Forest Map. Zonally the locality is at the upper border of the Canadian Life-zone (Storer, MS).

Danforth (1950:19) described the environment in which he found the species, on July 8, 1949, on the Firefall Ledge below Glacier Point, elevation approximately 6,300 feet. The general region was bare granitic rock, the south portion rising vertically to Glacier Point, the north portion sloping gently toward the valley floor. The ledge itself had a steep eastward slope. Water of a small snow-seep or spring followed the ledge-cliff contact, forming tiny puddles 8 to 10 inches across and a yard or so apart. Granite gravel had accumulated to a depth of 1 or 2 inches. On this material were lush moss banks of perhaps a square foot in extent and several penstemons. The salamanders were in the moist, but not wet, granite earth, underneath small, flattened rocks. In the several areas investigated, conditions were the same, with each rock having 2 or 3 salamanders under it. There were also many black beetles. The whole ledge is in direct sunlight for only 3 hours or so a day, and the temperature of the water keeps the microarea quite cool. Aside from the small volume of seep water, the region is quite arid and is only some 20 yards up the ledge from the ash and burnt bark resulting from the firefall.

At the head of Lyell Canyon, near Donohue Pass Trail, Tuolumne County, California, at an elevation of about 10,800 feet, on July 6, 1948, William Riemer and I found 11 individuals (adults, immatures, and young). They were discovered on an east-facing rocky slope above a meadow with a small lake. The area was at timber line. There were scattered white bark pines and a sparse growth of heather and grasses. Animals were found in two areas. In the first, 6 were found in a distance of 20 to 25 feet and in the second, 5 in a distance of 30 feet. The two localities were about 125 feet apart. Although we searched diligently for several hours in other areas on the slopes surrounding the meadow, no other animals were found.

An adult salamander was discovered at 9:15 A.M. under a rock (6 to 8 by 15 by 17 inches) that lay at the edge of accumulated soil in a shallow rocky gully. The soil was black to deep brown, composed of both coarse and very fine particles of decomposed granite with some organic material. Roots of grasses that grew along the upper side of the rock extended beneath it. The soil was soaking wet. There was a trickle of water ½ inch deep flowing within 10 inches of the salamander. In moisture conditions the situation reminded me of the niche of *Plethodon dunni*. The body temperature of the salamander was 7.1°C.; the water was 9.2°C.; the air temperature, 6 inches above the ground in the shade, was 9.0°C.; the substratum upon which the animal rested was 8.5°C.

The collection site had been in the sun for about 1 hour. Heavy frost had been noted on the grass, in the valley of the Lyell Fork of the Tuolumne River, but no frost was seen in the area of collection. The water was the warmest feature of the microenvironment, probably because it had passed over rocks at the head of the gully that had been warmed by the sun. The locality was a nearly level silted area (slope about 15° to the east) about 12 feet long by 3 to 4 feet wide. Above and below it were granitic boulders and other patches of accumulated soil, often with growth of grasses and heather. The salamander rested on soil near a massive, gently sloping, glacial-polished granitic surface that was warmed by the sun. Nearly all the rocks in the area possessed weathered glacial polish and there were numerous cracks between and beneath them providing retreats for the salamanders. A small patch of snow, from which water was flowing over the rocks and into the gully, was situated 30 feet above and to one side of the collection site. Another adult and several juveniles were found in the same area in rather similar situations. (Pl. 39, figs. 1 and 2.)

Behavior.—Nocturnal, but there are several records of activity in the daytime (Adams 1942:192). The species may be active from early May to late August. When disturbed this urodele may elevate its tail and head, arching the body downward.

Webbing of the feet, which increases the friction surface of the foot, facilitates locomotion over rock surfaces. When relaxed, the bottoms of the feet are shallowly cup-shaped, rendered more completely so by the fleshy webbing of the toes. When the moist, fleshy, somewhat wrinkled foot surface is placed against the substratum, effective adhesion occurs, especially when the animal walks on smooth glacial-polished surfaces.

Another adaptation associated with the climbing habit lies in the struc-

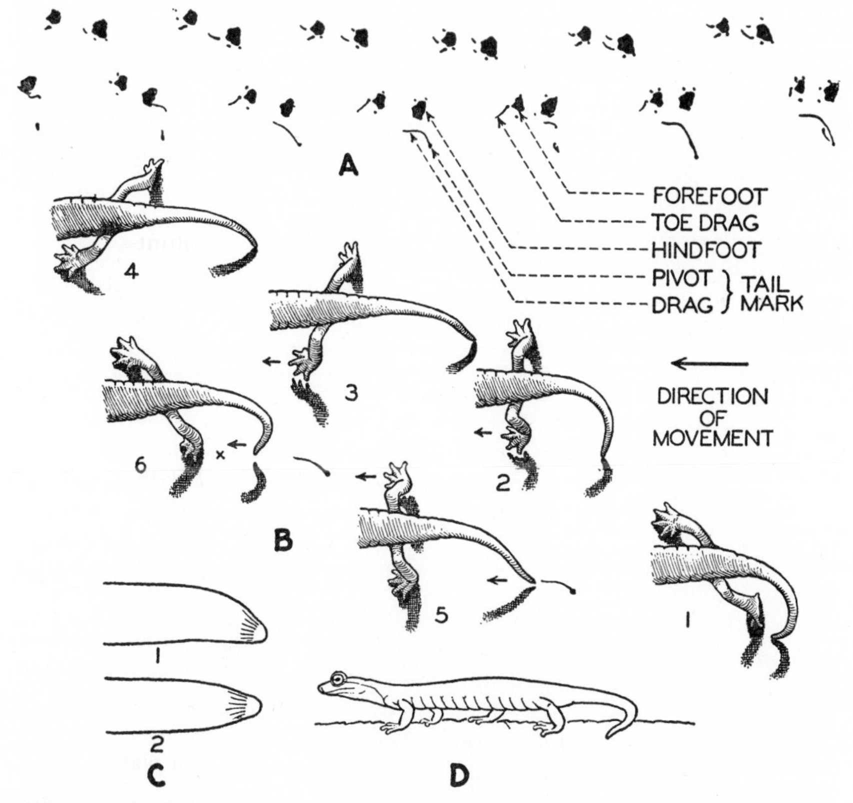

Fig. 19. A. Track of an adult male *Hydromantes platycephalus* made by allowing the animal to wallow in black ink and then walk across the drawing paper. These are the actual footprints retouched to render all marks solid black, but in no way altered in shape or position. The surface of the paper sloped at an angle of 30° toward the bottom of the page. Note the position of the tail mark. The hind foot falls behind the forefoot; there is no overstepping of the forefoot.

B. Diagrams 1 to 6 and back to 1 show successive stages (as frames in an animated film) in a single, completed tail movement. By means of shadows, the relationship (whether in contact or lifted) of the hind feet and tail to the substratum is indicated. Arrows indicate direction of movement of limbs and tail. The mark to the right of the tip of the tail in diagrams 5 and 6 corresponds to that labeled "tail mark" in A. The mark "x" behind the left hind foot in drawing 6 indicates the place where the tip of the tail is to be placed against the ground.

C. Diagram 1 is a lateral and 2 a dorsal view, in outline, showing the blunt tip of the tail in *H. platycephalus*.

D. Sketch showing, in lateral aspect, the position of body and tail in a typical walking pose.

ture and use of the tail (fig. 19). The short, muscular, blunt-tipped tail is employed like a walking stick. When an individual progresses along an inclined surface, the tail is curled so that the tip projects downhill. The tail is braced against the ground each time the hind foot on the downhill side is lifted. When the animal climbs uphill, the tail may be swung alternately from side to side, synchronized with the movements of the hind feet, bracing occurring from side to side as the feet are lifted. The tail is used in a less regular fashion when the salamander crawls on level surfaces. Juveniles as well as adults employ the tail in this manner (Stebbins, 1947:2-3).

At the type locality an adult salamander was removed from its hiding place beneath a fragment of granite and was placed on a nearby glacial-polished surface with a slope of 40°. The animal crawled with facility over this surface using the tail action described. The animal remarkably matched its background. Much of the granite in the area was lighter in color than the salamander; however, in the seepage areas, where the animals were most often found, were patches of rust-colored granite. When on such rock the background resemblance was almost perfect.

Food.—Terrestrial arthropods such as centipedes, spiders, termites, beetles, and adult and larval flies are eaten. The pedicelled tongue may be protruded with great speed and accuracy to a distance nearly half the length of the body (excluding the tail) to secure moving prey.

Reproduction.—Bishop (1943:455) states that females taken August 1 had well-developed ovarian eggs which showed as elongate light patches on either side of the belly. Specimens in the Museum of Vertebrate Zoology possessed ova as follows:

Specimen (MVZ No.)	*Date*	*Locality* (California)	*Number of Ova*	*Size of Ova* (mm.)
26183	June 26, 1938	Top of Half Dome, 8,930 ft., Yosemite National Park	6	2.8 to 3.8
26179	June 26, 1938	Top of Half Dome, 8,930 ft., Yosemite National Park	7	3.1
46009	Aug. 4, 1948	3 mi. S of Sonora Pass, 9,000 ft., Tuolumne Co.	14	2.0 to 2.7
46008	Aug. 4, 1948	3 mi. S of Sonora Pass, 9,000 ft., Tuolumne Co.	11	2.4 mm. (average) (2 other females taken on this date from this locality had small ova)

Females with large ova in the summer and the presence of young in early summer, following melting of the snow, suggest that development occurs when the animals are underground. Snow prevents surface activity throughout most of the range of the species from November, December, or January to April, May, or June. The species may be viviparous, but this has not been established.

William Riemer and I found what appeared to be recently born young on July 6, 1948, at the type locality. Adams (1942:193) recognizes 3 age groups: young of the year, animals between 1 and 2 years old, and animals more than 2 years old.

Remarks.—The pigmentation of living animals (7 individuals) from Half Dome differs in some respects from that of animals (17) from the type locality and Sonora Pass (6) in having less light-colored (guanistic?) blotching. In turn, the 6 animals from Sonora Pass appear more heavily guanistic than those from the type locality, about 50 miles in an air line to the south. The salamanders of Sonora Pass seem to have smaller and more closely spaced dark areas dorsally and the guanism of the gular area seems heavier. Geographic variation in pigmentation is thus evident.

ILLUSTRATIONS OF SALAMANDERS

Plate I

California Newt *Triturus torosus.*

Subspecies

Torosus, MVZ 27520, Las Trampas Creek, 500 feet, 1 mile north of Saint Mary's College, Contra Costa County, California. Skin texture based on MVZ 33134 from 2½ miles east of Moraga, Contra Costa County, California. × ¾

Adult male in aquatic stage, MVZ 27496, creek by Thompson Road in Lafayette, Contra Costa County, California. × ¾

Sierrae, MVZ 33105, Big Creek Unit of Kings River Experimental Range, 1,200 feet, Trimmer, Fresno County, California. × 1

Torosus, MVZ 9364, Boulder Creek west of Cuyamaca, San Diego County, California. × 1

Newts from this locality are characteristically, grotesquely warty, a condition that may be pathological. Note the distortion of the eyelids and nostril by the swellings.

TERRESTRIAL STAGE AQUATIC STAGE (MALE)

TRITURUS TOROSUS

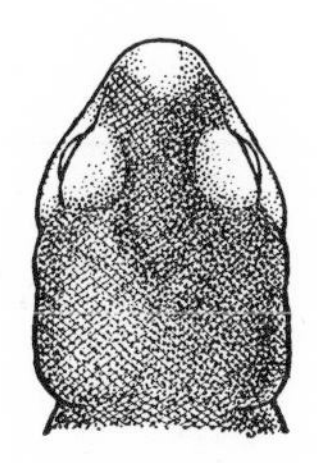

TRITURUS T. SIERRAE

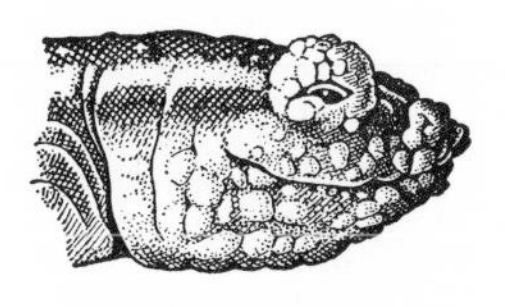

TRITURUS TOROSUS (KLAUBERI)

Plate 2

Western Red-bellied Newt *Triturus rivularis,* MVZ 25832, Frank C. Clarke Ranch, 7 miles southwest of Laytonville, Mendocino County, California. × 1

TRITURUS RIVULARIS

Plate 3

Pacific Giant Salamander *Dicamptodon ensatus,* MVZ 35484, Waddell Creek, 100 feet, 4 miles east and ½ mile north of Ano Nuevo Point, Santa Cruz County, California. × ½

Northwestern Salamander *Ambystoma gracile,* MVZ 44360, 4 miles north of Orick, 100 feet, Humboldt County, California. × ⅔

Olympic Salamander *Rhyacotriton olympicus,* MVZ 8503, Staircase Camp, Mason County, Washington. × ⅘

Long-toed Salamander *Ambystoma macrodactylum,* MVZ 50204, 4 miles southwest of Chester, Plumas County, California. × ¾

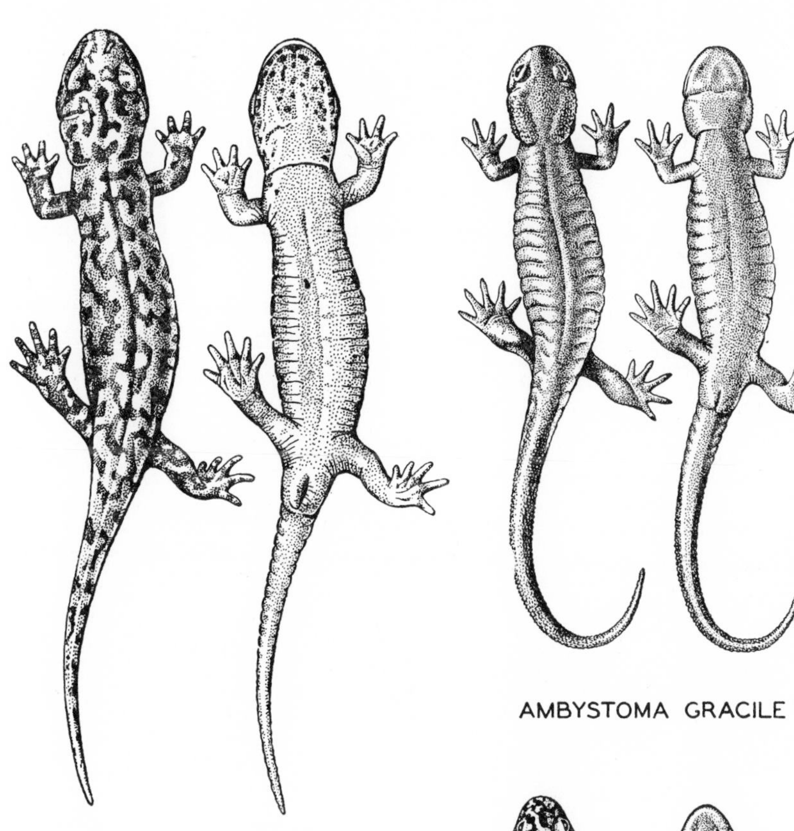

AMBYSTOMA GRACILE

DICAMPTODON ENSATUS

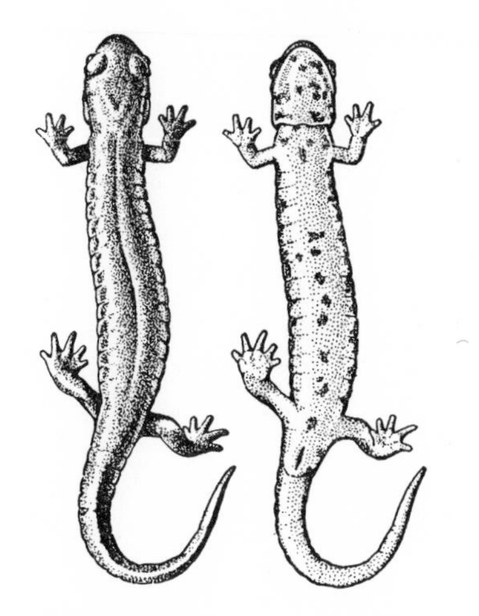

RHYACOTRITON OLYMPICUS

AMBYSTOMA MACRODACTYLUM

Plate 4

Olympic Salamander *Rhyacotriton olympicus.*

Subspecies

Variegatus, 1.3 miles west of Burnt Ranch Post Office, Trinity County, California. nat. size

Olympicus, stream at the south end of Lake Cushman, Mason County, Washington. nat. size

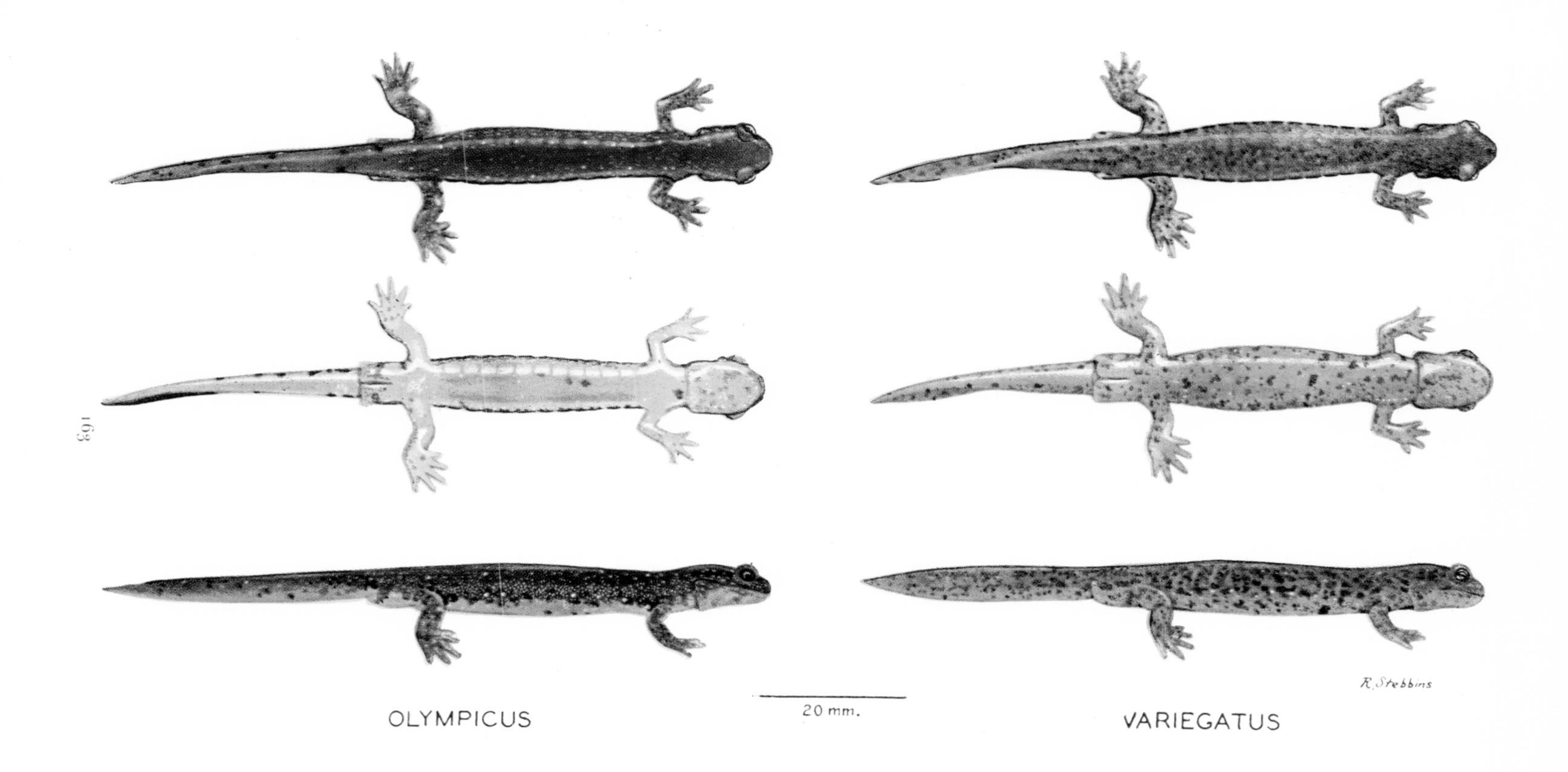

RHYACOTRITON OLYMPICUS

Plate 5

Tiger Salamander *Ambystoma tigrinum.* × ⅓

Subspecies

Californiense, MVZ 10684, Oakdale, Stanislaus County, California.

Mavortium, MVZ 26949, 3 miles west and 3 miles north of Clovis, Curry County, New Mexico.

Melanostictum, MVZ 41376, Mount Rainier National Park, Washington.

Nebulosum, MVZ 29481, Lapoint, Uintah County, Utah.

CALIFORNIENSE

MAVORTIUM

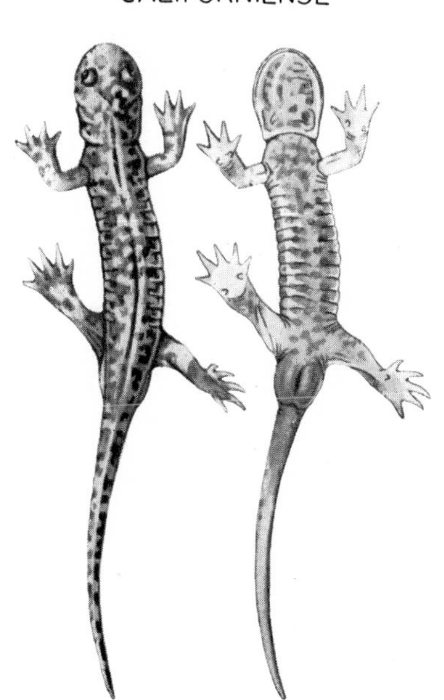

MELANOSTICTUM

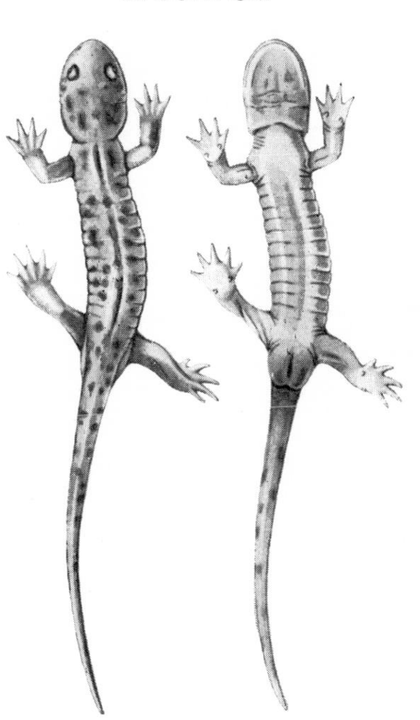

NEBULOSUM

AMBYSTOMA TIGRINUM

AMBYSTOMA TIGRINUM

PLETHODON NEOMEXICANUS

Plate 6

Tiger Salamander *Ambystoma tigrinum* (subspecies *mavortium*), Jornada del Muerto, 8.7 miles west and 22.8 miles south of New Bingham Post Office, Socorro County, New Mexico. × 3/4

New Mexican Salamander *Plethodon neomexicanus*, Jemez Mountains, 8,750 feet, 12 miles west and 4 miles south of Los Alamos, Sandoval County, New Mexico (type specimen, adult male, MVZ 49033). × 5/6

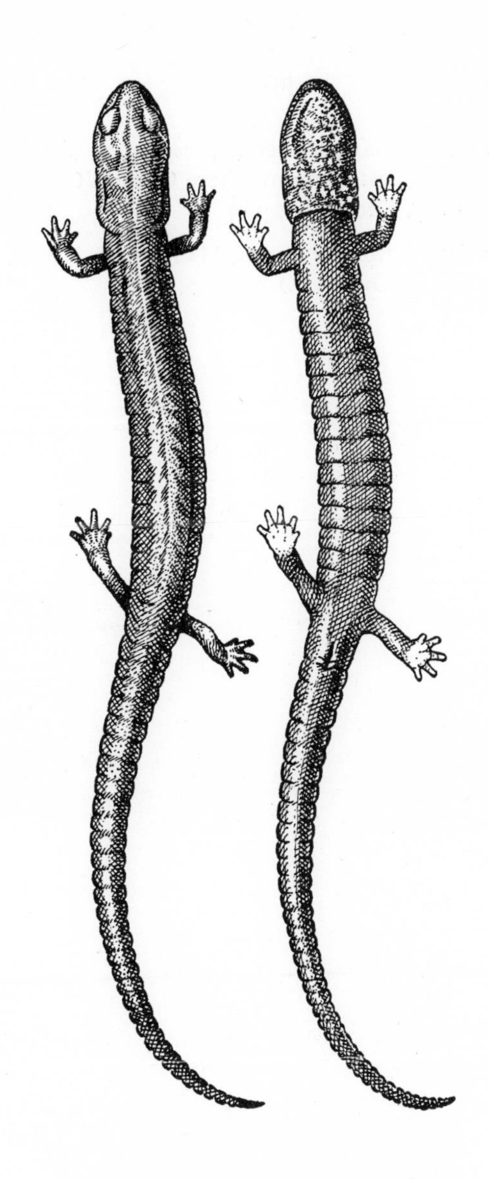

PLETHODON ELONGATUS
Plate 7

Del Norte Salamander *Plethodon elongatus,* MVZ 19141, 5 miles southeast of Requa, Del Norte County, California. × 1⅕

Plate 8

Western Red-backed Salamander *Plethodon vehiculum,* MVZ 42430, Fogarty Creek, ¼ mile east of point where Oregon Coast Highway crosses creek, Lincoln County, Oregon. × 1⅕

Dunn Salamander *Plethodon dunni,* MVZ 18576, Rogue River, 11 miles above its mouth, Curry County, Oregon. × 1⅕

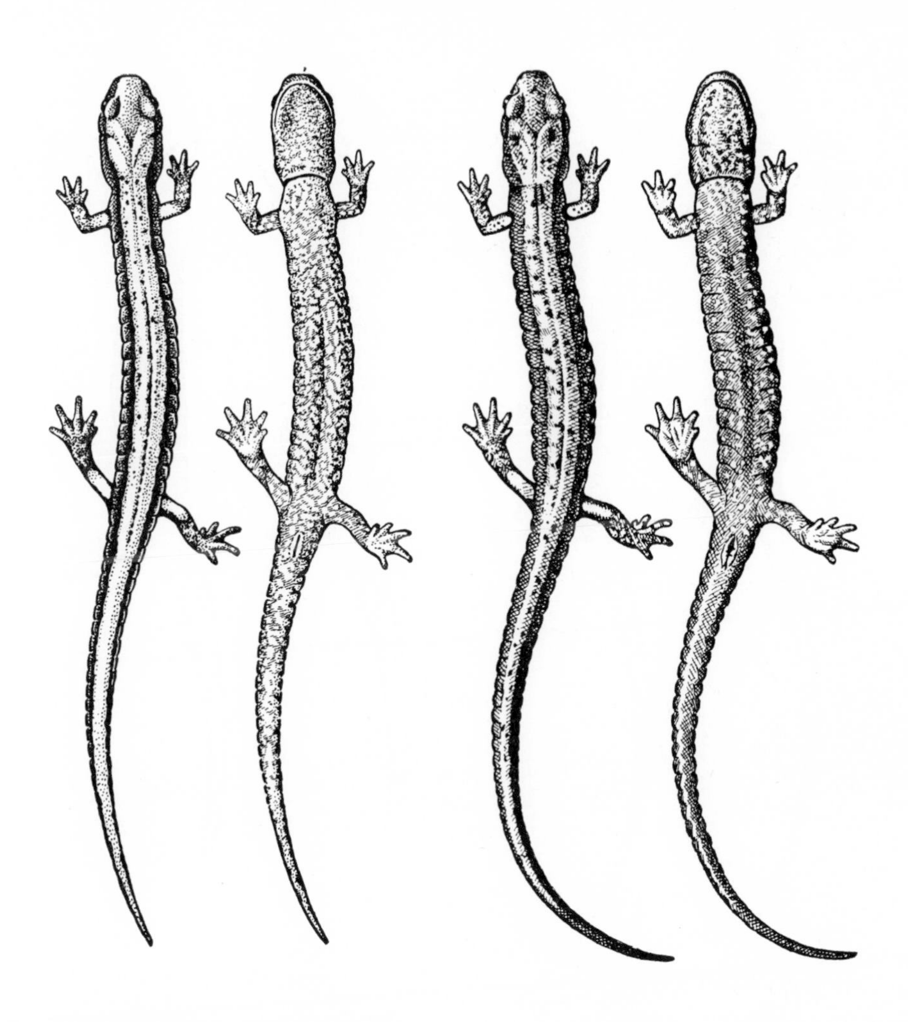

PLETHODON VEHICULUM PLETHODON DUNNI

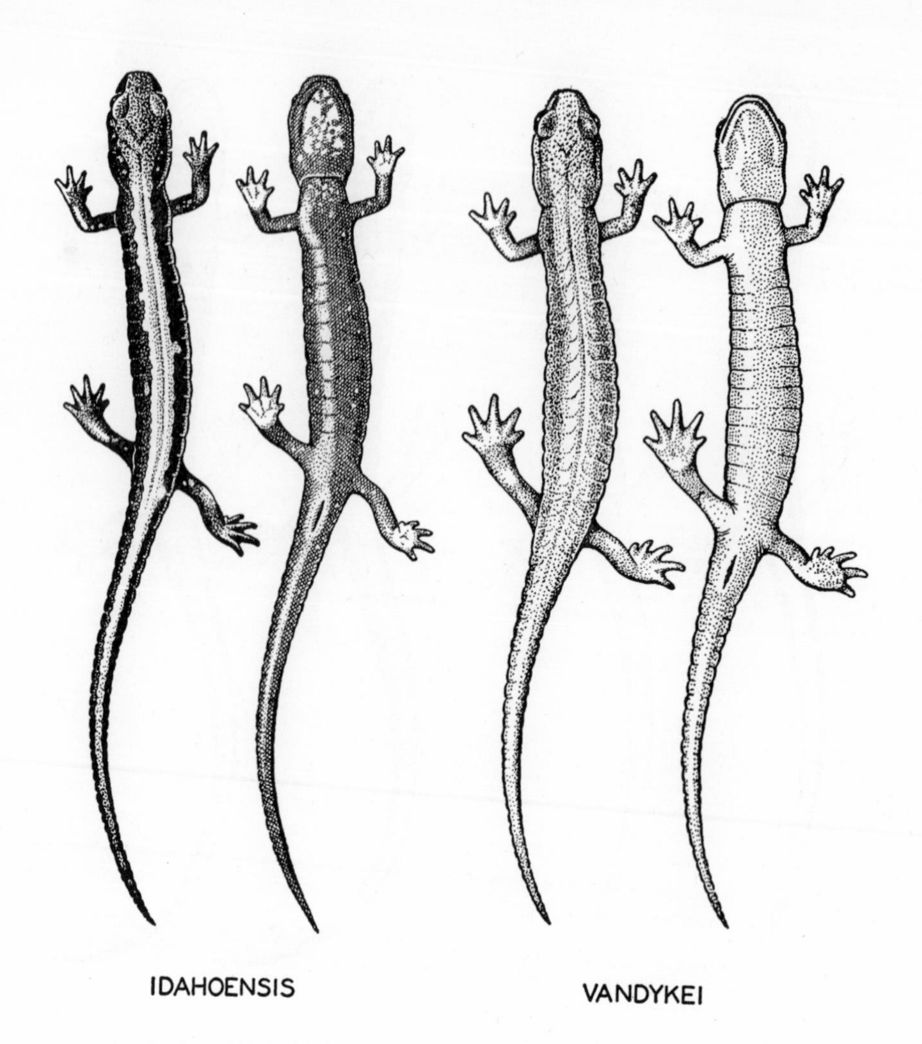

PLETHODON VANDYKEI

Plate 9

Van Dyke Salamander *Plethodon vandykei.*

Subspecies

Idahoensis, CPS 2711, type locality, northeastern corner of Coeur d'Alene Lake, on the shore of Wolf Lodge Bay, 2,160 feet, Kootenai County, Idaho. × 1

Vandykei (based on CPS 1157 and 5319), coastal Washington. × 1

Plates 10 and 11

Eschscholtz Salamander *Ensatina eschscholtzii.*

Subspecies and Intergrades

1. *Eschscholtzii,* adult ♀, Madelia Canyon, Sherman Oaks, Santa Monica Mountains, Los Angeles County, California. × ½
2. *Xanthoptica,* adult ♀, Redwood Regional Park, Oakland, Alameda County, California. × ½
3. *Oregonensis,* adult ♂, ½ mile south of Paradise Lake, King County, Washington. × ⅔
4. *Picta,* adult ♀, 3 miles north of Klamath, Del Norte County, California. × ¾
5. *Oregonensis-platensis* intergrade, adult ♀, 23.5 miles north of junction U.S. 299 and 99 on U.S. 99, Shasta County, California. × ½

6-10. Ventral views of foregoing animals.

11. *Eschscholtzii,* adult ♂, same locality as 1.
12. *Xanthoptica,* adult ♂, Berkeley, Alameda County, California.
13. *Oregonensis,* adult ♂, same individual as 3.
14. Juvenal *oregonensis,* 23 mm. in snout-vent length, from Portland, Multnomah County, Oregon.
15. Juvenal intergrade between *oregonensis* and *platensis,* 20 mm. in snout-vent length, from same locality as 5.
16. *Platensis,* adult ♀, 100 yards southwest of Indian Caves, Yosemite Valley, Mariposa County, California. × ½
17. *Platensis-croceater* intergrade, adult ♂, Kern County Park, 11 miles northwest of Kernville, Kern County, California. × ½
18. *Croceater,* adult ♀, 1 mile southwest of Fort Tejon, Kern County, California. × ½
19. *Croceater-klauberi* intergrade, adult ♀, Crystal Creek, north side of San Bernardino Mountains, West Cushenbury Springs, San Bernardino County, California. × ⅗
20. *Klauberi,* adult ♀, near Julian, San Diego County, California. × ½

21, 23, 25. Ventral views, respectively, of *platensis, croceater,* and *klauberi.*

22. Juvenal *platensis-croceater* intergrade, 26 mm. in snout-vent length, from same locality as 17.

24. Juvenal intergrade between *croceater* and *klauberi,* 28 mm., from same locality as 19.

26, 28, 30. Juvenal *platensis, croceater,* and *klauberi,* measuring respectively, in snout-vent length, 30, 37, and 28 mm.

27, 29. Dorsal and ventral views of *xanthoptica-platensis* hybrid from Jawbone Ridge, Tuolumne County, California. × ½

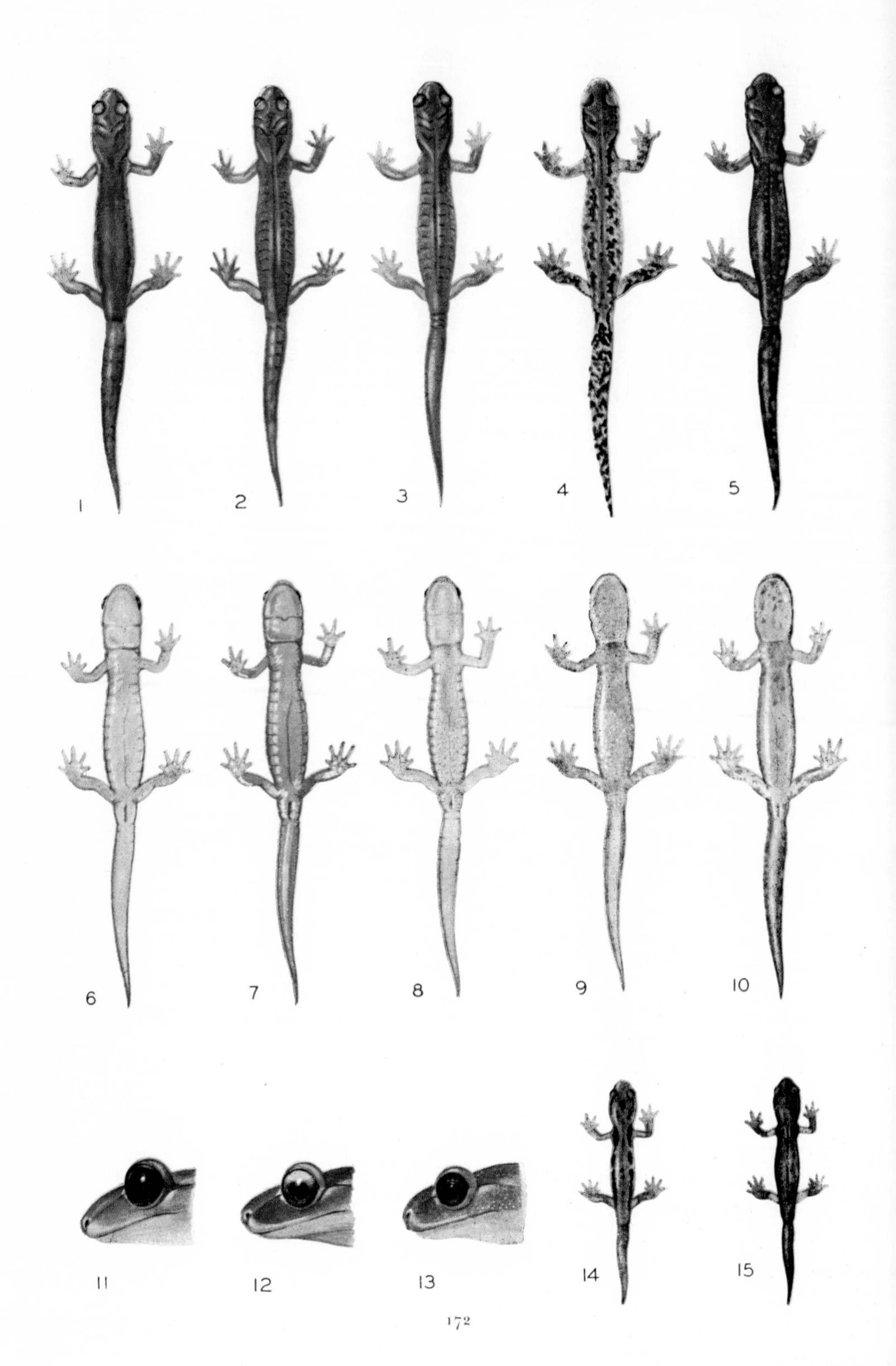
1
2
3
4
5
6
7
8
9
10
11
12
13
14
15

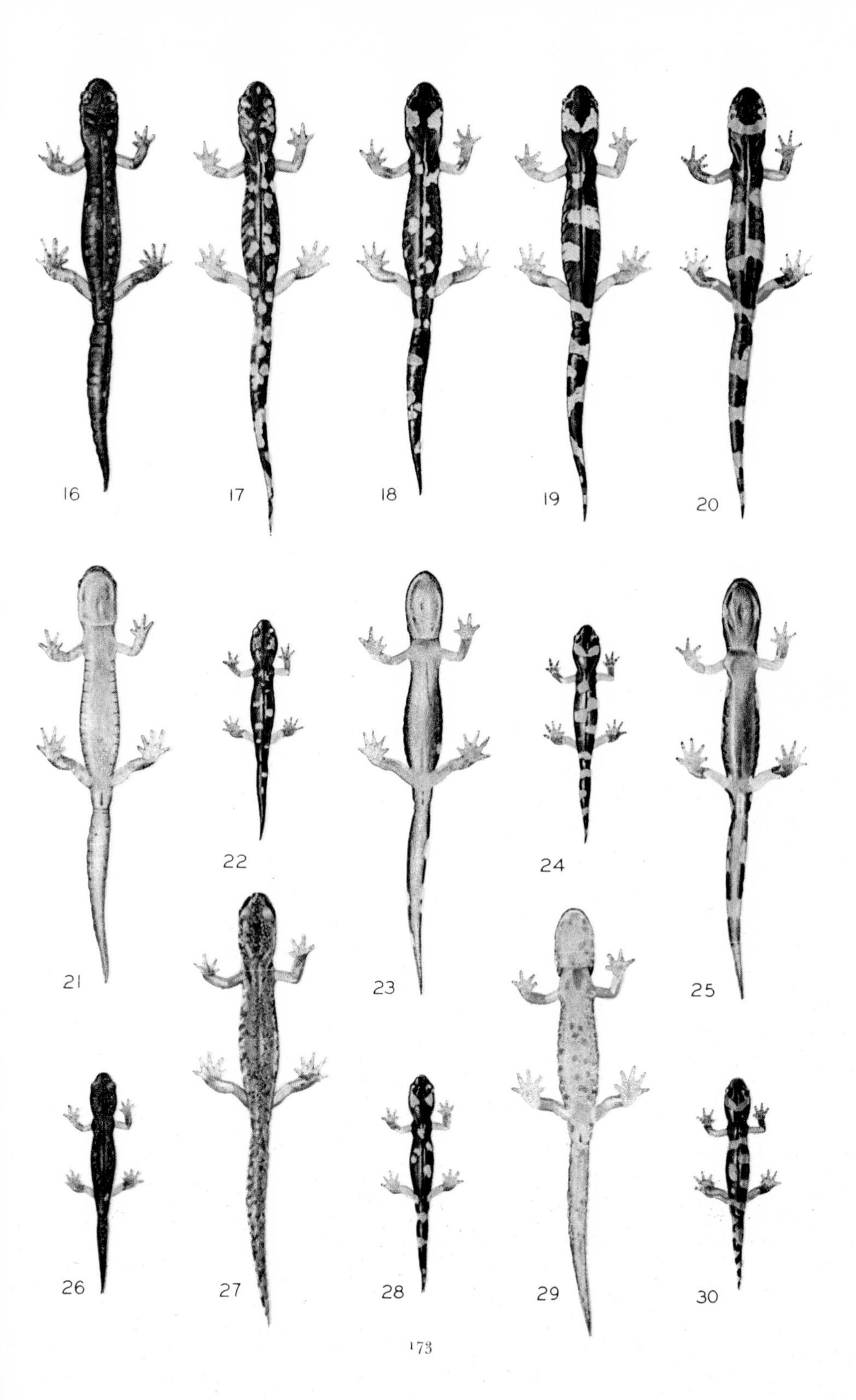
16
17
18
19
20
21
22
23
24
25
26
27
28
29
30

Plate 12

Mount Lyell Salamander *Hydromantes platycephalus,* type locality, 1 mile northeast of Mount Lyell, 10,800 feet, Tolumne County, California. × ¾

Oregon Slender Salamander *Batrachoseps wrighti,* JRH 1051, 8.5 mi. (by highway 50) southeast of Sandy, Clackmas County, Oregon. × ⅚

California Slender Salamander *Batrachoseps attenuatus,* MVZ 52090, Pinehurst, Contra Costa County, California. × ⅘

Pacific Slender Salamander *Batrachoseps pacificus,* JRH 932 and 934, Santa Rosa Island, Santa Barbara County, California. × ⅘

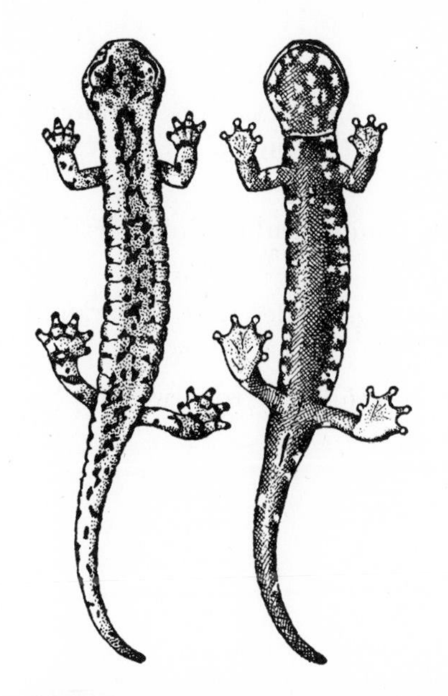

HYDROMANTES PLATYCEPHALUS

BATRACHOSEPS WRIGHTI

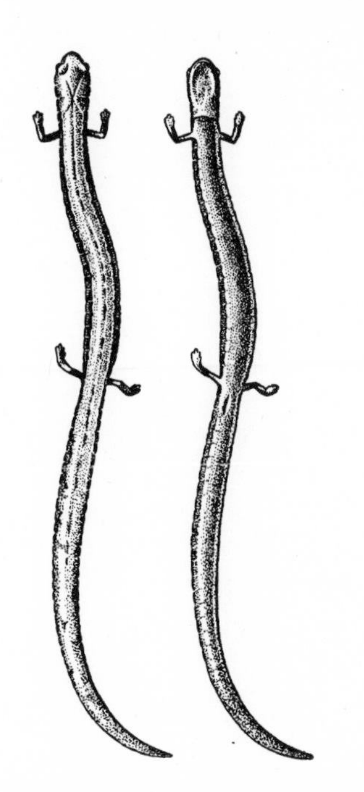

BATRACHOSEPS ATTENUATUS

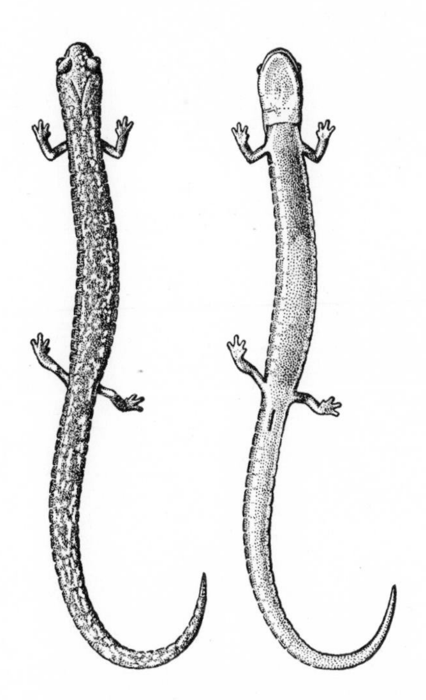

BATRACHOSEPS PACIFICUS

Plate 13

Sacramento Mountains Salamander *Aneides hardii,* Sacramento Mountains, about 1½ miles east of Cloudcroft, Otero County, New Mexico. × ⅚

Arboreal Salamander *Aneides lugubris,* 1 mile southeast of Inverness, Marin County, California. × ⅚

Black Salamander *Aneides flavipunctatus,* 3.9 miles west of Saratoga Creek, Santa Clara County, California. × ⅚

Clouded Salamander *Aneides ferreus,* 11.9 miles by road west of Navarro, Mendocino County, California. × ⅚

ANEIDES HARDII

ANEIDES LUGUBRIS

ANEIDES FLAVIPUNCTATUS

ANEIDES FERREUS

Frogs and Toads

FROGS AND TOADS

Order Anura

Characterization.—No neck constriction, head and trunk fused; no costal grooves; tail absent in metamorphosed individuals (caudal appendage in Ascaphidae not true tail); urostyle may represent fused caudal vertebrae; limbs 4, commonly unequal in size, hind limbs large, modified for leaping, typically webbed; skin smooth or warty; nostrils valvular; lungs present, sometimes reduced; eyelids movable in most, with nictitating membrane; external ear (eardrum) evident in many; teeth in both jaws, only in upper jaw, or absent; vomerine teeth present or absent; tongue usually present and protrusible (absent in some and not protrusible in others); well developed voice in males of many; larva with fused head-body and typically with compressed tail with dorsal and ventral fins; larva with external gills early in development which are replaced by internal ones; gills covered with operculum that opens through spiracle, commonly on left side of head-body; fore and hind limbs develop more or less together but forelimbs inside operculum; eyes without movable lids; larval mouth parts of horny mandibles and fringes of labial teeth; no true teeth as in urodele larva; external fertilization (Ascaphidae and possibly Pipidae excepted); amplexus pectoral or pelvic; fecundation of eggs as they are extruded; over 1,700 species (Storer, 1943:607).

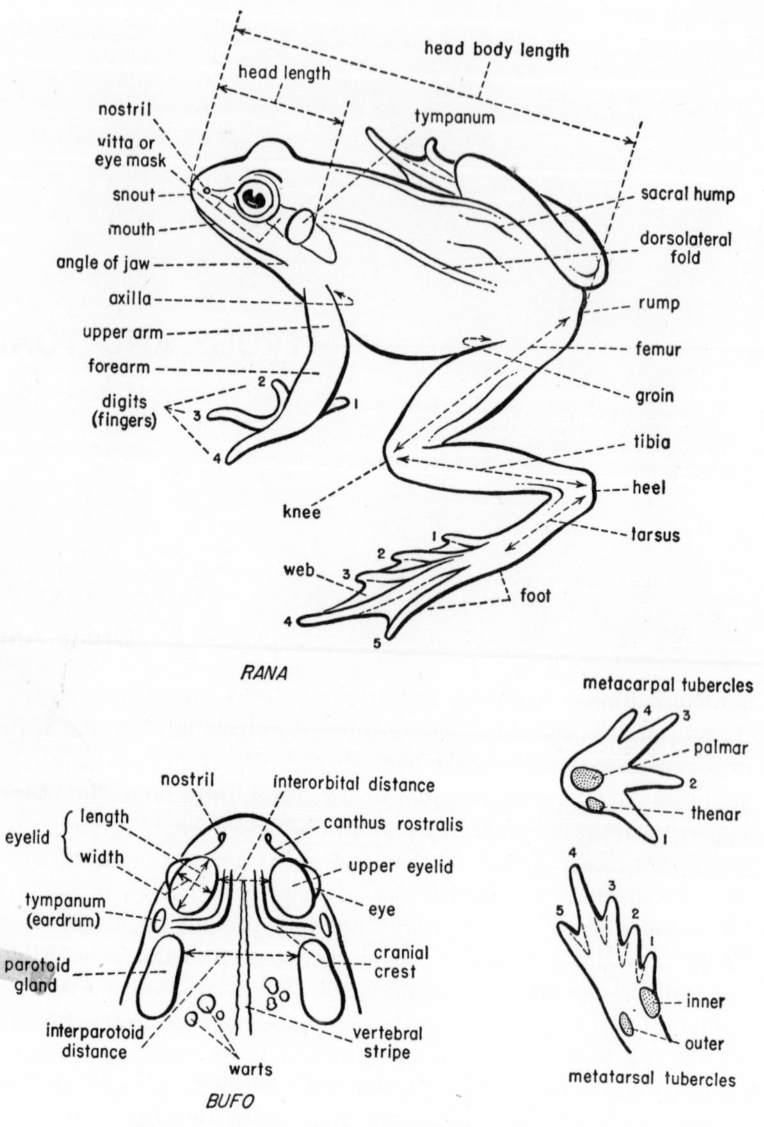

Fig. 20. External characteristics of anurans.

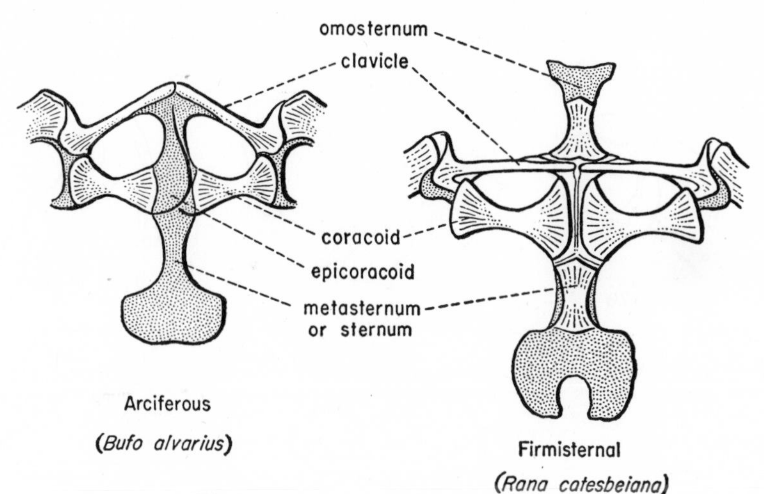

Fig. 21. Anuran pectoral girdles.

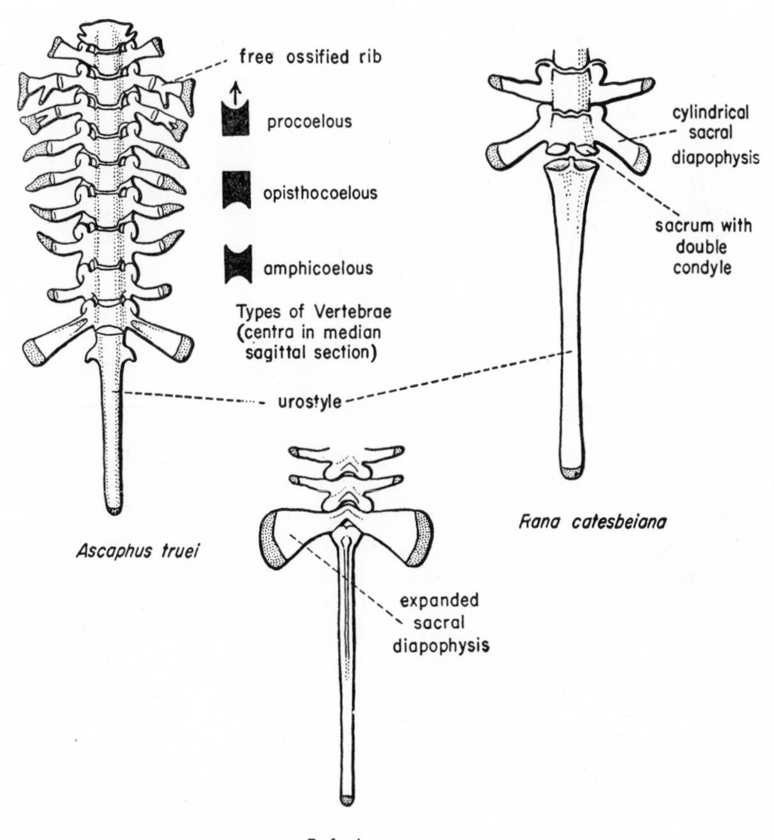

Fig. 22. Vertebral structures of anurans. In the drawings of centra in median sagittal section, the arrow points anteriorly.

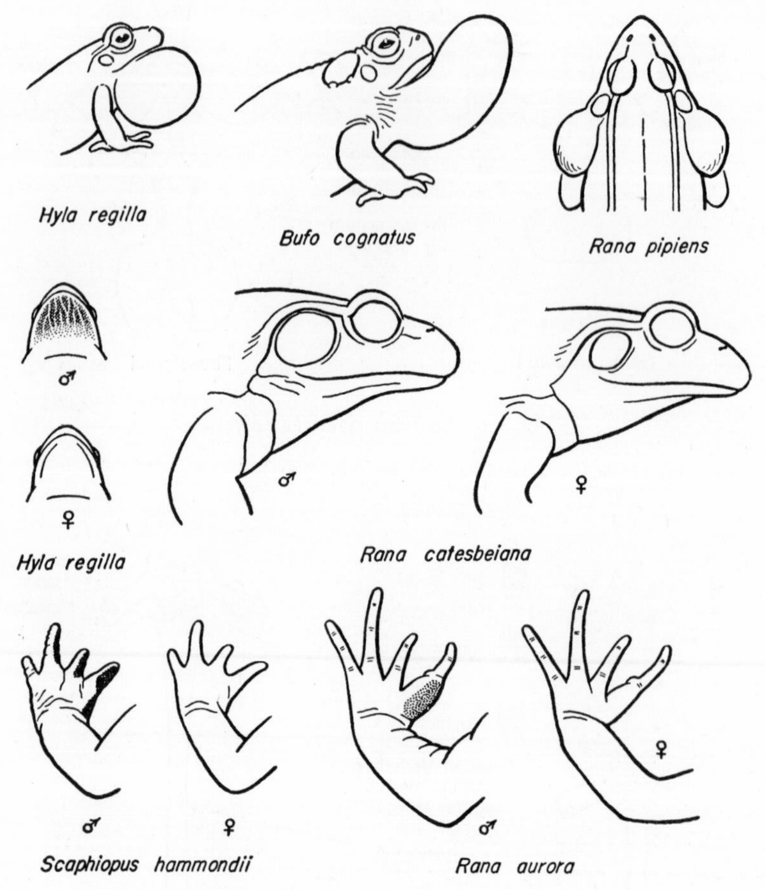

Fig. 23. Sexual differences among anurans. Expanded vocal sacs—spherical (*Hyla regilla*); sausage-shaped (*Bufo cognatus*); lateral (*Rana pipiens*). Discolored and longitudinally pleated skin of deflated vocal sac in male *Hyla regilla* contrasted with throat of female. Differences in size of eardrums in male and female *Rana catesbeiana*. Nuptial excresences on fingers in male *Scaphiopus hammondii,* absent in female. Enlarged basal portion of first finger and presence of nuptial pad in breeding male *Rana aurora* contrasted with first finger of female.

ACCOUNTS OF SPECIES

Key to Families
Figure 24

1*a*. Outer (5th) digit of hind foot broadest (1); male with taillike process from which vent opens (3), female with shorter anal tube; eye with vertically elliptical pupil (sometimes nearly round in preserved specimens) (18); metatarsal tubercles not sharp-edged; free ossified ribs present (fig. 22) .... Ascaphidae, *Ascaphus truei,* p. 188

1*b*. Outer digit of hind foot not broadest (6); no taillike process or anal tube; eye with horizontally oval pupil (19) or, if vertical, associated with black, sharp-edged, spadelike, inner metatarsal tubercle (16); no free ossified ribs 2

2*a*. (1*b*) With transverse fold of skin behind eyes, usually extending completely across head (4); in ours, size small, adults approximately 4/5 to 1½ inches; head narrow and snout pointed (4); transverse ridges on roof of mouth, one in palatine region, the other farther posteriorly, bounding anterior margin of oesophagus (5) .... Microhylidae. *Microhyla carolinensis,* p. 388

2*b*. No transverse fold of skin across head behind eyes, or if present, associated with circular disc of raised skin on underside of body; size commonly larger; head not especially narrow and snout not so pointed; no transverse ridges on roof of mouth 3

3*a*. (2*b*) Body stocky, limbs relatively short, waist broad (9); parotoid glands usually present (Pelobatidae excepted); no dorsolateral folds (9) 4

3*b*. Body slender, limbs long, waist narrow (8); no parotoid glands; dorsolateral folds present (8) or not 5

4*a*. (3*a*) Pupil vertically elliptical (vertically oval to round when widely dilated) (18); parotoid glands absent or indistinct; teeth in upper jaw; single metatarsal tubercle (inner one) black, with sharp cutting edge (16) (sharp-edged tubercle also present in some bufonids, as *Bufo cognatus, B. compactilis,* and *B. hemiophrys* but outer metatarsal tubercle present); skin often delicate and smooth, occasionally somewhat warty .... Pelobatidae, p. 194

4*b*. Pupil horizontally oval (19); parotoid glands present, usually distinct; no teeth in upper jaw; 2 metatarsal tubercles, not sharp-edged (with exceptions noted above) (17); skin commonly extensively warty .... Bufonidae, p. 225

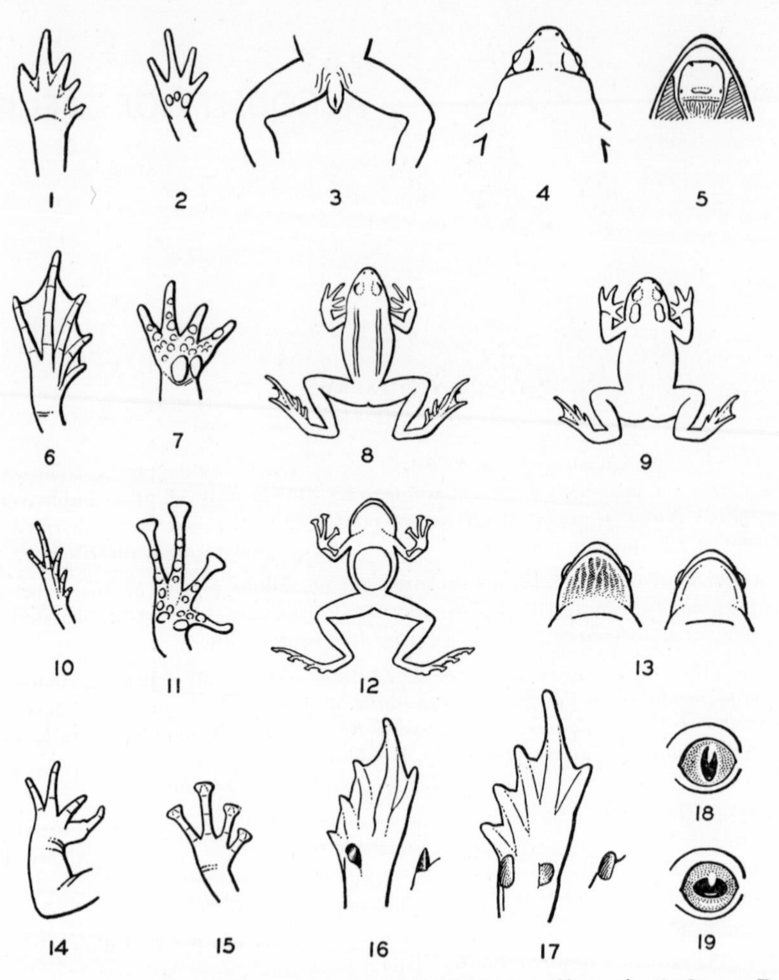

Fig. 24. 1-3, *Ascaphus truei;* 4-5, *Microhyla carolinensis;* 6, 8, 14, *Rana aurora;* 7, 9, 17, 19, *Bufo boreas;* 10, *Pseudacris nigrita;* 11, 12, *Eleutherodactylus latrans;* 13, 15, *Hyla regilla;* 16, 18, *Scaphiopus hammondii.*

5*a*. (3*b*) Eardrum thin, semitransparent, well defined; circular fold of skin forming large disc on venter (12); prominent, pointed tubercles on underside of joints of toes (subarticular tubercles) (11); throat of male not dark colored .. Leptodactylidae, p. 218

5*b*. Eardrum opaque, well defined or not; no circular fold of skin on venter; tubercles at joints of toes, rounded and often weak; throat of male dark-colored (13) 6

6*a*. (5*b*) Intercalary cartilages present; tips of toes with broad adhesive pads (15) or not; hind toes with or without a web (6, 10); no enlargement of base of first finger in male; no dorsolateral folds .... Hylidae, p. 294

6*b*. No intercalary cartilages; tips of toes without adhesive pads (14); hind toes fully webbed (6); first finger thickened basally in male (14) dorsolateral folds usually present (8) .... Ranidae, p. 330

BELL TOADS

Family Ascaphidae (Liopelmidae)

Structure.—Pectoral girdle arciferous; vertebrae amphicoelous; 9 presacral vertebrae; free ossified ribs (2 pairs); urostyle in *Ascaphus* articulated to single condyle (2 in *Liopelma*);[3] sacral diapophyses dilated; 2 tail-wagging muscles although no true tail; in male vent opens from tail-like prolongation of body that serves as copulatory organ; teeth in upper jaw but none in lower; vomerine teeth present; tongue large, rounded or pear-shaped, nonprotrusible, only slightly free posteriorly; lungs reduced, with attendant increase in specific gravity; pupil vertically oval (*Ascaphus*) or triangular (*Liopelma*); tympanum and Eustachian tubes absent; parotoid glands present (as postocular ridges in *Ascaphus*); terminal phalanges simple; fingers free, toes slightly webbed; outer metatarsals separated by web, inner one reduced.

Larva with mid-ventral spiracle posteriorly situated on body, large cyclostomous mouth, and stout muscular tail. Mouth not cyclostomous and spiracle on left side of body (except *Microhyla*) in all other anuran larvae considered here.

Habits.—Eggs laid in rosary-like strings. Fertilization internal (external in nearly all other salientians). Amplexus pelvic. These toads commonly frequent riffly cold streams.

Range.—There are 2 genera and 4 species in the family: *Liopelma* (3 forms: *hochstetteri, hamiltoni,* and *archeyi*) confined to New Zealand; and *Ascaphus,* restricted to northwestern United States and British Columbia, Canada.

---

[3] Fitzinger (1861:218) spelled it *Leiopelma.*

AMERICAN BELL TOAD

Ascaphus truei Stejneger
Plate 19

Range.—From southwestern British Columbia, south in coastal regions of Washington and Oregon (essentially west of the crest of the Cascades), into northwestern California as far south as central Humboldt County; also known from Washington and Adams counties in Idaho and as far east as the vicinity of Glacier National Park, Montana, east of the Continental Divide. (Pl. 55.)

Type locality.—Humptulips, Grays Harbor County [formerly Chehalis County], Washington (Stejneger, 1899:900).

Description.—STRUCTURE. Adult small, usually under 2 inches exclusive of "tail"; in general form, resembles *Hyla regilla;* pupil vertically oval (sometimes nearly round in preserved specimens); no cutting tubercle or "spade" on hind foot (oval inner metatarsal tubercle present); no tympanic membrane; nostrils widely separated, 1½ to 1¼ times interorbital distance; fifth toe broadest toe of hind foot; usually 3 conspicuous oval palmar tubercles arranged roughly in transverse row; skin smooth or with varied development of minute tubercles; in some, scattered brown-tipped tubercles are evident on undersides of thighs, pelvic area, abdomen, chest, and forelimbs, scarce in gular area; others may lack tubercles. COLOR. Dorsal ground color varies, old rose to brick red, creamy white, gray, and brown to almost black; dorsal pattern of dark streaks and blotches of varied development; eye stripe commonly present; area from tip of snout to transverse line on head bisecting eyelids, somewhat lighter (dull yellow to greenish) than remainder of head; below white to yellowish white with yellow color becoming most intense in femoral region; upper iris pale copper or apricot buff and middle and lower iris drab (based on 2 individuals from Humboldt County, California). SEXUAL DIFFERENCES. Male with vent opening from taillike prolongation of body that serves as copulatory organ; smaller, with longer legs, and usually less brightly colored than female. Breeding male with enormously enlarged (2 to 3 times normal size) forearm and inner palmar tubercle; white horny patch present on forearm where inner palmar tubercle touches it when arm folded, and occasionally inner palmar tubercle, inner side of first 2 fingers, and round spot on forearm black; underside of forearm gray, thickly dotted with white; underside of "tail" greatly congested (Gaige, 1920:5).

Habitat.—Found principally in well-forested areas in the Canadian and Transition life-zones. Permanent, relatively swift, mountain streams of low temperature seem requisite. Noble and Putnam (1931:101) believe that fish enemies, especially trout, tend to restrict the species to the smaller mountain brooks. Gaige (1920:2) collected individuals in small dashing streams above Lake Cushman, Washington, in water usually under 40°F. (4.4°C.) even on the warmest days. Svihla and Svihla (1933:38) found tadpoles in a small, cold, swift-flowing stream which emptied into the South Fork of the Snoqualmie River about 10 miles east of North Bend, Washington. The water was 10°C. at 1:00 P.M. Ricker and Logier (1935:46) found the temperature in small streams in British Columbia, inhabited by this species, to range through a minimum of 10° to 12°C. and a maximum of 11° to 14°C. Noble and Putnam (1931:97) state that apparently by increasing the temperature of the stream bed, removal of timber (by fire or logging) causes the disappearance of these toads. Above timber line, streams may reach 16°C. (August 27). The species was not found in streams with a large amount of decaying vegetation or lacking exposed stones.

Fitch (1934, MVZ field notes) on May 21, 1934 found this frog along the Smith River, 7 miles above its mouth, Jackson County, Oregon. At a place along the creek where coarse gravel had been scraped away, where water seeped down the bank, an *Ascaphus* was caught as it hopped over the stones. It may have been on a nearby log. A second individual was found a few yards away. It was crouched head downward on a bare spot on a nearly vertical sandstone bank which was damp and nearly covered with moss. Both animals were males. The creek along which the frogs were captured was of swift-flowing water, averaging about 6 feet wide and 3 or 4 inches deep. It was densely shaded by giant trees of broadleaf maple and by ash, bay, alder, tan oak, and Douglas fir.

An adult female and immature obtained by me, 10.6 miles west of Dyerville (by road to Honeydew), Humboldt County, California, were discovered near a seepage 5 feet from a well-shaded cascading stream. There were several quiet pools along this stream. The temperature of the water was 10.5°C. The ground was littered with alder and bay leaves. The water of the seep trickled through numerous small rootlets of these trees. Both individuals, about 10 inches apart, were situated at the base of a sword fern among dead leaves near the edge of the seepage. They were exceedingly difficult to see against the shaded broken background of leaves and rootlets. The light patch on the head of the animals was highly disruptive. The canopy at the collection site was nearly 100 per cent

(April 24, 1948) but would have been almost zero in winter. Vegetation at the site consisted of bay, alder, Douglas fir (only a single tree nearby), sword fern, oxalis, and horsetail (*Equisetum*).

Behavior.—Both adults and larvae occur in shallow mountain streams. Here they sometimes may be found, if stones are lifted from the bottom, when they are not otherwise evident. At night or on cool, damp days, or after drenching rains, the adults may leave the streams and crawl about on the banks. Phillips Putnam, quoted by Slevin (1928:82), found it difficult to find *Ascaphus* along creeks after a heavy rain (Skokomish River region, Washington). They were found in greater numbers on land. One individual that had not begun to absorb its tail was found over 100 feet from water. Putnam states, "I have always had the best luck collecting during a long dry spell. Now I know the reason to be that when it is wet, what few of them there are leave the water, and during a dry spell, lack of moisture forces them back again to the water."

This toad commonly seems to be solitary but J. Slevin (Van Denburgh, 1912:260) found 3 adult males together at a small pool on Mount Rainier and I found an adult female and a subadult a few feet apart on the bank of a small stream near Dyerville, Humboldt County, California. The species impresses me as being rather sluggish. A subadult (about 1¼ inch in snout-vent length) found by me hopped only 8 or 10 inches when aided by a 5° slope. An adult female covered 4 or 5 inches at each leap. When placed in an aquarium both animals swam rather slowly, frequently using their hind legs alternately.

The larvae tend to face upstream clinging by their suctorial mouths to stones. They are found both in swift and quiet water and sometimes even in waterfalls. They may occasionally be found out of water on spray-drenched surfaces.

Alden Miller (MVZ field notes) found tadpoles of this species on August 14, 1949, at Big Lagoon, elevation 250 feet, Humboldt County, California. They were found in a small stream in deep redwoods back of the Hammond Lumber Camp. The stream here dropped 20 feet in 100. It flowed down among rocks, partly moss-covered; there were quiet pools with fine silt bottoms. Most of the bottoms, however, were gravel and the water was moderately riffled. There was little splashing at this season. The larvae varied remarkably from full black with white tail tip to brown (mottled) with the same white tip. They were scattered in the larger pools chiefly from a little below the road up about 200 yards, where they seemed to stop. No more than 6 were seen in a single pool. They invariably attached with the great sucking mouth and usually avoided gravel.

A rock surface, flat or vertical, was chosen; not always, in this slow-moving water, with the head into the current. One was seen on the surface of a rock over which water was running 3 inches above a pool. The water did not completely cover its back. Keith Murray found one adult which was lying in the bottom of a 6-inch pool partly under a rock. It appeared very sluggish; moreover it was thin and weak-muscled. When held for some time it would jump as a frog, not a toad. The larvae seemed particularly hard-bodied as we picked them up, and the body-lashing was vigorous and through a wide arc. They generally were conspicuous and the tail marking seemed to be of no help in concealment.

Slater (1934a:141) believes the importance of temperature control in keeping this frog in captivity is overemphasized. He has kept them in the laboratory in unchilled water. Larvae that were kept in the laboratory a few days at Tacoma, Washington, were transported successfully by auto to Eugenc, Oregon, and back. Their water was not iced or changed.

Voice.—The species is apparently nonvocal. There is no vocal sac nor are there sac openings.

Food.—The following items have been recorded: spiders, beetles, a geometrid larva (16 mm. in length), and sowbug-like isopods. (Gaige, 1920:4; Van Denburgh, 1912:264; Fitch, 1936:639.)

Reproduction.—The season is long, from May to September. Gaige (1920:5) in the Lake Cushman region of Washington, found females with large eggs and males with enlarged forearms and anal region from June 27 into early September. Noble and Putnam (1931:97), in the same area, found pairs in amplexus from June 12 to July 6. Females with distended ovaries were noted throughout July.

Noble and Putnam (1931:98) and Slater (1931:62-63) have made observations on breeding behavior. Males crawl about on the bottoms of mountain streams in search of females. When a female is found the male may attempt to throw her on her back, perhaps thereby producing in her a state of tonic immobility. Slater (1931:62-63) observed mating. The female extended her hind limbs to form a narrow **V**. The male flexed his sacroiliac joint so that his pelvis made nearly a right angle with his vertebral column. The copulatory organ was bent forward by muscular manipulation to nearly a right angle to the pelvic girdle. Noble and Putnam (1931:99) state that the forward position of the copulatory organ is maintained by 2 postpubal cartilages (found in no other salientian) with additional strengthening by vascular pads. The male, when in amplexus, may fold his hands, interdigitating his fingers, beneath the female.

EGGS. Commonly deposited in rosary-like strings, arranged in globular masses, and attached to under surfaces of stones in cold running water; surfaces are adhesive causing them to stick together in rods and clumps; when widely spaced, jelly stalk may be observed binding them in tangled chain; eggs are surrounded by single gelatinous envelope, measuring 8 mm. to outer surface (Noble and Putnam [1931:100] state that there are 2 envelopes and a thin vitelline membrane. Livezey and Wright [1947:214], however, show only 1); ovum unpigmented, 4 to 5 mm. Females induced to lay eggs in captivity by implanting of fresh anterior pituitary substance, deposited in clutches of following sizes: 28, 34, 36, 38, 47 (average, 37) (Noble and Putnam, 1931:100). Livezey and Wright (1947:191) give number of eggs per mass as 35 to 50.

LARVA. Mature tadpole 35 to somewhat over 50 mm. in total length (to 60 mm., Mittleman and Myers 1949:62); upper tail fin not extending onto body; anus median; spiracle slitlike, located in ventral midline, posterior to mid-point of body. Distinctive large round mouth, occupying over ⅓ ventral surface of body; labial tooth rows appear as transverse dark lines in mouth, formula $\frac{2\text{-}3}{7\text{-}8\text{-}9\text{-}10}$ (Wright, 1929:3); $3/11$ or $3/12$, last lower rows exceedingly minute and occasionally imperfect (Mittleman and Myers, 1949:61); upper mandible a centrally situated, broad, transverse band of horny material, lower mandible not evident or represented by tiny tubercle of horn hidden beneath upper; papillae on lower lip. Coloration noniridescent black or blackish brown speckled with black; eyes dark; tail dark like body, or obscurely or strongly spotted with creamy white, tip creamy white with light area margined posteriorly by dark band; occasionally light markings of tail rose or flame color. (Pl. 27.)

Larvae in the laboratory did not hatch until one month after the eggs were laid (Noble and Putnam, 1931:100). The adhesive organ develops early. It is shaped like an **A** with the apex forward. Upon hatching the larva holds to the bottom of the dish by this organ rather than by its mouth. In nature the tadpole spends at least one winter in the stream after hatching. Two size groups of tadpoles in streams on August 3 and 31 are mentioned by Noble and Putnam (1931:101)—a group of metamorphosing larvae (year-olds at least) and another series 17 to 20 mm. in total length. Tadpoles in the field have been observed to climb 10 to 20 cm. out of the water, in spray-drenched areas, by using their suctorial mouths. Presumably these excursions are for richer food, in the form of algae and moss on rocks, than can be obtained from the swift waters of the stream.

Myers (1931) found tadpoles in a swift cold brook, about 1 yard wide and a few inches deep, a tributary of the Eel River, near U.S. Highway 101, 6 miles north of Dyerville, Humboldt County, California. The brook was in a dense redwood stand. All the tadpoles seen were in the swifter part of the stream, clinging to the bottom. When dislodged, they quickly attached to other stones. They were heavily mottled and clouded with blackish on a dull grayish background. This color included the tail fin.

The distal end of the tail for the last 6 to 7 mm. was jet black with a conspicuous, round, milk-white spot at the tip. All the larvae were approximately the same size, the largest 50 mm. in total length. Metamorphosis of larvae occurs from July into September. Ricker and Logier (1935:46) believe that it occurs in the second season following hatching.

Remarks.—The vestigial tail muscles, free ossified ribs, amphicoelous vertebrae, the inguinal clasp of the male, and the single median adhesive organ of the larva are considered primitive characteristics. On the other hand, these toads are highly modified for life in cold running water. Loss of the tympanum and absence of the voice are probably related to life in a habitat where the noise of turbulent water drowns out other sounds. Introduction of sperm into the cloaca of the female insures fertilization in moving water. As is found in other mountain brook amphibians, the lungs, which function in part as hydrostatic organs, are reduced. The cloacal appendage, according to Noble and Putnam (1931:101), may be considered a forerunner of the penis of reptiles, for the corpora cavernosa lying in the ventral wall of the cloaca form a large part of the structure. The sucker-like mouth facilitates attachment of the larva to the substratum, and the absence of external gills is probably related to the high oxygen content of the cold, agitated waters. Reduction of the tail fin and the stout musculature of the tail parallels caudal structure in certain other mountain brook amphibians such as, for example, the salamander, *Rhyacotriton*.

KEY TO SUBSPECIES[4]

1a. Eye (horizontal distance between anterior and posterior junctures of lids) to snout-vent ratio 13.6 per cent or more; combined vomerine count 7 or less. *Range.* Del Norte, Humboldt, and Siskiyou counties, California .... *A. t. californicus* Mittleman and Myers

1b. Eye to snout-vent ratio 13.5 per cent or less; combined vomerine count 8 or more 2

2a. Eye to snout-vent ratio 11.85 per cent or less; head width to snout-vent ratio 35.2 per cent or less. *Range.* Oregon and Washington, in the Cascade-Sierra and Pacific Border provinces .... *A. t. truei* Stejneger

2b. Eye to snout-vent ratio 12.31 to 13.50 per cent; head width to snout-vent ratio 35.6 to 38.6 per cent. *Range.* Northern Rocky Mountain Province in Idaho, western Montana, adjacent British Columbia, and probably extreme [eastern?] Washington and Oregon .... *A. t. montanus* Mittleman and Myers

[4] This key is included because I believe knowledge of the variation expressed by it is of value. I question, however, the desirability of applying names to the variants on the basis of these differences alone.

SPADEFOOT TOADS

Family Pelobatidae

Structure.—Frog- or toadlike in form; pectoral girdle arciferous; vertebrae procoelous or opisthocoelous, sacral vertebrae procoelous or less commonly opisthocoelous; 8 presacral vertebrae; free ossified ribs completely lacking; urostyle attaches to single condyle; sacral diapophyses dilated; teeth in upper jaw; vomerine teeth frequently present; pupil horizontal or vertically elliptical (all our species); tympanum distinct or indistinct; parotoid and pectoral glands present or absent; terminal phalanges simple; ours with single black inner metatarsal tubercle, with cutting edge; ours with 2 or 3 metacarpal tubercles, less sharply defined than in our bufonids; skin relatively smooth to uniformly roughened with small warts.

Mature larvae of species considered here small (3/4 inch in *couchii*) to large (to 3 inches in *hammondii*), pale gray, olivaceous, to blackish; snout short, body often broadest just behind eyes; eyes close together well up on head; mouth completely encircled by papillae, except for small area occupied by first upper labial tooth row (sometimes no gap in papillary ring); papillary fringe usually not emarginate laterally; spiracle on left side, below lateral axis; anus median, opening at base of ventral fin; labial teeth 2/4 to 5/5. (Pls. 27 and 28.)

Habits.—Nocturnal, terrestrial, and burrowing. The egg clusters are grapelike, resembling those of *Rana* but are smaller and are elongate and cylindroid (instead of rounded). The eggs of our species possess 1 or 2 jelly envelopes. They are commonly deposited in temporary rain pools.

Range.—Distributed across the northern hemisphere from Mexico and the United States to southeastern Asia and the Philippines. The family extends into the southern hemisphere in the East Indian region where representatives occur in the western part of the Indo-Australian Archipelago, but none reaches New Guinea or the Aru Islands. One subfamily is restricted to the Seychelles islands (Noble, 1931:492). The genus *Scaphiopus* is the only one in the Western Hemisphere. It ranges from the west to the east coast of the United States and from southern Canada (British Columbia) and New England south on the Mexican Plateau to its southern edge at Oaxaca and to Cape San Lucas.

Remarks.—American spadefoots are sometimes placed in a separate family, the Scaphiopodidae. Those who have worked on both the Old and

New World forms, however, appear to be unanimous in the belief that they are exceedingly close to each other. Hence I have included the American species in the Pelobatidae.

External differences separating the adults of species of spadefoot toads are not pronounced, and the problem is further complicated by variation in characters with age. Structural differences in the skulls are useful but such characters can not be employed readily in field identification.

Stejneger and Barbour (1943:37-39) treated the forms of *Scaphiopus* considered here as distinct species. However, Linsdale (1940:200) felt that *bombifrons* and *hammondii* were in the same species and that probably a third race *intermontanus* should be recognized. Wright and Wright (1949:112-20) also hold this view. Overlap in characters and the apparent allopatric nature of the distribution of *hammondii* and *intermontanus,* lead me to treat *intermontanus* as a race of *hammondii,* until it is shown that they are specifically distinct. In view of the overlap in the range of *hammondii* and *bombifrons* in New Mexico and elsewhere, these forms have been treated as distinct species although in time it may be shown that they intergrade somewhere to the north.

The phenomenon of acceleration of tadpole development should be investigated. The effect of changes of chemistry, pressure, and temperature of the water as well as the diet of the tadpoles should be studied.

Sexual isolation in areas where several kinds of spadefoots occur together (as at Las Vegas, New Mexico) has been studied by Bragg (1945). He (1945:70-71) summarizes his observations on this subject as follows: Spadefoot toads which inhabit the same region (ecologically as well as geographically) tend to be sexually isolated during breeding by two types of factors, (a) psychological and (b) ecological. Psychological isolation is the more important and is made effective through two phenomena, the differences in behavior of the males in securing mates and the marked interspecific attraction of spadefoot breeding calls. Ecological isolation is only partial and involves differential responses to amounts of rain as well as possible specific selection of breeding sites. The latter may be more psychological than ecological, however, due to the marked attraction for others of the call of the first spadefoot to arrive at a given pool.

The difference in behavior patterns of males in securing mates requires explanation. Bragg (1945:61) reports that the male of *S. bombifrons* calls repeatedly from one place without much moving about. Females attracted by the call swim to the male. The male pays little attention until touched by one of them, whereupon clasping occurs. In *hammondii* the male swims about almost continuously while calling and rushes toward any other spadefoot in the vicinity attempting to clasp it, whether male or female. A seized male is released when he croaks. Since female *hammondii* respond markedly to the call of the male, any female caught by a male is most likely to be of the same species.

KEY TO SPECIES[5]
Figure 25

1*a*. Spadelike process (inner metatarsal tubercle) sickle-shaped in adults, 3.9 to 5.7 mm. in length (3); width of eyelid equal to or slightly less than interorbital space (1); eye as long as snout or little shorter (2); no frontoparietal fontanelle (revealed by dissection) (4); frontoparietal interorbital space wide, not modified, and with skin in adults rather tightly attached to cranium; skin of back rather uniformly tuberculate; color generally light brown to yellowish green in life, with mottlings of darker color, most pronounced in female; size large (to over 3 inches); tympanum and parotoid glands present but indistinct .... Subgenus *Scaphiopus*. *Scaphiopus couchii*, p. 197

1*b*. Spadelike process cuneiform, in adults 2.9 to 3.5 mm. in length (7); width of eyelid 1½ to 1⅓ times (occasionally equal to or less than) interorbital distance (5); length of eye 1½ to nearly twice length of snout (6); frontoparietal fontanelle present (or modified one as in *S. h. intermontanus*) (11, 12); frontoparietal interorbital space narrow, modified; skin somewhat glandular and loosely attached to cranium; irregularly placed warts of variable size on upper surfaces; color dusky above, often with several broad longitudinal light-colored areas; size smaller (rarely much over 2 inches); tympanum indistinct or absent; parotoid glands absent .... Subgenus *Spea* 2

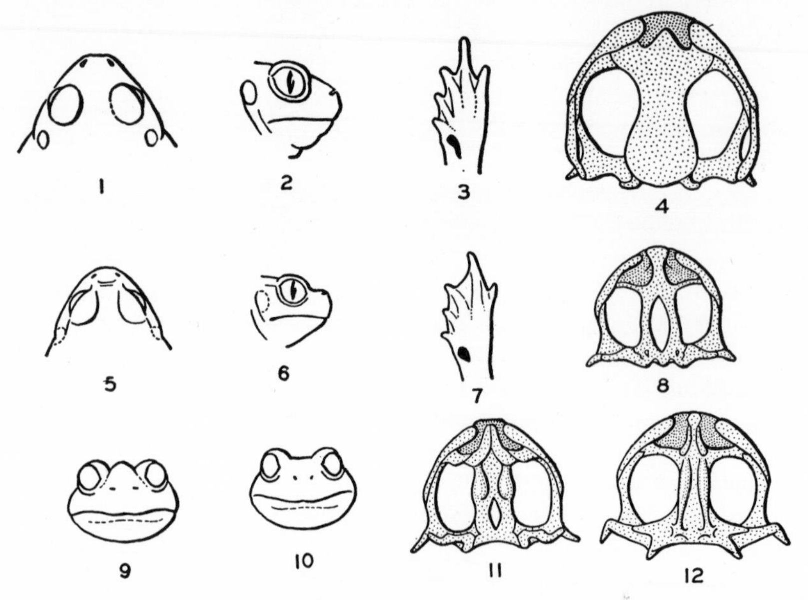

Fig. 25. 1-4, *Scaphiopus couchii;* 5-8, 10, *S. hammondii;* 9, 11, *S. bombifrons;* 12, *S. hammondii intermontanus.*

[5] Characters largely as given by Tanner (1939).

2*a*. Interorbital osseous bosses (11) giving rise to protuberance in interorbital area (9) (bosses revealed by dissection), boss present on either side of frontoparietal fontanelle (glandular prominence in interorbital region in *intermontanus* must not be confused with bony bosses) .... *Scaphiopus bombifrons,* p. 202

2*b*. No interorbital bosses present (8) .... *Scaphiopus hammondii,* p. 207

Subgenus *Scaphiopus*

Adults large, to over 3 inches snout-vent; skin of back tuberculate; color generally greenish in life; frontoparietal bone broad and well formed, extending well into nasal region, not highly modified; no frontoparietal fontanelle; metatarsal spade generally sickle-shaped. Eggs small and dark in color. Tadpoles small, commonly 1 inch or less in total length; color very dark gray or bronze, sometimes nearly black (black when preserved).

According to Tanner (1939:6) three species belong to this subgenus: *Scaphiopus couchii, S. holbrookii,* and *S. hurterii. Holbrookii* and *hurterii* are not considered here. The subgenus occurs in eastern, southern, and southwestern United States and in Mexico.

COUCH SPADEFOOT

Scaphiopus couchii Baird
Plate 14

Range.—Southern Arizona, southern and eastern New Mexico, southwestern Oklahoma, and most of Texas except extreme eastern part. In Mexico recorded from the states of Tamaulipas, Nuevo León, Coahuila, San Luis Potosí, Chihuahua, Zacatecas, Sonora, Baja California, Nayarit, and Sinaloa (Smith and Taylor, 1948:35). (Pl. 55.)

Type locality.—Río Nazas, Coahuila, and Matamoros, Tamaulipas, Mexico (Baird, 1854:62).

Description.—STRUCTURE. Differs from *hammondii* and *bombifrons* in following ways: no frontoparietal fontanelle; frontoparietal interorbital space wide, not modified, and with skin of adults rather tightly attached to cranium; size large, adult to over 3 inches; fingers and parts of hind limb including tibia, foot, and toes relatively longer than in *hammondii* (readily apparent if series of individuals of similar size compared); 2 or 3 metacarpal tubercles, thenar largest, palmar usually consisting of 2 small tubercles, closely associated, together nearly equalling thenar; metatarsal digging tubercle glossy black, usually distinctly sickle-shaped; tympanum circular, between 1/3 and 1/2 size of eye, indistinct; parotoid gland present but indistinct; skin of back rather uniformly tuberculate. COLOR. Above, in life, generally dull brownish yellow to bright greenish yellow with an irregular coarse network of brown; amount of light and dark color varies greatly, from irregularly arranged light spots on dark ground to light-colored ground, marked with dark (Dickerson, 1920:58); below whitish. SEXUAL DIFFERENCES. As in *hammondii* but in addition a pattern difference —male having less well-defined dorsal light markings than female. During breeding period, male has greater webbing of feet (Bogert and Oliver, 1945:339).

Adult male, RCS 3322, obtained July 23, 1949, at 10.5 miles north-northeast of Douglas, Cochise County, Arizona: Above greenish yellow with green reticulations of vague outline; black flecks, about 1/8 to 1/4 inch apart scattered over dorsal surfaces; below whitish to cream; seat patch and under surface of tibia light purple; underside of feet purplish; area immediately below anus cream-colored; nuptial pads on toes deep purplish brown; nictitating membrane edged with bright lemon yellow; iris well filled with pale greenish gold with pale coppery tinge.

Stroud (1949:232) collected an individual at night on a white substratum at White Sands National Monument, New Mexico. It was completely white except for the eyes and the metatarsal spades. In the laboratory, however, it gradually darkened, approaching the color typical of the species. All other individuals collected in the dune area were white. Specimens procured outside the dunes were light in color but not nearly so light as those from the dunes. The first one taken was obtained on the night of July 4, 1946.

Habitat.—Ruthven (1907:503) on August 1, 1906, found this species breeding in a shallow rain pool on the floodplain of the Santa Cruz River near Tucson, Arizona, in mesquite association. Bragg (1944a:525-26) reports the species restricted to the short-grass plains in southwestern Oklahoma. It commonly breeds in transient pools. Individuals live in burrows, frequently under objects.

Near Douglas, Arizona, at the locality mentioned above, this species was found on July 24, 1949, breeding in temporary rain pools in mesquite-yucca association. (Pl. 40, fig. 1.)

Behavior.—Largely nocturnal. *Couchii* that were breeding in the same area with *hammondii,* 20 miles west of Saltillo, Coahuila, Mexico, were noted in smaller, shallower pools than *hammondii* and in running water in ditches. The choruses were small, varying from 1 to 8 males. The species were segregated (Blair, 1947:67).

At the Steam Pump Ranch at the foot of the Santa Catalina Mountains, Arizona, Ortenburger and Ortenburger (1926:101) found that "On every occasion when there was a heavy rain these toads were found in daytime as well as at night." July 7, after the first hard rain, was the first date on which the eggs were found.

Voice.—The voice of this spadefoot is readily distinguished from that of *hammondii* and *bombifrons*. It is a baaing sound much like that of a sheep. Ortenburger (1925:19) likens it to the bleat of a lamb. There is generally a slight drop in pitch toward the end of the call. It has much of the quality of a human moan, suggesting someone in pain. It suggests to me a drawn out "wow" or "meow." Strecker (1908:203) has written it, "yē-ŏw" and that of the female as, "ŏw." He states that the cry of the male is loud and resonant and is repeated at intervals while that of the female is a short grunting note uttered several times, with shorter intermissions. Blair (1947:67) notes the call as a "bleat." King (1932:175) describes it as a "plaintive bellow." The voices of individuals I heard near Douglas, Arizona, seemed to be pitched at G or A below middle C. I found I could best imitate the sound by giving a rather hoarse, drawn out "wow" with declining inflection and of sighing quality.

The animals at Douglas, Cochise County, Arizona, heard July 24, 1949, called irregularly. Three or 4 notes were given at about 3-second intervals followed by a pause, but there was much variation in rate and in length of the interval between vocalizations. When an animal was calling vigorously, 3 to 5 seconds between calls was about average. A single call lasted ¾ to 1¼ seconds. These records were made at a water temperature of 19.5°C. Muddy ground 3 feet from the water's edge was 19.8°C.; the time was 12:05 A.M. The call is much different from the snoring, metallic cry of the Hammond spadefoots with which the Couch spadefoots were associated.

King (1932:175, near Tucson, Arizona) reports the species as beginning to call just after dark and continuing until just before dawn. They call both from the edge of muddy pools and while swimming; the latter call may be muffled. The male exerts his whole body in producing his call, drawing in his hind legs as the vocal pouch is protruded. During the calling, the vocal pouch of the male expands not only at the throat but also at the sides—over the arm insertion and on the sides of the breast (Dickerson, 1920:59).

During the calling from the floating position, the limbs are outstretched and the vocal pouch expands above the water. The call appears to require considerable effort, and when the sac is fully expanded the toad's back is arched sharply backward almost submerging the animal except for the head and vocal pouch. As one approaches a calling individual, the voice seems to come from each bush or tuft of grass that lies between the animal and the observer, even when the toad is 100 or more feet away. The call is highly ventriloquial (W. J. Riemer, 1949, MVZ field notes).

Reproduction.—Season, April to August (Livezey and Wright, 1947: 192), during periods of heavy rain. King (1932:175) gives the height of the breeding season in the vicinity of Tucson, Arizona, as between July 11 and 15. At this locality eggs numbered 6 to 24, and occurred in clumps, fastened in irregular masses to any solid object in the water, just below the surface. The eggs hatch in 1 or 2 days. The tadpoles grow rapidly and in a week are sufficiently developed to make their way into the mud at the bottom of the puddle. All have vanished by 2 weeks. The males outnumber the females 4 to 1. Ruthven (1907:503) describes males singing while amplexing females. The clasp is inguinal.

EGGS. Attached to vegetation in water usually less than 6 inches in depth; deposited close together in rather firm cylinder 6 mm. across; including jelly, eggs somewhat smaller than in *hammondii* and with single jelly coat; ovum black above, cream below, 1.4 to 1.6 mm.; jelly envelope, 2.5 to 3.5 mm., loose; complement of 350 to 500 per female (Livezey and Wright, 1947:192).

I found 2 egg clusters on July 24, 1949, 10.5 miles north-northeast of Douglas, near U.S. Highway 80, Cochise County, Arizona. These were arranged in a roughly cylindrical mass, each cluster attached to a grass blade. The eggs were situated in water about 8 to 10 inches deep, 6 feet from shore in a temporary rain pool. One egg measured 1.6 mm. across the ovum and 3.4 mm. to the outer surface of the jelly envelope.

LARVA. Mature tadpole smaller (approximately 18 to 24 mm. in total length) than in *hammondii* and *bombifrons*, although adult larger; similar in general form to other species, although head seems less broad in relation to body; in specimens from near Douglas, Arizona, body tended to be slightly wider than head; less heavily pigmented ventrally than in *hammondii*, intestine of preserved specimens appearing clearly over most of ventral surface of body. (Pl. 27.)

Labial tooth formula $\frac{2}{4}$, usually $\frac{4}{4}$, rarely $\frac{5}{4}$, $\frac{3}{4}$, or $\frac{5}{5}$; mouth encircled with papillae in continuous row or inconspicuously broken in middle of upper labium; inner papillae scarce; first upper row of teeth very short or absent; second row continuous, sometimes barely broken in middle; third row with wide median interval 2 to 3 times first row; fifth row may be present on each side or only one side; usually 4 rows of teeth on lower labium, first 2 not continuous in middle, last 2 continuous; interval of second row very short; last lower row of teeth 2½ to 3 times in next to last row; sometimes an additional short row may occur above the normal first row. (Pl. 28.)

General aspect of ground color coppery bronze with golden spots or sheens and much iridescence; under close scrutiny observed to be black dorsally, finely dotted with old gold, light grayish vinaceous, vinaceous fawn or orange cinnamon, sometimes bright greenish yellow, spots sometimes join to form network dorsally; below spotted except around spiracle; intestine shows through skin; spots scarcer anteriorly; upper half of tail musculature spotted, some of lower half and tail tip free of spots; upper and lower tail crests transparent, but stippled finely with small black melanophores, most abundant in dorsal fin; iris black with spots and dots of colors described for dorsum of body. (Larval description largely from Wright, 1929:20.)

Larvae, all about ⅜ to ½ inch, exclusive of tail, obtained July 24, 1949, at 10.5 miles north-northeast of Douglas, Arizona: Above rather uniform olive brown, under magnification seen to be blackish overlaid by close network of old gold (lipophores?); on close inspection with unaided eye, skin looks closely stippled with gold; dark spot present on either side, median to and somewhat behind eyes; pupil ringed with gold and iris elsewhere blotched with gold with coppery tinge, in color like dorsum of body; tail musculature with rather dense concentration of golden flecks dorsally, split longitudinally by melanic color at base of dorsal fin; sides of tail musculature sooty to black, suffused for basal ½ to ⅔ with pale gold flecks; tail membranes translucent but dorsal fin with scattered melanophores and few lines and spots of gold; abdomen with dense layer of guanophores ventrolaterally but layer thins out centrally where only fine stippling occurs, viscera showing through; ventrolaterally guanistic color has an ash-gray cast; region of gill chambers and throat blackish.

Subgenus *Spea*

Adults small, seldom over 2½ inches snout-vent; irregularly placed warts of variable size on head, back, and upper surfaces of legs; pigmentation generally gray, brown, or olivaceous centrally on back with whitish on sides and venter; adults average smaller than in subgenus *Scaphiopus* and distance between nasal opening and orbit and interobital width proportionately less; frontoparietal fontanelle present (or a modified one, as in *intermontanus*); frontoparietal and temporal bones greatly modified; metatarsal spade generally rounded (cuneiform). Eggs relatively large and light-colored. Tadpoles large, to nearly 3 inches; color usually light to medium gray or brown, seldom very dark (except when preserved); rounded and full-bodied.

According to Tanner (1939:11) this subgenus constitutes a division of toads that are closely related in external and skull characters. Two species (three if *intermontanus* is considered of specific rank) are included—*Scaphiopus hammondii* and *S. bombifrons.* The subgenus ranges from the Great Plains to the Pacific Coast and south into Texas and Mexico.

CENTRAL PLAINS SPADEFOOT

Scaphiopus bombifrons Cope

Plate 14

Range.—Largely east of the Rocky Mountains, from North Dakota and Montana south at least to Chihuahua, Chihuahua, Mexico (C. M. Bogert, *in litt.*), and possibly west into southern Arizona (Ajo–Gila Bend area, AMNH 53058). Ranges eastward to western Missouri and extreme western Oklahoma. Cope (1889:308) records this form (under *Spea hammondii bombifrons*) from Fort Benton and Blackfoot Fork, Montana, and Camp Thorne, Yellowstone. Cope's records may not all be of this species. However, he did make a distinction between *bombifrons* and *intermontanus* (as races of *hammondii*). *Intermontanus* resembles *bombifrons* in possessing a protuberance between the eyes, although in the former it is basically glandular rather than osseous.

The record for extreme western Montana, shown on the distribution map (Pl. 55) has not been verified.

The range overlaps that of *hammondii* in New Mexico and western Oklahoma, probably also in Colorado, Arizona, and in Chihuahua, Mexico. (Pl. 55.)

Type locality.—Three localities mentioned: Fort Union on the Missouri River, latitude 48°N; Platte River, 200 miles west of Fort Kearney; and Llano Estacado, Texas (Cope, 1863:53).

Description.—STRUCTURE. Resembles *hammondii* but possesses bony prominences between eyes that give rise to an interorbital boss (boss gives forehead and snout of *bombifrons* more of a sloping profile than *hammondii*), is generally less rugose in skin texture, internarial distance averages greater, and voice is said to be different. Bragg (1941:92), in vicinity of Las Vegas, New Mexico, where the two forms occur together, was able to distinguish them readily by their calls. *S. h. intermontanus* may possess glandular prominence in interorbital region, not to be confused with bony protuberances. In *bombifrons* glandular area lies above and in front of osseous boss, usually amplifying its appearance externally. Dissection of protuberance may be necessary for determination of its character.

Smith (1934:435) states that the tip of the first toe of the hind foot is apparently invariably black and corneous to north but is more variable to the south, in Oklahoma occurring in only about 50 per cent of the individuals encountered. The condition rarely occurs in *hammondii* and probably only on the extreme eastern limit of its range. Specimens of *hammondii* (in the Museum of Vertebrate Zoölogy) from near Santa Maria, Santa Barbara County, California, however, possess such corneous toe tips.

Cope (1889:307) thought the similarity between *bombifrons* and half-grown *cognatus* sufficiently close to constitute an instance of mimetic resemblance. The animals can be distinguished, however, by the pupil difference (vertical in *bombifrons*, horizontal in *cognatus*) and the single black sharp-edged metatarsal tubercle in *bombifrons* (two tubercles in *cognatus*). In some *S. bombifrons* the end of the snout and frontal convexity are covered with a layer of black horn, in each area the horny layer forms an oval shield; patches of horn may be confluent and occasionally may extend on the dorsum as a broad horny stripe. Cope (*loc. cit.*) believed the shields were due to constant pressure and friction of the earth resulting from burrowing activities. Although the animals burrow with their hind limbs, the snout is employed in keeping a passageway open to the surface. The character is not constant, however.

COLOR. Body above dark grayish olive with darker spots and blotches of sooty color and with a scattering of minute cream-colored tubercles; cream-colored spot on either side and above vent; forelimbs and upper surfaces of hind feet grayish; tubercles on upper surface of femora pale yellow; iris pale gold with tracery of black; edge of nictitating membrane cream; below white; spades glossy black; underside of forefeet and toes of hind feet flesh-colored (based on adult female MVZ 49096, from 9 miles east of Fort Sumner, De Baca County, New Mexico). SEXUAL DIFFERENCES. Male with blackish throat and cornified fingers.

Habitat.—Largely mixed grass prairies of central United States. In general similar to that of *hammondii*. Gilmore (1924:1, 5) says that east of Colorado Springs, Colorado, *bombifrons* occurs in low rolling hills where the soil is a mixture of sand, gravel, and loam and is generally quite dry. The adult toads are found at depths of from a few inches to several feet. For breeding, the species chooses temporary ponds, not permanent lakes, although these are available. Ponds occupied are roadside mudholes and low areas in fields with water ranging from a few inches to a few feet in depth. The water of the breeding ponds is muddy and warm. The vegetation consists of such microscopic plants as have passed the winter in a resting condition in the dried mud at the bottom of the ponds. Marsilea, some of the coarser grasses, sedges, and rushes may be present. Animal life is rich and varied including protozoa, rotifers, smaller worms, larvae of aquatic beetles, bugs, and Diptera in small numbers. The dominant fauna consists of crustaceans such as phyllopods, cladocerans (*Daphnia*, etc.), and copepods (Gilmore, 1924:5, 6).

The resistance of the species to drought conditions is shown by an observation of Moore (1937:226). At Stillwater, Oklahoma, on May 27, numerous tadpoles of this species, many with hind legs visible, were observed in a transient pool. On June 1st, the larvae were floundering in mud and slime due to the evaporation of water from the pool as the result of a continuous high wind. On June 3rd, at 3:00 P.M., no water was left. The tadpoles were closely packed together, their tails in the moist earth, their backs encrusted with dry soil, and their bodies inclined at about 45°. On June 4th, about 25 per cent of the larvae were dead, but in the late afternoon rain replenished the water of the pool. About 75 per cent of the larvae survived 1½ days of direct sunlight. (The maximum temperature [on June 4] was 84°F.)

Behavior.—Near Colorado Springs, Colorado, there is usually a short season of heavy rains in the early summer. The rainy period is preceded and followed by periods of dryness. Spadefoots appear with the rains. Over a period of 4 years, Gilmore (1924:3) recorded the dates of the first appearance of these toads. From 1921 to 1924, they were as follows: May 31, June 1, June 15, and May 31 (after 13 days of drizzling rain).

Kellogg (1932a:36, under the name *hammondii*) notes that the young may emerge at night, during summer, independent of rains. "Along the Powder River near Powderville in Montana, on June 15, 1916, while lying upon my cot, I heard a curious rustling in the dry leaves about our tent. Upon investigation with a flash light many small spadefoot toads were found. They were hopping about in the dry leaves which were scattered about on the sandy soil. When hunted with a flash light they endeavored to burrow out of sight and but a few minutes were required for them to entirely conceal themselves. These spadefoots made circular holes in the ground and yet in sandy soil it is very difficult to find the place where they have burrowed down, for in most cases it seems as if they pulled the hole in after them. After the breeding season is over, they take more pains in constructing their burrows as they are well rounded and resemble somewhat an earthen jar with a narrow top. Around this opening there is present some sticky matter which may aid in the ensnaring of insects. I have usually found this toad most plentiful in sandy areas, especially along the banks of streams though they occur on the elevated plains from Kansas to Montana. The call of this toad is quite weird and unusual, and may be likened to the squawk of some animal when severely injured, or a resonant *ye-ow*. Once heard this distinctive call is not likely to be forgotten."

Voice.—Concerning the singing of this spadefoot, Smith (1934:430) writes, "The males sing while floating in the water, with legs outstretched and vocal sacs distended. The latter is divided, as in *hammondii,* and is broader than long." The effect of the song has been described as "weird plaintive cries, hoarse and woeful."

Food.—The following foods have been recorded: ADULTS—flies, hymenopterans, moths (saturniids, noctuids, notodontids, and others), beetles (carabids, cicindelids, chrysomelids, and scarabaeids), bugs of several kinds, including pentatomids, and miscellaneous spiders (Bragg, 1944a: 532).

LARVAE. The larger tadpoles feed on smaller ones, shrimps, and insect larvae. The mouth of the spadefoot tadpole is admirably adapted for a diet of living animals. The horny jaws are constructed for seizing and holding the prey and they are capable of being opened to accommodate large prey. The median horny recurved tooth (of variable occurrence) on the roof of the mouth is not found in herbivorous tadpoles. The lips are flat and thin, probably assisting in the capture and holding of the prey. Food is not swallowed whole as with the adults but is held in the jaws and sucked or torn to bits. There is unusual development of the mouth muscles. There is great variation in length of the intestine, some tadpoles seem never to have had a long intestine. Probably they are departing from their ancestors in adjusting to a new diet. The long intestine has not been eliminated but is in the process of reduction. It exists early in larval life and is replaced later by a shorter one (Gilmore, 1924).

Reproduction.—Similar to that of *hammondii*. Breeds after heavy rains in spring and summer, in temporary pools usually of considerable size. Resorts to flooded fields and, less commonly, buffalo wallows, ditches, and cattle tanks. In Morton County, Kansas, this species has been observed by Dr. E. H. Taylor to breed as early as June 8 and as late as August 8 (Smith, 1934:430). Livezey and Wright (1947:199) give the breeding season as last of May to August.

Gilmore (1924:3, Colorado) says, "Very soon after reaching the water, mating begins. The males grasp the females just in front of the [hind] legs. The process of mating and egg laying occupies from twenty-four to forty-eight hours. If rains continue the adults may remain in the water for several days; but more commonly they leave the pond immediately after the eggs have been laid." Amplexus is inguinal.

C. W. Goldsmith (Storer, MS), reporting on the spadefoot east of

Colorado Springs, Colorado, says that there is successional breeding, 2 or 3 times in one season in single pools. There are commonly 2 or 3 days of activity at a given pool. In leaving the breeding site, the animals may cover 60 to 150 meters in a night. There are commonly 1 or 2 nights of rapid centrifugal movement away from the pool, after which movements become more random.

EGGS. In elliptical masses greatly variable in size, consisting commonly of from 10 to 50 to occasionally 250 eggs (Livezey and Wright, 1947:199). The clusters are attached to vegetation or other support in the water. The incubation period in the field seems to be less than 48 hours (Gilmore, 1924:4).

LARVA. Structure (based on 9 larvae from 4 to 5 miles southwest of Erick, Beckham County, Oklahoma, obtained June 12, 1946, by Arthur N. Bragg): size large, in the Oklahoma animals ranging from 47 to 66 mm. (average 58 mm.) in total length; body ovoid in dorsal aspect, sometimes almost round, broader than deep; tail with pointed tip, longer than body in all individuals, near 1½ times body length; dorsal and ventral tail fins about same depth as tail musculature at its base; fins deepest near mid-point of tail; dorsal fin extends on body to immediately in front of hind legs but not beyond point midway between hind legs and spiracle; spiracle low, almost ventral; eyes close together, nearer mid-dorsal line than lateral outline of head; nostrils close together, closer to eyes than to tip of snout; anus median, at edge of ventral fin where it joins body. (Pl. 27.)

Labial disc encircled by continuous row of papillae, interrupted but slightly in middle of upper lip; teeth 4/4, 3/4, rarely 5/4 (Wright, 1929:3). (Pl. 28.)

Dorsal surface of head-body mottled sooty and dull olive yellow; under magnification, superficial irregular flecking and spotting of gold chromatophores; throat light gray, mottled with pale greenish gold; viscera concealed by layer of metallic cream pigment with pinkish cast; dorsal tail fin translucent but mottled pale yellow and ash gray; flecks of metallic gold overlying yellow and gray mottlings; upper part of tail musculature olive, lower part dull yellow with olive cast; ventral tail fin translucent, with a few gold flecks; iris gold. (Based on larvae, RCS 4676, 2¼ inches in total length, obtained June 5, 1950, 2 miles northeast of Lawrence, Douglas County, Kansas.)

According to Gilmore (1924:4-5, east of Colorado Springs, Colorado) the newly hatched tadpole is slightly less than ¼ inch in length. The maximum length of the mature larva is about 2½ inches but a few individuals may reach 3 or 3¾ inches. The larvae vary greatly in size. Thirty-six to 40 days may be required for completion of transformation.

According to Bragg (1941:93), fully grown tadpoles are readily differentiated from those of *hammondii* in Colorado and New Mexico by the lack of a "muttonchop" appearance (jaw muscles less well developed) and the absence of beaked and notched jaws. Several of the animals from Oklahoma, upon which the foregoing structural description of the larva was based, however, possessed a weak beak on the upper jaw and a shallow notch in the lower. Furthermore, I have observed larvae of *hammondii* in California that lacked the beak and had weakly notched lower jaws. These characters hence cannot be strictly relied upon in distinguishing the larvae of these two species. In New Mexico the two species have been found together in the vicinity of Las Vegas, of Fort Sumner, and in the Jornada del Muerto.

HAMMOND SPADEFOOT

Scaphiopus hammondii Baird
Plates 14 and 15

Range.—Southern British Columbia, Washington, and Oregon, east of the Cascade Mountains, into California and northern Lower California; eastward through Arizona, New Mexico, western Texas into northwestern Oklahoma; also in Idaho, possibly western Montana, Wyoming, Nevada, Utah, and Colorado. In California absent from considerable portions of the deserts and from the higher mountains, although at Deep Springs Valley, Inyo County, it occurs at an elevation of 5,000 feet and near Whitmore Tub, Mono County, at 6,800 feet. In Mexico, reported from the states of Baja California, Chihuahua, Coahuila, Nuevo León, Tamaulipas, and Sonora (Smith and Taylor, 1948:36). If *multiplicatus* is considered a race of this species, the range would include also the states of San Luis Potosí, Guanajuato, Jalisco, México, Distrito Federal, Puebla, Veracruz (western), Zacatecas, Durango, Aguascalientes, Guerrero, and Oaxaca. (Pl. 55.)

It has been reported from Great Falls, Montana, but I have not verified this record.

Type locality.—Fort Reading (near Redding, Shasta County), California (Baird, 1859b:12).

Description.—STRUCTURE. Adult 1½ to 2½ inches; toadlike in form; large protuberant eyes with vertically elliptical pupil (pupil usually broadly oval in living individuals observed in dim light and sometimes in preserved specimens); tip of snout slightly elevated in profile, nostrils opening upward (large eyes and short thick snout give face pug-dog appearance); no well defined parotoid glands; eardrum indistinct or not evident; no interorbital osseous bosses; frontoparietal fontanelle present or absent; interorbital space narrow; skin somewhat glandular and loosely attached to cranium; metacarpal tubercles as in *couchii* except small palmar tubercle may be set off more from outer metacarpal tubercle; prominent inner metatarsal cutting spade, glossy black in color, typically rounded; no outer metatarsal tubercle; fingers and parts of hind limb, consisting of tibia, foot, and fourth toe, relatively longer than in *couchii;* skin commonly smooth and delicate, with small rounded tubercles but sometimes quite roughened. COLOR. General tone of dorsum dusky green, olive, dull gray-green, light gray, purplish gray, or rarely pale yellow, with scattered spots and blotches of darker color, sooty to dark brown; usually with irregularly outlined broad longitudinal stripes of ash white, gray or yellowish olive, one on each side, passing posteriorly from upper eyelids, and sometimes one on either side extending backward from tympanic region; stripes sometimes broken, particularly in female; dorsal markings sometimes obscure, especially when animal in dark phase; tubercles of skin sometimes tipped with orange or reddish, best defined in young individuals; below whitish, becoming purplish, pinkish, or dull yellow ocher in area of seat patch and on undersides of limbs; undersides of feet tend toward dusky or pinkish purple; toes may be buff; tubercles of forefeet pinkish; region about vent cream; usually unmarked ventrally; 2 cream to orange spots above and lateral to anus; iris variegated with pale yellow, ash gray, pale copper, or flesh color, brightest around the pupil; edge of nictitating membrane pale yellow. JUVENILE. Yellow-brown above with reddish or orange-brown warts; iris coppery to coppery gold; below cream with faint pinkish iridescence, changing to buff on seat patch (based on animals about ½ inch in length from Sink Valley, 4 miles southeast of Alton, Kane County, Utah, obtained June 30, 1949). SEXUAL DIFFERENCES. Male averages slightly smaller than female, with light olive to olive-tan (blackish in preservative) throat (throat of female dusky [Storer, 1925]); during breeding period inner and upper surfaces of inner 3 fingers, and area from innermost finger onto inner surface of wrist brown or dark brown to blackish in color, composed of many tiny papillae (magnification required for observation) which aid in holding slippery body of female during amplexus.

Habitat.—Frequents short-grass plains and alkaline flats in arid and semiarid regions. In Oklahoma this species has been taken only in the northwestern portion, in the short-grass plains. Its eastern limit practically coincides with the broad ectone between the short- and mixed-grass prairies (Bragg, 1944a:525). Intermittent and permanent pools of water, irrigation canals, reservoirs, edges of streams, and rain pools are frequented for breeding.

In California I observed this species on June 20, 1949, at Deep Springs Valley, Inyo County, at 5,000 feet, an arid region largely surrounded by mountains that are covered with a scattering of piñon pines and juniper. The toads were found in canals in slowly flowing clear water and in standing water in a short-grass meadow. The meadow area constituted only a few acres of the valley floor which was arid and covered, except for an extensive alkaline flat, with scrubby xeric vegetation.

Scaphiopus hammondii was associated with *Bufo boreas exsul. Scaphiopus* was heard calling at night and in the daytime. Seven adults were found scattered along the bottom of a canal, resting fully exposed to the sun, and 2 individuals were found in shallow water at its edges. Hundreds of larvae were present and these, like the adults, were in the quieter water of the canal.

In the vicinity of the type locality of *S. h. intermontanus,* 9 miles south-southeast of Salt Lake, Salt Lake County, Utah, Herndon Dowling and I found a large number of spadefoots, Woodhouse toads, and swamp cricket frogs. The animals were calling from a flooded field. The surrounding country was farm land but apart from irrigated areas, was dry. It had not rained for about 3 weeks and it had been warm for several days.

Water stood in the field to about 10 inches, over an area 40 to 50 yards wide. Clumps of partly submerged weeds were scattered about and in some places formed extensive patches. There were a number of smaller pools, 6 to 10 feet across and 1 or 2 inches deep around the larger pool. Some of these were in grassy places but others were on bare ground. The water of all the pools was cloudy.

We arrived about 10:30 P.M., attracted to the place by the strong spadefoot chorus. As we waded into the larger pool, using head lamps for illumination, the chorus began to diminish but I was able to find 2 animals. They were sprawled at the surface in water about 8 inches deep. The animals were in open water among the weedy growth, 25 to 30 feet from shore.

We finally resorted to locating animals by eye shine as they became increasingly less inclined to call. My attempts at imitation did not stimulate them. Eye shines, pink in color, were most readily picked up at 25 or 30 feet. By this means we located and collected 18 animals in about 30 minutes. Three pairs were found in amplexus.

Calls of individuals were ½ to ¾ of a second in duration. The sounds suggested wă-ă-ă, ă-ă-ă, or hw-ă-ăh. The water was 18.0°C.; the air 14.3°C. at 11:00 P.M.

At Sink Valley near Alton, Kane County, Utah, on June 30, 1949, many mature and metamorphosing larvae and recently transformed young were found in a short-grass pasture in a shallow basin formed by slumping of soil in the wetter part of the meadow. The tadpoles were found in muddy water in cattle hoof-marks and in 2 small pools, each about 5 feet across and 3 to 4 inches deep. The water in these pools was 27°C. at about 3:00 P.M. With one scoop of our dip net (12 inches in diameter), over 150 tadpoles were captured. The pasture was almost level, about 1/4 mile across, and was bordered by basin sagebrush. Piñon pines and juniper bushes covered the surrounding low hills.

Along the Virgin River at Bloomington, Washington County, Utah, July 2, 1949, choruses were heard on either side of the river in sedge areas near the banks. The animals were not found in chorus in the exposed pools of the bare damp sand of the river bottom, although a few isolated individuals were found. The river was about 1/4 mile across with several shallow channels of running water and a number of scattered shallow pools. Tamarisk, willow, a few cottonwoods, sedges, and grasses occurred along the banks. Barren eroded hills and mesas adjoined the river.

Near Douglas, Cochise County, Arizona, July 24, 1949, these toads were in chorus along with *Scaphiopus couchii* in temporary pools formed by a recent thundershower. The locality was in the yucca-mesquite association. (Pl. 40.) Sixteen miles northwest of Pima, Graham County, on the same date, individuals were heard and seen in an earthen reservoir, 75 feet square. The water was muddy and 12 to 16 inches deep. Clumps of grass and a broad-leafed weed grew on the 6-foot sloping banks. The surrounding country was semiarid but cultivated. *Bufo cognatus, B. woodhousii,* and *B. debilis* were also calling from this reservoir.

Behavior.—Nocturnal. Secretive. In the daytime and during dry weather, much time is spent below ground, often in a self-made burrow. The burrow is constructed by digging backward into soft earth by means of the hind feet, which are equipped with horny digging spades. Soil falls over the toad concealing it from view. Ordinarily no open burrow remains.

Harry Snook (MS) has, on two occasions, found spadefoots in the loose earth mounds of pocket gophers. Areas underlain with hardpan favor formation of lingering pools where the larvae can develop, but in such areas it is difficult to believe that the adults can penetrate the ground. They may make use of the burrows of other animals. Use of burrows has been observed by Henry Fitch at the San Joaquin Experimental Range near O'Neals, in the foothills of the Sierra Nevada. After it was fully dark adult spadefoots emerged from burrows of kangaroo rats (Storer, MS). Five miles west of Kerman, Fresno County, January, 1938, A. E. Culbertson of Fresno, when digging for kangaroo rats, found individuals 14 to 18 inches under ground. At the Experimental Range at O'Neals individuals emerged with the first soaking rains in mid-October, 1950, according to Nathan Cohen, resident at the Range.

Mud cracks in the bed of a dried-up irrigation ditch near Maggie Creek, Nevada, were used as places of retreat by recently transformed individuals (July 4). Stamping on the ground drove the animals to the surface where they were conspicuous and easily captured (Ruthven and Gaige, 1915:16). At Sink Valley, Kane County, Utah, on June 30, 1949, we similarly found recently metamorphosed individuals occupying mud cracks near the edges of rapidly drying pools. Little and Keller (1937:218) found adults in August (1931) and September (1932) in newly excavated cellars at the Jornada Experimental Range, New Mexico. There were evidences of gelatinous coats or jelly layers that spadefoots secrete about themselves while buried over dry periods.

When handled these toads may give off an odor suggesting popcorn or roasted peanuts. Some persons in handling them experience an allergic reaction characterized by sneezing and discharge from the nasal membranes.

Spadefoots are seldom seen except during their breeding congresses, but Bragg (1944a:519) believes that their surface scarcity is not as great as is generally supposed. Linsdale (1938:23) found individuals foraging in daylight hours in Smoky Valley, east of the Toyabe Mountains of Nevada. A few were seen at midday on clear, hot days—that is, with temperatures between 95° and 100°F. Huge numbers of adults on occasion emerged there independently of rainfall. These amphibians are most likely, however, to be found at night in the vicinity of pools resulting from violent rains.

Appearance of large numbers of these toads late in the season has been reported in eastern Oregon. In August, 1912, and again in October, 1924, near Blitzen, Harney County, many of these toads appeared after heavy rain. In October, 1927, R. C. Steele observed a "toad migration" in northern Klamath County. These were probably spadefoots (Jewett, MS in Storer, MS).

Voice.—The well-developed voice of the male is probably related to the nature of the breeding sites. These are usually of ephemeral character and of scattered occurrence, requiring quick assembly of the sexes from considerable distances. The voice is loud, the number of croaks averaging 75 or 80 a minute as based on individuals observed in New Mexico by Little and Keller (1937:218). It carries well, being heard a half-mile or more. The voice has been variously described. It has been likened to ". . . a loud purr of a cat but at the same time having the metallic mechanical sound of grinding gears" (Ortenburger, 1925:19) and, for the species in Uintah County, Utah, as ". . . a soft, though very penetrating *kwak,* low-pitched with something of the quality of the vibrating of a heavy rubber band" (Wood, 1935:101). Englehardt (1918:77, Utah) describes the voice as ". . . a loud crah-crah-rah, repeated at short intervals. . . ." Storer (1925:155) describes an individual note as ". . . a low-toned rather prolonged *tirr-r-r-r,*" each note lasting about ½ second with about 2-second intervals when the animals are singing in full chorus. Different individuals croak at different times and in slightly different keys. Blair (1947:67) noted that males called both while swimming and while sitting in shallow water. He notes the call as a "snore-like cry."

At Deep Springs Valley, Inyo County, California, June 19, 1949, in a meadow in a spring area about 7 miles south of Deep Springs Post Office, we heard the snorelike cries of spadefoots. The sounds were ventriloquial; the singers were difficult to find. A calling individual was found with hindquarters immersed, head and throat at the water's edge, in a shallow quiet pool. The animal's throat swelled into a spherical pouch with each call. It called alternately with another individual, suggesting that they were communicating, but this syncopation may have been accidental. The individual notes lasted about one second. On two occasions when timed, the animal gave 32 croaks per minute. This was at 8:35 P.M., at an air temperature, 1 inch above the ground, of 16.8°C., and a water temperature taken near the toad of 13.3°C. Among the individuals heard, the pitch varied 2 full notes. There was no great chorus. Some half-dozen well-spaced groups of 3 or 4 individuals seemed to compose the lot.

Near Bloomington, Washington County, Utah, on July 3, 1949, several *Scaphiopus* were calling among a large number of chorusing *Bufo punctatus* in a temporary pool. The spadefoots called infrequently until W. J. Riemer hit on a good imitation, after which they called incessantly. An individual, evidently in response to the imitation, sometimes gave 4 or 5 calls in 5 seconds but the rate varied considerably. Single calls lasted ½ to 1 second. I can imitate the call best by an inspiration with the vocal chords completely relaxed and the mouth well open, producing the lowest note of which I am capable and saying "walk" or "kwalk." The note is given a rattling or rasping quality. The call may at times have a slightly rising inflection. In chorus the sounds suggest a man sawing wood.

Individuals near Douglas, Cochise County, Arizona, on July 24, 1949, produced, about as above, 3½ to 4 calls every 5 seconds. This was at 12:10 A.M. in water at a temperature of 19.5°C. The duration of individual calls varied from ¾ to 1¼ seconds. The sounds were snorelike but with more of a mechanical quality. They also suggested the purring of a cat, but were stronger and hoarser. Individuals were found floating with limbs outstretched in the center of a pool 25 by 10 feet and 8 to 10 inches in depth. The vocal pouch was observed as bilobed, furrowed longitudinally; and upon inflation the singer arched his back, probably owing to elevation of his foreparts by the buoyancy of the distended sac.

Sixteen and a half miles northwest of Pima, Graham County, Arizona, on July 24, 1949, a sound like the quacking of a duck was heard in a chorus of *Bufo cognatus, B. woodhousii,* and *B. debilis.* I waded out into the shallow water of an earthen reservoir, imitating the sound and thereby stimulating the singer to call. When within about 6 feet I turned on my flashlight and found a spadefoot floating with limbs outstretched, the forelimbs against a grass blade. As the animal quacked, the gular area expanded only slightly, as a narrow oval swelling, the long axis of which extended along the midline of the throat. This may have been a female, but the animal escaped.

Food.—Tanner (1931:172) examined the stomach contents of 5 individuals from Utah. These contained insects of the following kinds: ants, beetles (tenebrionids [*Eleodes*], carabids, and 1 larval dytiscid), a grasshopper, an ichneumonid, and a cricket (gryllid).

Reproduction.—Apparently there is no definite breeding season. Breeding is often initiated by torrential rains and extends from mid-February to August, considering the species as a whole. Temporary pools are commonly frequented. In California croaking of this species may be heard in volume most often following heavy rains in the spring, as in February, March, and April, and the eggs may be deposited then. Small larvae were reported by Burgess (1950:49) as early as February 25, 1947, on the west side of the San Joaquin Valley, Fresno County, and by Storer (1925:158) on March 11, 1923 at Bellota, San Joaquin County. Metamorphosing larvae were discovered May 3, 1921 at Arroyo Seco, Los Angeles, and large larvae and some completely metamorphosed toads, 3 miles east of Whitmore Tub, Long Valley, Mono County, at 6,800 feet, on July 12-13, 1922. Logier (1932) found mature and transforming tadpoles on July 2, 1928, in a large temporary pond near Summerland, British Columbia.

Seven miles south of Deep Springs School, Deep Springs Valley, Inyo County, California, hundreds of larvae were found on June 20, 1949. These were in canals and shallow overflow areas in a meadow. Water is evidently permanent here. The tadpoles were of all sizes, but none was found about to metamorphose although some were 1½ inches, or so, in total length and possessed small hind limbs. They swam leisurely, individuals occasionally hanging nearly vertically as they gulped at the surface. They were in the quieter water of the canal and an especially large concentration of them was found in a turbid area. Elsewhere the water was largely clear.

At Current Creek, Nye County, Nevada, on June 22, 1949, larvae of two sizes, 10 to 12 mm. and 25 to 35 mm. in total length, were found. They were in a quiet pool adjoining the creek. Fully mature tadpoles with hind limbs well developed, and transforming individuals were found in a mud puddle in a pasture in Sink Valley, 4 miles northeast of Alton, Kane County, Utah, on June 30, 1949. The water was so muddy that the larvae could be seen only when they came to the surface. Many larvae of about the same size (about ½ inch in body length) were found in a rain pool on July 21, 1949, at Fry, Cochise County, Arizona.

Five miles south of Holbrook, Navajo County, Arizona, on July 29, 1949, mature, light gray larvae were found in muddy pools along an intermittent stream course. The water was reddish brown due to a suspension of fine soil. At one place about 75 tadpoles were concentrated in water about 1 inch in greatest depth in an area of approximately 2 square feet. Some larvae rested on the bottom near the edges of the pool, with their backs breaking the surface film. The water was 34.2°C. at 2:30 P.M. Deeper, cooler water was available. What intense illumination these larvae face, living as they do in arid and semiarid regions in exposed shallow pools, commonly lacking protective vegetation or other shelter. The frequent turbidity of the water may help to protect them.

Little and Keller (1937:218), at the Jornada Experimental Range in New Mexico, found egg clusters on dead vegetation after the first heavy summer rain on the morning of July 12, 1932. Cope (1884:14) states that eggs are deposited in July and August, at Santa Fe, New Mexico.

EGGS. Masses deposited in temporary pools attached to plant stems, grass, or the upper surfaces of small rocks. Ovum greenish olive, 1.47 (1.0—Livezey and Wright, 1947:192) to 1.62 mm. in diameter; 2 jelly envelopes, inner one, 1.63 to 1.94 mm., outer one 3.25 to 4.44 mm.; occasionally attached to vegetation by stalk 5 to 10 mm. long (*loc. cit.*); complement of perhaps 300 to 500 eggs per female; deposited in an irregular cylindrical mass 6 to 25 mm. in diameter (*loc. cit.*), containing 10 to 42 eggs (average 24). Eggs may hatch in 5 to 7 days or less. (Also from Storer, 1925.)

LARVA. May reach nearly 3 inches (71 mm., Storer, 1925:159) but transformation at smaller size (1 to 1½ inches) is more common. Body broadest just behind eyes, tapering gradually posteriorly and sharply anteriorly; snout short; tail about 1⅓ to 1¼ times head-body length; depth of tail musculature at its base about ½ to ⅓ of depth of body; greatest width of tail near its mid-point, fins at that point each about equal in height to width of tail musculature; dorsal fin originating well posteriorly on body; eyes close together, well up on head, interorbital width about same as distance from outer edge of eye to contour of side of head, as viewed from above; anus median, emerging in base of ventral fin, sometimes displaced laterally with folding of base of fin; spiracle low on left side, below lateral axis. (Pl. 27.)

Mouth rather small, to outer papillated margin 1/3 or less width of body as viewed toward mouth; mouth when widely open nearly circular, ringed by small, low papillae 1 or 2 rows deep, except for narrow gap in upper lip which bears short labial tooth row (some individuals may lack this gap); labial teeth in 2/3, 2/4, 3/3, 3/4, 4/4, or 5/4 rows; 1 or 2 labial teeth to groups of half dozen or so may be scattered about in area lateral to mandibles and between definitive labial tooth rows; these small groups of teeth make designation of tooth formula somewhat arbitrary; in representative 4/4 combination, first upper row short, in length between 1/3 and 1/4 of second row; second row divided at midline, extending laterally to near papillary fringe; third row represented by 2 segments, each same length as first row, 1 on either side of upper mandible; fourth row 1/2 to 1/3 length of first. Lower rows as follows: first situated next to lower mandible, consisting of 2 widely separated, laterally situated segments each slightly shorter than segments of third upper row; second about same length as second upper row, similarly divided medially; third like second; fourth undivided, between 1/2 and 2/3 length of third. (Based on mature larvae, about 1 1/2 inches in length from Fry, Cochise County, Arizona. In absence of muttonchop appearance and well-developed beak on upper jaw, these larvae are like *S. bombifrons*.) In larvae 2 1/4 inches long (hind limbs small) from 5 miles southeast of Millett Post Office, at 5,500 feet, Nye County, Nevada, first upper labial row absent or extremely short; papillary ring continuous when first labial row absent; upper mandible may or may not have beak. (Pl. 28.)

At some localities distinguishable from larvae of *S. bombifrons* by exceptionally well-developed jaw muscles, which give a muttonchop appearance, and presence of beak at tip of upper jaw that fits into notch in lower (Bragg, 1941:93); not all *hammondii* larvae, however, possess a beak and well-developed jaw musculature.

General coloration above light gray, olivaceous, greenish olive, brownish olive, dark brown, or greenish black; below cream or silvery with salmon to coppery iridescence (bluish black or slaty in alcohol); intestine in some may be discernible centrally. Larvae are capable of slow color change from light to dark phase.

Tadpoles at Deep Springs Valley, California, were olivaceous above, apparently the result of the association of melanophores and pale yellow guanophores (or xanthophores); tail marked with spots and blotches of pale yellow-olive on a dull olive-brown background of tail musculature; tail fins translucent with some melanic flecking dorsally; belly metallic yellowish cream or pale greenish yellow with coppery or pinkish iridescence; dark crescents, one behind each eye, opening anteriorly (these may overlie the brain and facial nerves) and a dark spot at anterior base of dorsal fin; iris with extensive dense flecking of pale gold, like body. Larvae from Current Creek, Nevada, resembled above but seemed to have less definite cephalic crescents and fewer pale yellow-olive blotches on tail beyond extensively guanistic area at tail base.

Larvae from Sink Valley, Utah, resembled the Deep Springs and Current Creek tadpoles but were pale gold or buff above with coppery iridescence, averaging lighter than the latter. Mature larvae at Fry, Arizona, were sooty above with coppery tinge; below light purplish gray with coppery abdomen and blotches of pale gold on throat; visceral region covered by solid layer of coppery guanistic color, superficial to which were whitish to cream blotches of closely set guanophores; tail musculature sooty, lightening basally, with pale yellow to coppery blotches composed of closely set guanophores (?) on basal half of tail; no cephalic crescents. Mature larvae, 5 miles south of Holbrook, Arizona, were gray above with pinkish tinge; dark cephalic crescents were replaced by pale copper patches; venter uniformly ash gray with coppery iridescence; throat blotched with pale greenish gold.

Larval development is rapid, and is said to speed up with evaporation of water from the breeding pond. Concentration of chemicals in the water (such as iodine), increased temperature, or other factors may be involved. Under laboratory conditions, Burgess (1950:51) reports the minimum length of the larval period as 25 days and the mean as 51 days. In the field, development from the egg to the time the toad leaves the water requires about one month (30 to 40 days). With respect to chemistry of the water, the experiment of Burgess (*loc. cit.*) is of interest. He found that laboratory growth of tadpoles in alkaline water from temporary rain pools (in which they were found in the field) was more rapid than that of tadpoles in tap water. Both groups of larvae had equal nutritional opportunities. The colloidal solution of field water contained a large proportion of chlorides, carbonates, and bicarbonates.

Scaphiopus larvae are notable in their habit of emergence while the tail is still of considerable size. Recently metamorphosed individuals from a number of localities in California measured 16.5 to 31.0 mm. in total length (Storer, 1925:159). The digging reflex is present upon transformation.

Remarks.—Bragg (1945:69-70) considers this species and other spadefoots as exemplifying well the anuran xeric breeding pattern which includes the following tendencies: (1) lack of a definite breeding season; (2) use of temporary water; (3) initiation of breeding behavior in nature by the coming of rain; (4) hastened development of the larva; (5) possession of a rather loud voice by the male; (6) marked attraction of males as well as of females by the breeding call of the species, thus tending to build up large congresses quickly.

Other modifications or adjustments related to the xeric environment are: (1) The presence of a relatively smooth skin and metatarsal spades that have been considered adaptations for burrowing. (2) The ability to withstand considerable dehydration, even slightly greater than that of the rough-skinned form, *Bufo boreas* (Thorson and Svihla, 1943:378). The average per cent of loss of body water in reaching the vital limit was 59.5 (47.6 average per cent of the body weight) for *S. hammondii* and was 55.8 (44.6 per cent of the body weight) for *B. boreas.* (3) Nocturnal and secretive habits (the vertically elliptical pupil is related to vision in dim light). (4) The ability of the tadpoles to use both plant and animal food and also their cannibalistic tendencies. In regard to cannibalism Bragg (1946:92) has remarked: (a) the xeric pattern of reproductive behavior exemplified by *Scaphiopus* is exactly and nicely fitted for survival of the young; (b) despite this, even under the best of conditions many tadpoles may be lost through excessive or fast evaporation; (c) such pools produce many animals in relation to the ultimate plant food and this makes competition among animals of all groups intense; (d) it follows from these conditions that fast rate of development and cannibalistic tendencies of typical spadefoot tadpoles tend to favor their development.

SUBSPECIES
Figure 26

(Characters largely from Tanner, 1939:17-18)

1a. Frontoparietal fontanelle present (3); interorbital region unmodified—no glandular prominence or longitudinal bony ridges; head shorter and narrower with less internarial space (11.7 to 14.0 [aver. 13.1] times in body length)[6] (1); forearm, femur, and whole foot shorter; skin less warty. *Range.*—From southern British Columbia through Washington, Oregon, and California into northern Lower California and onto Mexican

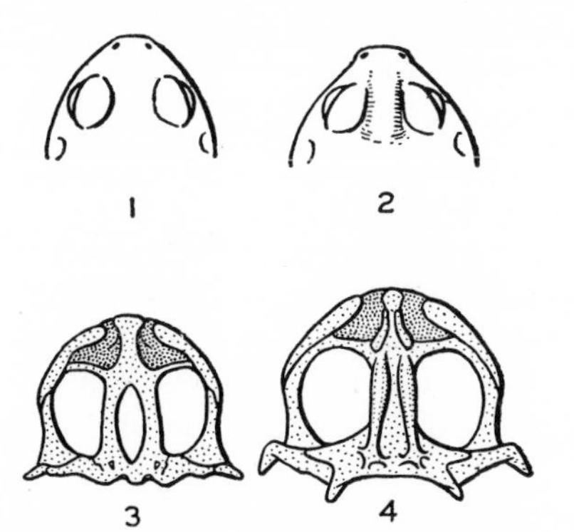

Fig. 26. 1, 3, *Scaphiopus hammondii hammondii;* 2, 4, *S. h. intermontanus.*

[6] Calculations based on Tanner's (1939) figures.

Plateau, eastward through Arizona, New Mexico, western Texas into northwestern Oklahoma; also in Idaho, western Montana, and southwestern Colorado (where intergradation with *multiplicatus* of Mexican Plateau occurs is unknown) . *S. h. hammondii* Baird

1*b*. Frontoparietal fontanelle absent (4); prominent longitudinal ridges in interorbital region, formed by frontoparietal bones; interorbital space may be filled with glandular prominence, not to be confused with osseous bosses of *bombifrons;* head longer and broader with greater internarial space (10.0 to 13.2 [aver. 11.9] times in body length)[6] (2); forearm, femur, and whole foot longer; skin wartier. *Range.*—According to Tanner (1939) largely confined to the Great Basin in Nevada, Utah, northern Arizona, southwestern Wyoming, most of Idaho, except extreme northern part, southeastern Washington, and eastern Oregon .... *S. h. intermontanus* Cope

LEPTODACTYLIDS

Family Leptodactylidae

Structure.—Froglike or toadlike forms; pectoral girdle arciferal; vertebrae procoelous; presacral vertebrae typically 8; ribs absent; sacral diapophyses cylindrical or slightly dilated; maxillary teeth present or absent (*Engystomops*); vomerine teeth present or absent; pupil horizontally oval; tympanum usually distinct, often semitransparent; parotoid glands occasionally present; digits tapered or with expanded tips; terminal phalanges T-shaped or simple; many species with circular fold of skin on ventral surface of body; in some fold confined to abdomen, not reaching femora, and in others it forms semicircle posteriorly on abdomen, not extending across chest; dorsolateral folds present or absent.

The single species occurring in our area has no aquatic larval stage. Full development occurs within the egg.

Habits.—Aquatic, arboreal, terrestrial. *Eleutherodactylus,* the genus considered here, deposits its eggs in terrestrial situations, in moist crevices in cliffs or in a pit in the ground under a rock. The species *E. recordii* in Florida lays its eggs in vegetable debris and leaf mold, in depressions in woods. Members of the genus *Leptodactylus* produce foam nests in pockets in the ground. Upon hatching the heavily yolked larvae live for a time in the liquefied foam in the center of the froth. With the coming of rain they are washed into nearby pools where they continue their development.

Range.—Principally South and Central America with a few species extending into the United States (Florida, Texas, southern New Mexico and Arizona) and the West Indies.

Remarks.—Noble (1931:496) treats this group of frogs as a subfamily of the Bufonidae stating: "They are more primitive than the toothless genera, but as they have given rise to toothless bufonids in different parts of the world, it makes a more natural system to group toothed and toothless genera together as a single family."

Davis (1936), however, on the basis of the presence of Bidder's organ in all genera of Noble's subfamily Bufoninae, with the single exception of the African genus *Nectophryne,* raises the subfamily to family rank and reinstates the family Leptodactylidae. *Nectophryne* is provisionally referred to the latter.

BARKING FROG

Eleutherodactylus latrans (Cope)
Plate 14

Range.—Central and western Texas south into Mexico to San Luis Potosí. In Mexico known from the states of Coahuila and San Luis Potosí (Smith and Taylor, 1948:63). Probably also in southern New Mexico, southeastern Arizona, and possibly Sonora, Mexico.

Koster (1946:173) found a frog of this genus 12 miles northwest of Carlsbad, Eddy County, New Mexico. Identification of the species as *Eleutherodactylus latrans* was confirmed by Dr. A. H. Wright of Cornell University. Probably the *Eleutherodactylus* of southern Arizona belongs with the form from New Mexico and Texas, although there is insufficient material on hand unequivocally to establish this. (Pl. 56.)

Type locality.—Helotes, Bexar County, Texas (Cope, 1880:25).

Description.—STRUCTURE. Adult to approximately 3 inches: circular fold of skin on belly forming large ventral disc; head large and broad; transverse fold of skin across head behind eyes; toes without web, with T-shaped terminal phalanges; prominent subarticular tubercles present; tympanum distinct, thin, 1/3 to 1/2 size of eye opening, cavity of ear may be evident through it; 3 metacarpal tubercles arranged in transverse row; 2 metatarsal tubercles, inner one slightly larger than outer one; no tarsal fold. COLOR. Specimens in Museum of Vertebrate Zoölogy, MVZ 28777 and 28778, from southern Sonora, Mexico, tentatively regarded as *E. latrans,* are colored in alcohol as follows: above light purplish brown with conspicuous blotches and spots of dark brown (MVZ 28777 was referred to by the collector as "black-spotted"); limbs tend toward banding of dark brown; below yellowish; iris speckled with whitish above and below pupil.

An individual, from near Carlsbad, New Mexico, after a few minutes in formalin was described by Koster (1946:173) as follows: "most of dorsum greenish, darkest on head and neck; venter plain white; upper jaw whitish with vertical green bars; a double whitish line extending across the anterior part of the interorbital area; an irregular whitish line, extending most of the distance between the interobital lines and the interscapular region; body with numerous dark green spots, the more posterior ones faintly outlined with whitish; band across back between the arm insertions and forelimbs ivory; a greenish bar on the wrist and forearm and a faint one on the upper arm; hind limbs lighter green than the back with darker green bars, these more or less outlined with lighter."

Habitat.—Frequents rocky areas in canyons—cliffs or rocky hillsides. Found in crevices or under rocks and in caves or even wells. Permanent water is not necessary. In Texas it has been found in the limestone ledges of the cliffs that front the Edwards Plateau. On several occasions specimens have been caught in mousetraps.

Strecker (1910b:73) writes of the occurrence and habits of *Lithodytes* [=*Eleutherodactylus*] *latrans* in Texas, "This frog . . . has in all probability an extensive range, but, on account of its peculiarly secretive and nocturnal habits, has been overlooked by the most eminent herpetologists who have visited Texas. Its distribution is entirely dependent on the presence of the exposures of white limestone which enclose many of the streams of the central and southern sections of the state."

Strecker (1910b:75-76) found *E. latrans* in Texas in the vicinity of Waco at Flat Rock Creek, McLennan County (Hewitt Section, altitude 625 to 655 feet). The creek was an intermittent stream flowing through a stretch of prairie land. There were banks of soft, shaly white limestone, filled with cavities and fissures. Large fragments had broken loose from the bluffs from time to time and strewed the bed of the stream. The rocky bluffs were low, averaging less than a dozen feet.

Observations were also made at Nameless Gully, 3 miles north of Waco, heading near Walker's Crossing on the Bosque River. Again there were banks of soft shaly limestone, here interspersed with stretches of yellow clay. At the highest point, the bluffs were only about 20 feet, but averaged about 15 feet for a distance of about a quarter of a mile. The gully was dry during the greater portion of the year. A few small water pockets were fed by tiny springs but the moisture evaporated so rapidly that a running stream was seldom formed. The majority of the hollows in the bed were filled with rain water. A few of them were as much as a foot in depth, but the average was only 3 or 4 inches. The bluffs were constantly shaling off and the bed of the gully was strewn with small, shattered masses of limestone. The hill on the east side was covered with a heavy growth of rock cedar, *Juniperus sabinoides,* and the one on the west side with numerous trees, shrubs, and vines of many species.

An individual was found in Madera Canyon, in the Santa Rita Mountains, Arizona, about 1943, by Dr. C. Vorhies accompanied by John Hendrickson and others. It was discovered, according to Hendrickson (oral communication), under a large boulder in a canyon in which there was much rock and little soil. Hendrickson informs me that it was after the first summer rains had started. These rains commonly come by mid-July. The calling of this individual led to its discovery.

Another individual was collected by Sam Davidson on October 1, 1927, in Madera Canyon, Santa Rita Mountains, Arizona (Slevin, 1931: 140).

According to Wright and Wright (1949:368) W. L. Chapel (1945) said he caught a good-sized frog with a prominent ventral disc which he thought must be *Eleutherodactylus* but it was lost. It was found in Parker Canyon, northeast of Roosevelt Reservoir in central Arizona. There are limestone outcrops in that region.

Koster (1946:173) found a frog of this genus on September 5, 1944, 12 miles northwest of Carlsbad, Eddy County, New Mexico. The amphibian was discovered under the tent where it apparently had sought shelter during a violent storm in which about 1.6 inches of rain fell in 15 hours. The region for several hundred yards about the location was a grassy plain with a scattering of shrubs. The canyon of the Pecos was about ½ mile distant, and a small rocky hill projected above the plain about ⅓ mile away. Identification of the animal as *E. latrans* was confirmed by Dr. A. H. Wright of Cornell University.

An individual, assigned by Bogert and Oliver (1945:405) to *augusti* was obtained by Seth Benson of the Museum of Vertebrate Zoölogy, 2 miles east of Guirocoba, Sonora, Mexico, April 10, 1939. Benson noted on the field tag, "caught in a mousetrap under a rock near water."

A specimen, MVZ 28777, collected by Charles Sibley, on May 5, 1939, at an elevation of about 1,800 feet at Agua Marin, 8.3 miles west-northwest of Alamos, Sonora, Mexico, was recently discovered in the collection of the Museum of Vertebrate Zoölogy, identified as *Hyla arenicolor.* The frog is a male, 42 mm. in snout-vent length. Sibley's notes say, " 'Black-spotted Frog' (?) In well—12′ deep; 3′ square—vertical sides—very little water."

Behavior.—Mocquard (1899:160) has published notes on the related form *Hylodes* [=*Eleutherodactylus*] *augusti,* taken from the field notes of M. Diguet. So little is known of the habits of frogs of this genus that these observations may prove of value in obtaining information on *latrans*. From these notes Kellogg (1932b:102) provides the following translation:

"*H. augusti* appears to be essentially nocturnal, which explains its rarity in collections. Cope had already made known some facts regarding their habits, after the data furnished to him by Mr. G. W. Marnock, who discovered it [regarded here as *E. latrans*] in Texas. In confirming these details for me, Mr. Diguet has been good enough to add to them the following information: 'This batrachian is encountered in the territory of Tepic in damp ravines at the commencement of the rainy season; that is, the end of June and July. Its voice is resounding and can be heard at a distance after sunset. At this time, it is found attached upon certain smooth-barked trees, such as the Burseras, the color of which is the same as that of the animal.'

"This last observation of Mr. Diguet has its importance, in that it establishes for us the significance of the ventral disk: It is, undoubtedly, an *adhesive disk*. The fingers, in fact, lack terminal disks and are only feebly swollen at their extremities; the animal therefore can not maintain itself along vertical surfaces except by means of this ventral disk. Furthermore as this disk can not be other than an organ of attachment, the progression of this batrachian upon the trunks of trees or in the vertical cracks of rocks, where it has been found by Mr. G. W. Marnock in Texas, must be effected by leaps: This is actually the case and Mr. Diguet has seen it constantly leaping from one branch to another when it tried to hold on.

"Mr. Diguet has never encountered *H. augusti* during the day, but [only] at night with the aid of a light. He was able to capture eight specimens, seven males and one female, in the vicinity of small puddles of water on the western slope of the Cerro San Juan, territory of Tepic. He had at first grasped a male, next a female, whose sex he identified by the presence of ovaries loaded with eggs, which the transparency of the abdominal wall let be seen; he held this female upon the ground and saw arriving successively 6 other males which followed her and which he seized."

Strecker (1910b:73, Texas) says it is a land animal, hiding in caves and fissures during the daytime, and, excepting during the brief breeding period, venturing abroad only at night. It does not appear to be perfectly at home in the water at any time and specimens observed by Strecker made no attempt to conceal themselves by diving, but swam clumsily across small pools and sought to escape by leaping up the bank on the opposite side. A breeding pair remained in amplexus close in to the bank.

Dickerson (1906:164) says the species moves about in a slow stilted manner with body and tarsi elevated. She suggests that this type of locomotion may be correlated with its habit of living among limestone rocks. Strecker (1910b:81, Texas) states that the younger specimens have much shorter limbs and do not look so odd. At times the species is sluggish and rather easily captured, but as a rule retreats into caves and fissures at the slightest alarm.

Voice.—The species is appropriately referred to as the barking frog. John Hendrickson, one of my associates, who has heard the animal in Arizona, described the voice as resembling the rapid yapping of a fox terrier. Strecker (1910b:81-82, Texas) refers to it as a short doglike bark ending in a metallic ring. It is usually uttered at night or during heavy showers; rarely in the morning.

Food.—Strecker (1910b:82, Texas) reported the elytra of a ground beetle and the remains of many spiders and ants in the stomach of one example.

Reproduction.—Noble (1927:90) writes that the diagnostic characters of the life history of *Eleutherodactylus* are the terrestrial mode of egg laying, the large eggs with 2 or more resistant capsules devoid of peduncles or "foam," the absence of tadpole mouth parts, the presence of a premaxillary egg tooth, and a broad, highly vascular tail.

EGGS. Number per female in the form in Texas, about 50; ovum large, 6.0 to 7.5 mm.; eggs deposited in terrestrial situations, in moist or rain-filled cracks or crevices in rocky cliffs and ledges or in caves. Breeding may occur over a long period, apparently during any rainy period from February to May. (Largely from Livezey and Wright, 1947:188.)

Jameson (1950) reports on the eggs and manner of development in this species, settling the long-standing question of whether it is a terrestrial or aquatic breeder. On the night of April 29, 1949, he and several others traced a calling individual to its position under a large rock on the side of a canyon near the Medina River, 18 miles west of Medina, Bandera County, Texas. Under the rock was found a cluster of 67 eggs in a small pocket of the rich soil usually found under rocks of the Edwards Plateau. The pocket was about 4 inches deep and filled with a mixture of eggs and mud. Capture of the male near the eggs suggested that he remains with them until they hatch. The moisture was possibly formed by the urine of the male. It was difficult to explain otherwise the presence of so much moisture in the pocket when it had not rained in the locality for several days. The soil around the pocket was quite firm and devoid of moisture. This dry condition prevailed under other rocks turned in the area at the time. Jameson hypothesizes that the male may prevent dehydration of the eggs by wetting the egg mass with the contents of his bladder.

The eggs were removed and incubated in flowerpots filled with sand, set in a bowl of water, and covered by a piece of glass. When first observed in the laboratory the eggs possessed embryos with limb buds and slightly differentiated fingers. The mouth was formed and the olfactory pits evident. The heart was beating. The tail was well expanded and quite vascular; it completely surrounded the developing embryo. There was no evidence of gills or gill slits. The operculum was not present and the intestinal tract lacked the typical amphibian coiling. Development continued through a typical *Eleutherodactylus* pattern through various stages until the formation of an "egg-tooth" just before the last specimen died on June 2, 1949. Jameson estimates the total period of development from fertilization to hatching may vary from 25 to 35 days.

Strecker (1910b:79, Texas) says of *E. latrans,* that two specimens collected in March were only about 1½ inches in length, suggesting that it requires from 2½ to 3 years for this species to become full-grown.

Remarks.—*Eleutherodactylus latrans* is evidently close to the Mexican form *E. augusti.* Dugès in Brocchi (1879:21-22) described *Hylodes* (=*Eleutherodactylus*) *augusti,* basing his description on a specimen from Guanajuato, Mexico. Cope (1880:25-26) described *Lithodytes* (=*Eleutherodactylus*) *latrans* from material obtained in Texas by G. W. Marnock. These species were referred to the genus *Eleutherodactylus,* the form *augusti* by Slevin (1931:140) and the species *latrans* by Stejneger and Barbour (1917:34). According to Kellogg (1932b), Mocquard concluded that *E. augusti* was identical with Cope's *E. latrans* from central Texas but a direct comparison by Kellogg of Mexican specimens with the cotypes of *E. latrans* did not entirely confirm this assumption. Kellogg, however, found no constant structural features that would distinguish specimens from these two areas.

Evidently the first frog of this genus to be reported in Arizona was obtained by Sam Davidson in Madera Canyon, in the Santa Rita Mountains. It was sent to Dr. Doris Cochran, of the United States National Museum, who in turn allowed Dr. Remington Kellogg to examine it. According to Slevin (1931:140), on the basis of its peculiar dorsal spotting it was referred by Kellogg to *augusti* rather than to *latrans* of Texas. In 1942, Wright and Wright (1949:366) saw this specimen and concluded it superficially appeared to be *E. latrans.* This impression was reinforced by seeing Mulaik's (University of Utah) material of young with light crossbands from Kerrville, Texas. Koster's (1946, Carlsbad, New Mexico) material and the Wrights' material from Boerne, Texas, also showed the light transverse band. On a later page (367 *op. cit.*), following measurements, the Wrights state that Slevin's (1931) specimen is *E. latrans.*

Three specimens in the Museum of Vertebrate Zoölogy, from southern Sonora, Mexico, I suspect, on biogeographical grounds and from a comparison with Slevin's (1931) specimen in the collection of the California Academy of Sciences, belong in the same species with the animals from southern Arizona. This conclusion is tentative, however, because of the inadequacy of the material.

On the basis of the Sonoran specimen (MVZ) from Guirocoba, Bogert and Oliver (1945:405) listed the form *E. augusti* for Sonora and questioned the specific distinctness, from *augusti*, of Taylor's (1940) *tarahumaraensis* and Cope's (1880) *latrans*. Smith and Taylor (1948:64, footnote), however, reject the suggestion that *tarahumaraensis* and *augusti* are in the same species. They state that these two species are the most widely different of the entire group of *Eleutherodactylus* to which they belong.

Were I to follow Bogert and Oliver (1945), I should regard the form in Arizona as *augusti* but I have learned from Bogert (oral communication) that the suggestion in the Sonoran paper was probably not valid. I, hence, follow Wright and Wright (1949) in regarding the animals of Texas, New Mexico, and Arizona as *latrans*.

TOADS

Family Bufonidae

Structure.—Pectoral girdle arciferal; vertebrae procoelous; presacral vertebrae typically 8; ribs absent; urostyle attached to double condyle on sacrum; sacral diapophyses dilated; maxillary teeth absent; tongue elliptical or pear-shaped, entire and free posteriorly; pupil horizontally oval; tympanum distinct or absent; parotoid glands present; terminal phalanges simple; 2 metatarsal tubercles, innermost largest; warts numerous in most.

Mature larvae of species considered here (genus *Bufo*), from about an inch (*B. b. exsul*) to 2 inches (*B. b. halophilus*) in length; often black but sometimes tan, olive, or gray; snout longer and eyes less closely situated than in spadefoot tadpoles; body oval in dorsal aspect; mouth with papillae confined to sides and papillary fringe emarginate midway on either side; spiracle on left side; anus median; labial teeth 2/3. (Pls. 29 and 30.)

Habits.—Terrestrial, aquatic, and fossorial. Species of the genus *Bufo*, considered here, deposit their eggs in gelatinous strings (*B. punctatus* excepted), in aquatic situations.

Range.—Practically world-wide in distribution except for colder regions. The single genus *Bufo* with ten species is considered here. This genus is world-wide except for New Guinea, Polynesia, Australia, and Madagascar. In the Americas it occurs in the Hudson Bay region, Labrador, Aleutian Islands, and along the southern coast of central Alaska southward through North and Central America into South America.

Genus *Bufo*

Structure.—Adults from 3/4 (*B. quercicus*) to about 9 inches (*B. marinus*) in total length; body typically squat and stout, and limbs relatively short; webbing of hind feet generally less developed than in frogs (*Rana*); palmar and plantar tubercles usually prominent; a large palmar tubercle and varied development of thenar tubercle (situated at base of first finger); a pair of metatarsal tubercles, rounded or sharp-edged, inner tubercle largest; skin usually warty; parotoid glands present; cranial crests prominent to absent; no teeth; tympanum usually evident; pupil of eye typically horizontally oval.

Range.—World-wide except for New Guinea, Polynesia, Australia, and Madagascar (Noble, 1931:503).

Key to Species
Figure 27

1*a*. Dorsal surface of femur with conspicuous, much-enlarged wart (sometimes with several large warts) or (and) wart or group of warts on tibia (1); one or more conspicuous enlarged warts at angle of mouth (3); fold of skin on tarsus (8) 2

1*b*. No conspicuously enlarged wart(s) on femur or tibia (5); with (8) or without (12) fold of skin on tarsus 5

2*a*. (1*a*) Prominent cranial crests that curve around behind eyes (2); size large, 3 to over 6 inches; skin relatively smooth; dorsal coloration largely uniformly olivaceous or dark brown; enlarged warts on both tibia and femur (1); tympanum nearly or same size as eye opening (3); (juveniles may lack leg glands and may have small, light-colored spots on back) .... *B. alvarius*, p. 229

2*b*. Cranial crests absent or obscure (6); enlarged wart(s) on tibia only (5); size averages smaller (seldom over 5 inches); warts (commonly pitted and often conspicuous) present on body; tympanum 1/4 to 1/2 size of eye opening (7) 3

3*a*. (2*b*) Parotoid glands not sharply defined (10); skin relatively smooth; tarsal fold reduced; size smaller, adults 1 3/4 to 2 1/2, occasionally to 3 inches 4

3*b*. Parotoid glands usually sharply defined (6); skin rough; tarsal fold usually conspicuous (8); size larger, adults to 5 inches .... *B. boreas*, p. 234

4*a*. (3*a*) Parotoid glands large, interparotoid distance less than width of gland (10) or about same width or less than width of eyelid (10); seat patch light-colored, essentially unmarked; chest and belly usually with few scattered dark spots; sexes differ in coloration .... *B. canorus,* p. 245

4*b*. Parotoid glands smaller (6), with interparotoid space usually at least twice width of gland (6); seat patch black or sooty with numerous white specks; chest and belly heavily marked with black; sexes similar ...... *B. boreas exsul,* p. 234

5*a*. (1*b*) Cranial crests absent 6

5*b*. Cranial crests present, or prominent boss between eyes 13

6*a*. (5*a*) Distance between eyes ½ width of upper eyelid or less (10); parotoid glands large but often not well defined, with interparotoid distance less than width of gland or about same width or less than width of eyelid (10); skin relatively smooth, few or no minute tubercles between warts; sexual differences in coloration —male uniformly colored, or nearly so; female with dark spots and blotches outlined with whitish on ground color lighter than ground color of male .... *Bufo canorus,* p. 245

6*b*. Distance between eyes nearly equal to, equal to, or greater than width of upper eyelid (6); parotoid glands usually well defined, with interparotoid space usually at least twice width of gland or (in *debilis*) twice width of eyelid (13); skin rough, tuberculate between warts (*B. boreas exsul* excepted); no sexual dichromism 7

7*a*. (6*b*) Outer metatarsal tubercle with sharp cutting edge (16) 8

7*b*. Outer metatarsal tubercle without sharp cutting edge (19) 10

8*a*. (7*a*) Boss on snout, sometimes extending as horny protuberance posteriorly between eyes (17) 9

8*b*. No boss on snout or in interorbital region 21

9*a*. (8*a*) Cranial crests prominent, often diverging from boss on snout (4); ranges south of *B. hemiophrys* .... *Bufo cognatus,* p. 249

9*b*. Horny protuberance on head between eyes, extending from snout to posterior portion of eyelids, sometimes with median longitudinal furrow (17); North Dakota, and Canada in Alberta, Manitoba, and Northwest Territory .. *Bufo hemiophrys,* p. 263

10*a*. (7*b*) Parotoids round, same size or smaller than upper eyelids (9) .... *Bufo punctatus,* p. 280

10*b*. Parotoids large and elongate, longer than upper eyelid 11

11*a*. (10*b*) Size small, adults approximately 1½ to 2 inches; head flattened (14); snout protuberant, pointed or subacute (13); no vertebral stripe; ground color in life greenish or yellowish with small ink-black bars, spots, and flecks ...... *Bufo debilis,* p. 259

11*b*. Size larger, adults approximately 1¾ to 5 inches; head not flattened, snout rounded (7); vertebral stripe usually present, sometimes absent; gray, brown, or olivaceous above marked with larger spots and blotches of dusky to black 12

12*a*. (11*b*) Membranous flap of skin on tarsus extending from inner metatarsal tubercle almost to heel (8); vertebral stripe present (some juveniles excepted) .... *Bufo boreas,* p. 234

12*b*. No flap of skin on tarsus (12); vertebral stripe present or absent 20

13*a*. (5*b*) A prominent horny boss between eyes extending from posterior portion of eyelids to snout (17) .... *Bufo hemiophrys*, p. 263

13*b*. Separate cranial crests present (18) 14

14*a*. (13*b*) Parotoid gland small, usually same size or smaller than upper eyelid, commonly almost perfectly round (9); prominent lump on upper jaw above corner of mouth but below tympanum, projecting beyond general contour of head, as viewed from above (9) .... *Bufo punctatus*, p. 280

14*b*. Parotoid gland elongate, usually larger (in length, width, or both) than upper eyelid (15); no prominent lump on upper jaw at corner of mouth 15

15*a*. (14*b*) Dorsal pattern of large dark blotches often outlined with lighter color, lighter than ground color (4); blotches often symmetrically situated, tending to be paired 9

15*b*. No dorsal pattern of large, paired blotches outlined with light color 16

16*a*. (15*b*) Well-defined fold of skin on tarsus extending along inner surface from inner metatarsal tubercle almost to heel (8) .... *Bufo boreas*, p. 234

16*b*. No fold of skin on tarsus (sometimes row of warts or low rounded ridge but no membranous flap of skin) (12) 17

17*a*. (16*b*) Eyes widely spaced, separated by about 1½ to 2 times width of eyelid (13); cranial crests, when evident, curve around eyelids, closely applied to them; head depressed (14); dorsal ground color green or yellow-green in life with many small spots and bars of inky black; size small, to 2 inches .... *Bufo debilis*, p. 259

17*b*. Eyes larger, more closely set, separated by approximately width of eyelid or slightly more (18); cranial crests when present more rectilinear, not closely applied to orbital region (18); head not notably depressed (7); dorsal ground color olive, gray, or brown, largely unmarked or with large dark markings (seldom inky black), usually in form of spots or blotches; size larger, 2 to 5 inches 18

18*a*. (17*b*) Boss on snout (4); well-defined cranial crests diverging posteriorly from boss .... *Bufo cognatus*, p. 249

18*b*. No boss on snout; cranial crests weak (15) or strong (18) with interorbital portions parallel; crests sometimes absent 19

19*a*. (18*b*) Inner metatarsal tubercle with cutting (usually black) edge (16); no vertebral stripe .... *Bufo compactilis*, p. 255

19*b*. Inner metatarsal tubercle with rounded (usually brown) edge (19); vertebral stripe present .... *Bufo woodhousii*, p. 286

20*a*. (12*b*) Vertebral stripe present; venter rougher and usually dark blotches on chest and upper sides; males with dark throat .... *Bufo woodhousii*, p. 286

20*b*. No vertebral stripe; venter less roughened and usually immaculate; males with light-colored throat .... *Bufo microscaphus*, p. 266

21*a*. (8*b*) Inner metatarsal tubercle sickle-shaped and usually black-edged (16); thenar tubercle not prominent; vocal sac of male sausage-shaped when inflated, forming dewlap when deflated; adults commonly 3 to 3½ inches .... *Bufo compactilis*, p. 255

21*b*. Inner metatarsal tubercle rounded and usually brown in color (19); thenar tubercle usually prominent; vocal sac of male rounded when inflated; adults commonly 2½ to 2¾ inches .... *Bufo microscaphus*, p. 266

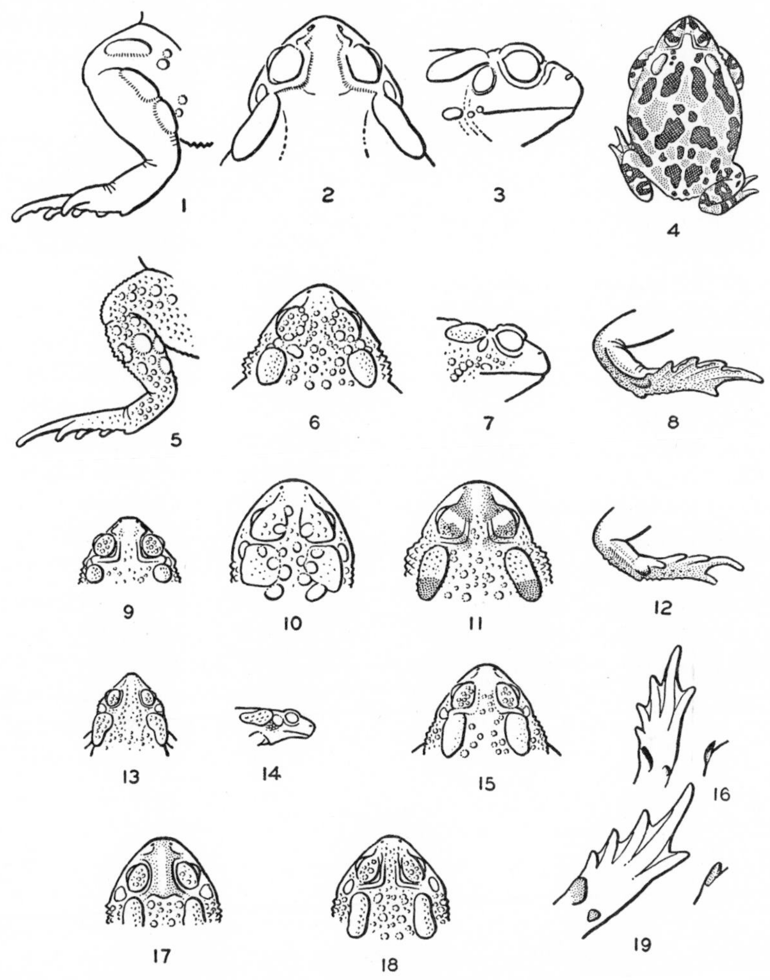

Fig. 27. 1-3, *Bufo alvarius;* 4, *B. cognatus;* 5-8, *B. boreas;* 9, *B. punctatus;* 10, *B. canorus;* 11-12, *B. microscaphus californicus;* 13-14, *B. debilis;* 15-16, *B. compactilis;* 17, *B. hemiophrys;* 18-19, *B. woodhousii.*

COLORADO RIVER TOAD

Bufo alvarius Girard
Plate 15

Range.—Southeastern California in Imperial County, and central and southern Arizona south at least to near the southern border of Sonora and probably into Sinaloa, Mexico. In Arizona found at least as far north as the Humbug Gold Mines, 6 miles north of Castle Springs, Yavapai County. May range into extreme southern Nevada and southwestern Utah, although as yet there are no authenticated records. (Pl. 56.)

In the United States this toad inhabits principally the drainages of the Colorado and Gila rivers. In the Colorado it may extend as far north as Bloomington, southwestern Utah, but this has not been established. At this locality a farmer told me of the discovery of a toad so large that it nearly covered the blade of a shovel. It was found in an irrigated field. The toad was described as sluggish and of bluish-gray color.

Type locality.—Valley of the Gila and Colorado rivers (Girard, in Baird, 1859a:26).

Description.—STRUCTURE. Our largest toad—adult to approximately 7 inches; skin relatively smooth for a toad, with small scattered warts and many minute tubercles; warts light-colored in life, set in blackish areas in young individuals, but dark blotches obscure or absent in larger animals; parotoid glands almost kidney-shaped, divergent posteriorly, 2 to 3 times as long as wide, smooth to the touch; interparotoid distance between anterior ends of parotoid glands, 3 to 4 times width of gland; cranial crests prominent, crescent-shaped, closely applied to inner margin of eyelid; canthus rostralis raised into a ridge and continuous with preorbital ridge and sometimes cranial crest; tympanum nearly or same size as eye opening; one to several prominent round warts, usually in a row, extending posteriorly from angle of jaw, especially conspicuous because of surrounding rather smooth skin; one to several dorsally situated femoral warts—one usually elongate and much enlarged, standing out from surrounding smooth or slightly warty skin; one to several enlarged tibial warts; membranous fold of skin on inner side of tarsus, usually well defined; 2 metacarpal tubercles, thenar smaller; 2 metatarsal tubercles, rather small considering size of toad, outer one reduced; femur short, in large part concealed by body skin. COLOR. Above uniformly dark brown to brownish green, olive, greenish olive, or grayish with some warts often pale orange or orange brown; below cream or dirty white, unmarked, or throat and chest mottled with gray; toes brown or reddish brown; small whitish area commonly present at anterior corner of eye; iris bronze to rust-colored. JUVENILE. Specimens reported by Bogert and Oliver (1945: 339) from Sonora, Mexico, were dark gray above with numerous small white spots commonly bordered by black; below usually with some spotting, principally in gular and pectoral regions. Juvenal specimen in Museum of Vertebrate Zoölogy has leg glands reduced and warts on back cream to whitish, set in dusky spots. SEXUAL DIFFERENCES. Throat and chest of female mottled with gray (Dickerson, 1920:106); first finger of male may be swollen basally and first and adjacent two fingers may possess nuptial pads.

Adult, RCS 3194, 4½ inches in snout-vent length, obtained on July 14, 1949, 1½ mile north-northeast of Ajo, Pima County, Arizona: Ground color above light olive gray on limbs, becoming greenish olive on upper surface of body; cranial crests and canthus rostralis brownish olive; spots of rust, lightening to yellow ocher on sides and limbs, often, but not invariably, associated with warts, especially dorsally on body; warts at angle of jaw and posterior part of upper jaw whitish; below cream; tips of toes and foot tubercles brown; iris pinkish orange or rust, grading to pale yellow around pupil, with horizontal blackish streak coinciding with pupil.

Habitat.—Dwells in arid regions but appears to be dependent, to a considerable extent, upon the presence of permanent springs or streams. Has entered the Imperial Valley of California with the development of irrigation. Usually inhabits lowlands but a juvenile obtained by Bogert and Oliver (1945:339) at Guirocoba, Sonora, Mexico, was found at 4,000 feet. Mr. Bogert tells me he has seen these toads around habitations in Arizona, 2 or 3 miles from water. Near Florence Junction they were breeding in temporary pools. Professor Thornber (Ruthven, 1907:506) states, "One usually sees the toads [Tucson, Arizona] a few days before the beginning of the summer showers, and their presence is taken as a sign of rain."

Ortenburger and Ortenburger (1926:102, Arizona) report that with few exceptions these amphibians were found in the wet places around the cattle watering-troughs of the ranches in mesquite areas. In the daytime they hid in hollows under the troughs.

Two specimens were collected (Kauffeld, 1943:343) in a water pocket in the rocks at 3,100 feet in Bear Canyon, in the Santa Catalina foothills northeast of Tucson, Arizona, in the plant association consisting of sotol, cholla, sahuaro, ocotillo, and palo verde. These were obtained July 11, 1941, at 9 P.M.; the temperature was 90°F. There had been sufficient rain to bring the toads out in numbers. On the night of July 13 a chorus of giant toads was heard from a ditch near the Sells-Robles road, southwest of Tucson.

Near Ajo, Pima County, Arizona, on July 14, 1949, 3 half-grown individuals were captured on the bank of a small stream that smelled strongly of hydrogen sulphide. The water was clear but there was much black tarlike silt over the bottom and on the grass at the sides of the creek. The stream was generally 1½ to 3 feet wide, but the toads were found around a pool 12 feet wide and 8 to 10 inches deep. Flow between such pools was moderately fast. The stream was probably fairly permanent as it came from a large silting basin of a copper mine which was under continuous operation. Mesquite, palo verde, and large creosote bushes were common along the stream. There was a dense growth of grass extending 3 to 5 feet from the water's edge. The surrounding country was nearly level, with the vegetation predominately creosote bush and sahuaro cactus.

This species was also observed at Peña Blanca Springs, Santa Cruz County, Arizona, on July 16 and 17, 1949. This locality is in the Pajarito Mountains near the Mexican line. The valley in the vicinity of the springs was 100 to 150 yards wide with a sand and gravel bottom and surrounding rocky peaks. There were oaks of several kinds and walnuts, the latter most common on the valley floor. The only water was at a covered spring, in a drinking trough for cattle, and in a small seepage area 50 yards below the covered spring. Grass had begun to grow, but according to a line rider, there was only dry grass a month ago. He said that about 2 weeks before we came, it had rained off and on for a week. July 16 was the first rain since then. About 9:00 P.M., on that date, we found 3 large *B. alvarius,* one perched on top the concrete side of the cattle tank, about 2½ feet above the ground. The exterior of the trough sloped 55° to 60°. It is difficult to see how such a heavy-bodied anuran could reach this position. The other 2 toads were found on damp soil near the tank.

Large size, a handicap in seeking underground shelter, and a smooth skin, subject to drying, are characteristics that tend to restrict the species to water in its desert habitat, according to Storer (1925:166-67).

Behavior.—Nocturnal. Semiaquatic. Seems to be more aquatic than most toads. Capable of considerable change in color from a dark brown phase to olive green or grayish.

Although summer rains usually initiate the activity of this species, wet weather was not responsible for the appearance of individuals observed by Arnold (1943:128), southwest of Tucson, Arizona. The first individual was seen on the night of June 22. There had been no rain for at least 2 months. Others were seen on June 26 and 29. At about 9:00 P.M. on the night of July 1, the first light rain of the summer commenced. Four individuals were observed at about 2:20 A.M. and others were seen several days later.

Voice.—Regarding the voice, Mearns (1907:113) states that after early summer rains which formed a large shallow lake near Buenos Ayres, Arizona, "These large toads then filled the air with their loud cries, which increased until a deafening roar was produced." Thornber (Ruthven, 1907:506) says regarding these toads at Tucson, Arizona, "I assure you there was no lack of noise that day or night, the croaking being incessant." Wright and Wright (1942:61) describe captive males as clucking like contented chickens or chickens when sleepy at night. Dickerson (1920) describes the protesting sound as a gentle chirping. This author also says that when held this toad jerks spasmodically and vibrates its entire body.

The observations of Mearns and Thornber need confirmation. They may have confused choruses of *Scaphiopus* or some other form with this species.

Thermal data.—At Peña Blanca Springs, Arizona, on July 17, 1949, subadult in shallow puddle on wet dirt road after thunderstorm, active, body 21.0°C.; water 21.8°C.; 8:30 P.M. Rowood, Arizona, on July 14, 1949, subadult active on highway, surface dry, body 21.5°C.; 1:30 A.M.

Food.—The following have been recorded: spiders; insects—grasshoppers, beetles (carabids, scarabaeids, ostomids, meloids, chrysomelids, and tenebrionids), hemipterans (coreids), hymenopterans (ants), lepidopterans (noctuids, adults and larvae); a centipede; small lizards (*Holbrookia* and others). (King, 1932:175-76; Bogert and Oliver, 1945:339-40; Ortenburger and Ortenburger, 1926:102.)

Reproduction.—Season, probably May to July (Livezey and Wright, 1947:194), but not adequately known. Two females collected at Alamos, Sonora, Mexico, between August 27 and September 2 contained mature eggs in the oviducts (Bogert and Oliver, 1945:339).

EGGS. Laid in long (400 inches) ropelike strings, 7,500 to 8,000 eggs. Deposited in temporary pools or shallow streams in water 12 to 18 inches deep, usually after first heavy summer showers. Strings with continuous gelatinous encasing; single jelly envelope, 2.12 to 2.25 mm. in diameter, average 2.20 mm., rather loose but distinct in outline; ovum 1.14 to 1.70 mm., average 1.40 mm., black or dark brown above and light tan below; 12 to 28 eggs per inch (Livezey and Wright, 1947:193).

LARVA. Apparently has not been described. Metamorphosis is rapid. Ruthven (1907:506) quotes Professor J. Thornber of the University of Arizona: "I do not think it is more than a month's time from the egg stage to the time when the young toad hops away with his tail nearly absorbed." Further, Thornber reports findings eggs in Sabino Canyon, Santa Catalina Mountains, about June 15, 1903: "A small stream of water came down from the mountains as the result of rain above, and these toads appeared in abundance pairing almost immediately. On that day every female was laying eggs. The eggs were laid in the clear stream of water, which was perhaps a foot to eighteen inches deep."

Remarks.—The virulence of the poison of the skin glands of this species is of interest. Several published and a number of unpublished observations suggest that this poison is of considerable potency. Musgrave (1930) reported that a wire-haired fox terrier bit one of these toads and killed it. The dog died within 2 or 3 minutes after the attack. A large police dog appeared, touching his nose to the toad. A few moments later, after the police dog had gone no more than 100 feet, his front legs crumpled beneath him and he pitched forward. He gathered himself only to tip backwards, his legs and body paralyzed. He later recovered. Miss D. M. Cochran (see Musgrave and Cochran, 1930:98) states that she has handled these toads without ill effect. An associate, John Hendrickson, informs me that he observed a bulldog worrying one of these toads. After the dog had mouthed the toad for about an hour, he began coughing and frothing at the mouth and some paralysis appeared. He was unable to get to his feet for a while, but eventually recovered.

WESTERN TOAD

Bufo boreas Baird and Girard
Plate 16

Range.—From southeastern Alaska through British Columbia, Washington, Oregon, California, into northern Lower California; also in Idaho, Montana (except extreme eastern part), western and central Wyoming, Nevada, Utah (mountains and higher plateaus), and northwestern and central Colorado, probably to as far south as Cumbres Pass, Conejos County. (Pl. 56.)

Type locality.—Columbia River and Puget Sound (Baird and Girard, 1852b:174-75).

Description.—STRUCTURE. Adult approximately 1¾ (subspecies *exsul*) to 5 inches; numerous pitted and minutely tuberculate warts on dorsum; tympanum about ¼ to ½ size of eye opening; parotoid and leg glands prominent; parotoid gland oval, smooth, or somewhat tuberculate, about same size or somewhat larger than upper eyelid; interparotoid space about twice width of gland; cranial crests absent or occasionally faintly evident, especially in large preserved individuals; usually well-developed fold of skin on tarsus (poorly developed in *exsul*), extending from inner metatarsal tubercle almost to heel; 2 rounded metatarsal tubercles, inner one larger. COLOR. General coloration above gray, blackish, dusky brown, yellowish, or dull green; white, greenish or yellowish vertebral stripe present, sometimes broken; warts commonly light-colored, usually brownish, often with reddish centers, commonly set in black blotches which may unite; limbs tend to be dark-spotted or banded; small, usually well-defined, white patch in front of eye, principally on lower lid; patch sometimes absent but when present usually more conspicuous than in other toads; below whitish, buff, or yellowish with varying amounts of dark spotting (dark markings most abundant in subspecies *exsul*); underside of feet yellowish, brown, or sooty with cream, yellow, tan, or brown tubercles; iris with bronze, greenish, or yellowish markings concentrated above and below pupil. JUVENILE. May be more spotted ventrally, under surfaces of feet more brilliant yellow—yellow orange or light orange, and warts more rust-colored than adult. SEXUAL DIFFERENCES. Female larger, heavier, and stouter than male especially in early spring when carrying eggs. Male has smoother skin and develops brown patches on inner surfaces of fingers during breeding season; there is no discoloration of throat.

Subspecies *exsul,* obtained June 20, 1949, 7 miles south of Deep Springs Post Office, Inyo County, California (general description): Juveniles with yellow-orange tubercles on undersides of feet; above olivaceous; under magnification black areas dorsally and laterally seen to be subdued by pale gold flecks (xanthophores?); dorsal stripe cream; seat patch sooty, with whitish tubercles; pupil rimmed with gold with slight coppery tinge; golden flecking of iris becomes less marked peripherally. In larger animals pale gold chromatophores of sides are less evident or absent, revealing underlying black color; foot tubercles tend toward whitish or cream; longitudinal dorsal area (about ⅓ width of body) may be olive green (xanthophores [?] overlying melanic ground color) but dark spots and flecks of ground color may show through; some larger individuals dark dorsally, lacking olive-green suffusion; iris brownish with numerous flecks of pale gold or cream; pupil margined by pale gold, most pronounced dorsally.

Adult of subspecies *nelsoni,* RCS 2916, obtained June 20, 1949, 2 miles south of Beatty, Nye County, Nevada: Ground color above brownish buff; warts brown, those on sides orange brown or nearly orange; parotoid glands orange brown; orange color of warts most pronounced on side of head and neck; foot tubercles dusky brown; venter buff, pale yellow, or cream; seat patch with faint dull orange-pink tinge; vertebral stripe cream or pale yellow; iris marked with pale gold and broken by horizontal dark stripe.

Adult of subspecies *boreas,* RCS 3466, obtained August 22, 1949, 10.9 miles west of Hebron, Jackson County, Colorado: Ground color above olive gray becoming brownish gray next to dorsal stripe; stripe pale yellow with greenish tinge; warts brown; below ash white with numerous black markings; seat patch cream or faint buffy cream; metacarpal tubercles tan, set in sooty ground color; metatarsal tubercles light grayish brown; iris with many closely set pale copper markings above and below pupil; pupillary ring gold; horizontal bar of blackish coinciding with pupil.

Habitat.—Occupies a variety of habitats from sea level to high mountains (to about 10,000 feet in Colorado). Occurs in relatively dry to humid situations. Found in open valleys and meadows, about lakes and streams and, less commonly, in heavily wooded regions. (Pl. 40, fig. 2 and Pl. 41, fig. 1.)

Adults at Pyramid Lake, Nevada, were in water quite noticeably saline. Most of the time during the day must be spent in the water since the banks are practically devoid of vegetation or shade of any sort. At this locality the species appears to have become as highly aquatic as are frogs (Brues, 1932:282).

Near Beatty, Nye County, Nevada, on June 20, 1949, *B. b. nelsoni* was obtained among sedges, 8 to 10 inches from the edge of an alga-covered pool. The water was clear and quiet although this pool was connected with others by rather rapid flow. The surrounding country was creosote-bush desert. The Amargosa River, of which the above pool is a part, makes possible the occurrence of *B. boreas* in this arid country. The vegetation of the river bottom consists largely of grassland with scattered cottonwoods; tules and sedges occur in the marshy areas. Drainage is to the southwest, but the river is intermittent and disappears for considerable distances south of Beatty.

Ten miles west of Hebron, Jackson County, Colorado, on August 22, 1949, *Bufo b. boreas* was found along a slowly flowing, clear mountain stream where there were quiet pools and several beaver ponds. Vegetation along this watercourse consisted of aspens and willows, with scattered lodgepole pines. Basin sagebrush and grass were present in open areas.

Myers (1942b) has described in detail the habitat of *exsul:* "Deep Springs Valley is an isolated depression in the desert mountains of northeastern Inyo County, California. It is elongate in form, trending northeast by southwest, about twelve miles long and five miles broad at its widest part. The lowest part of the valley, at its wide southwestern end, is a flat area about three by five miles, of almost exactly 5,000 feet elevation, although the rest of the gently rising valley floor is also very level. Surrounding Deep Springs, the White and Inyo Mountains rise to heights of 7,000 to 8,000 feet. Westgard Pass, through which one enters the valley from Owens Valley to the west, reaches 7,276 feet, and the top of the pass into the southern arm of Fish Lake Valley, on the east, is at 6,374 feet. The lowest entrance to the valley appears to be the dry, narrow, and now virtually unused Soldier Pass, from the dry northeastern corner of Deep Springs Valley into Eureka Valley on the southeast; the top of this pass appears to be at approximately 5,400 feet.

"Like other desert valleys to the east of the Sierra Nevada, Deep Springs is exceedingly dry, and on its floor the vegetation consists of sparse low desert brush (*Chrysothamnus*). The surrounding mountains support growths of juniper and piñon.

"The valley has few sources of water. Aside from washes carrying water only during infrequent desert rains, I know of only three. Wyman Creek, the course of which leads into the northern end of the valley, contains a little water, at least in its upper reaches, most of the year, and tiny Antelope Spring, on the west side of the valley, appears to be permanent, but neither of these contributes water to the valley floor, except during exceptionally heavy rains. The chief water source is formed by the Buckhorn or Deep Springs, which flow from the base of the southeastern valley wall just above the sink. These springs issue from the rocks for a distance of a mile or more, but only a few of them have a strong flow. The flow from the more southerly springs forms a marshy area of several acres, the water finally draining down into a shallow lake of alkaline, sulphurous water that sometimes reaches a diameter of a mile or more. There is also a smaller pond of good water between the springs and the lake.[7] The marshy area and the watercourses through it emit a strong sulphurous odor. Much of this is apparently due to sulphur bacteria, but some of the springs themselves must carry sulphur.

"In the late Pleistocene, the whole of the desert area in which Deep Springs Valley is set down was relatively well watered and supported a rather lush vegetation and forests. Since that time progressive aridity has made the region one of the most forbidding in North America, and the amphibian populations, no less than those of the fishes, have managed to exist only in the relatively few and widely separated areas watered by desert springs. The Deep Springs toad has probably been cut off from communication with surrounding populations for a very long time. The high passes into the valley are dry and are as impassable barriers to amphibians as to fishes, even during the infrequent rains. Soldier Pass, into Eureka Valley to the south, is not much higher than the floor of Deep Springs Valley, but it is dry and its southern slope is long, since the floor of Eureka Valley is much lower than that of Deep Springs. Toads might get out, but toads almost certainly would not get in by this pass. Parenthetically, nothing is known of the toads of Eureka Valley, if any exist there."

Behavior.—Generally nocturnal and crepuscular, but in some parts of its range diurnal activity occurs. *Bufo b. exsul* at Deep Springs Valley, Inyo County, California, on June 20, 1949 was as active in the daytime as at night. *Bufo boreas boreas* near Hebron, Jackson County, Colorado, on August 22, 1949, were found in numbers in the daytime. The species is largely terrestrial but enters water to breed. It may seek shelter in the daytime beneath boards, logs, rocks, and other surface objects or in rodent burrows. Some individuals have been observed to return regularly to the same retreats, exhibiting pronounced localization of movements. Locomotion on land is by hopping or walking, heavy-bodied individuals usually preferring to walk. The gait is awkward and often slow; tracks indicate that the hind toes may be dragged. When swimming, the fore-

[7] This pond now contains carp, according to Hubbs. *Cyprinodon* has recently been introduced into the marshy watercourses by R. R. Miller.

limbs are usually extended posteriorly but occasionally anteriorly; propulsion is accomplished principally by means of the hind limbs, commonly kicked together but sometimes alternately.

At Deep Springs Valley, California, this toad (subspecies *exsul*) was abundant on June 20, 1949. I counted 25 in 10 feet along a canal 2½ to 3 feet wide. In walking about one had to exercise care to avoid stepping on them. Myers' (1942b:8) estimate of 600 to 700 toads for the spring area would not apply this year. The animals must have been present in thousands. Mostly they were within a few feet of water but several dozen were discovered over 30 feet away, upon dry soil. Perhaps 30 or 40 were seen 10 to 15 feet from water. The animals seemed quite fearless. We repeatedly walked to within a few inches of them and many were easily taken in hand. They rested exposed or in sparse clumps of grass or pockets in the soil along the streams and canals. Occasionally one would dive to the bottom kicking with the hind legs alternately or together and would come to rest on the mud or beneath a streamer of filamentous green algae. Most of the bottom, however, was bare mud. There seemed to be as many animals active at 10:40 A.M. as there were at 9:00 P.M. the night before. Unless pressed, the toads seemed to prefer to walk rather than to hop.

Thermal data.—*Bufo b. boreas* swimming in stream, water 18.4°C.; air, 1 inch above ground 24.8°C.; 4:00 P.M. Adult in shade in grass, body 16.7°C.; 4:10 P.M. Adult sitting in water ½ inch deep, water 22.1°C.; body 22.2°C.; 1:45 P.M. (10.9 miles west of Hebron, Jackson County, Colorado, August 22, 1949). See also the table on page 239.

Voice.—Weak. During breeding activity or when handled, the male may utter a birdlike chirping sound consisting of mellow, tremulous notes. Storer (1925:177) compares the voice of *B. b. halophilus* heard in chorus ". . . to the voicings of a brood of young domestic goslings. The call of each male is uttered for a second or two and repeated at short intervals so that a practically continuous chorus issues from a breeding colony." The species does not possess an enlarged resonating vocal pouch. Calling may occur in the daytime as well as at night.

Food.—A highly beneficial species, eating numerous kinds of harmful insects. However it may be somewhat troublesome if present in large numbers in the vicinity of apiaries. Eckert (1934:93) found that the species at Davis, California, ate large numbers of bees. The toads came to the hives just after sundown when the bees were clustered at the entrances. On hot summer nights the insects may remain clustered out all night and a number of them will be busily engaged in ventilating the hive by fanning. Observations on moonlit nights revealed the presence of a large number of toads in different parts of the apiary, 16 being

THERMAL DATA

Deep Springs Valley, 7 miles south of Deep Springs Post Office, Inyo County, California, June 20, 1949, 12 individuals of subspecies *exsul*. (Data compiled by Ernest L. Stebbins.)

Individual	*Time* (A.M.)	*Size* (mm.)	*Temperature, °C.*			*Conditions of occurrence*
			Body (cloacal)	*Substratum*	*Air* (½ inch above surface in shade)	
1	8:30	55	23.4	27.6	24.7	In shade of tuft of grass, 25 feet from water
2	8:35	50	22.6	25.2 (dung heap)	24.5	On cow pie, no shade, 30 feet from water
3	8:40	51	24.4	27.6	23.8	Walking in sun, 20 feet from water
4	8:50	52	22.6	26.2 (dung heap)	26.8	Sitting quietly on dung, 20 feet from water
5	8:53	43	24.2	26.2 (dung heap)	26.8	Sitting quietly on dung, 20 feet from water
6	9:05	47	23.8	28.2	26.8	Walking in sun, 10 feet from water
7	9:15	50	22.0	26.2 (slightly damp)	26.4 (over slightly damp soil)	Resting in shade of grass, 10 feet from water
8	9:30	51	21.2	20.8 (water)	26.8	On bottom of stream 8 inches deep and 2½ feet wide
9	9:35	45	22.8	20.8 (water)	26.8	Swimming—swam 25 feet
10	9:40	40	21.6	20.8 (water)		Resting at edge of stream, in water; 240 gular pulsations per minute*
11	9:55	45	21.6	20.8 (water)		" but 212 gular pulsations per minute
12	10:05	52	21.8	20.8 (water)		" but 200 gular pulsations per minute

* Gular pulsations were taken for one minute of steady breathing, however the toads stop their gular movements for periods of 10 seconds or more and vary intensity of respiration.

counted around one row of 12 hives. Some were seen sitting at the entrances of hives with their forefeet on the bottom boards. The stomach and colon of one medium-sized toad contained 33 heads of bees, 7 elytra of beetles, 31 ants, 4 small arachnids, and some extraneous vegetable matter. Twenty-two individual droppings were examined in which a total of 514 heads of bees was found (an average of 23.3 bees each). The largest number of heads in any one dropping was 38 while the smallest was 13. Predation of this sort, of course, can be easily prevented by elevation of the hives.

Other foods recorded: Crustaceans—a crayfish and a sowbug; arachnids—spiders; insects—grasshoppers, trichopterans (caddisflies); lepidopterans (moths and larvae), dipterans (mosquitoes [*Culiseta* sp.] and deer flies), beetles (tenebrionids [*Eleodes*], scarabaeids, elaterids, weevils, hydrophilids, carabids, silphids, dytiscids, staphylinids, coccinellids, cicindelids, and beetle larvae). (Ellis and Henderson, 1915:254; Tanner, 1931:174-75; Schonberger, 1945:121; Burger and Bragg, 1947:62.)

Several dozen *B. b. exsul* from Deep Springs Valley, Inyo County, California, obtained June 20, 1949, were killed in a jar of formalin along with 4 or 5 adult *Scaphiopus hammondii*. The animals were killed shortly after capture. In the bottom of the jar were found a number of regurgitated *Scaphiopus* tadpoles. These larvae were abundant in a canal where most of the toads were captured. Examination of stomach contents of 6 *exsul* some months later revealed remains of snout beetles, ants, and lepidopterous larvae but no tadpoles. It is unknown whether the toads or the spadefoots had eaten the larvae; perhaps both had fed on them.

Reproduction.—Considering the species as a whole, the season is long, extending from January to September—for *boreas,* March to September, with the crest in June and July, and for *halophilus,* January to July (Livezey and Wright, 1947:195). Cope (1884:18) found the race *boreas* in voice in a pond near the shore of Pyramid Lake, Nevada, in July, 1882. Storer (1925:176) states that in the central part of California most spawning occurs in March, April, and May and that Camp (MS) says this toad breeds from January to June in southern California. At higher altitudes breeding probably is delayed until June or July. According to Storer (1925:177), 12 to 15 pairs (*halophilus*) ordinarily constitute a breeding population at any one spot. Great congregations of thousands of individuals, as in some other species of *Bufo,* have not been observed. In assuming the position of amplexus, the male usually mounts the female from behind, holding her with his forelimbs in the axillary region.

Burger and Bragg (1947:61-62) found that this species exercised little discrimination in the selection of breeding sites. Any body of water without a strong current and with gradually descending banks at some point on its margin were used. Tadpoles were found in a roadside puddle with approximate dimensions of 3 feet by 6 inches and at Taylor Reservoir, the largest lake in Colorado. They were found in beaver ponds and glacial kettle ponds alike.

EGGS. In masses of up to 16,500 eggs as calculated for subspecies *halophilus* by Storer (1925:178). Eggs extruded in 2 strings which often become greatly entwined in vegetation along margins of ponds, reservoirs, and streams. Deposited in shallow water, ordinarily not deeper than 12 inches and often less than 6 inches. Gelatinous encasing about eggs continuous; 2 jelly envelopes; no partitions separating individual eggs; ova mostly in double (occasionally triple) row within jelly tube; outer envelope may be 4.89 to 5.29 mm., somewhat loose but distinct; inner envelope may be 3.54 to 3.82 mm., distinct; ovum 1.65 to 1.75 mm. (*halophilus*) or 1.50 to 1.75 (*boreas*), jet black above, white or cream below; 13 to 52 eggs per inch, average 27 (Storer, 1925:178; Livezey and Wright, 1947:195).

LARVA. Up to 56 mm. in total length (*halophilus* from Stockton, California, Storer, 1925:179) but often much smaller; larvae from Arroyo Seco near Los Angeles obtained April 15, 1923, ranged from 10 to 34 mm. and well-developed hind limbs were present on one individual only 27 mm. in length (Storer, 1925:179); body tapered behind, broadest between eye and spiracle; eyes nearer lateral margin of body than dorsal midline; tail fins narrow, widest near mid-point of tail; greatest height of dorsal fin nearly same as musculature at tail base; ventral fin similar in height to dorsal; anus median, emerging in ventral fin; spiracle on left side of body near middle. (Pl. 29.)

Upper mandible slightly bowed in outline, lower well developed, broadly **V**-shaped; labial teeth 2/3 (1/3, *exsul*)—first upper row longest, extending entirely across mouth; second interrupted medially; first, second, and third lower rows successively shorter, although similar in length, not divided at center; papillae only at sides of mouth. (Pl. 30.)

General coloration dull blackish, or dusky, with no red or yellow; under surface slightly paler, but with little or no iridescence; tail fin clouded, but without spots, marked with dense minute melanic stippling, especially in dorsal fin; muscular portion of tail solidly blackish; iris blackish (based on subspecies *halophilus,* principally from Storer, 1925: 171-72).

In life individuals from Oakland, Alameda County, California, obtained May 12, 1951, were olivaceous dorsally; under magnification head-body noted as closely flecked with metallic pale yellow, belly with salmon metallic (guanistic?) flecking; iris with gold markings suggestive of adult.

Larval description by Burger and Bragg (1947:63), based on animals from the Gothic region, Gunnison County, Colorado, corresponds to Storer's description, but maximum total length given as 34 to 47 mm.; tail tapering to blunt tip; dorsal fin extending anteriorly short distance past anus and disappearing onto body. Burger and Bragg described color of their specimens (in alcohol) as ". . . heavily colored above with a dark-brown pigment, often having a bluish tinge; ventrum of body slate-colored with lighter blue blotches that tend to form transverse bands on each side of abdomen; median ends of these bands more or less fused to form two lines that converge posteriorly and enclose an immaculate slate-colored wedge-shaped central area; area beneath head anterior to level of eyes and ventral surfaces of hind limbs also light blue in color; musculature of tail opaque with a yellow tinge, densely flecked with large dark-brown chromatophores so as to give a brown granular effect; dorsal and ventral tail fins semitransparent and with scattered small dark-brown chromatophores, dorsal fin appearing more densely pigmented in preserved material because of presence of more coagulated blood."

Larva of *B. b. exsul,* obtained by me 7 miles south of Deep Springs Post Office, Inyo County, California, June 20, 1949 were colored as follows: Body solid black, lightening slightly ventrally, with minute pale gold flecks on sides becoming scarcer posteriorly; only few pale gold flecks laterally at base of tail musculature; iris flecked with gold; tail fins translucent, stippled with melanophores.

Storer (1925:179) mentions small larvae as 9 mm. and 10 mm. in total length. They feed by scraping algae and detritus from the bottom film. Metamorphosis is usually completed in less than 3 months, hence the breeding pond need not be permanent. Sometimes, however, the pond dries before they have transformed. Wright and Wright (1949) give the time required for metamorphosis as 30 to 45 days for *boreas* (transforming from July to September at 9.5 to 12.0 mm.) and 28 to 45 days for *halophilus* (transforming from April to August at 12 to 15 mm.). Sexual maturity is probably reached in 2 or 3 years.

An individual lived 6 years in the Philadelphia Zoölogical Garden (Conant and Hudson, 1949:3).

Key to Subspecies

Figure 28

1*a*. Heavily mottled with black on whitish, sometimes almost solid black above; below whitish heavily spotted and blotched with black, especially posteriorly; seat patch dark with white spots and blotches; skin between warts smooth; adult size small, up to about 2 inches . . . . *B. b. exsul* Myers

1b. Dorsal dark mottlings fainter; below light colored, without spots or with few on chest (occasional individuals may have more extensive spotting); seldom with uniformly dark seat patch; skin between warts tuberculate; adult size larger, to about 5 inches 2

2a. Head narrow wedge-shaped, with elongate, pointed snout (1); size smaller (usually under 3 inches); elbows and knees not meeting when limbs adpressed to sides; feet smaller, with reduced webbing (6); skin smoother (male *halophilus* excepted). *Range.* Southern and eastern Nye County and northern Lincoln County, Nevada[8] . . . . *B. b. nelsoni* Stejneger

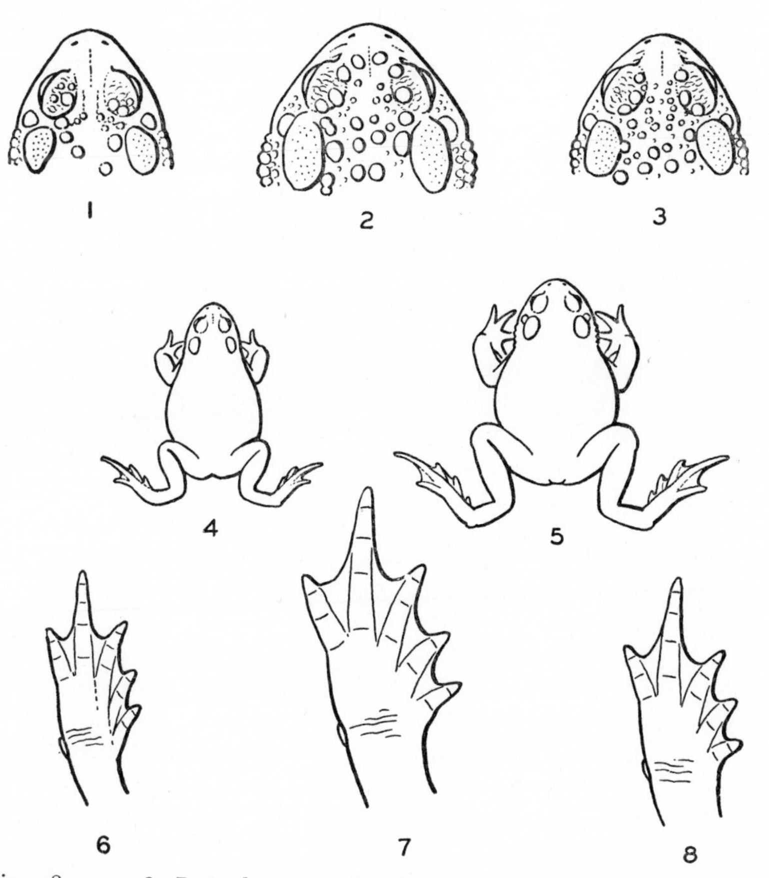

Fig. 28. 1, 4, 6, *Bufo boreas nelsoni;* 2, 5, 7, *B. b. boreas;* 3, 8, *B. b. halophilus.*

[8] "So far known from three separated localities, but most characteristic population is in the upper part of the Amargosa River. Apparently this toad is more closely restricted to water than even its near relatives which inhabit more humid districts" (Linsdale, 1940: 204).

2*b*. Head broader, blunter, with rounded snout (2, 3); size larger; elbows and knees meeting when limbs adpressed to sides; feet larger and more fully webbed (7, 8); skin rougher (male *halophilus* excepted) 3

3*a*. Eyes smaller with interorbital distance greater (2); head narrower; hind foot broader, greater than 36 per cent of body length, measured from first to fifth toe (7); size larger; tendency toward somewhat heavier ventral blotching. *Range*. From southeastern Alaska through British Columbia (including Vancouver Island), Washington, and Oregon into northern California; also in Idaho, western Montana, western and southern Wyoming, Nevada (except southern part), Utah, and northwestern and central Colorado .... *B. b. boreas* Baird and Girard

3*b*. Eyes larger with interorbital width less (3); head broader; size smaller; foot breadth less than 36 per cent of body length (8); less webbing than in *boreas* (8); general color lighter and less ventral blotching. *Range*. Throughout California except for northern part, southeastern deserts, and higher mountains of the Sierra Nevada; in northern Lower California .... *B. b. halophilus* Baird and Girard

Remarks.—Myers (1942b) described the toad of Deep Springs, Deep Springs Valley, Inyo County, California as a species, *Bufo exsul*. This population is apparently isolated, confined to Deep Springs Valley which is ringed by mountains. The animals are highly aquatic, almost froglike in habit. I prefer to view this form as a subspecies of *Bufo boreas* rather than as a distinct species. Although it is smaller, more darkly pigmented, and has a somewhat smoother skin—in structure, general aspects of coloration, and voice, it is like this species. *Bufo boreas nelsoni* occurs in similarly isolated populations and its morphological divergence from *boreas* stock seems to me not to differ in extent in any clear way from that of *exsul*. The relationship of *exsul* to the *boreas* complex is not essentially different from that between *boreas* and *nelsoni* or, for that matter, in some other species, the relationship of certain differentiated insular populations from mainland stocks. See Myers (1942b:12-13) for an alternative opinion.

In regard to *exsul*, Myers (1942b:13) sounds the following pertinent warning: "*Bufo exsul* has perhaps the most restricted range and the fewest living representatives of any known amphibian. It is a queer and interesting relict, and it is to be hoped that herpetological collectors will not too greatly reduce the population. The Natural History Museum of Stanford University is ready to supply reputable institutions really needing specimens with material from its relatively large series. It is also to be hoped that the proprietors of the Deep Springs School will not endanger the existence of this strange creature by the introduction of bullfrogs or other predators into its small territory, a reprehensible type of destruction that has become all too common in desert spring areas of the Southwest."

A study of variation in this and other species of *Bufo*, using live material for more complete analysis of coloration, is needed. Individuals from Walker Creek, 4 miles southwest of Olancha and Diaz Lake near Lone Pine, Inyo County, California, and from several localities at intermediate elevations in the Sierra Nevada (as the floor of Yosemite Valley) suggest that *Bufo canorus* may be a high mountain differentiate of *B. boreas.* It is probable that interbreeding between *boreas* and *canorus* occurs along the east-west drainages of the western and perhaps eastern slope of the Sierra.

Burger and Bragg (1947:64) observe that the dorsal coloration of adults from the Gothic region of Colorado is darker than that of typical specimens of *B. b. boreas* from the Pacific Northwest. Further, in the Gothic animals the skin between the warts is smoother, the warts are less pronounced, and the parotoid glands are larger and more oblong and not so elevated; the head is larger and broader; size is smaller (maximum 83 mm. in contrast to 125 mm. for *B. b. boreas*); and the dark ventral markings are more numerous and more irregular (tending to unite irregularly). "In some characters the Gothic toad shows variation from *Bufo boreas boreas* in the direction of *Bufo exsul* Myers." A close similarity to *B. b. nelsoni* is suggested by descriptions of the latter. I may add that there is also similarity to *Bufo canorus,* probably to be viewed as convergence, since both types are high mountain forms. *Exsul,* in turn, appears to me in many respects like a small black *B. canorus,* although lacking the sexual dimorphism in coloration of the latter.

YOSEMITE TOAD

Bufo canorus Camp

Plate 16

Range.—High Sierra Nevada of California, usually above 6,500 to over 10,000 feet. The species is known from 2 miles southwest of Sonora Pass, 8,700 feet, Alpine County, in the north to near the top of Kaiser Pass, 9,200 feet, Fresno County, in the south. The species seems to be absent from the high altitudes of Placer County and from the Sierras south of Kings River, where its place is taken by *B. boreas halophilus,* which there goes to a high elevation (Camp, 1916a:62).

Type locality.—Porcupine Flat, 8,100 feet, Yosemite National Park, Mariposa County, California (Camp, 1916a:59).

Description.—STRUCTURE. Size small, adult 1¾ to 3 inches; in general appearance resembles *B. boreas* but interparotoid space narrow, usually same as or less than width of gland; parotoid glands large, rounded, as broad as length of eyelid, sometimes rather poorly defined and merging with smaller warts; interorbital space narrow, usually less than width of upper eyelid; cranial crests absent or, rarely, weakly developed; tympanum 1/3 to 1/2 size of eye opening; snout rounded in profile; above with moderate numbers of rather smooth but pitted warts; enlarged tibial wart usually present as in *boreas;* 2 rounded metacarpal tubercles, thenar 1/3 to 2/3 size of palmar tubercle; 2 light-colored, often brownish, rounded metatarsal tubercles, inner one larger; skin froglike, relatively smooth and moist. COLOR. Females and immatures: Strikingly dark and light-colored above; warts large, often dark-colored, lightening centrally, each set in a dark blotch, most blotches connected; blotches outlined with fine tracery of cream to yellowish, lighter than ground color; blotching extends onto feet and on top and sides of head and on parotoid glands; vertebral line narrow, somewhat irregular, and sometimes broken, whitish to yellowish in life; below whitish or pale yellow with varying amounts of spotting and blotching, especially on abdomen and chest; some individuals, including juveniles, largely unmarked ventrally; iris commonly with numerous flecks of coppery or brassy color on dark background. SEXUAL DIFFERENCES. Male smaller than female and with less conspicuous warts largely because they are not set off by dark blotches as in female; male frequently almost uniformly colored dark olivaceous to olive green or with small spots of black edged with narrow yellowish or whitish margin; female contrastingly marked with large spots of black outlined with whitish and with touches of yellow and rust in dorsal pattern. Most pronounced instance of sexual dichromism among North American anurans. As with other toads during breeding season, male develops roughened light to dark brown skin on upper and inner sides of inner three fingers.

Habitat.—Occupies the Canadian, Hudsonian, and, to a lesser extent, the Arctic-Alpine life-zones. Frequents wet mountain meadows at elevations usually above 6,500 feet (Storer 1925:184). Individuals are commonly solitary when not breeding. They occur in damp situations beneath stones, logs, and other surface objects and in rodent burrows. The species breeds in pools, lakes, small streams, and in meadows in water from melting snow.

Behavior.—May be active in the daytime, especially during the breeding period. It is a hardy species, hibernating during the cold season, emerging in April, May, June, and July, and retiring in September and October.

Voice.—Males make a mellow, long-sustained trilling sound of 10 to 20 or more notes uttered rapidly and given repeatedly at frequent intervals.

The song has a ventriloquial quality. The specific name, *canorus*, refers to this melodious trill (Camp, 1916a:62). When singing is done in chorus, songs of individuals overlap so that a continuous sound is produced. There is some difference in pitch at which the several members of a group sing, varying perhaps with the size of the individual. Choruses at different elevations may begin as early as May 20 and last until July 9, singing occurring in the daylight hours and into the early evening (Grinnell and Storer, 1924:659-60).

Food.—Includes a wide variety of insects and the like. An individual captured at Porcupine Flat, Yosemite National Park, June 29, 1915, contained 2 tenebrionid beetles, several weevils of various species, numerous large ants and 1 centipede, besides some red fir needles probably taken incidentally (Grinnell and Storer, 1924:660).

Reproduction.—Breeds in late spring and early summer. Camp (1916a: 62) states that breeding begins as soon as the snow melts from the Sierran meadows, June 1 to July 15. Many females captured at this time contained mature eggs. On May 20, 1919, near Chinquapin, south of Yosemite Valley, Grinnell and Storer (1924:659) found males out and trilling loudly. Some probably emerge toward the end of April and a few may be out until early October. Wiggins (1943:197) collected an adult female on August 11, 1942, that was crawling toward a small pool in a meadow. She possessed eggs ready for spawning. At the head of Lyell Canyon several individuals were depositing eggs July 16, 1915 (Grinnell and Storer, 1924:660). Males precede females to the breeding sites.

EGGS. Undescribed.

LARVA. Closely resembles larva of *B. boreas* but smaller except for subspecies *B. b. exsul;* labial teeth 2/3. A comparison was made between 8 mature larvae of *Bufo canorus* (SNHM 2936) from Peregoy Meadow, Yosemite National Park, California, collected on June 20, 1928, with 11 larvae, of similar growth stage, of *Bufo boreas* (MVZ 9961), from 7 miles south of Red Bluff, Tehama County, California, collected May 6, 1924. The *canorus* larvae are darker, the intestines scarcely or not at all visible; the viscera can be easily seen in all the *boreas* larvae; the dorsal fin is transparent, marked with few relatively large branched melanophores in *canorus,* is similarly transparent but closely stippled with numerous punctate melanophores in *boreas;* the snout appears shorter in *canorus.* To what extent these differences can be relied upon is unknown. The specimens have been preserved for a long but similar length of time. Methods of preservation may have differed. (Pls. 29 and 30.)

Myers (1930a:62-63) found many tadpoles on June 20, 1928, in the vicinity of Peregoy Meadow (7,100 feet), Yosemite National Park. These were of two sizes, the smaller ones about 10 mm. and the larger mature tadpoles about 28 or 30 mm. Some of the larger ones transformed that night, the tiny toadlets measuring 10 mm. Tadpoles were found in holes not more than 6 or 8 inches in diameter that were almost filled with fine mud and vegetation. The holes may have been made by cattle. Seepage water kept them filled. The water in the holes was very warm but must have become rather cold at night.

Remarks.—As mentioned under *B. boreas,* it appears that *canorus* is a close relative of *boreas.* Professor Culbertson of Fresno State College informs me that both *B. boreas* and *B. canorus* occur in a meadow at the top of Kaiser Pass, elevation about 9,200 feet, above Huntington Lake, Fresno County, California. Mr. Culbertson states that he has never found an individual of *B. boreas* more than about 2 inches long at this locality, although at a lower elevation (7,000 feet) there are many large individuals but no *canorus.* He suspects it is possible that some of the smaller *boreas* in the range of *canorus* might be breeding individuals, crossing to some extent with *canorus.* There seems to be considerable variation in the parotoid glands. Similarity of the young of *canorus* and *boreas* make their identification difficult.

I have seen individuals from Yosemite Valley (Yosemite Museum specimens) that are intermediate between *canorus* and *boreas* in dorsal markings and appearance of the parotoid glands.

The habitat of *canorus* is such that isolation and semi-isolation of populations occurs. These toads inhabit mountain meadows that are of scattered occurrence and are commonly separated by rocky terrain in which the toads are scarce or absent. Such separation favors local differentiation. Thus in a group of these toads from Reds Meadows near Devil's Post Pile, the parotoid glands are light-colored, contrasting with the darker pigmentation of the head and body. In Tuolumne Meadows, in air line about 15 miles away, another population occurs that largely lacks contrastingly colored parotoids. These populations, although only a few miles apart, are in the headwaters of two distinct drainages, that of the San Joaquin and the Tuolumne rivers, respectively. The headwaters of the two are adjacent, while the junction of the Tuolumne River with the San Joaquin in the Great Valley of California lies about 75 miles north of where the San Joaquin River leaves the foothills of the Sierra. The desirability of further study of geographic variation in the species is evident.

GREAT PLAINS TOAD

Bufo cognatus Say
Plate 17

Range.—From Logier, Alberta, Canada, south through eastern Montana, Wyoming, Utah, southern Nevada, southeastern California (along the Colorado River and in the Imperial Valley), into Mexico including northern Lower California; eastward to Minnesota and Arkansas; in North and South Dakota, Nebraska, Colorado, Kansas, Oklahoma, New Mexico, and Texas. In Mexico, reported from Chihuahua, Coahuila, Durango, San Luis Potosí, and Baja California (Smith and Taylor, 1948:41). (Pl. 57.)

Type locality.—Arkansas River (in Colorado, probably between the present site of La Junta and the Colorado-Kansas boundary [Grinnell and Camp, 1917:140]). (Say, 1823:190.)

Description.—STRUCTURE. Adult approximatetly 2 to 4½ inches; above with numerous small warts of rather uniform size; head relatively small, broadly triangular in dorsal aspect; well-developed cranial crests, divergent posteriorly and meeting anteriorly at boss on snout; snout blunt and rounded; parotoid glands usually tuberculate, rarely smooth, widely separated, 2½, or more, times width of gland, same length or slightly longer than length of eyelid, usually about 1½ to 2 times as long as wide; tympanum vertically oval, ⅓ to ½ size of eye opening; interorbital area about same width as eyelid; legs short, much of femoral portion is concealed within hind portion of body; single large palmar tubercle; inner metatarsal tubercle flat, commonly with sharp edge; outer tubercle smaller, also sometimes rather sharp-edged; ventral surface coarsely granulated, sometimes minutely tuberculate. COLOR. Ground color above generally yellowish, brown, greenish, or gray, with usually symmetrically placed large dorsal and lateral dark blotches (often greenish in life); dorsal blotches commonly in 4 pairs; blotches with irregular outline and commonly edged with lighter color than ground; when light color prominent, animal may appear obliquely striped; when blotches outstanding toad may appear spotted; upper eyelid with central dark stripe or blotch; limbs blotched dorsally; narrow light vertebral stripe may or may not be present; below unspotted, cream to white, with yellow or orange-yellow seat patch, often with pinkish tinge. JUVENILE. Cranial crests may be absent or obscure in very young individuals; 4 to 8 pairs of large dark spots on dorsal surface and smaller spots on sides, similar to adult; very young toads may have whole dorsal surface dotted with small, brick-red spots. SEXUAL DIFFERENCES. Vocal sac of male bluish or purplish black, sausage-like when inflated. When deflated loose thin skin of sac may be partly tucked under flap of skin of gular area; small area of sac may appear posterior to this flap. Female reaches larger size than male. Male has first finger and sometimes 2 adjacent ones more or less cornified.

Juvenile, RCS 3326, about 25 mm. in snout-vent length, obtained on July 24, 1949, 32 miles northeast of Douglas, along U.S. Highway 80, Cochise County, Arizona: Ground color above, light purplish gray; spots suffused with olive green centrally, edged with black; spots margined with cream; dorsal tubercles orange yellow; iris with pale gold, tinged with rust; throat white; underside of body ash white; underside of feet dull orange yellow.

Summarization of colors of adults, obtained July 14, 1949, at Rowood, Pima County; 2 miles north-northeast of Douglas, Cochise County; and 16.4 miles northwest of Pima, Graham County, Arizona: Ground color above light buff-brown, dusky olive green, dark olive, or whitish to cream; dorsal symmetrically arranged blotches and spots, dark olive green, olive green, or light olive green, edged with sooty or black; spots sometimes obscure, especially when animal in extreme light or dark phases; symmetrically placed spots edged with light greenish yellow; vague blotching of light olive green between spots; warts light yellowish brown; cranial crests and boss on snout light olive brown; ventral stripe ash gray, poorly defined or not evident; outer edges of upper eyelids yellowish brown or tan; spots on lower sides dark yellowish olive; below cream, or creamy white; seat patch yellowish, dull orange yellow, or pinkish yellow; tips of hind toes and foot tubercles purplish brown to black; skin between tubercles purplish; foretoes purplish sooty to yellowish brown; metacarpal tubercle may be light yellowish brown; nuptial pads brown to purplish black; vocal sac sooty anteriorly, purplish posteriorly; iris brassy or coppery, with old gold around pupil; inner posterior surface of tibia and upper surface of hind foot sometimes yellowish but no yellow in groin, axilla, or femoral areas.

Habitat.—Grassland to desert areas, varying considerably in different parts of the range. Found in arid and semiarid regions, usually in the lower, damper sections of such areas. Frequents irrigation canals, flood plains of rivers, temporary rain pools, and reservoirs.

Ortenburger and Ortenburger (1926:103) found the species in Arizona almost always in the vicinity of watering troughs where it was associated with *Bufo alvarius*.

Bragg (1940b:329) says, "From the bulk of the evidence available, it may be concluded that *Bufo cognatus* is primarily a toad of the grasslands biome which is able to extend its range into deserts of the Sonoran zone in limited numbers along irrigation ditches and similar low-lying areas where sufficient moisture is available. Under climatic conditions resulting in a mixed-grass prairie, however, it tends to avoid the lower areas, thus automatically becoming excluded from woodlands and the flood plains of streams."

At Rowood, Pima County, Arizona, on July 14, 1949, a chorus of these toads was found in a seepage area near the silting basin of a mine. The toads were in a shallow pool 12 by 75 feet and about 1 inch deep. Most were calling from the bases of bushes (bull nettle [*Solanum elaeagnifolium*] and an undetermined plant) that stood in the water. Mesquite and creosote bushes were present about the pool.

Behavior.—Nocturnal but sometimes diurnal, especially during the breeding period. Strecker (1910a:19-20, Texas) observes that this species is more diurnal in habit than most toads, having been seen in the streets, on cloudy days, as late as 11:00 A.M. and as early as 3:00 P.M., and at the springs at all hours of the day. Usually, however, they come out of their burrows about an hour before dusk. Bragg (1937b:273-74) captured a small male soon after 10:30 A.M. on a warm, showery day in central Oklahoma (air temperature 26°C.).

Bragg (1940, Oklahoma) found the species uncommon about human habitations and street lights. On several occasions in central Oklahoma he (1940a:14) observed these toads moving along roads on moonlight nights in the springtime, hundreds of individuals all hopping in the same direction and feeding as they progressed. The species spends considerable time underground, since the period favorable for activity may last for only a few weeks in spring or summer. It is capable of burrow construction as observed by Bragg (1937b:274) in Oklahoma where individuals were found in shallow basins into which their bodies fitted neatly and flush with the surface of the ground. The animals burrow by backing into the ground with a shuffling movement of the hind feet; the sharp-edged cornified tubercles facilitate submergence. When annoyed this toad may assume a defensive attitude common to many anurans. The lungs are inflated, thereby increasing the size of the body; the head is lowered and the eyes often depressed into their sockets.

Voice.—Well developed in the male—a shrill, harsh, vibrating, prolonged trill. When calling, the vocal pouch becomes enormously distended, projecting sausage-like upward and in front of the head and equaling in bulk ⅓ of the body (fig. 23). At close range a chorus of these toads may be almost deafening.

According to Dickerson (1920:101) the female rarely makes any sound. The male, in addition to his trilling, produces sounds resembling the squawk of a toy doll. Ortenburger and Ortenburger (1926:103) refer to the call as ". . . a chirp somewhat like that of a sleepy little chicken."

A chorus at Rowood, Pima County, Arizona, July 14, 1949, was composed of 15 or 20 males. The singers were mostly under bushes, sitting in shallow water. Their vocal sacs, when inflated, did not touch the water. Frequency and duration of the trills of 2 individuals were timed as follows: 1.—(8) 10 (11) 6 (12) 7 (10) 8 (11) 10 (11) 10 (15) 13 (13) 10 (12); 2.—(11) 7 (14) 7 (17) 11 (13) 10 (16). Numbers in parentheses represent lengths of sustained trills, and the others represent intervals between trills, all in seconds. The song is a rattling, raucous trill, essentially on one pitch. It starts and stops abruptly. It suggests a pneumatic hammer but has more musical quality. The clattering of this chorus was heard at a distance of about ½ mile. When among the singers it was difficult to carry on a conversation because of the volume of the sound. Individual calls varied in vibration rate and slightly in pitch. One singer in the open allowed me to bring my flashlight to within 15 inches of him. When he trilled the translucent, bubble-like membrane of the vocal sac vibrated in unison with a fluttering of the sides of the body. In the flashlight beam the vocal sac appeared as a dark, vertically oval patch when deflated, but flared into a short sausage when distended.

Thermal data.—At the foregoing locality, 2 adult toads were found with body temperatures of 22.2° and 22.0°C. at 1:30 A.M.; air 1½ inch above the water 23.0°C.; water 21.6°C.; mud at the edge of the pond 23.5°C. The animals were sitting in shallow water of the seepage area, trilling.

Food.—Destroys many noxious insects. An effective enemy of overwintering cutworms in Oklahoma. Value to agriculture on a yearly basis of individual toads of this species in Oklahoma has been estimated at $25 apiece (Bragg, 1943:38). Foods recorded: Lepidopterans (moths), flies, beetles (tenebrionids [*Eleodes*], carabids [*Agonoderus, Harpalus,* and *Platynus*], and elaterids [*Elater* and *Ludius*]). (Little and Keller, 1937:218-19; Hartman, 1906:228; Tanner, 1931:176.)

Reproduction.—According to Bragg (1940b:435) these toads breed only after rain in spring and summer when the temperature exceeds 12°C. Breeding sites in central Oklahoma include buffalo wallows, flooded fields, and the edges of extensive temporary pools. They do not use ditches, "tanks" (relatively permanent pools) in pastures, streams or lakes, and they have never been known to breed in excessively muddy water. They use only relatively clear shallow water. They breed usually in large congresses built up by the reaction of males to one another's calls. The season of activity is from April to September (Livezey and Wright, 1947:194).

EGGS. A single female may lay 20,000 eggs, which are deposited after heavy rains in temporary pools, permanent springs, and small streams, attached to debris near the bottom (Livezey and Wright, 1947). Eggs in strings with continuous gelatinous encasing; 2 envelopes present, decidedly scalloped, almost beadlike, appearing laminated; outer layer distinct and firm, 1.72 mm. at narrowest point, 2.05 mm. at thickest point in single row, 2.66 mm. in double row, inner envelope 1.60 mm.; partitions separating individual eggs; ovum 1.20 mm., black above and white below; single or double strings rarely have double row of eggs within one tube (Livezey and Wright, 1947:194).

Bragg (1937b:283) states that "Sight plays little or no part in sex recognition; a calling male clutches any toad which happens to touch him. Males when clasped or handled 'protest' by chirping. Females often make the same respiratory movements but do not chirp. Females, once clasped, are retained tenaciously; males are soon released. Amplexation is axillary and a male in the wrong positions works till he obtains the correct one.

"Egg laying is a long process. Amplexation occurs at night, but the eggs are often not all laid till the afternoon of the next day. Typically the eggs are produced in two long strings wound about in the space of two or three feet at the bottom of the pool. The eggs, and presumably the sperm, are emitted at intervals, a few at a time." Eggs in the laboratory may hatch in 53 hours (Bragg 1936b:20).

LARVA. To 28 mm. in total length at metamorphosis—average of 13, 21 mm.; in these, head-body to 12 mm. (average 11 mm.) and tail to 16 mm. (average 10 mm.) (Bragg, 1937a:228, Oklahoma); hind limbs appear at about 15 mm. (Smith, 1946:96, Kansas) to 20 to 25 mm. (Bragg, 1936b:18, Oklahoma); dorsal fin highly arched, extending to level of juncture of tail with body, or somewhat more anteriorly; tip of tail obtuse; spiracle sinistral; anus median, in anterior margin of ventral fin.

Labial teeth 2/3, last lower row, on average, can be contained 2¾ to 3 times in first lower row; first upper labial tooth row and first and second lower rows about same length; median space in second upper row about same length as one of lateral segments (based on Smith, 1946:95, Kansas —part of Smith's material obtained July 2, 1938, 1.5 miles east of Meade County State Park, Kansas). (Pl. 30.)

Early tadpole (at about 5 mm. in total length) almost black with ventral coloration lighter than dorsal; fairly sharp line laterally, dividing dorsal and ventral colors; line passes from head region just dorsal to external gills and then curves ventrad to anus; at tadpole length of 8 mm., color pattern more definite; under magnification gray background evident, largely obscured dorsally and laterally by closely set oval black areas (melanophores?); between tip of snout and nares is fan-shaped darker area that narrows posteriorly toward eyes and passes between them as dark line along mid-dorsal line of back; silvery chromatophores on most dorsal surfaces posterior to eyes, tending to aggregate in 5 areas—2 such areas situated one on either side posterior to eyes; second pair posterior to these on posterior part of body, and fifth just anterior to tail and median in position; 3 posterior patches may merge to form crescent-shaped marking; in larger larvae all 5 areas tend to unite; ventral surface of head mostly unpigmented, therefore nearly uniformly gray although bordered laterally by black descending from sides; anteriorly on abdomen gray color extends obliquely caudo-laterad, reaching spiracle; chromatophores tend to invade these lateral gray areas; remainder of abdomen covered fairly evenly by golden chromatophores; eyes large and black; tail fins translucent, dorsal one with black dendritic pigment spots, ventral one clear; at 20 to 25 mm., when hind legs begin to appear, dorsal surface mottled with brown and gray and, although still quite dark, distinctly lighter than earlier; under magnification silvery areas seen to be conspicuously interwoven with black ones; ventral surface markedly lighter than dorsal; throat with greenish-yellow iridescence which extends caudad along sides of abdomen, gradually shading into grayish green; central portion of abdomen with reddish iridescence marked with very fine black and golden spots; viscera earlier readily seen through body wall, now slightly or not at all visible; tail fins about as earlier but with some dark flecks now in ventral fin; iris golden (Bragg, 1936b).

Bragg (1937b:283) states, "Tadpoles hatch by passing through jagged holes one of which appears opposite each in the gelatinous envelopes. Upon hatching the larva moves slowly away from the jellies by means of its cilia and finally attaches to some object by means of the adhesive organ. Later, when it begins locomotion by muscular action, it swims in a spiral, turning either to the right or to the left." About 1½ months after the eggs are laid, metamorphosis starts at a tadpole length of 26 to 29 mm. (Bragg, 1940b:435). Strecker (1910a:19) says, ". . . metamorphosis of the tadpole is said to take less than two weeks." Bragg (1940b:436) suspects adult size may be reached in 2 years by some individuals but not by others for 3 or 4 years. Dickerson (1920:101) believes that at least 5 years are required for full growth, judging from the decidedly different sizes of individuals found in the spring. Storer (1925:191) thinks at least 4 and possibly 5 years are required.

Remarks.—Casual inspection of specimens in the Museum of Vertebrate Zoölogy from California and Arizona suggest that they have less contrasting and often smaller dorsal spots than those from Nevada and Colorado. The more southerly animals seem rougher.

SONORAN TOAD

Bufo compactilis Wiegmann
Plate 17

Range.—Southeastern New Mexico, Texas to the eastern timbered region, southwestern Kansas, western Oklahoma; south into Mexico. In Mexico recorded from the states of Sonora, Chihuahua, Coahuila, Nuevo León, Tamaulipas, Durango, Zacatecas, Guanajuato, Michoacan, Jalisco, Veracruz, Distrito Federal, Puebla, and Oaxaca (Smith and Taylor, 1948:40). (Pl. 57.)

Type locality.—Mexico (Wiegmann, 1833:661-62). According to Smith and Taylor (1950:329), Xochimilco, Mexico. I am unaware of the basis for this restriction.

Description.—STRUCTURE. Adult 2 to somewhat over 3½ inches; no enlarged glands on hind legs; no fold of skin on tarsus; no sharp canthus rostralis; interorbital space equal to or slightly less or greater than width of eyelid; cranial crests weak or absent, no boss on snout; head short and thick; snout blunt, rounded in profile; tympanum vertically oval, ½ size of eye opening or smaller; parotoid glands separated 2½ to 3 or more times width of gland; parotoid gland elongate oval, nearly smooth or minutely tuberculate, equal to or slightly greater in width than upper eyelid, commonly half or once again as long as wide; rather uniformly warty above; pupil horizontally oval; femur short as in *B. cognatus;* large oval palmar tubercle; thenar tubercle small or absent; 2 metatarsal tubercles, inner one largest, both sharp-edged, usually glossy black or dark brown; outer metatarsal tubercle may be sickle-shaped. COLOR. Above generally gray with greenish cast or light brown marked with small olivaceous, dull yellowish-green or blackish spots but sometimes largely unspotted; anterior and posterior eye corner each with a conspicuous white marking; no dorsal stripe; warts of back tipped with brownish orange to red in life; below white or cream without spots; iris well filled out with pale yellow to pinkish beige with pupil margined above and below with gold to pale brass. JUVENILE. Soft gray-brown above with bright red tips to the warts, and with a few black spots and many irregularly placed moss-green patches. SEXUAL DIFFERENCES. Female averages larger than male. Male in life may have buff-colored area with olivaceous center on throat and dark nuptial pads on foretoes. Vocal sac of male sausage-shaped when inflated; when deflated folds of thin skin are covered by flap of thicker skin that extends posteriorly.

Habitat and behavior.—Inhabits arid and semiarid regions such as deserts and prairies. Generally nocturnal. Much inclined to burrow. When an enemy approaches it may flatten itself on the ground until it looks like a circular lump of earth. Often found associated during breeding congresses with *Scaphiopus couchii.*

Voice.—A loud shrill trill. Of the call Dickerson (1920:103-4) states that it is loud, penetrating, and harsh in quality, about one call per second with a short pause between calls, pitched about 2 octaves above middle C(D). The notes were maintained at this pitch for some minutes, when abruptly there was a distinct drop, followed quickly by a rise again to the original pitch.

Ottys Sanders (*in litt.*) compares the voices of *Bufo cognatus* and *B. compactilis* of the Texas plains: *Bufo cognatus,* a rapid rattle with a tremor, moderately high pitched and loud; *Bufo compactilis,* a brief trill (1 second duration, 1 second interval), moderate in pitch.

Reproduction.—Breeds after rains to mid-July (Livezey and Wright, 1947:193) with a few individuals still later. Assembles in large numbers during the breeding period. Utilizes rain pools (including muddy ones), irrigation and cattle tanks and other quiet water for breeding.

EGGS. Deposited in long coils in temporary pools. Eggs in strings with a single continuous gelatinous encasing; envelope slightly scalloped; gelatinous tube tightly coiled; envelope 1.8 to 2.4 mm., average 2.0 mm., distinct; ovum 1.2 to 1.6 mm., average 1.4 mm., brown or dark gray above and yellow below; 11 to 17 ova per inch (Livezey and Wright, 1947:193). Eggs may hatch in 2 days.

LARVA. Description largely based on 7 preserved tadpoles with hind limbs well developed, provided by Arthur N. Bragg, collected on June 11, 1946, 2.7 miles east of railroad at Granite, Greer County, Oklahoma. Total length from 29.1 to 36.4 mm. (24 to 28 mm. according to Wright and Wright, 1942:79); head-body length 11.7 to 12.4 mm., greatest depth 5.75 to 6.40 mm., greatest width 6.4 to 7.5 mm.; tail 17.3 to 24.0 mm., greatest height 4.8 to 6.1 mm.; body elongate oval in dorsal aspect, broadest about at mid-point, not deep; tail fins low, greatest height of dorsal fin about at mid-point, ½ to ⅔ greatest depth of musculature; tip of tail rounded to subacute; spiracle on lateral axis, midway between eye and posterior margin of body, opening oval, directed backward and slightly upward; eyes well up on head, situated about midway between lateral outline of head and mid-dorsal line; nostril about midway between eye and tip of snout, slightly nearer eye; intestine shows through skin of belly; anus median, opening at edge of ventral fin close to juncture with body. (Pl. 29.)

Labial teeth 2/3, labial rows of nearly equal length although last two lower ones progressively shorter than first lower row; second upper row with median space 1/3 to 1/2 length of one of lateral segments; labial papillae in single row on either side of mouth, emarginate medially. (Pl. 30.)

In preservative, above on head-body rather uniformly purplish brown lightening to cream or pale yellowish on snout and at sides of root of tail (in life drab or light grayish olive); some suggestion of dark brownish spotting; melanophores rapidly disappear on upper sides, only few scattered blotches extending to lateral axis and very few scattered and clumped melanophores on abdomen; throat usually wholly lacking melanophores; some suggestion of metallic silvery pigment flecks on upper sides, especially behind eyes, possibly remnants of more extensive pigment of this type; throat pale yellow; intestine light reddish tan, probably from color of contents; in life, light tan to pinkish cinnamon below; iris with close, pale yellow stippling above and below pupil; blackish areas anterior and posterior to pupil; tail fins translucent, with sparse scattering of minute melanophores in dorsal fin and very few or none in lower; tail musculature yellowish cream, unpigmented, except for irregular series of spots and blotches that tend to unite to form more or less continuous stripe full length of side of tail.

A transformed individual of this species lived 4 years and 3 months in the Philadelphia Zoölogical Garden (Conant and Hudson, 1949:3).

Remarks.—In build, form of the vocal pouch, and in the sharp-edged foot tubercles, this species shows an affinity with *B. cognatus.*

Superficially it resembles *Scaphiopus* in its short femur, the size and distribution of the warts and in the cutting sole tubercles. *Scaphiopus,* however, differs in having a vertical pupil and a single metatarsal tubercle.

It is close in structure and pigmentation to *Bufo microscaphus.* The remarks to follow are based on 7 adult *compactilis* from Texas and New Mexico and 11 adult *microscaphus* (6 *californicus* and 5 *microscaphus*) from scattered localities in California and Arizona: The two forms show no significant differences in general proportions but *compactilis* reaches larger size, 3 to 3 1/2 inches, while *microscaphus* ranges from about 2 1/2 to 2 3/4 inches. They are similar in the general rugosity of the dorsal surfaces (excluding the subspecies *microscaphus*) including both the warts and the brown-tipped tubercles and they are similar in the texture of the skin of the ventral surfaces. The shape, position, and surface texture of the parotoid glands is essentially the same and cranial crests are weak.

The greatest structural differences lie in the character of the foot tubercles. The thenar tubercle is better defined (usually stands out more sharply against a background of smaller tubercles) in *microscaphus*. The centrally situated palmar tubercle appears the same in the two forms. The inner metatarsal tubercle is margined with black and is sharp-edged and elongate (sickle-shaped) in *compactilis*. It is more rounded, brown, and blunt-edged in *microscaphus*. The outer tubercle is similar in size in the two forms but in *compactilis* it tends to be black, is sharper, more elongate, and has a cutting edge. This tubercle in *microscaphus* is conical and brownish. *Compactilis* differs from *microscaphus* in having a vocal sac that is sausage-shaped when expanded. The expanded sac is round in *microscaphus*. When deflated the thin skin of the sac in *compactilis* is covered by an anterior flap of thicker skin that forms a kind of dewlap, not present in *microscaphus*. In neither form is the throat notably discolored. The principal differences in pigmentation are: *Microscaphus* tends toward a light-colored transverse stripe across the head, lightening of the pigmentation of the parotoid glands, anteriorly, and the presence of light-colored blotch over each sacral hump and one in the nuchal area. Such markings are not (or seldom) evident in *compactilis*. Both forms tend to have dark spots and blotches dorsally and both lack a vertebral stripe. Both are usually unspotted ventrally except the subspecies *compactilis* of *B. compactilis*.

Although it is conceivable that *compactilis* and *microscaphus* may intergrade, this has not been shown. Few specimens of the two forms are known from Mexico (actually *microscaphus* is of dubious occurrence, see p. 266). The ranges of typical *microscaphus* and *compactilis* are widely separated to the north. A connection between the two in New Mexico seems unlikely. Specimens of a *microscaphus*-like toad from Mimbres, Grant County, New Mexico, although approaching *compactilis* in size, are less like it than is *Bufo microscaphus californicus* from California and northern Lower California.

I regard the differences in vocal sacs and foot tubercles as trenchant.

Subspecies[9]

1*a*. Venter dark-spotted; warts on dorsal surface rougher, tips hardened; dorsal spots small, numerous; cranial crests better developed. *Range*. The main Mexican Plateau from its southern edge in Puebla and Jalisco northward to Chihuahua and perhaps to adjacent New Mexico and western Texas; on the east possibly to central Nuevo León .... *B. c. compactilis* Wiegmann

1*b*. Total or near total absence of ventral markings; absence of spines on the warts; presence of fairly well-defined pattern of dorsal spots. Cranial crests very low and poorly defined. *Range*. Northern Nuevo León northward to northern Oklahoma and probably southwestern Kansas; southeastern New Mexico .... *B. c. speciosus* Girard

[9] Characters as given by Smith (1947:7, 9)

LITTLE GREEN TOAD

Bufo debilis Girard
Plate 15

Range.—Southwestern Kansas, western half of Oklahoma, western and central Texas, southeastern Colorado, New Mexico, and southeastern Arizona; in Mexico in states of Sonora, Chihuahua, Coahuila, Durango, Nuevo León, Tamaulipas, and Zacatecas (Smith and Taylor, 1948:42). (Pl. 57.)

Type locality.—Lower part of the valley of the Rio Bravo (Rio Grande del Norte), and in the province of Tamaulipas (Girard, 1854:87). Smith and Taylor (1950:345) give the type locality as the "lower part of the Rio Grande del Norte," Tamaulipas, Mexico.

Description.—STRUCTURE. Adult around 1½ to 2 inches; head flattened; parotoids large and elongate, situated obliquely on shoulders; tympanum slightly over half size of eye opening; snout pointed in dorsal aspect; cranial crests absent or consisting of narrow ridge closely applied to inner margin of eyelid, reaching tympanum in postorbital region; crests most evident in preserved specimens, probably due to shrinkage; large palmar and much smaller thenar tubercle; two metatarsal tubercles, inner one slightly larger than outer one; skin above with numerous small warts capped with brown-tipped tubercles; below granular, with many much smaller tubercles than those on back (observed under magnification). COLOR. Description based on adults from 26 miles south-southwest of Bingham Post Office, Socorro County, New Mexico (animals provided by Charles Lowe). Ground color above greenish with warts largely yellow, commonly capped with a brown tubercle; yellowish color particularly noticeable on snout, eyelids, and parotoid glands; dorsal ground color variable—some individuals more yellowish than others; above with numerous irregular inky-black spots; prominent black bar bisecting each eyelid; hind limbs barred with black; groin, undersides of femoral region, and sides of belly light-colored, with pinkish or light purplish tinge; belly centrally with light bluish cast; iris with pale gold markings.

Adult, RCS 3320, obtained July 23, 1949, 10.5 miles north-northeast of Douglas, Cochise County, Arizona: Light yellowish green above with yellow to orange-yellow tubercles; each tubercle minutely tipped with dot of brown, situated in center of yellow area; body and limbs above marked with ink-black bars, spots, and blotches; below whitish to cream; posterior part of gular area reddish purple, anterior part dark purplish brown;

margin of upper and lower jaws light yellow to cream; undersides of forefeet dull reddish orange with some yellow in it; concealed surfaces (when limb folded) of hind limbs not yellow although rear of femoral region near vent with closely set, light yellow tubercles; iris with flecks of pale gold and pupil margined above and below with gold.

Juvenile, RCS 3425, 12 mm. in snout-vent length, obtained August 10, 1949, 9 miles east of Fort Sumner, De Baca County, New Mexico: Ground color orange or yellowish orange above, with this color most intense on tubercles; under magnification ground color appears composed of close network of light grayish-yellow xanthophores (?) with orange lipoid (?) color on tubercles; limbs slightly more yellowish than body; black markings on body and limbs with orange or yellowish-orange tubercles in some of larger marks; below white except seat patch which is light grayish tan; undersides of limbs light blue-gray; underside of feet orange yellow; iris with orange flecking above and below pupil and orange pupillary ring.

Habitat.—Calling adult males were found by Charles Lowe, Jr. within 10 to 20 inches of the edge of temporary pools formed by summer rains during August, 1947, on the arid plains of the Jornada del Muerto, Socorro County, New Mexico. They were commonly found occupying the same situations as *Ambystoma tigrinum, Bufo cognatus, Scaphiopus couchii* and *Scaphiopus hammondii.* Calling posts were usually in grass or weedy growth, and often at the base of shrubs. *Scaphiopus* was not observed to call from such terrestrial situations. Occasionally *B. debilis* was observed calling in the water close to the edges of the ponds. When so observed, it used vegetation for support and kept only part of its head out of water. It was never observed floating prone as *S. hammondii* or sitting on the bottom in shallow water as *S. couchii.* When light was shone upon a calling individual, it usually became quiet and settled down close to the ground. The ventriloquial nature of the call, combined with concealing behavior, small size, and the cryptic effect of the green, yellow, and brown dorsal coloration made these little toads difficult to find even when known to be only a few inches away.

It is possible to obtain this species in quantity only a few days in each year, when they are in their breeding pools or have been driven from their burrows by heavy rains. *Bufo debilis* is a toad of the mesquite prairie, and with the aid of a flashlight an occasional specimen may be found in such environments even on a dry summer night, but the collector may be compelled literally to walk miles in an effort to find such scattered examples (Strecker, 1910a:10, Texas).

Near Douglas, Cochise County, Arizona, on July 23, 1949 at 10:30 P.M., I was attracted by *Bufo cognatus* clatter to a roadside rain pool where I found *B. debilis.* Two individuals were discovered a foot apart near the bases of clumps of grass on mud 3 feet from the edge of the pool. They were trilling. Mesquite, creosote bush, and Russian thistle were plants in the area.

Sixteen miles northwest of Pima, Graham County, Arizona, on July 24, 1949, between 8:30 and 9:00 P.M., I found four species of anurans calling from an earth bank reservoir—*Bufo cognatus, B. woodhousii, Scaphiopus hammondii,* and *B. debilis*. The reservoir was about 75 feet square with mud bottom and sloping earth banks 6 feet high. The water was muddy, 12 to 16 inches deep. Clumps of grass and a broad-leafed weed formed a dense growth along the banks. At least 4 *debilis* were calling. One was found 12 feet from shore among the leaves and stalks of a sparse clump of grass in water 1 foot deep. Only his hind limbs touched the water. He was perched with his body at an angle of 45°. His gular pouch appeared gray and spherical when inflated.

Behavior.—Call a cricket-like, prolonged trill. Charles Lowe, Jr., who has observed this species in south-central New Mexico, describes the call (*in litt.*) ". . . a sharp trill that is relatively high-pitched as compared to *Bufo cognatus* and the harsh notes of *Scaphiopus*."

The calls of an individual observed 2 miles north-northeast of Douglas, Arizona, were timed as follows: (4) 8 (4) 5 (3) 5 (3) 8 (4) 5 and again (3) 9 (7) 8 (3). The figure in parentheses is the duration of the trilling, the other the interval between calls, in seconds. The mud surface on which the toad rested was 20.4°C.; the water of a nearby rain pool 22.0°C. The call was a rapid trill sustained at one pitch. It was suggestive of *Bufo punctatus* but was less musical, of more mechanical quality. It also possessed some of the quality of the note of *Microhyla*. It is a mixture of a buzz and a whistled trill.

Reproduction.—In Texas *debilis* breeds in April and May in what are usually termed prairie sinks, i.e. small temporary ponds and in roadside ditches, according to Strecker (1926:10).

EGGS. Strecker (1926:10) says of the eggs in Texas, that they ". . . are in small strings and are attached to grass and weedstems."

LARVA. Apparently has not been certainly described although Smith (1934:444-45), has reported what he presumes to be the larvae of this species.

"A series of *Bufo* larvae, apparently undescribed, were collected September 6, 1933, in small pools at the rocky bottom of a small, nearly vertical-sided tributary of Schwartz Canyon, near Indian River in Comanche County, Kansas, in which region *debilis* is known to exist. It is impossible to state definitely at present what species these larvae represent, but I would suggest *debilis*. Their description follows (Pl. 30):

"Labial teeth 2/3, outer margins about even; outer row in upper labium not divided, second row sometimes divided, but never distinctly, the lateral halves but slightly separated if at all; rows of teeth in lower labium not divided, or nearly uniform length, the outer somewhat shorter than the others; upper mandible less than half the length of the adjacent rows of labial teeth; lower mandible sharply bent medially, forming an angle of about 100-105°; labial papillae confined to sides, the length of the lower part of one side about 1/6 the circumference of the lower labium; length of the upper part of one side about 1/8 to 1/9 the circumference of the upper labium; orbitonarial distance about half the distance between nares and snout, interorbital distance slightly greater than internarial; diameter of orbits about 1/5 greater than orbitonarial distance; spiracle sinistral, below lateral axis of body; anus median; tail 1/3 longer than head and body; tail musculature at base about 1/2 total diameter of tail at base; insertion of caudal fin about 1/3 the distance between insertion of hind legs and spiracle; total diameter of tail (dorsoventral) nearly uniform throughout, slightly tapering toward distal end, broadest in middle; tip of tail rounded.

"Dorsal surface of body uniformly stippled with black; ventral surface of body same, except for a broad median, sharply defined, transparent 'stripe' from anus to between mouth disk and spiracle, very conspicuous in life; ventral caudal fin practically uniformly transparent, dorsal caudal fin with scattered, irregularly outlined, comparatively large, spots of pigment; tail musculature stippled as body."

Strecker (1926:10, Texas) says the larvae of *debilis* are slightly smaller than those of *punctatus,* and their metamorphosis is accomplished rapidly. Upon returning to a pond where *debilis* had been found breeding 20 days earlier, Strecker discovered that it was almost dry, only a few mudholes remaining. In one of these were a few belated tadpoles, and in the grass along the banks he found two small toads with tails.

Remarks.—*Bufo debilis* was described by Girard (1854:87) from the lower part of the valley of the Rio Bravo (Rio Grande del Norte), and in the province of Tamaulipas. In the same article (p. 88), a related form *B. insidior* was described from material collected by Thomas Webb in Chihuahua, Mexico. Dr. Webb was attached to Commander Bartlett's party in the survey of the United States-Mexican boundary line. Kellogg (1932b:50), however, synonymized these forms under *debilis.* Campbell (1934:3) under the name *debilis* and Kauffeld (1943:343) under the name *insidior* have since recorded toads of this group in Arizona. A question arises regarding the treatment of *insidior* and *debilis.* Shall they be considered distinct species as Girard (1854) described them? Taylor (1936) and Smith and Taylor (1948:42) evidently hold this view. Is *insidior* sufficiently distinct to be removed from the synonymy of *debilis?* If so, Bogert and Oliver (1945:410) strongly suspect that it will be at the subspecific level. These authors believe some modification in view regarding the ranges of the two forms may be necessary.

There is also some question regarding application of the name *insidior*. Bogert and Oliver (1945:410) write, "Unless the type or other specimens from Chihuahua more closely resemble the Arizonan and Zacatecan individuals than the Texan specimens, the applicability of the name *insidior* to the former is open to considerable question." I regard these two forms as of the same species, hence the name *debilis* is applied. It appears first in Girard's description.

CANADIAN TOAD

Bufo hemiophrys Cope
Plate 18

Range.—North Dakota, northwestern Minnesota, and Canada in Alberta, Manitoba, and Northwest Territory. Seton (1918:83) says it is abundant everywhere in Manitoba from Winnipeg and Shoal Lake to Brandon, from Boissevain to Winnipegosis, and probably throughout the province. (Pl. 57.)

Type locality.—Pembina and Turtle mountains, North Dakota (Cope, 1886:515-16).

Description.—STRUCTURE. Adult to slightly over 3 inches; 2 metatarsal tubercles, inner one large and moderately sharp-edged; half or more of femur free of body skin; parotoid gland oval; snout short, rounded; horny protuberance on head between eyes extending from snout to posterior portion of upper eyelids, sometimes with median longitudinal furrow, and with sides parallel; tympanum relatively small; numerous rounded warts on back. COLOR. Above greenish or brownish with dark spots; reddish tubercles set in spots; whitish vertebral stripe; irregular brown stripe on sides with dark reticulations below it; legs and feet with dark bars; below light-colored with dark ventral spotting. JUVENILE. Cranial crests absent in very young animals, appearing with increase in size and becoming more and more completely united with age. Immature individuals may have crests united anteriorly and posteriorly. SEXUAL DIFFERENCES. Throat of male dark-colored; nuptial pads on foretoes during breeding period.

Habitat.—Vicinity of lakes and streams. Breckenridge (1944:63, Minnesota) writes, "Specimens of this toad have been taken from pond and stream margins and in dirt-floored cellars." It may be found active at night on sandy beaches of lakes.

Harper (1931b:68) writes that two of these toads were collected on May

15, 1914, in a muddy pool on the wooded slope between the business district of Edmonton and the Saskatchewan River, Canada. On May 18 one was seen at Rochester and two in a small pool by the river at Athabaska Landing. Here they were heard trilling at night. The species was again noted in voice on May 25 along the Athabaska several miles above Little Buffalo River, and on May 31 near the mouth of Firebag River, where it was common. On May 18, 1920, a single toad was heard trilling along the east branch of the Athabaska Delta, at a temperature of about 40° to 45°F. On August 10, two very small specimens were collected by Hamilton Laing on the sandy bank of MacFarlane River near its mouth.

Behavior.—Seton (1918:83) describes the voice of this toad in spring as ". . . a soft trilling, uttered about twice a minute and lasting about three seconds each time."

Reproduction.—Breeding occurs in the shallow water of ponds, lake margins, or other water, beginning in May. They transform at 3/8 to 1/2 inch (9 to 13.5 mm.). (Wright and Wright, 1942:83.)

Breckenridge (1944:63) found this toad on the night of June 7, 1943, calling in rain-filled roadside ditches near Crookston in Polk County, Minnesota; and again on May 8, 1944, near Herman in Grant County, many males were found calling in the grassy margins of recently swollen ponds. "A clasping pair was found. The egg string being laid was like a long, single string of jelly-coated black beads, each bead about 1 mm. in diameter, the distance between beads slightly less than 1 mm. The toads and eggs were collected and the eggs were placed in an aquarium. On June 12 the young had hatched and were wriggling their way from the jelly. Five series of tadpoles were preserved at intervals until July 19, when they were about 20 mm. long, with hind limbs well developed. At this stage they were compared with tadpoles of the American toad. Pigmentation, width of dorsal tail crest, extent of dorsal crest onto the body, tail outline, mouth structure, and position of spiracle and eyes all seemed identical with those of the American toad."

LARVA. Based on preserved specimens loaned by Professor W. J. Breckenridge, obtained July 3, 1943 at Crookston, Minnesota; 4 tadpoles ranging from 10.0 to 14.3 mm. in total length. Largest specimen, total length 14.3 mm.; head-body 6.20 mm., greatest width 4.25 mm., greatest depth 3.30 mm.; greatest depth of tail, approximately midway on tail, 3.0 mm.; tip of tail rounded; dorsal fin sharply reduced shortly before reaching body; outline of head-body narrowed slightly at juncture of head with body; anus median, opening at edge of ventral fin near body; spiracle slightly above lateral axis about midway between posterior edge of eye and posterior outline of body, opening vertically oval and directed backward and somewhat upward; eyes well up on head, interorbital distance about equal to distance between dorsomedian edge of eye and outline of head, as viewed from above; nostril nearly midway between eye and tip of snout but slightly closer to eye. (Pl. 29.)

Labial teeth 2/3, first row continuous across upper labium from one papillary fringe to the other; second row with median space about 4/5 length of one of lateral segments; 3 lower rows progressively shorter, last about equal in length to upper mandible; single row of oral papillae at either side of mouth, indented medially. (Pl. 30.)

In alcohol tadpoles sooty to black on body, lightening slightly ventrally on abdomen and on throat, latter lightest portion of body; tail musculature colored like body, dark above, lightening slightly ventrally; tail fins translucent, finely stippled with brownish melanophores, most abundant dorsally; melanophores of dorsal fin more abundant toward juncture of fin with body; melanophores of ventral fin largely confined to juncture of fin with tail musculature; under magnification body observed to be extensively covered with rather close stippling of melanophores, most abundant dorsally but largely absent on throat.

Through the generosity of Dr. Breckenridge, I present the following information on the tadpoles, loaned by him: These are in 6 lots collected in June and July, 1943, at Crookston, Minnesota, on different dates during the period of development.

Date	*Number of specimens*	*Size* (mm.)		*Stage of development*
		total length	*head-body*	
June 12	17	4.0		Tail shorter than body, fins weak; sucker prominent; recently hatched
June 14	6	5.8		External gills; paired sucker
June 16	5	7.2	2.7	Gills nearly covered by operculum; paired ventral sucker
June 21	4	7.7 to 10.2	3.1 to 4.3	Internal gills; operculum sealed except for spiracular opening; small hind limb buds
July 3	4	10.0 to 14.3	4.3 to 6.2	Similar to preceding, but limb buds more prominent
July 19	1	20.4	8.9	Hind limbs conspicuous; knee joint present, toes forming

Remarks.—In structure this form is close to *B. cognatus*. The boss on the head, tendency toward sharp-edged metatarsal tubercles, character of the vocal sac, and pigmentation, especially of immatures, bear this out. The two forms occupy contiguous ranges but so far as I know do not overlap in range.

COPE TOAD

Bufo microscaphus Cope
Plate 18

Range.—The subspecies *californicus* occurs along arroyos and river courses in coastal areas of California from near Santa Margarita, San Luis Obispo County, to the Rio Santo Domingo, Lower California. It ranges inland in California along the Mohave River at least as far as Victorville, San Bernadino County.

The subspecies *microscaphus,* disjunct in range from *californicus,* occurs in scattered localities in the northern tributary drainages of the Gila River in central Arizona. Specimens from the Cave Creek and Verde River drainages, indicate an intermixture of the characters of this form and *woodhousii*. Localities where pure *microscaphus* seems to occur lie along the more westerly tributaries, the Agua Fria and Hassayampa rivers. The form also occurs in the Big Sandy drainage which joins the Bill Williams River of western Arizona and probably near Fort Mohave on the Colorado River, immediately south of the southern tip of Nevada.

In southwestern Utah it exists in Zion National Park and vicinity and occurs in association with *woodhousii* in the vicinity of Saint George and evidently also at Bellevue (Englehardt, 1918:78). These localities are in the upper Virgin River. Association with *woodhousii* also occurs at other, more westerly, localities along the Virgin River into Nevada. Where the two forms occur together, individuals are found that exhibit an intermixture of their characters.

In Nevada, toads from the upper Meadow Valley Wash and Las Vegas are close to this subspecies but exhibit some variation in the direction of *Bufo woodhousii*.

Toads from the lower Meadow Valley Wash and at its juncture with the Virgin River, and along the Colorado River to Willow Beach, about 9 miles below Boulder Dam, are closest to *woodhousii* but show some tendencies in the direction of *microscaphus*.

Individuals of uncertain affinity but showing *microscaphus* characters of low crests, rounded parotoids, and unstriped dorsum have been found in the following localities outside the range given above: Rose Creek Lodge, Headwaters Rose Creek, at 5,300 feet, Gila County, Arizona; Point of Pines, south side of White Mountains (University of Arizona specimen); Mimbres, Grant County, New Mexico; and Rio Gavilan, 7 miles southwest of Pacheco, at 5,700 feet, and Meadow Valley, 5 miles south of Garcia, at 7,500 feet, Chihuahua, Mexico. All these localities, except the Mexican ones, lie in the Gila River drainage. (All but the University of Arizona specimens are in the Museum of Vertebrate Zoölogy of the University of California.) (Pl. 58.)

Type locality.—Cope (1867:301) based his description of *Bufo microscaphus* on specimens collected by Dr. Elliot Coues and H. B. Möllhausen. Coues' specimens were obtained during his travels over the "Territory of Arizona," chiefly near the 35th parallel and along the valley of the Colorado from Fort Mohave to Fort Yuma. Möllhausen was a member of the party headed by Lt. J. C. Ives that explored the Colorado River from its mouth to near the 36th parallel, or near the present site of Boulder Dam. Specimens collected by him (USNM 4106 and 4184, listed by Cope) were obtained from the "upper Colorado region."

Two specimens in the United States National Museum are catalogued as types of *Bufo microscaphus*. Miss Doris Cochran (*in litt.*) informs me that she believes them to be the types (=cotypes). There is an old label with them in Cope's handwriting, which appears to establish their identity. Dr. Stejneger, who was extremely careful about such matters, picked out the Cope types from the United States National Museum collection, and the record concerning the two specimens (now USNM 4184, each specimen so labelled) is not questioned by him, which, according to Miss Cochran, means he accepted the specimens as valid type material. Miss Cochran states that their original number was USNM 4106 but some clerk unfortunately made a double entry for this number and the two toads were later renumbered 4184. Included with the specimens is an Ives expedition label bearing the identification *Bufo woodhousii,* written, according to Miss Cochran (*in litt.*), by herself, as Dr. Stejneger then considered *woodhousii* and *microscaphus* synonymous.

The larger of the two specimens possesses a pattern of prominent, well-spaced, rather uniform spotting on a beige or nearly ash-gray ground color. This style of coloration is not mentioned in Cope's original account nor in a later (1889:270) description of the "type" of *Bufo microscaphus.* In the 1867 report (*supra cit.*) he speaks of the upper surfaces as blackish and in 1889 as uniformly dark green. The first was, at least in part, a general description, based on a number of individuals, whereas the second was that of a single specimen. The light-colored, dark-spotted dorsum of the United States National Museum specimen could be, but I believe not likely so, the result of bleaching with age. Cope's descriptions, however, leave no doubt that they were based on the unstriped weak-crested toads of the lower Colorado drainage.

Shannon (1949:307) regards one of the cotypical specimens as a "normal appearing *B. w. woodhousii*" and designates the other as the lectotype of *Bufo woodhousii microscaphus.* In my opinion both toads are *microscaphus,* although the larger, pale individual, referred to above, is more conspicuously spotted than any other *microscaphus* I have seen. This individual is a female, 69 mm. in snout-vent length. It resembles *microscaphus* more than *woodhousii* in its smooth skin, weak cranial crests, absence of a dorsal stripe, and unmarked venter. I am unsure which toad was chosen by Shannon as the type, but I suspect it was the smaller individual which to me is most typically *microscaphus.* Shannon (1949:307) gives Fort Mohave, Mohave County, Arizona, as the type locality, by restriction.

Description.—STRUCTURE. Adult 2 to approximately 3 inches, most individuals about 2½ inches; cranial crests low, weak, and occasionally absent, interorbital portions parallel or slightly divergent posteriorly; postorbital ridge usually clearly evident; parotoid glands oval, generally as wide or wider than, and usually 1½ times or less, length of upper eyelid, generally more rounded than in *B. woodhousii,* inner margins parallel to posteriorly divergent, surfaces minutely tuberculate (rough to touch) to smooth; interparotoid distance approximately twice width of gland; tympanum present, relatively smooth, vertically oval, about ⅓ to ½ size of eye opening; snout blunt, rounded in profile; no enlarged gland on hind leg or membranous flap of skin on tarsus; metacarpal and metatarsal tubercles essentially as in *B. woodhousii;* warts of dorsal surface variable in size, low, and with few or no tubercles (*microscaphus*) or more prominent and with small brown-tipped tubercles (*californicus*); ventral surfaces generally less granular than in *woodhousii.* COLOR. Dorsal ground color variable—greenish gray, gray-brown, yellow-brown, or reddish brown; warts generally reddish brown, rust, to tan, largest ones usually set in dusky blotch which sets off lighter color of wart; some blotches unite; blotching most common in *californicus.* Outer edge of eyelids and anterior portion of parotoid glands often colored like warts; an obtuse **V**-shaped light-colored mark on head with each arm of **V** crossing an eyelid centrally, or somewhat anterior to its center, and generally extending to edge of lid; no vertebral stripe but usually light-colored area between parotoid glands and light patch in front of, or on, each sacral hump; these patches colored like anterior portion of parotoids. Limbs generally spotted or blotched with dusky color dorsally, blotches sometimes forming irregular bands on hind limbs; generally no black variegations on posterior surface of femur or with only few scattered dark blotches; below typically unmarked, whitish to yellowish or light yellowish orange; iris silvery, light yellowish gray, to pale gold, speckled with black. JUVENILE. Warts closer together and relatively larger than in adult; structurally resembles *B. punctatus* but differs in having larger, more oval parotoids (*punctatus* has small round parotoids), less flattened head and less acute snout; ground color above ash white (*californicus*) to light olive or salmon (*microscaphus*); warts reddish brown to yellowish brown; dorsal dark marks conspicuous, at least in young *californicus;* underside of feet yellow to yellow orange, brighter than in adult. SEXUAL DIFFERENCES. Male with throat colored essentially like rest of underparts, not dark as in *B. woodhousii, B. punctatus,* and others; distinguished from female during breeding season by presence of brown nuptial pads on inner three fingers.

COMPARISON OF *Bufo woodhousii* AND *Bufo microscaphus* FROM BLOOMINGTON, WASHINGTON COUNTY, UTAH

Coloration	*woodhousii*	*microscaphus*
Dorsal markings	More contrasting, variegated	Largely absent, dorsum nearly uniformly colored but usually with light patch between parotoids and one in vicinity of each sacral hump
Vertebral stripe	Typically whitish, well defined	Absent or rarely present and diffuse
Transverse stripe on head intersecting eyelids	←Sometimes present→	
Light iris color	Generally less abundant	Generally more abundant
Pigmentation of ventral surfaces	Chest and upper sides spotted	Typically lacks dark spots on chest and upper sides
Color of posterior surface of femur	Yellow orange with black reticulations (orange color also present on posterior and inner surface of tibia and in groin)	Faint cream or absent; no black reticulations
Structure		
Skin	Brown-tipped tubercles dorsally Generally rougher ventrally	Tubercles without corneous tips, usually not brown-tipped dorsally Generally smoother ventrally
Foot tubercles	←Similar→	
Cranial crests	More prominent	Less prominent or absent

Subspecies *californicus* (from Myers, 1930b:77, based on animals from Rincon, San Diego County, California): Upper surfaces various shades of dull brown with greenish tinge; warts of back tipped brownish; dorsal blotches black; hind border of tarsus and rump largely black, warts whitish; under surfaces yellowish white, unmarked; enlarged warts behind angle of mouth, largely whitish; iris silvery or slightly yellowish gray, speckled with black.

Subspecies *microscaphus* (summary of field notes on coloration of adults): Ground color above highly variable—reddish brown, cinnamon, pale gray, pale sooty gray, pale yellowish brown, grayish brown, yellowish buff, olive gray, purplish gray with pink, or light brownish gray. Warts rusty, yellowish brown, reddish brown, brown, tan, or light purplish or pinkish brown; outer edge of eyelids and anterior portion of parotoids often colored like warts; light eyelid markings and light mark on back between parotoids (sometimes elsewhere), pale reddish, tan, light buff, pale pinkish buff, in keeping with general tone of ground color. Dark markings on body and limbs light sooty brown, sometimes with olive green; below pale yellow, cream, whitish, or light yellow with orange; seat patch buff orange, pale yellowish orange with reddish tinge, or light carmine; undersides of feet yellowish orange with pinkish cast, tan, or purplish brown, with tubercles and toes tipped with brown or black; forefeet with dull-yellow-ocher to buffy-brown tubercles and brown or sooty brown toe tips; groin often pale yellow and areas of hind limb, concealed when limb flexed, pale yellow with orange cast; iris cream to pale gold, often with coppery or pinkish cast, often lightening to pale gold around pupil, forming pupillary ring. (Based on adult animals from 2.6 miles southwest of Springdale and Bloomington, Washington County, Utah; 1.2 miles north of Littlefield, Mohave County, and Rose Creek Lodge, Rose Creek, Gila County, Arizona; and Mimbres, Grant County, New Mexico; animals obtained between July 1 and August 7, 1949.)

Area of hybridization between *woodhousii* and *microscaphus,* Bloomington, Washington County, Utah (July 5, 1949): At this locality the toads tended strongly toward either *Bufo microscaphus* or *B. woodhousii;* there was approximately 1 intermediate to 6 unmixed animals (of 43 animals, 23 were classed as *microscaphus,* 14 as *woodhousii* and 6 as hybrids).

Habitat.—The subspecies *californicus,* in California and northern Lower California, occurs in the Lower and Upper Sonoran life-zones but it is probably most common in the latter. It frequents arroyos of semi-arid character where streams are frequently intermittent. Miller and Miller (1936:176) found 3 individuals near Santa Margarita, San Luis Obispo County. The area was characterized as follows: There were low hills with occasional sparse stands of Digger pine among oaks. The animals were found along a river bottom with marginal growths of oaks and cottonwoods on sandy beaches with willow and mule fat thickets bordering the stream. There was a small flow of clear water that gave promise of continuing well through the summer. The stream subdivided frequently and at places formed comparatively quiet pools in the gravel, as much as 18 inches deep.

Although they were abundant on dry sand 500 feet or more from the river, Tevis (1944:6) found none of these toads at Rio Santo Domingo, Lower California, on nonsandy soil. Sandy river banks and washes seem clearly to be favored by this toad.

On May 5, 1946, John Davis and I obtained 10 *californicus* on a broad sandy beach along the Mohave River, 3 miles north of Victorville, San Bernardino County, California. Several individuals were found emerging from the sand at the base of a cottonwood tree 250 feet from the river.

Others were discovered hopping about on the exposed sand between this tree and the willow-fringed bank of the river. (Pl. 42, figs. 1 and 2.)

I observed the subspecies *microscaphus* near Springdale, Washington County, Utah, on July 1, 1949. The animals were active at midday. I caught 4 half-grown individuals at the edge of an oat field on muddy soil from overflow of an irrigation ditch. The field was fringed by willows and cottonwoods. The Virgin River was 100 yards away. The surrounding country was of rocky, arid hills with yucca, piñon, and juniper. Other individuals were found on the damp sandy soil near the river.

Again at Bloomington, Washington County, Utah, on July 2, 1949, *microscaphus* was common along with *woodhousii* on the dirt roads, in marshy areas, along the banks of the Virgin River, along irrigation ditches, and in the oat and alfalfa fields. All sizes from young to adults were found at all times of day and at night. Larvae were found near the river in a seepage area bordered by tamarisk, where there was much green grass, sedge, and tules. *Rana pipiens* larvae were also abundant there.

Behavior.—Individuals observed at Bloomington, Utah, July 2 to 5, 1949, were very active, hopping instead of walking. Adults sometimes covered 18 inches in a single jump. They hopped high and fast like the species in California. Larvae swam with moderate speed. They blended well with the substratum and sometimes partly buried themselves on coming to rest. Thermal data are presented on page 272.

Voice.—The voice of *californicus* is a clear, prolonged, musical trill. Myers (1930) says it suggests the voice of *Bufo americanus*. Miller and Miller (1936:176) found three animals trilling, spaced about equally along a ¼ mile of stream bed. According to them there is considerable resemblance in the voice of this toad to the louder, more raucous call of *cognatus*.

I heard this species on March 9, 1951, on the Sweetwater River, San Diego County, California. The voice is a nearly clear trill lasting 2 to 14 seconds, usually 8 to 10 seconds. It may be written w o o ē ē ē ē ē ē. It commonly begins with a slurring rise in pitch, beginning at about G to C (middle C) below F. Upon reaching F it is sustained at one pitch to the end of the call whereupon it is ended abruptly. The slurred portion may last ⅕ the length of the song in a call that lasts 5 seconds. Among our western toads, the voice resembles that of the desert toad, *Bufo punctatus,* but differs in being slightly less clear and in having a slurred introduction. There is indeed some resemblance also to the call of the Great Plains toad, *B. cognatus,* but it is less metallic and forceful. The vocal sac is a nearly perfect sphere and when inflated is white or pink in color.

Food.—Five specimens from Utah (Zion National Park) studied by

THERMAL DATA

Locality	*Date*	*Time**	*Size*	*Temperature, °C.* *Body*	*Substratum*	*Air* (½ inch above surface in shade)	*Conditions of occurrence*
Utah (Washington County) 2.6 mi. SW of Springdale, Virgin River	*1949* July 1	1:25-1:30	1¾ inches	32.5	33.0 (soil)	31.7	Damp mud of alfalfa patch
			2 inches	30.5			Alfalfa field
				29.0 33.6 30.4			Damp sand 20 feet from river
Bloomington	July 2	9:00 A.M.	2 inches	22.0			Virgin River bottom
	July 3	7:35 7:38 8:00 8:05	adult adult adult adult	24.3 23.5 23.0 23.5			Actively hopping about cultivated fields

* P.M. unless otherwise indicated.

Tanner (1931:178, under the name *Bufo compactilis*) contained the following: insects including a sand cricket (stenopelmatid), beetles (carabids, elaterids, a staphylinid, and a tenebrionid [*Eleodes* sp.]), a bug (pentatomid), ants, a bee (*Apis mellifica*), a moth larva; snails (*Oreohelix cooperi*); plant fragments.

Reproduction.—From the first of March to the first part of June appears to be the breeding season of *californicus*. Robert Saunders found the species abundant in April and active as late as June 20 at Blue Point Camp, 10 miles north of Piru, Ventura County, California.

EGGS. Livezey and Wright (1947:193) describe eggs obtained by A. Wright, May 6, 1942, at Green Valley Falls Public Camp on the Sweetwater River, California, as follows (these were presumably the eggs of *californicus*): Laid in tangled strings on bottom of pool among leaves, sticks, gravel, mud, etc.; several thousand eggs. Deposited in strings with continuous gelatinous encasing; one envelope present, 5.62 to 6.12 mm., average 5.77 mm., distinct and relatively firm; ovum 1.25 to 1.62 mm., average 1.42 mm., black above and gray below; average 42 eggs per inch, arranged in string in 2 or 3 irregular rows.

I obtained eggs on March 9, 1951 in the Sweetwater River (San Diego County, California). They were found on a clean sand bottom in water about 1-inch deep. They agree with the foregoing description except that some strings had only a single row of eggs and none had three. Ova measured 1.75 mm. in strings with a double row and 1.90 mm. in those with a single row.

LARVA. Structurally larvae of *californicus* from near Victorville, San Bernardino County, California, fit closely the description of Youngstrom and Smith of *B. woodhousii* (p. 292) from Lawrence, Kansas, except that they ranged to larger size, 16.8 to 34.2 mm. in total length and I find the outer, lower labial row exceeded in length by the inner row, 1/5 to 1/2 the length of the inner row. Larvae of *B. m. microscaphus* (some of them possibly *woodhousii-microscaphus* hybrids) from Bloomington, Washington County, Utah, ranged to 36.3 mm. and in 4 larvae whose mouth parts were examined the outer, lower labial row was the same length as the inner, the second row being slightly longer than the other two in 2 larvae and the same length in the third; the fourth larva had the outer row about 5/6 the length of the inner. The samples from Utah and California are essentially indistinguishable structurally. (Pls. 29 and 30.)

These samples have been compared in coloration as follows (based on 4 *californicus* from Mohave River, 3 miles north of Victorville, San Bernardino County, California, and 4 larvae [some possibly hybrid] from Bloomington, Washington County, Utah): Pale gold stippling more extensive dorsally on the body in *californicus* than in Bloomington larvae;

the pale gold pigment forms a rather solid layer over the melanic ground color, but there are a few gaps here and there giving the dorsum a somewhat mottled appearance. The general aspect of the dorsal coloration is similar in the two forms but is somewhat darker in Bloomington larvae; *californicus* has slightly more extensive pale gold color in the eye than Bloomington larvae and there is a heavier guanistic layer ventrally on the body, the belly appearing white in life with pinkish iridescence. In the Bloomington larvae the abdomen is covered with a more diffuse, thinner layer than in *californicus,* the layer appearing gray or dull white with a pinkish cast; similar color differences exist on the lower side of the tail musculature where whitish guanistic patches are better defined in *californicus* than in Bloomington larvae; in both forms the tail membranes are translucent. In summary, the basic differences between these larvae lies in the amount of guanism, *californicus* exceeding Bloomington larvae.

Subspecies

(Characters largely from Shannon, 1949)

1a. Parotoids elongate and nearly parallel; skin relatively smooth; dorsal spotting reduced or absent (animals from Vegas Valley, Nevada, have fine black punctations dorsally). *Range.* Southwestern Utah, southern Nevada, central, western, and northwestern Arizona .... *B. m. microscaphus* Cope

1b. Parotoids broadly oval and generally more divergent; skin rougher; dorsum with dark spots. *Range.* Coastal California from northern San Luis Obispo County through Santa Barbara, Ventura, Los Angeles, San Bernardino (along Mohave River, as at Victorville), and San Diego counties into northern Lower California to Rio Santo Domingo .... *B. m. californicus* Camp

Nomenclatural history.—Revival of the species, *Bufo microscaphus* Cope (1867), including in it, as a subspecies, *Bufo californicus*[10] Camp (1915), requires explanation.

Cope (1867) described *microscaphus* from material obtained in Arizona in the general area of the 35th parallel and probably somewhere along the Colorado River between Fort Mohave and Fort Yuma (see "type locality," p. 267). Later, however, he came to regard *microscaphus* as a variant of *Bufo columbiensis* (=*Bufo boreas*) and in 1889 placed it in the synonymy of this species. The name *compactilis* gradually came to be applied to Cope's toads (*microscaphus*) because of the morphological similarity to the Great Plains and Mexican form, *Bufo compactilis* Wiegmann (1833).

[10] Described by Camp (1915) as a subspecies of *B. cognatus* but established as a separate species, *B. californicus,* by Myers (1930).

In 1940 Linsdale, following a study of the toads of southern Nevada, reported a breakdown in characters between *Bufo woodhousii* and the presumed southern Nevada *compactilis,* particularly near the junction of the Virgin and Colorado rivers. Comparison of the *compactilis*-like toads of southern Nevada and southwestern Utah with the Californian species, *B. californicus* Camp (1915), revealed no significant structural differences, although there were minor differences in pigmentation. These facts led Linsdale to suggest that *B. compactilis, B. woodhousii,* and *B. californicus* were in the same species, and since *compactilis* was the oldest name, they were placed as subspecies of this form.

Shannon (1949) however, did not regard the *compactilis*-like toads of southern Nevada, southwestern Utah, and western Arizona as in the same species with *compactilis* from the Great Plains and Mexico. Therefore he revived for the former, Cope's name, *microscaphus.* He followed Linsdale, however, in considering *woodhousii, californicus,* and the unstriped toads of southern Nevada and adjacent areas (*microscaphus*) as subspecifically related, but as subspecies of *woodhousii.*

I agree with both Linsdale (1940) and Shannon (1949) in considering *Bufo californicus* and the unstriped low-crested toads of southern Nevada and nearby areas as in the same species. However, I treat them as subspecifically related to neither *compactilis* or *woodhousii* but rather as together composing a separate species, *Bufo microscaphus.* Two subspecies are recognized, *microscaphus* and *californicus.* I hesitate to place *woodhousii* and *microscaphus* in the same species because of uncertainties regarding the degree of reproductive compatibility between them. More field work and perhaps breeding tests can be expected to show what nomenclature is the best expression of the evolutionary relationships of these animals.

Biogeographic considerations.—*Relationship between* BUFO MICROSCAPHUS MICROSCAPHUS *and* BUFO MICROSCAPHUS CALIFORNICUS. Despite the fact that *microscaphus* and *californicus* are now separated, their ranges must at one time have been continuous.

According to Miller (1946:52) the theoretical evidence for a once continuous watercourse between Death Valley and the lower Colorado River Basin is good. Mohave River may have discharged alternately into Death Valley Lake and toward the Colorado River, or it may have once directly connected with the Colorado River through a series of lakes east of Barstow. The occurrence of the fish *Cyprinodon* in the Death Valley system demands a connection with the basin of the Colorado River and the presence of a fossil *Cyprinodon* in the region suggests that the connection was an early one, possibly late Pliocene or Early Pleistocene. The marked distinctiveness of the Recent fish fauna of the Death Valley system is in harmony with the view that the drainage has been isolated for a long time. A toad like *Bufo microscaphus* would not require a continuous watercourse for dispersal and could maintain its connection with adjacent populations through its ability to move about on land, long after such an aquatic connection was severed.

Bufo microscaphus exhibits a disjunction in range similar to that of *Scaphiopus hammondii* and *Hyla arenicolor.*

Relationship between BUFO MICROSCAPHUS *and* BUFO WOODHOUSII (Fig. 29, p. 278). Localities for *B. m. microscaphus* are known from, or are closely associated with, 3 major drainages: (1) the northernmost one, in relation to the range of the species, is the combined Meadow Valley Wash and Virgin River drainages that meet and join the Colorado River at Lake Mead in Nevada. I include here also the isolated Las Vegas area and the presumed type locality near Fort Mohave; (2) a centrally situated one, the Big Sandy River which flows south to join the Bill Williams River, which in turn drains west, emptying into the Colorado River near Parker Dam; (3) a southeasterly one, the Gila River, specifically its northern tributaries in central Arizona. These tributaries flow south to join the southwesterly flowing Gila which joins the Colorado River at Yuma, Arizona, about 50 miles above its mouth.

In both the northern and southern parts of the range there are places where *microscaphus* is found in association with *Bufo woodhousii.* In these areas interbreeding evidently occurs since animals exhibiting characters of both species are present. At certain localities in the northern drainage, structurally homogeneous populations exist that show slight tendencies in the direction of either one form or the other. Whether mixed populations occur in the centrally situated Bill Williams River drainage is unknown, but all individuals so far obtained have been *microscaphus.* Animals have been procured at the following localities: Wikieup and vicinity, in Mohave County (Shannon, 1949, 3 individuals [SDSNH]; a University of Arizona specimen); Santa Maria River, 30 miles west-northwest of Congress, Yavapai County (Shannon, *in litt.*, 29 individuals), and Cabin area, northeast slope of Aspen Peak, at 6,200 feet, Hualpai Mountains, Mohave County (Allan Phillips' specimen).

Consider first the northern drainage. All individuals from Zion Canyon (17, one with faint stripe) and near Springdale (9) are *microscaphus.* These localities are near the headwaters of the Virgin River. At Saint George, however, about 35 miles in an air line down river, a mixed population exists. Of 43 animals collected July 2 to 4, 1950, 23 seemed clearly referable to *microscaphus,* 14 to *woodhousii,* and 6 were regarded as hybrids, a ratio of 6 essentially typical animals to 1 exhibiting clearly a combination of characters of the two forms. At Bellevue, in the headwaters of the Santa Clara River, a tributary of the Virgin River that joins the latter near Saint George, another mixed group may occur (see Engelhardt, 1918:78).

A mixed population comparable to that at Saint George also occurs on the Virgin River beyond the Nevada boundary at Mesquite, Nevada. Here the proportions were 9 *woodhousii,* 4 *microscaphus,* 6 intermediates, a ratio of slightly over 2 to 1, with *woodhousii* predominating, rather than *microscaphus,* the reverse of the situation at Saint George. At Bunkerville, 5 miles farther southwest, of 13 male specimens (MVZ) obtained March 28, 1923, 11 were assigned to *woodhousii,* 1 to *microscaphus,* and 1 as an intermediate. Both the *woodhousii* and *microscaphus* showed slight tendencies in the direction of the opposite form.

The shift in the direction of *woodhousii* at Mesquite and Bunkerville may be related to the proximity of nearly pure *woodhousii* some 25 to 30 miles in an air line to the southwest where the Virgin River is joined by the Meadow Valley Wash. An intervening population between Saint George and the Mesquite-Bunkerville localities in the vicinity of Littlefield, Arizona, may be nearly pure *microscaphus.* Six specimens are available to me. These all seem to be *microscaphus,* but the small size of some of them makes determination somewhat uncertain. Shannon (1949:310) lists an "intergrade" from this area.

In Nevada, all the toads from upper Meadow Valley Wash, Indian Spring in the Virgin Range, and Vegas Valley are near *microscaphus* and are quite uniform structurally. Some do, however, show traces of *woodhousii* in the height of the cranial crests and in having faint suggestions of a dorsal stripe. As suggested by Linsdale (1940) the occurrence of these toads in three far-separated places seems to indicate that the species moved into the region when it was more humid than it is now. There would be little hesitancy in assigning them to *microscaphus* except for the toads in the immediate vicinity of the Virgin and Colorado rivers. These show perceptible traces of *microscaphus* but they are essentially of the *woodhousii* type. The isolated Vegas Valley population of *microscaphus* (4 adult specimens available) exhibits fine dark spotting, different from that so far observed in other parts of the range. Shannon (1949:309) regards 2 of these individuals as intergrades, evidently because of a faint suggestion of a dorsal stripe. Toads from the Lake Mead area and 9 miles below Boulder Dam are near *woodhousii,* but differ from the typical form in their smaller size (2 to 2½ inches), reduced ventral spotting, and pale dorsal coloration. To what extent these characters are due to the influence of *microscaphus* genes or to local environmental effects, apart from such influence, is unknown.

Evidently the situation is similar in the southeastern area of junction

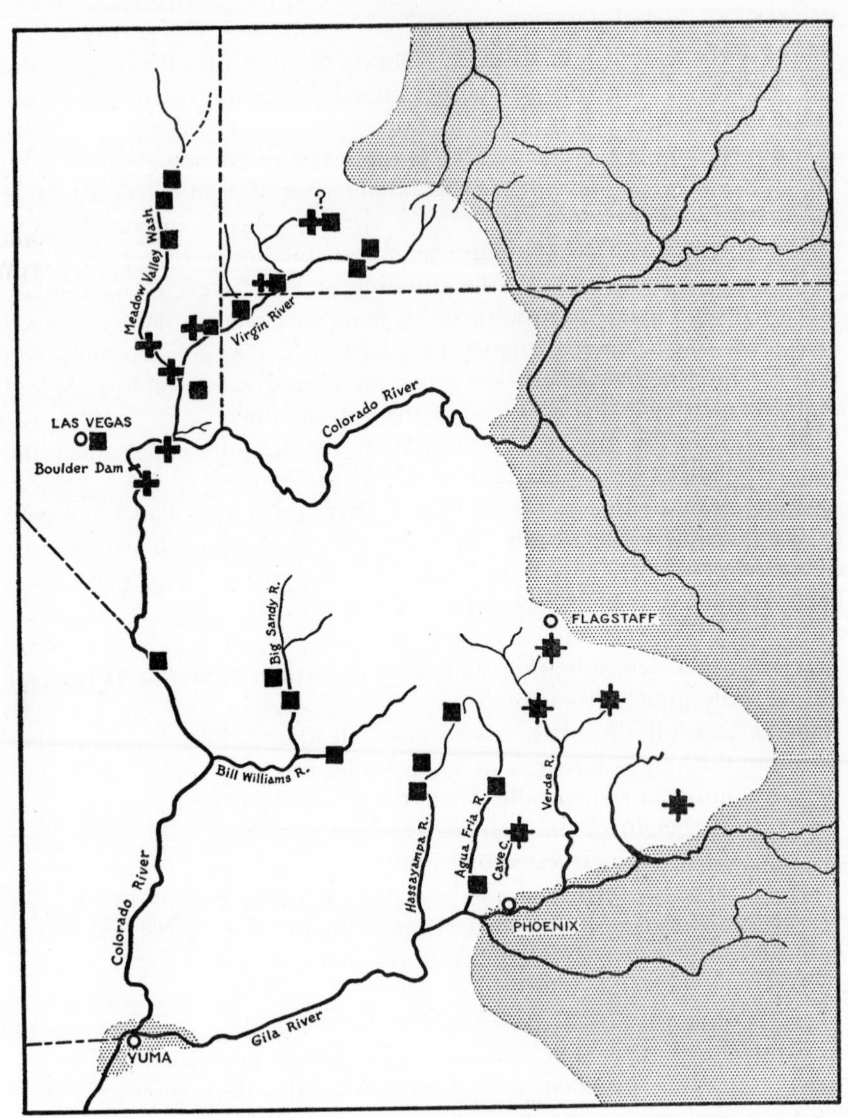

Fig. 29. Map showing the relationship between *Bufo microscaphus* and *Bufo woodhousii* in Arizona, Utah, and Nevada. The black squares represent localities from which typical or nearly typical *microscaphus* are known. The black crosses are localities for *woodhousii*. Where a cross and square are united, both kinds of toads are present, with hybridization occurring between them. The dominant type in such areas is shown by enlargement of the symbol for that type. The questioned hybrid locality in Utah is based on the literature. The black symbols in the lower right quadrant (squares superimposed on crosses) are "intergrade" localities based on the literature (Shannon, 1949), except for the one to the extreme

of *microscaphus* and *woodhousii.* Dr. Shannon informs me that merging of characters is not smooth. Plotting his (1949) locality records reveals that intergrades (to use Shannon's term) occur in the Cave Creek drainage (1 specimen) and the headwaters of the Verde River (Oak Creek Canyon area—5 *microscaphus,* 2 intergrades [Coconino National Forest]; Long Valley—4 intergrades; Camp Verde—3 intergrades and 1 specimen listed under *Bufo woodhousii* as slight intergrade). These streams flow almost due south to join the Gila River. Parallel drainages to the west, respectively the Agua Fria and Hassayampa rivers harbor *microscaphus* (Agua Fria–Rock Springs [3 specimens], Marinette [1 specimen] and Hassayampa-Wickenburg and vicinity [28 specimens], Yarnell [12 specimens], and Prescott and vicinity [11 specimens, 1 with a question]).

I have seen only a few specimens from these areas (of "intergradation") hence cannot comment on the nature of the variation. In view of the type of variation at Saint George, Utah, and Mesquite, Nevada, it appears that the localities and specimens are too few and scattered to determine whether or not there is mergence or gradation through a series of intermediate types (intergradation). Perhaps the relationship between *microscaphus* and *woodhousii* in these areas is not greatly different from that in the northwest. I have seen, for example, what to me was a typical specimen (University of Arizona) of *microscaphus* from Long Valley, an area in which "intergrades" are known (Shannon, 1949).

If the toads listed under *Range,* page 266, from localities outside the currently recognized range of *microscaphus,* prove to belong to this species, it would appear that there may be further geographic overlap in the ranges of *microscaphus* and *woodhousii* types.

Relationship between BUFO MICROSCAPHUS *and* BUFO COMPACTILIS. *B. microscaphus* has many features in common with *B. compactilis* of the Great Plains and Mexico. The weak cranial crests, rounded parotoids, and absence of the dorsal stripe are points of similarity. Differences lie in the character of the foot tubercles (sharper edged in *compactilis*), the degree of tubercle development of the skin of the back (greatest in *compactilis*), the shape of the expanded vocal sac, and perhaps the position of the parotoids (Shannon, 1949). There is greater similarity in the metacarpal tubercles between the southern subspecies of *compactilis* (*compactilis*) and *microscaphus* than between the latter and *B. compactilis*

---

right, which is based on specimens in the Museum of Vertebrate Zoölogy. Stippled areas indicate the range of *Bufo woodhousii.* At most of the localities for this species (represented by crosses), along the Virgin River, the lower Meadow Valley Wash, and the Colorado River proper the toads show characters in the direction of *microscaphus.*

speciosus. On the other hand *B. c. speciosus* and *B. microscaphus* resemble one another in being essentially unmarked ventrally. *B. compactilis compactilis* possesses a black-spotted venter (Smith, 1947).

The Chihuahuan toads, assigned tentatively to *microscaphus* (see page 266, under *Range*), although similar in most respects to *microscaphus,* possess a dark-spotted venter, in this respect resembling the southern subspecies of *compactilis.* Were it not for the rounded metatarsal tubercles and somewhat greater tubercle development, these toads might be assigned to *compactilis.* The character of the vocal sac is unknown.

To what extent the similarity between *microscaphus* and *compactilis* is indicative of close relationship or, on the other hand, parallel evolution, is unknown. The differences in vocal sacs of the males of the two forms is marked. *Compactilis* has an elongate sausage-shaped sac like *Bufo cognatus.* The vocal sac of *microscaphus* is round like that of *Bufo woodhousii.*

I am unable at present to accept the view that *woodhousii* and *compactilis* are in the same species even granting the existence of a *compactilis*-like subspecies of *woodhousii, Bufo w. microscaphus* (Shannon, 1949). The vocal sac difference, along with the extensive range overlap between *woodhousii* and *compactilis,* make a specific relationship between these two forms appear unlikely.

DESERT TOAD

Bufo punctatus Baird and Girard
Plate 17

Range.—Southwestern Kansas, western and southern Oklahoma, Texas, except southeastern part, New Mexico, Arizona, southern Utah, southwestern Colorado, and southern Nevada, deserts of southeastern California. Recorded in Mexico from states of Tamaulipas, Coahuila, Nuevo León, Chihuahua, San Luis Potosí, Sinaloa, Sonora, Guanajuato, and Baja California (Smith and Taylor, 1948:46). (Pl. 58.)

Type locality.—Rio San Pedro (Devil's River), tributary of the Rio Grande, Val Verde County, Texas. (Baird and Girard, 1852a:173.)

Description.—STRUCTURE. Adult approximately 1¾ to 3 inches; body covered with numerous small warts of varying size; parotoid gland nearly perfectly spherical, minutely tuberculate, smaller than, or about same size as, upper eyelid, as viewed from above; juncture of canthus rostralis and preorbital ridge prominent, sometimes forming almost wartlike lump near eye; interorbital area broad, often 1¼ to 1½ times greater than width of upper eyelid; eyelids with numerous closely set small warts; no well-defined postorbital ridge, but rather, a laterally situated wart between eye and parotoid gland; cranial crests absent or weak, closely applied to eyelids; snout pointed in dorsal aspect; head generally depressed; tympanum round to vertically oval, about half size of eye opening; no markedly enlarged warts on hind limbs; 2 metacarpal tubercles, large rounded palmar tubercle, and thenar tubercle ⅓ to about ½ size of palmar; metatarsal tubercles rounded, inner one larger; occasionally suggestion of tarsal fold. COLOR. Warts rusty or buff, commonly set in small black blotches which give spotted appearance; general dorsal coloration pale, often grayish, brownish olive, or reddish brown, of variable hue; no vertebral stripe; below whitish, cream, or buff, unspotted, or with scattered dark flecks, especially in pectoral region; considerable orange color may be present on ventral surfaces of feet; eyelids frequently bicolored, light anteriorly and dark posteriorly; iris bronze. JUVENILE. Brick-red tubercles dorsally; feet with pale yellow ventral surfaces; seat patch lavender, otherwise whitish below; usually with black spots ventrally, more common than in adult. SEXUAL DIFFERENCES. Male averages smaller than female, with dark throat and generally darker coloration. Nuptial digital pads of male dull yellowish brown or grayish brown, not conspicuous but clearly evident in life. Parotoid glands average slightly higher in male than in female (Storer, 1925:195). Vocal sac spherical when inflated.

Adult female, RCS 3109, obtained July 3, 1949, 4.6 miles south-southwest of Saint George, Washington County, Utah: Ground color light sooty olive; light areas on back and sides dull whitish with faint brownish or pinkish tinge; tubercles brick red, including those on limbs; touch of light orange in axilla and groin; below white with faint bluish cast on abdomen; seat patch light pinkish purple; horizontal cream streak just below vent, extending out onto femora; undersides of feet light orange yellow with pinkish cast; surfaces of hind limbs, concealed when limbs folded, faint dull yellow; iris pale copper, pupillary ring gold.

Adult male, RCS 3110: Differs from RCS 3109 principally in having light yellow on face (especially on margin of upper jaw), absence of light areas on back, more yellow on upper surfaces of feet, and discolored throat.

Adult male, RCS 3111: Resembles RCS 3109 but ground color with brownish suffusion; anterior gular area yellowish orange; nuptial pads on fingers, light yellow-brown; iris reddish copper with gold pupillary ring.

Habitat.—Frequents rocky canyons in deserts or semiarid regions where there are springs or seepages. Persistent pools along intermittent stream courses, springs, cattle tanks, reservoirs, and probably occasionally temporary rain pools, provide breeding places. Found from below sea level in Death Valley, California, to approximately 6,500 feet in Colorado (Cockerell, 1927:112). Distribution is spotty, coinciding with the occurrence of water in the relatively dry regions inhabited. (Pl. 41, fig. 2.)

Johnson, *et al.* (1948:255) found desert toads in May and June in and about springs and small, temporary pools in rocky canyon bottoms between 4,000 and 5,000 feet in the Providence Mountains area, California. None was found in midwinter. The apparent altitudinal restriction resulted from the fact that the springs and residual pools used as breeding sites by the toads were most abundant along the bases of mountains, where the rocky canyons were deepest and narrowest.

Ortenburger and Ortenburger (1926:103) in Arizona found 3 individuals some distance from water, one a half mile away, another over a mile. The first was in the open mesquite association. The others were on sand among boulders in a dry stream bed in a canyon.

In dry periods seeks shelter underground. An individual recorded by Burnett (1926:3) was taken from a prairie dog burrow, in sandy loam, near McElmo Creek, Montezuma County, Colorado, on July 30, 1925.

At Bloomington, Washington County, Utah, on July 2, 1949, this species was heard trilling as we walked about over the sandy Virgin River bottom. The bottom was about ¼ mile wide at this location. There was little water although the sand was generally wet. There were, however, several channels of moving water, 2 to 3 inches deep and 30 to 40 feet across. In addition there were scattered shallow pools. There was no vegetation except along the banks. An adult individual was caught 100 yards from the nearest bank which was covered with a growth of sedge. Many individuals seemed to be calling from the exposed sand and pools well out toward the center of the river bottom. *Bufo woodhousii* and *Scaphiopus hammondii* were also found.

On July 3, 1949, we came upon a strong chorus of these little toads. Several hundred individuals must have been present in a shallow pool, evidently the result of an overflow from a nearby canal. There were many small puddles in hoofmarks of horses and cattle in addition to the main pool. There was a scattering of weeds and grass in and near the water. The muddy soil was reddish brown. Tamarisk grew along the banks of the earthen canal and creosote bushes were the conspicuous plants of the surrounding desert. Three *Scaphiopus hammondii* were joining in the chorus, but the abundant *Bufo woodhousii* of the cultivated lands and river bottom, ¼ to ½ mile away, were not represented. Many eggs and larvae of *B. punctatus* were present. Eggs were found, each covered with a film of dirt, singly and in clusters, one egg thick, on the mud bottom of the pool. Others, without a dirt covering were floating singly or in groups at the surface. The water at 5:10 P.M., July 4, was 32.6°C. at a depth of 1 inch.

Near Peña Blanca Springs, Santa Cruz County, Arizona, on July 16, 1949, 15 immature individuals were collected and others were seen along the bottom of a water-scoured rocky ravine in ocotillo, chilicote, oak association. No adults or larvae were found. The toads were discovered under rocks and in nooks and crannies, as well as in exposed places, along the rocky canyon bottom, often near natural "tanks" of standing water. *Hyla arenicolor* and *Microhyla carolinensis,* both adults and larvae, were also found.

Behavior.—Nocturnal but occasionally diurnal. An active and alert species.

Voice.—A bird- or cricket-like trill of relatively high pitch. Faint chirping notes may also be given. Trills may last 4 to 10 seconds with intervals of comparable duration.

At Bloomington, Washington County, Utah, on July 3, 1949, we observed the breeding activity of these toads. In the beam of our flashlights the expanded vocal pouches of the males appeared as almost perfectly round white spheres. Singing males sat erect with their vocal sacs clear of the water. Some sang sitting in shallow water with only the hindquarters immersed; others were on the damp soil at the edges and on little bars and islands in the pool. Singers were spaced 1 to 3 feet apart except for pairs in, or those attempting, amplexus. Males attempting to clasp were energetic. Some leaped a foot or more, landing upon nearby individuals and immediately attempting an embrace. Their aim was good. Occasionally the animal seized was another male and in some instances both individuals were seen with vocal pouches distended as they sang together. Such pairs usually soon separated.

Isolated calling males were timed in their trilling as follows: 1.—(6) 7 (5) 14; 2.—(8) 9 (8) 8 (10), hopped away; 3.—(7) 11 (7) 12 (7) 11 (8) 9 (8) 9 (7) 8 (4). The figures are seconds, those in parentheses measure the duration of the trill, the others intervals between trills. The song is a rapid trill, on one pitch, terminating suddenly. I can imitate it best by tipping my head forward, allowing saliva to accumulate behind my lips. A whistle produced on inspiration is given a trilling quality as air passes over and through the saliva. The pitch of the song seemed to vary between C and C#, 2 octaves above middle C.

Food.—Hemipterans (box-elder bugs and mirids), beetles (*Eleodes* and others) and hymenopterans (ants and bees), have been recorded (Little and Keller, 1937:219; Tanner, 1931:179-80). Little and Keller (1937), at the Jornada Experimental Range in New Mexico, found that adults in May and June, 1935, generally had empty stomachs.

Reproduction.—Breeds from April to September, most commonly in May (Livezey and Wright, 1947:192). In Death Valley, found spawning at the end of the first week in April, 1917 (J. Grinnell, MS). Breeding is probably often initiated by rains. On August 28, 1947, C. Bogert (*in litt.*) found an enormous breeding chorus in a rocky arroyo 20 miles west of Saltillo in Coahuila, Mexico.

EGGS. Commonly deposited on bottoms of small, shallow, often rock-bound pools. Eggs laid singly, in short strings, or sometimes as loose, flat clusters on pond bottom; one gelatinous envelope present, 3.2 to 3.6 mm., very sticky; ovum 1.0 to 1.3 mm., black above and white below (Livezey and Wright, 1947:192). Campbell (1943:3), observing at Peña Blanca Springs, Arizona, states that on July 21, 1933, ". . . the bottoms of the pools were covered with eggs, some of which floated to the surface where they collected in masses. Those which we brought into camp began to hatch in 36 hours."

LARVA. (Based on 10 mature larvae [MVZ 42848] with hind limbs well formed, from Quail Spring, San Bernardino County, California, July 2, 1946, collected by the author.) These measure 33 to 37 mm. in total length; in specimen 37.0 mm. long, head-body 13.6 mm.; tail, including fins, about same height as greatest depth of body; fins widest somewhat posterior to mid-point of tail; greatest height of dorsal and ventral fins similar and each same as greatest width of tail musculature, viewed laterally; tip of tail rounded; dorsal fin originating well posteriorly on body; spiracle sinistral, midway on body, below lateral axis; anus median, emerging at base of ventral fin; body ovoid in dorsal aspect, broadest behind mid-point; eyes well up on head, interorbital distance about equal to distance between outer contour of eye and contour of head as viewed from above; nares about ⅓ distance from anterior eye corner to mouth. (Pl. 29.)

Labial teeth ⅔, first upper row extending completely across mouth to lateral papillary fringe; second row slightly shorter and narrowly divided at midline; lower 3 rows of similar length, about as long as second upper row; papillary fringe confined to sides of mouth. (Pl. 30.)

Generally black with bronze flecks on venter; large larvae with tendency toward faint mottlings of lighter color on blackish ground; tail translucent, with rather evenly spaced black dots; iris bronze. (Coloration from larvae obtained at Lost Palms Canyon, Riverside County, California.)

Closely similar to tadpoles of *Bufo boreas* (as based on comparison with preserved larvae of *boreas* from near Red Bluff, Tehama County, California, collected in 1924). *Punctatus* has coarse spotting and blotching of dorsal fin in contrast to minute uniform stippling in *boreas.* The tail markings are more like those of *canorus* (p. 247) but are still coarser and are more abundant. The snout is longer and body less rotund than in *canorus*. To what extent these differences in the preserved specimens can be relied upon is unknown.

Tadpoles of two size groups were found (Johnson *et al.,* 1948:257) on May 27, 1938, in the shallow, sun-warmed water that flowed out over granite rocks from Rock Spring in the Providence Mountains area of California. The total length of 44 of the smaller-sized tadpoles (after nearly 2 years in alcohol) varied between 8.3 and 13.5 mm. (average 11.2 mm.). In 7 of the larger tadpoles length varied between 27.9 and 37.7 mm. (average 34.5 mm.). On May 30 the larger tadpoles at the spring were nearly metamorphosed, the more advanced of 2 individuals saved, measuring 15.1 mm. in head-and-body length and 6.2 mm. in vestigial tail length.

Camp (1916c:512), at a water hole at the south end of the Turtle Mountains, California, found larvae and some metamorphosing young toads May 28, 1914, apparently of this species. Young measured 9.4 to 10.5 mm. in length. On August 26, 1933, newly metamorphosed toads were so abundant at Peña Blanca Springs (?), Arizona (Campbell, 1934:3) that it was difficult to avoid stepping on them. They were hopping about in midday on the hot sand and gravel of the canyon bottom.

Larvae and eggs of this species were found 2.6 miles southwest of Springdale, Washington County, Utah, on July 1, 1949. Large numbers of very young tadpoles, probably recently hatched, were found in quiet protected water at the edge of the Virgin River. The substratum was largely of reddish-brown mud, overlying rocks. There was no vegetation in the pools. The water was 1 to 2 inches deep. As the water was clear and there was no protective vegetation in the pools, the tadpoles were exposed to direct sunlight most of the day. Eggs were found resting singly or in small unattached groups, a single egg thick, on the mud bottom. They were completely coated with a muddy film. They resembled small, round lumps of earth. Most were found with a small black embryo about ready to hatch.

Twenty-six adult males in a series from Pachalka Spring in the Providence Mountains area, California, obtained May 31, 1939, were separable into two size groups, 42 to 45 mm. and 49.0 to 51.9 mm. (Johnson *et al.,* 1948:257).

WOODHOUSE TOAD

Bufo woodhousii Girard
Plate 18

Range.—In the United States, it is principally an inhabitant of the Great Plains but it also occurs west of the Rocky Mountains. The range in Mexico is little known. It occurs along the Columbia River in south central part of Washington and north central Oregon, in extreme eastern Oregon, Idaho, southern and eastern Montana, Wyoming, southwestern North Dakota and all but eastern South Dakota, Nebraska, western Iowa, western Missouri, Kansas, Oklahoma, Texas except eastern part, Colorado, Utah, New Mexico, Arizona, extreme southern Nevada (Lake Mead area), and extreme southeastern California. Kellogg (1932b:72) records the species as ranging westward in the northern part of its range to near the junction of the Umatilla and Columbia rivers (Umatilla). In northern Mexico it is found in Chihuahua, Sonora, and Durango (Smith and Taylor, 1948:40). (Pl. 58.)

Wright and Wright (1949) and others consider *fowleri* a subspecies of *woodhousii.* This form occupies most of eastern United States, from southern New Hampshire, southeastern Ontario, southern Michigan, and southeastern Iowa south to the Gulf of Mexico in eastern Texas and Louisiana. It appears to be absent from the southern portions of Mississippi, Alabama, and Georgia, and from southeastern North Carolina, eastern South Carolina, and from Florida. I follow Blair (1941:416) in viewing *B. woodhousii* as specifically distinct from *fowleri.*

Type locality.—New Mexico. Province of Sonora, Mexico, and in the San Francisco Mountains [Coconino County, Arizona] (Girard, 1854:86).

Description.—STRUCTURE. Adult to over 5 inches; cranial crests prominent; interorbital portions parallel or slightly divergent posteriorly; parotoid glands elongate, from about 1½ to nearly 2 times length of upper lid, inner edges divergent posteriorly, smooth to touch but pitted and sometimes minutely tuberculate; interparotoid space about 2 to 2⅔ width of gland; tympanum large, vertically oval, from half to nearly same size as eye opening; snout blunt, rounded in profile; no enlarged gland on hind leg or membranous flap of skin on tarsus; 2 metacarpal tubercles, palmar 2 to 5 times larger than thenar tubercle; 2 metatarsal tubercles, usually blunt-edged, inner one much enlarged, 2 to 5 times larger than outer tubercle; warts on dorsal surfaces of body of variable size and distribution, conical, usually with brown-tipped spiny tubercles. COLOR. Above dull yellowish brown or grayish, with greenish, drab, or olive cast, sometimes almost black or nearly tan; warts tipped with pale red, reddish brown, to brown; parotoid glands usually uniformly colored; eyelids uniformly colored or with dark blotch or bar centrally situated near inner margin of lid; dark marking set off by light color anteriorly and posteriorly to it; yellow on lower sides and portions of femur concealed when limb flexed; warts light-colored, commonly brownish, often surrounded by relatively narrow black fringe; whitish vertebral stripe present; limbs tend to be dark-banded dorsally; below usually with small dark flecks, especially laterally in pectoral region, sometimes with median-dark breast spot; ground color below pale yellow, dusky cream, to beige; iris abundantly marked with metallic yellow to cream, in life. JUVENILE. More whitish ventrally than adult; no yellowish-orange color on posterior surface of femur or in groin and axilla; reddish-brown tubercles present dorsally; undersides of feet pale yellowish orange (based on young from Yuma, Yuma County, Arizona, obtained July 9, 1949). SEXUAL DIFFERENCES. Male with dark throat, most evident during breeding season; dark throat stippled with small, light-colored warts and set off by cream to beige lower-jaw margins; vocal sac spherical when inflated; brown nuptial pads on inner 3 fingers. Female reaches larger size, is usually lighter-colored, and usually possesses somewhat more rugose skin than male.

Combined description of 3 adult males, RCS 3015-17, obtained June 28, 1949, 2 miles southwest of Joseph, Sevier County, Utah: Above light olive to grayish brown, suffused with greenish to dark olive, particularly about warts and in leg markings; cranial crests, from nostrils posteriorly, brown; tips of fingers and toes yellowish brown to almost reddish brown; nuptial pads deep rose; enlarged metatarsal tubercle reddish brown or cinnamon brown; vertebral stripe prominent, ash white to pale cream; posterior surface of femur, dorsal and inner surface of foot, and inner side of tibia, concealed when limb flexed, orange yellow; groin and axilla also orange yellow; below opaque yellowish cream; seat patch orange yellow with reddish tinge; gular area sooty, speckled with numerous, closely set cream tubercles; pale gold to cream iris with blackish tracery. The ground color of these animals changed from dark to light olive during 15 minutes' exposure to the sun.

Adult male, RCS 3159, obtained July 9, 1949, 2 miles east of Center Street on 1st Street, Yuma, Yuma County, Arizona: Light-colored areas dorsally and dorsolaterally, pale whitish buff; vertebral stripe pale whitish buff, with diffuse outline; dorsal darker areas greenish gray; groin, rear of femur, rump, inner and posterior surface of tibia, upper surface of hind foot and axilla, yellow with orange tinge; parotoid glands nearly uniformly light brownish olive; warts with minute reddish-brown tubercles; vague transverse stripe on head intersecting eyelids, colored like vertebral stripe; below cream or light yellow with buffy tinge; throat sooty gray with faint pinkish cast; seat patch yellowish orange; hind toes and undersides of forefeet pinkish brown; tips of toes and large metatarsal tubercle brown with faint reddish cast; nictitating membrane edged with greenish yellow; iris pale gold, almost silver near pupil but pinkish peripherally.

Habitat.—Highly variable. Kellogg (1932b:74) points out that the habitat includes surroundings as diverse as the sagebrush flats of eastern Montana, the prairie fields among the chalk cliffs of western Kansas, the Hudsonian Zone mountainsides of eastern Colorado, the irrigation ditches that traverse the mesquite plains of New Mexico, and the bottom lands along the Colorado River near Yuma, Arizona. During May and June, according to locality, adults of this species may be found breeding in shallow, sluggish creeks, in irrigation ditches, or in fresh-water pools in the canyons.

Reports on occurrence by other authors, and personal observations are as follows: In Oklahoma it is found in wooded bottom lands, small gardens, and in sandy areas (Bragg, 1940a:9).

Marr (1944:480), reporting on this species collected in Oklahoma, Kansas, and Nebraska found it in grassland, in sand hills, near creeks, and in towns. They were common under street lights on hot nights, particularly in Beaver, Beaver County, Oklahoma, where as many as 8 or more individuals were observed under one light. An individual was removed from the burrow of a kangaroo rat (*Dipodomys ordii*).

Ruthven (1907:508), near Alamogordo, New Mexico, reported that all specimens were taken in the evening along irrigation ditches in the mesquite association on the plains. Probably the natural habitat, as with *B. punctatus,* is the canyons in the mountains where moisture is more abundant. It probably has extended its range to the plains with irrigation. It was not seen during the intense heat of the day but at about dusk these toads came out in numbers along the shallow ditches, especially near street lamps.

Taylor (1929:65), in Kansas found large adults in the prairie dog villages at night. They hid in the holes during the day.

Near Joseph, Sevier County, Utah, on June 28, 1949, at about 10:00 P.M., I became aware of a faint, distant trilling, suggestive of the sound made by high-tension wires or the wind blowing through telegraph lines. After walking about a quarter of a mile over basin sagebrush desert and farm land, I came to a pool 4 or 5 inches deep, 4 or 5 feet across, and approximately 10 feet long. The pool was near a large, fast-flowing canal situated in the Sevier River bottom. There were several tule clumps in the pool but otherwise little vegetation. The mud bottom could be clearly seen. An adult *B. woodhousii* was sitting in shallow water at the far side of the pool. Another was lying on the bottom near the base of a tule clump. The latter had probably submerged on our approach. The light-colored body of the toad was conspicuous against the dark mud. One hundred yards away an adult male was found trilling from a mat of submerged grasses at the edge of a large quiet pool bordered by sedges and willows. This individual, like the first, rested in quiet water with his hindquarters submerged. (Pl. 43, fig. 1.)

At Yuma, Yuma County, Arizona, on July 9, 1949, a chorus of these toads was heard along an irrigation canal among cultivated fields. The sides of the canal sloped about 50° and were of white concrete. The bottom was probably also concrete but was covered with dark brown sediment. The water was quiet. Its surface was about 12 feet across and its depth 10 to 12 inches. Here and there were clumps of green grass but in general there was little vegetation in the water. Twelve calling males were spaced 10 to 75 feet apart along 200 feet of the canal. Some had their hindquarters in the water; others rested on the steeply sloping bank at the water's edge. With the exception of 2 individuals, they were on the shadowed side of the canal. It was a bright moonlight night.

Behavior.—An active species, even during hot weather, seemingly more so than *B. cognatus* and others. Largely nocturnal but occasionally abroad in the daytime. In Oklahoma, Bragg (*sup. cit.*) found that the young were more inclined to be diurnal than the adults. As with most toads, this species may retreat by burrowing into the soil. Burt (1932:79) found partly grown individuals beneath shallow mounds of sand in sandbanks near Antioch, Nebraska. The species may feign death when roughly handled. Thermal data are presented on page 291.

Voice.—Near Joseph, Sevier County, Utah, on June 28, 1949, trilling of an individual (body temperature 15°C.) was timed as follows: 15 (2½) 11 (2¼) 12 (2½) ? (2½) 12 (2) 43 (2½) 18 (2½) 47 (3) 55 (2½). The parenthetical numbers are the trills in seconds, the others the intervals between trills. The pitch was about E (just above middle C) or perhaps ½ to 1 note lower. I can best imitate it by fluttering my tongue as rapidly as possible and whistling at the same time at a high pitch. The trill was sustained, for the most part, on one pitch but dropped suddenly, but slightly, at the end. When my companions and I approached with our light, the animal became quiet. We concealed the light and waited but there was no response. I tried a whistled imitation of the call, using a salivary trill (see the account of *Bufo punctatus*, p. 283), but although it seemed to me correct as to pitch it was not accurate as to frequency and force of the vibrations. I changed to a rapid tongue flutter, expelling air with considerable force and using the same whistle. This sound had much more volume and the vibrations seemed more nearly those of the toad's although they were not as fast.

The first time I tried the imitation, the toad called within 2 seconds after the imitation. I turned on my flashlight and observed the vocal sac expanded bubble-like in front of the animal's head. The sac was spherical from the front but somewhat oval in lateral aspect. Only the base of the sac touched the water and the toad's tympanic membranes were well above the surface. I kept the animal in the beam of the flashlight and attempted further imitations. Whereas previously he had been quiet for long periods and disinclined to call when illuminated, he now responded to each imitation. It was evident each time before he called that he was about to vocalize, for he erected his body and moved his forelimbs about slightly, as though attempting to get better footing. He puffed out his vocal sac slightly 2 to 4 times, partly filling it. This was followed by the trill and distension of the sac. When inflated the sac appeared dark gray at the tip, lightening basally. The toad responded to a tongue flutter without, as readily as with, a whistle.

At Yuma, Yuma County, Arizona, on July 9, 1949, at about 10:00 P.M., we heard cries suggestive of a newborn babe. The sounds also brought to mind the baa of a sheep, the bawling of a calf, or the voice of a barn owl, but more prolonged than the latter. The voice might be represented as "wh-e-e-e-e-e-e-e." The sounds were similar to, but not identical with, the calls of *Bufo woodhousii* in Utah. Individuals heard at Holladay, near Salt Lake City, June 18, 1950, were recorded as producing sounds suggesting "w-a-a-a-a-a-a-h." Theirs was a wheezy cry, and ended rather abruptly. The calling of an individual at Yuma, Arizona (body temperature 31.4°C.) was timed in seconds as follows: (1) 9 (1) 13 (1½) 8 (1½) 8 (1¼) 8 (1) 7 (1) 8 (1¼) 7 (1¼) 8 (1½) 7 (1½) 7 (1½) 9 (1½) 7 (1½) 9 (1) 7 (1) 6 (1¼) 5 (1¼) 8 (1½) 11 (1½) 9 (1¼). The pitch was about A or A-flat above middle C. An individual at a cloacal temperature of 21.3°C. at Holladay, Utah, gave 8 calls in 60 seconds, the cries varying in length from 1½ to 2½ seconds.

Food.—The following items have been recorded: Sowbugs; scorpions, centipedes, spiders; insects—orthopterans (grasshoppers, crickets [gryllids]), lepidopterans (noctuids [cutworms], other moths, and butterfly larvae), dipterans (tachinids and a syrphid), hemipterans (pentatomids—*Chlorochroa*, etc.), beetles (scarabaeids [*Diplotaxis, Cotalpa, Phyllophaga, Trox*, and *Hoplia*], weevils [*Calendra ochrea*, etc.], carabids [*Pterostichus, Harpalus, Elaphrus, Agonoderus*, and *Bembidion*], cucujids, tenebrionids [*Eleodes*], lady beetles [coccinellids], tiger beetles [cicindelids—*Cicindela oregona*], *Platynus*, chrysomelids [flea-beetles—*Psylliodes*], staphylinids [*Creophilus maxillosus*, etc.], elaterids, meloids, dytiscids), hymenopterans (ants, bees, bembicids, and a sphecid [*Sphex*]); plant materials—small sticks, leaves, grass, etc., probably taken incidentally (Marr, 1944:480; Smith, 1934:452; Force, 1925:26).

Pack (1922[107]:46-47) describes the congregation of these toads during a sugar beet webworm flare-up in the Benson district, Cache County, Utah, in August, 1921. "Most of the toads were of this year's brood, rang-

THERMAL DATA

Locality	Date	Time*	Size	Temperature, °C. Body	Substratum	Air (½ inch above surface in shade)	Conditions of occurrence
Utah	*1949*						
2 mi. SW of Joseph, Sevier Co.	June 28	11:00	adult	15.0	14.6 (water)	13.0	Sitting in shallow water with hindquarters immersed; trilling
2½ mi. S of St. George, Wash. Co.	July 4	4:20	nearly adult	29.6	29.0 (soil)	32.0	Active in the sun
Bloomington	July 1	11:30 A.M.			34.6		Larvae and recently metamorphosed toads in water at this temperature
	July 2	9:00	2 inches	23.0			Active on damp sand of Virgin River bottom
		9:05	2 inches	21.8			
	July 3	7:35	adult	23.4			
		7:40	adult	23.6	24.6 (soil)	24.3	Active in cultivated field
		8:05	adult	23.0			Ten inches from ground in sunflower-clover growth
	July 3		2 inches	22.0			Hopping across dirt road at dusk
			2 inches	22.5			
			2 inches	22.5			
	July 4		nearly adult	27.0			Active in alfalfa field
Arizona							
0.2 mi. E of Center St., on 1st St., Yuma, Yuma Co.	July 9	10:00	adult	31.4	33.4 (water)	30.2	Near water's edge on concrete side of canal, trilling
		10:20	adult	27.8			as above, trilling
			adult	30.2			
Fort Huachuca, Cochise Co.	July 21	10:40	adult	20.0			Squatting on dry surface at top of concrete dam

* P.M. unless otherwise indicated.

ing in length from one and a fourth to one and a half inches. I would estimate that in one field of about one square acre there were no fewer than one hundred toads.

"An examination of the stomach contents of a number of toads disclosed the fact that they were feeding exclusively upon the webworms and that every one was gorged to the limit. These small toads contained from 24 to 40 worms each, the limiting factor in quantity being the size of the stomach. A number of representative toads were weighed, and the stomach contents of each were then removed and weighed. It was found that the contained food represented 16 per cent of the total weight of the toad. If the toad fills its stomach four times every twenty-four hours, as Kirtland maintains, these toads were daily eating a mass of webworms two-thirds their own weight!"

Reproduction.—Bragg (1940c:319) reports the following for the species in Oklahoma: Breeds in a variety of places such as cattle tanks, ditches, flooded fields, backwashes of streams, artificial fish pools, reservoirs, sloughs, flood plains of rivers, often in shallow, muddy water but sometimes in deep water, to as much as 3 feet. Most breeding takes place after rain but some occurs irrespective of rain. Breeds over a considerable period, from March to July. Congresses are usually small, evidently composed of different individuals at different times.

EGGS. Deposited in tangled mass around vegetation or debris in practically any type of pool or stream; complement up to 25,650 eggs per female. Eggs in strings with single continuous gelatinous encasing; envelope 2.6 to 4.6 mm., average about 3.5 mm., distinct and relatively firm; ovum 1.0 to 1.5 mm., black above and tan to yellow below; one or two rows of 17 to 25 eggs per inch; long strings, 8 to 10 feet in length (Livezey and Wright, 1947).

LARVA. Tadpole small, maximum total length 23 mm.; tip of tail rounded, obtuse, not attenuated; dorsal fin extends to a point less than halfway between anus and vertical of spiracle; spiracle sinistral, below lateral axis, directed backward and upward at an angle of about 35° to 40°; opening of spiracle round or slightly oval; inner edge very slightly free from body; eyes dorsal to lateral axis, slightly nearer to median dorsal line than to lateral outline when viewed from above; anus median, opening distinctly higher than lower edge of ventral fin. (Pl. 29.)

Labial teeth 2/3; papillary fringe a single row confined to angles of mouth, sharply indented on each side, slightly below middle; medial edges of dorsal papillary fringe extend on each side exactly to lateral ends of first row of upper labial teeth; medial edges of ventral papillary fringe extend on each side to slightly medial of lateral edges of last (outer) row of lower labial teeth; on each side, dorsal portion of papillary fringe (i.e., portion dorsal to lateral indentation) slightly shorter than ventral portion; few small papillae in mouth disc above and below lateral indentations; first row of upper labial teeth continuous; second row divided by space about half length of either half; lateral edges of the two rows coincide; length of first row of upper labial teeth about 1⅓ times length of upper mandible; latter broadly U-shaped, shallow, its external edge finely denticulated; lower mandible V-shaped, its external edge finely denticulated; first row of lower labial teeth slightly indented medially, last (outer) neither indented nor broken, first row longest of the three, slightly longer than second, about twice length of last row; inner rows of upper and lower labia about equal in length. (Pl. 30.)

Body and hind limbs heavily pigmented with dark brown or gray to slate (specimens preserved in formalin appear more brownish); dorsal musculature of tail somewhat lighter than body; ventral musculature immaculate; fins with few scattered flecks of pigmentation, more numerous in dorsal fin than in ventral, latter being almost immaculate; black surface of eyes speckled with gold and pupil rim golden (Johnson, 1939: 163). (Largely from Youngstrom and Smith, 1936:630-31.)

Larvae, RCS 3376, obtained July 29, 1949, 0.8 miles north-northwest of Lakeside, near State Highway 173, Navajo County, Arizona (notes from 5 individuals of about 20 collected): Total length from 14.3 to 22.5 mm., most about 20.0 mm.; head-and-body length, 6.1 to 10.2 mm. In structure these larvae fit foregoing description by Youngstrom and Smith (1936) except as follows: spiracle on, or slightly above, lateral axis; no papillae discernible above and below lateral indentation of papillary fringe; outer upper row of labial teeth broken into 3 parts (in 2 individuals), central one shortest; inner lower row 1¼ to 1⅓ times longer than outer lower row and not indented medially.

After preservation larvae pigmented as follows: Deep brown above on head-and-body and tail musculature; tail musculature not noticeably lighter than body, although in some individuals there appears a scattering of small light-colored gaps in melanic ground color; tail fins nearly unpigmented; upper fin with 1 or 2 to a half dozen black, branched melanophores and brown stippling of melanophores toward anterior base; lower fin with none or 1 or 2 black, branched melanophores and no brown stippling; branched melanophores fan out from tip of tail musculature into fin at tip of tail; ventral ⅓ or ¼ of tail musculature immaculate; ventral surface of head-and-body blackened with melanophores, but such pigment largely absent on throat and reduced over intestine; intestine shows clearly in some individuals but is nearly wholly obscured in others.

In life, generally black above with scattered pale orange, pale yellow, or buff blotches on sides of head-and-body and upper surface of tail musculature; pale yellow to whitish (guanistic?) blotches along lower ⅓ of tail musculature; most of underside of body mottled with metallic-appearing, light-colored pigment, iridescent blue-green in sunlight; intestine not visible; throat gray; underside of tail light sooty gray, without guanophores; iris with fine speckling of pale orange, metallic-appearing pigment, most abundant immediately around and filling iris above and below pupil.

TREE-TOADS

Family Hylidae

Structure.—Pectoral girdle arciferous; vertebrae procoelous; ribs absent; urostyle attached to two condyles; usually with dilated sacral diapophyses; teeth in upper jaw; vomerine teeth usually present; tongue oval or heart-shaped, entire or variously nicked posteriorly, usually free but sometimes attached in varying degrees; pupil of variable shape (horizontally or vertically elliptical; triangular); tympanum evident or not; weakly developed parotoid glands sometimes present; intercalary bones or cartilages present, to which attach terminal phalanges that are usually claw-shaped; well-formed toe pads often present.

Mature larvae of species considered here small (*Pseudacris*) to medium (*Hyla arenicolor*), ranging from about 1 to 2 inches in total length; oral disc usually not emarginate; labial teeth $\frac{2}{2\text{-}3}$, dorsal fin often highly arched and extending well onto body; anus dextral; spiracle sinistral, on or just below lateral axis.

Habits.—Most are arboreal, some are aquatic, others are terrestrial, and some are somewhat fossorial. The eggs are single or clustered.

Range.—Confined to the New World with the exception of the genus *Hyla* (as recognized by Noble, 1931:508) which is world-wide in distribution except for gaps in the Indo-Malayan (including Borneo), Polynesian, Ethiopian, and Madagascan regions. There are three genera in the United States—*Hyla, Acris,* and *Pseudacris.* Three species of *Hyla* and one *Pseudacris* are treated here.

Key to Genera and Species
Figure 30

1*a*. Digital discs small (1, 2, 3); hind toes with or without web (1, 2); snout elongate (11); adult size small, 3/4 to 1 1/2 inches 2

1*b*. Digital discs larger (4, 5, 10); hind toes with web (4); snout blunt (12); adult size larger, to over 2 inches 4

2*a*. (1*a*) Dark eye stripe absent (6) or, if present, then with dorsal longitudinal dark lines, bars, or spots anteriorly on body (7) 3

2*b*. Dark eye stripe present (8); anterior portion of dorsal surface of body usually unmarked or markings confined to eyelids . . . . *Hyla wrightorum,* p. 327

3*a*. (2*a*) Hind toes with well-developed web (1); often a light-colored bar extending from eye to base of forelimb (6) .... *Acris gryllus*, p. 296

3*b*. Hind toes without webbing or only slightly webbed (2); no light-colored bar on side of head and neck (7) .... *Pseudacris nigrita*, p. 305

4*a*. (1*b*) Eye stripe present, usually well-defined (8, 9); web of hind toes moderately developed (4); margin of web concaved between toes when toes spread; toe pads smaller, less transversely expanded (4); skin of dorsal surfaces relatively smooth or weakly tuberculate 5

4*b*. Eye stripe absent; web of hind toes often greatly developed in individuals from California (5), moderately developed elsewhere (10); in those with well-developed web, margin of web may be nearly straight between individual toes when toes spread (5); toe pads larger, transversely expanded (5); skin of dorsal surfaces relatively rough .... *Hyla arenicolor*, p. 313

5*a*. (4*a*) Eye stripe extending to shoulder, or somewhat beyond (9); webbing of toes greater (4); commonly a dark mark on head between or behind eyes (12) .... *Hyla regilla*, p. 322

5*b*. Eye stripe long, extending well back along sides posterior to shoulder where it may break into several segments (8); webbing of toes less pronounced (3); usually no dark mark on head between or behind eyes although mark may be present on each eyelid .... *Hyla wrightorum*, p. 327

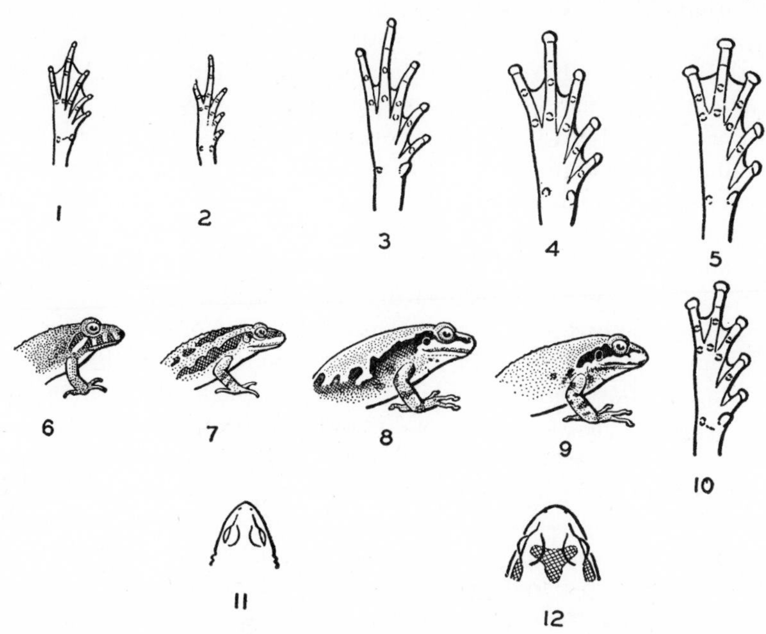

Fig. 30. 1, 6, 11, *Acris gryllus;* 2, 7, *Pseudacris nigrita;* 3, 8, *Hyla wrightorum;* 4, 9, 12, *Hyla regilla;* 5, *Hyla arenicolor* (from California); 10, *Hyla arenicolor* (from 10 miles north of Clifton, in White Mountains, Arizona).

CRICKET-FROG

Acris gryllus (Le Conte)
Plate 19

Range.—Eastern Colorado and eastern New Mexico east to the Atlantic seaboard; south through Texas to the Gulf of Mexico; north to Connecticut and New York and the Great Lakes region. In Mexico south to central Coahuila (Smith and Taylor, 1948:77, under name *A. crepitans*).

Dr. Paul Maslin informs me that in Colorado the species occurs in the eastern river valleys below 4,000 feet in altitude. He has collected the species at Wray, Yuma County, but the records for Greeley, Weld County, are based on *Pseudacris*. (Pl. 59.)

Type locality.—Probably Le Conte Plantation, Riceborough, Georgia (Le Conte, 1825:282).

Description.—STRUCTURE. Size small, adult ¾ to approximately 1⅓ inches, most about 1 inch; a hylid with ranid-like build; skin sometimes smooth but commonly roughened by numerous minute tubercles; rather prominent warts may be present in anal region; tympanum small and indistinct, about ⅕ to ⅓ size of eye opening; snout elongate and tapered; hind limbs long; digits with small toe pads, only slightly expanded; 2 oval metacarpal tubercles, inner one usually somewhat smaller than outer one; hind feet with well-developed web; web extending to within 1½ to 3 phalanges of tip of fourth toe; 2 round-surfaced metatarsal tubercles, inner one often only slightly larger than outer; distinct tarsal fold. COLOR. Ground color above gray, green, or various shades of brown to almost black; upper jaw barred with dark color; commonly light bar on face extending from eye region to base of forelimb; usually dark, often light-edged, triangular mark, with apex directed posteriorly between eyes, and anterior corners reaching eyelids; usually with dark marking on sides extending from above and behind axilla to region in front of groin; often small dark markings on back, setting off light-colored warts; commonly an irregular light-colored, often broad, vertebral stripe—whitish, reddish, or greenish in color; limbs barred and spotted with dark color; hind limbs particularly showing tendency toward well-defined bands (commonly 3); below whitish, unspotted, or with dusky spotting, mainly in gular area and on chest; conspicuous light-colored wart (s) usually present on either side of, and below, anus; posterior surface of femur commonly with dark-colored longitudinal stripe, bordered above and below by light color; iris bright orange to gray. SEXUAL DIFFERENCES. Male with gular area grayish black, yellowish in life (in spring), and with chest and gular region more commonly spotted than in female; female has slightly longer fingers (Smith, 1934:459, Kansas) and is larger than male; thumb of male with inconspicuous pad on inner side when breeding.

Adult male, RCS 3414, obtained August 7, 1949, at Carlsbad, Eddy County, New Mexico: Above olive brown with dark markings of blackish; small spots on back, and on upper surface of hind limbs, light orange; tubercles below vent cream; dark sooty longitudinal bar on femora bordered above and below by dull light yellow; line behind eye and markings at edge of upper and lower lips cream; belly white, resulting from dense guanistic layer; gular area sooty posteriorly, grading to brownish olive anteriorly; undersides of limbs light gray; seat patch sooty with cream-colored spots; iris gray above and below pupil, under magnification observed to be marked with pale yellow flecks; area anterior and posterior to pupil rust, composed of minute pale orange flecks; pale gold pupillary ring.

Adult male, RCS 3632, obtained March 18, 1950, 8.2 miles north of Quemado, near State Highway 85, Maverick County, Texas: Above brownish gray with small warts of brown; orange-buff area immediately anterior to groin and on anterior and posterior surfaces of femur; light-colored postocular bar, buff near eye grading to white in front of shoulder; throat deep olive; chest and abdomen white, under magnification color seen to be result of solid guanistic layer; undersides of limbs pale blue-gray with weak scattering of whitish guanophores; tips of toes orange buff; iris with ash-white patches above and below pupil, brown anterior and posterior to pupil; pupillary ring pale gold.

Habitat.—This species is mainly a lowland form inhabiting the grassy borders of streams, springs, ponds, lakes, ditches, and river overflow areas. It may occur in grassy meadows and in boggy or swampy places. It is terrestrial in habit but enters water to breed. It seems to prefer damp places on land rather than the water. It does not exhibit the climbing propensities of many other members of the family.

Linsdale (1927:76-77) reported on *A. gryllus* in the vicinity of Geary, Kansas, as follows: "This species was the most abundant amphibian within the limits of this area. It was found most abundantly at the edges of bodies of water in all parts of the area in spring although some were found on the shores of the lake [an old saucer lake] through the summer and until late in the fall.

"On February 2, 1924, several were found in the creek above the bridge. They were in the water above some old ice and below a top layer of new ice. All the frogs were stiff and floating and apparently they were dead.

"In the warm water of the springs and just below the springs a few frogs of this species were found throughout the winter.

"In the spring the number of individuals present at the edge of the water began to decrease after the first of May."

Smith (1934:459, Kansas) states that breeding sites are varied. Where the species is abundant, permanent lakes, streams, and springs always have their quota. The species may breed in and sing from temporary pools in pastures or at roadsides.

Breckenridge (1944:65) describes the habitat in Minnesota as consisting of small, meandering, gravel-bottomed streams flowing through grassy meadows. The frogs are found either in the water or in the grass or among the pebbles along the shores. Ruthven, Thompson, and Gaige (1928:38) say of the frog in Michigan, "The cricket-frog is a tree-frog that is almost entirely terrestrial in its habits."

Pope (1944:89-90), writing of the species in the Chicago area, says it occurs along the open marshy borders of pond, lake, and stream. Other plant-grown, aquatic situations such as grassy ditches, river overflow pools, bogs, and swamps are likewise frequented. He speaks of it as a "prairie frog."

At Carlsbad, Eddy County, New Mexico, on August 7, 1949, we camped about a quarter of a mile east of town, approximately 200 yards from the east bank of the Pecos River. It was a balmy, somewhat cloudy evening. About 8:00 P.M. I noticed a rattling sound suggesting that made by striking stones together. It was also somewhat like the low motorboat sound made by the Texas nighthawk. We hiked a quarter of a mile over a hill covered with low-growing mesquite, prickly pear, and cholla cactus, down into a rocky wash onto the grass and tule-bordered river bank. Tamarisk was common along the stream. We had thought the sounds were coming from a distance of about 100 yards. They seemed little louder now than when at camp. The callers were out in the stream, which here was about 75 to 100 feet across. The sounds seemed to come from masses of scum that had accumulated in shallow places and about grass and scattered tule clumps.

There were two groups of singers, about 50 feet apart, one composed of perhaps 5 or 6 individuals, the other of 3. I waded out in the direction of one of the groups, walking through water generally 2 to 8 inches deep, over a bottom of rocky ridges. In some places the rock was exposed or was covered with only a thin film of water. The current was not strong. The water was cool. In the light of my lantern I saw a cricket frog jump across a mat of scum, leaping 2 to 3 feet in the air and covering 3 to 4 feet at a jump. The singers were wary, seldom calling unless our light was out. William Riemer, from the bank, stimulated them to call by striking two pebbles together. I finally spotted a little fellow perched near the edge of a mass of scum. His tiny beadlike vocal sac was expanded. He had just finished calling. The sac was largely free of the water and scum although its base may have been immersed.

At 8.2 miles north of Quemado, near State Highway 85, Maverick

County, Texas, this frog was abundant along the margins of standing pools of water in a drying river bottom, cobbled with whitish water-worn stones. Mesquite, acacia, oaks, and patches of green grass were present on the river banks. Yucca and a low-growing, pale yellow-blossom acacia were present on the level or gently rolling surrounding terrane. Three pools were investigated. They measured respectively 100 by 20, 75 by 25, and 30 by 300 feet and were all about 1 foot in greatest depth. About the margins were floating masses of pale green algal scum and scattered masses out from shore. Algae were also present in places on the bottoms. The mud and moist stones at the edges of the pools were ash gray. The frogs were found by walking near the water's edge; they were rarely seen before they jumped because of their close matching of the background.

Behavior.—This species is an excellent jumper, capable of leaping 3 or 4 feet at a jump on a horizontal surface. It is a good swimmer although it seems to prefer the shore. Individuals frightened into the water may quickly swim back in a semicircle to the bank where they usually conceal themselves readily. These frogs in peninsular Florida, however, tend to seek shelter under objects on the bottom (Netting and Goin, 1945:308). The species seldom, if ever, climbs.

Marr (1944:480), commenting on this frog (under *A. crepitans*) collected in Texas, Oklahoma, and Kansas, states, "These frogs were invariably found near ponds and streams and generally on sandy banks. They seemed reluctant to enter the water and would hop along the shore in preference to entering the water. When forced to jump into the water they immediately returned to the shore. After several hops they seemingly tired and were more easily captured."

In animals observed by me near Quemado, Texas, I noted a change in behavior, presumably related to increased body temperatures. When I was collecting between 12:30 and 1:00 P.M., basking individuals were observed to leap from positions on shore 1 to 3 feet out into the water and to swim directly to the bottom, hiding under stones or masses of algae on the bottom. The frogs usually remained motionless as I moved their cover and seized them. Later, between 1:30 and 2:00 P.M., animals that jumped into the water darted about a short distance before hiding. Several were chased along the bank and some jumped out onto floating masses of algae and then quickly back to shore. The temperature of the water at this time was 25.3°C.; the air temperature, 1 inch above the ground in the shade near the edge of a pond, was 26.5°C.

These frogs are capable of rapid color change. The pattern may become obscure at the extremes of the dark and light phases.

Voice.—Pope (1944:89) says the call is a series of 30 to 40 ". . . sharp clicks like two pebbles or marbles being struck together, at first slowly and then more rapidly. . . . One that has been silenced through fright quickly revives if two pebbles are knocked together by a concealed observer." Choruses occur night and day during the breeding season.

Hudson (1942:25, Nebraska): "The cricket-like chirping of these abundant little frogs is a familiar sound about the marshy borders of streams and ponds from April to July."

The name is said to refer to the song rather than to small size and activity (Dickerson, 1920:155).

At Carlsbad, New Mexico, the individual song of this frog started slowly, at first a single "kick" or "gick," followed after one second or so by another, then speeding up to calls at half second intervals, finally reaching a rate of perhaps 5 or 6 sounds per second. The "kicks" were uttered quite irregularly and except for the first notes had a somewhat double quality. The song can be imitated well by striking stones together. The first notes are best produced by single direct strokes, the later ones by scraping the stones slightly as they are brought into contact. Riemer's stone imitations were so good that the frogs readily responded and much of the time I was unable to distinguish his sounds from theirs. The vocal sac is spherical.

Food.—The following items have been recorded: Spiders; a crayfish; insects—orthopterans, hemipterans (Thyreocorinae and *Adelphocoris* [*Calocoris*] *rapidus*), aphids (numerous pupae and wingless females), a caterpillar, dipterans (crane flies and *Chlorops*), beetles (coccinellids and elaterids), and ants (Hudson, 1942:25; Garman, 1892:342; Hartman, 1906:228).

Reproduction.—Season, February to October (Livezey and Wright, 1947:190) considering the species over its entire range. Pope (1944:88) says the breeding season was at its height on June 2 in southeast Iowa. In approximately the latitude of Chicago, breeding apparently begins in May and extends into July. Livezey (1950:140) says that in Texas, depending upon the weather, these frogs may be seen at any month of the year. Choruses have been recorded from February until October, with the peak of the breeding season evidently extending from the latter part of April through July.

The species breeds in shallow, quiet plant-grown water. Temporary roadside and pasture pools are also used. Amplexus is axillary.

EGGS. Livezey (1950:139-140) reports the following observations on the subspecies reaching our area: Three amplexing pairs were collected at Nelson Creek, Walker County, Texas, the evening of July 6, 1949. These were taken to the laboratory and placed in large aquaria provided with water, sand, and debris from the creek. During the night one female deposited several dozen eggs. These were laid singly and in small, irregular clusters containing two to seven eggs. Pine needles, twigs, grass stems, and leaves were utilized as places for deposition; several single eggs were also found on the sand in the bottom. In the small masses the eggs were held together by the adhesion of the gelatinous envelopes. Individual eggs were distinct in the mass, but the single egg or cluster shortly becomes difficult to discern as a result of the large amount of debris which sticks to the viscid jelly.

Ova were dark brown to black above and tan below, with an average diameter of 1.13 mm., the range being 1.06 to 1.17 mm. There is evidently no conspicuous capsular cavity. Examination with a binocular microscope revealed the presence of two gelatinous envelopes. The inner was distinct and not visible without optical aid, but the outer was quite distinct and firm. Measurements of these envelopes were: inner 2.34 to 2.74 mm., average 2.60 mm.; outer 2.98 to 3.70 mm., average 3.34 mm. From these data it is indicated that the eggs of *Acris g. crepitans* differ from those of *Acris g. gryllus* (providing published data on the latter are accurate). The former subspecies apparently has a somewhat larger ovum, two envelopes rather than one, and the average over-all diameter is slightly greater. This last criterion may, however, be a matter of samples examined.

Wright and Wright (1949:37 and 219) give 241 and 250 eggs as the complement for *Acris g. gryllus.* Ovarian counts indicate that *Acris g. crepitans* may have a larger complement of eggs per female than its southeastern relative. A gravid female taken April 12, 1947 from south of Huntsville, Walker County, Texas, contained 125 fully developed ova and about 100 ova in formative stages in the left ovary. Another specimen collected April 26, 1947 from the Brazos River, Palo Pinto County, contained a total of 315 eggs (192 in the right and 123 in the left ovary). A third ovarian count of a female collected at Huntsville, April 10, 1948, totaled 340 eggs (169 in the right and 171 in the left ovary). There was no difference in size or appearance of the eggs from the Walker County and the Palo Pinto County specimens.

The eggs are reported to hatch in 4 days (Breckenridge, 1944:66, Minnesota); the tadpole period may be 50 to 90 days or longer (Wright and Wright, 1942:101).

LARVA. Description based on 4 mature tadpoles from 7 miles west of Cuero, DeWitt County, Texas, obtained July 26, 1947, by Max Hecht, loaned through the courtesy of C. M. Bogert of the American Museum of Natural History. Total length 40.0 to 49.4 mm.; head-body 15.8 to 17.3 mm., greatest depth 8.8 to 11.5 mm., greatest width 10.9 to 12.9 mm., egg-shaped in dorsal aspect, broadest well behind eyes; greatest depth of tail near mid-point or somewhat anterior to mid-point, 9.6 to 11.2 mm.; greatest height of dorsal fin about same or slightly less than greatest depth of tail musculature; tip of tail acute or nearly so; dorsal fin originating on body near verticle through spiracle; spiracle on, or slightly above, lateral axis, directed backward and slightly upward, opening vertically elliptical; eyes situated well laterally, lateral outline of eye nearly reaching outline of head as viewed from above; distance between dorsomedian edges of eyes about twice distance from this edge to contour of head; nostril slightly nearer eye than tip of snout; anus dextral, opening near edge of ventral fin, at its base; muciferous crypts indistinct. (Pl. 31.)

Labial teeth 2/2; first row continuous across upper labium, extending between papillary fringes; second row with interspace about same or slightly less (rarely greater) than length of one of lateral segments; first lower row slightly shorter than second; second row about same length or slightly longer than first upper row; single row of labial papillae extending around mouth except for gap in upper labium occupied by long, first labial tooth row; labial papillae extending inward beyond ends of upper row little, if at all, differing in this regard from our other hylids; few or no inner papillae. (Pl. 32.)

In alcohol body flecked and spotted with dark brown on light grayish purple ground color; venter gray with viscera evident through abdominal wall; except for few flecks on throat and over gill chambers, venter without melanophores; tail musculature cream, blotched with brown, blotching reduced basally; tail fins similarly blotched, with markings increasing in abundance distally; tip of tail blackish brown, contrasting rather sharply with rest of caudal pigmentation; blackish tip flecked with light color. In life, according to Wright (1932:181-82, Okefinokee Swamp, Georgia), dorsal coloration dark olive buff, old gold, olive lake or sulphine yellow; belly, especially on sides and in gill region, light vinaceous fawn, shell pink, or pale salmon; ivory-yellow or cartridge-buff spots clustered on belly; such spots abundant on upper surface of body; area posterior to mouth parts without vinaceous fawn or ivory yellow; spots become almost continuous forming patch of lilac gray on throat; tail usually tipped with black; ivory-yellow or cartridge-buff spots on upper fin and part of musculature, reduced on lower fin and ventral portion of musculature; fins nearly transparent; iris ivory yellow above and below pupil and light coral red and black posterior and anterior to it; entire iris more or less marked with black mingled with two lighter colors mentioned. Orton (1947) has found the black tail tip, usually regarded as a diagnostic character of *Acris* tadpoles, is by no means of constant occurrence in Louisiana *crepitans*. The black tip was absent in specimens with a total length of less than 19.0 mm. and was present as a well-defined jet black tip in only 24.3 per cent of the larger tadpoles.

Near Saint Louis, Missouri, transformation in a colony was about over by September 18 (Boyer and Heinze, 1934:189).

Remarks.—Viosca (1923:43) recognizes two distinct species of *Acris* in Louisiana, an upland form, tentatively *A. gryllus* and one of the lowlands, *A. crepitans.* According to Viosca, wherever their ranges overlap, they are found side by side without interbreeding, each with its characteristic chorus and habits. Dunn (1938:153) agreed with Viosca that two species were involved. These have been contrasted as follows: *gryllus* smaller, has 3 phalanges of fourth toe free, instead of 2 to 1½ phalanges, and first toe partly free, instead of completely webbed; more rugose; anal warts less prominent; legs longer, heel extending beyond snout instead of failing to reach snout; thigh more definitely striped than in *crepitans.*

The observations of Orton (1947) in southeastern Louisiana tend to support Viosca's view. Orton found the tadpoles of *gryllus* and *crepitans* readily separable. The chief differences listed by her are tabulated below:

Character	*crepitans*	*gryllus*
Spiracle tube	Very short, not projecting out from body as a free tube	Long and conspicuous, projecting free from body wall
Stripes on side of snout	Light and dark stripe of about equal width	Light stripe very narrow and partly obliterated by encroaching dark pigment
Throat and chest	Throat light; a dark stripe begins below otic capsule and extends vertically down side of gill region, then transversely across chest	Entire throat dark, hence no separate dark band across chest
Sides of tail	Finely mottled and reticulated with grayish	Sharply flecked with dark in addition to some fine mottling
Dorsal surface of axial musculature	On body: pale with strongly contrasting dark saddle spots	On body: typically dark, seldom a conspicuous pattern
	On tail: usually with a linear series of rectangular dark spots, rarely a continuous dark stripe	On tail: dark pigment usually forms a continuous dark stripe except on the very thin distal part of tail

According to Neill (1950:152) two forms exist in east-central Georgia; one, an upland form, consistently displaying a squat, rather toadlike build, blunt snout, and a single, diffuse or irregular postfemoral stripe; the other, a lowland form, slender, with a sharp snout and one or two sharply defined postfemoral stripes. The calls of the two forms when heard together are distinguishable. He regards the former as *crepitans,* the latter as *gryllus. Crepitans* ranges in east Georgia southward to about 45 miles below the Fall Line, *gryllus* to 60 miles above this line, an overlap of 105 miles. The altitudinal relationship of the two forms in Georgia is the reverse of that in Louisiana where *crepitans* is the lowland form.

Smith (1934:461), however, did not find *crepitans* in Kansas. The variation in *Acris* there was well within that of *gryllus*. Netting and Goin (1945) described a race of *Acris gryllus* in Florida. This form, *dorsalis,* is said to differ from *gryllus* and *crepitans* in habits, thigh pattern, and wartiness. Harper (1947:39-40) considered *crepitans* a race of *gryllus* and, further, described a new subspecies, *blanchardi*. The range of this form is given as "Chiefly the Interior Plains and Interior Highlands of the United States; north to the southern parts of Wisconsin, Minnesota, and South Dakota; east to southwestern Michigan, northwestern Indiana, Illinois, southeastern Missouri, and northeastern Arkansas; south to southwestern Texas; and west to central Nebraska, eastern Colorado, and southeastern Arizona [New Mexico?]." It is distinguished from the nearest geographical representative, *A. g. crepitans* Baird, by slightly greater linear measurements, by decidedly greater bulk, by somewhat more extensive webbing of the toes, and by the more extensive dusky area on the posterior face of the femora in the vicinity of the vent. In general the dorsal color pattern seems to be less distinct in *blanchardi* than in *crepitans*.

Burger, *et al.* (1949:131-32) described *A. g. paludicola* from near Sabine Pass in Jefferson County, Texas. They diagnose this subspecies as a small, smooth-skinned frog, decidedly pink in life. According to these authors, it has the most pronounced digital pads and most obscure dorsal pattern of all members of the genus. It differs from *Acris gryllus* in lacking a prominent post-femoral dark stripe, in possessing extensive webbing (only the terminal joint, exclusive of the pad, the fourth toe is free of web), and in having slightly larger toe discs. It may be distinguished from *Acris crepitans* by the much larger discs, smaller size, and difference in color. Wright and Wright (1949) treat *gryllus* and *crepitans* as subspecies of the form *gryllus* and give an allopatric distribution, with *gryllus* confined to the central and southern Atlantic coast and the eastern Gulf coast and Florida. *Dorsalis* is not recognized. It appears we may have a problem here not unlike that of the leopard frogs, *Rana pipiens,* which exist as many locally differentiated populations. I have made no personal study of this group of frogs. I follow the systematic arrangement of Wright and Wright (1949).

SWAMP CRICKET-FROG

Pseudacris nigrita (Le Conte)
Plate 19

Range.—Widely distributed throughout North America. Ranges in the north to New Jersey and Pennsylvania, Lake Ontario, and to the swamp lands of northwestern Canada; in the south reaches east-central Arizona, northern New Mexico, the Gulf coast from Texas into peninsular Florida; in the west reaches north-central Arizona, northeastern and probably southwestern Utah, Idaho, and eastern British Columbia; extends eastward to the Atlantic seaboard. Apparently absent from considerable portions of the Great Plains (short-grass prairie) of Nebraska, eastern Colorado, and western Kansas. Ranges to over 11,000 feet in the Uintah Mountains of Utah. (Pl. 59.)

Type locality.—Not known. Species described by Le Conte (1825:282).

Description.—STRUCTURE. Adult 3/4 to 1 1/2 inches; resembles *Hyla regilla* (p. 322) but differs in following ways: head narrower, snout more pointed and elongate in our representatives; digital pads inconspicuous; hind foot without distinct web although amount of webbing varies considerably. Tympanum 1/3 to slightly over 1/2 size of eye opening; metacarpal tubercles not well differentiated from other small tubercles on undersides of forefeet; 2 round-surfaced metatarsal tubercles, outer one small, 1/2 to 1/3 size of inner one. This species has been considered a tree frog that has undergone much retrogression in structures adapted for arboreal and aquatic life (Dickerson, 1920:160). COLOR. Ground color above highly variable, brown, tawny, buff, greenish, olive, grayish olive, grayish, leaden to almost black; marked above with dark brown, deep olive, greenish, olive brown to blackish spots or stripes; typically three stripes on back, continuous or more or less broken into rows of spots, and stripe on either side extending from nostril through eye, half way or to groin; stripes on sides may consist of mottlings or spots; dorsal median stripe often broken into row of spots; dark triangle, spot, or stripe may (common in subspecies *triseriatus*) or may not be present between eyes; markings may become obscure at extremes of dark and light color phases; light cream, whitish, or light yellow line along upper jaw (white-spotted or plumbeous in race *verrucosa*); limbs commonly crossbanded or spotted with dark brown; below whitish, cream, or yellowish, sometimes blackish olive, unmarked; iris with flecks of pale yellow, greenish yellow, to coppery and with tendency toward horizontal dark bar. JUVENILE. Description based on individuals taken five miles east-southeast of Rabbit Ears Peak, Jackson County, Colorado, August 23, 1949, by William Riemer: Venter cream to golden with occasional tinges of greenish, posterior portion of abdomen usually most golden; dorsal ground color golden tan, golden olive, to tan-gray, first color type dominating; blotches ranging in definition from very prominent to almost complete absence; color of markings always darker than ground color and of either brown or olive hue, or both; no correlation between distinctness of blotches and ground color; lateral dark stripe forming eye mask always present anteriorly, from deep olive to sooty brown; width of stripe variable and stripe often broken behind head; upper lip light-colored, golden with either orange or greenish tinge; iris gold to copper, slightly more melanic in darker animals than in lighter ones. SEXUAL DIFFERENCES. Male has greenish yellow to dark olive throat and when breeding has nuptial pad on inner side of first finger. Female averages larger than male.

Adult, WJR 404, about 25 mm. in snout-vent length, obtained July 29, 1949, 0.8 mile north-northwest of Lakeside, State Highway 173, Navajo County, Arizona: Above pale buff yellow to cream with rusty cast; light tan on lower back and hind limbs; dorsal markings light yellowish brown; eye mask sooty; below yellowish cream; throat yellowish; underside of limbs and seat patch brown with purplish or pinkish cast; iris coppery with vague horizontal dark bar.

Subadult, RCS 3473, about 15 mm. in snout-vent length, obtained August 22, 1949, at Rand, Jackson County, Colorado: Dorsum and limbs bronze or light tan; dorsal markings sooty brown; eye stripe blackish brown; light line on upper jaw pale copper in front of eye; cream behind; below cream; seat patch and undersides of limbs tan; iris with upper edge of pupil with gold crescent and remainder flecked with copper or orange gold.

Habitat.—Terrestrial throughout most of the year, frequenting damp meadows, marshes, and swamps. Found on the ground or in low bushes and plants near the ground. May occur in damp woods where it hides under dead leaves, logs, and the like (Pope, 1944:94). Commonly breeds in the quiet, shallow water of ditches, ponds, lakes, marshy fields, and transient or permanent pools, often where there is low-growing vegetation. Carl (1943:46) reports this species as abundant and in full song during May and June in flood pools at Tupper Creek and in marshy backwaters of the North Pine River at Charlie Lake, British Columbia. This frog may at times be encountered a mile or more from the nearest standing water (Hudson, 1942:27, Nebraska).

Jacobs (1950:154) found the species in voice in late June, 1948, on the north shore of Lake Superior in Cook and Lake counties, Minnesota.

The frogs were in clear water of rock-bound pools, essentially free of vascular plants, a rather unusual breeding site.

Near Provo, Utah County, Utah, on June 27, 1949, 7 subadult and adult individuals were captured in a grassy area 15 to 20 feet from the water of Utah Lake. They were found in open areas among or bordering the sedges and tules of the lake margin. Wriggling of grass blades usually indicated the presence of a *Pseudacris* or a grasshopper. The grass patches were well illuminated, the air temperature, 3 inches above the ground in the shade, was 20°C. at 10:40 A.M. The damp soil in the sun was 33°C. There was ample shade, however, among the grass. Willows and cottonwoods grew nearby. The surrounding country was level, some of it marshy, and much of it cultivated.

At Lakeside, Navajo County, Arizona, on July 29, 1949, I found several *Pseudacris* in grass at the edge of a large quiet pond about 75 by 15 yards. The pond was sparingly margined with tules. Open grassy meadows and pine forest characterized the surrounding country.

Five miles east-southeast of Rabbit Ears Peak, Jackson County, Colorado, on August 23, 1949, this species was found in association with *Rana sylvatica, R. pipiens,* and *Bufo boreas* along a meandering willow-bordered stream in a broad grassy valley. The surrounding hills were of low relief and covered with aspens and conifers. Basin sagebrush occurred in extensive patches in the valley and on the lower slopes of the hills. The *Pseudacris* were found in grass or on damp soil near the edge of the stream.

Behavior.—This species is terrestrial. It is not a good climber or especially good swimmer, as tree-frogs go. Breckenridge (1944:68), however, found individuals calling halfheartedly from several feet up in grapevine tangles and other heavy undergrowth in Minnesota.

An individual slightly under 1 inch in snout-vent length, obtained at Utah Lake, Utah, was placed in a shallow quiet pool about 4 feet across. I threw it into the water 10 or more times, attempting to head it in the direction of the opposite shore, but it invariably turned and swam toward me rather than venture the distance to the opposite side. Another individual of similar size was tested as to jumping ability. It was placed on smooth, level, damp soil that was not sticky. It covered from 4 to 6 inches at a jump.

Voice.—The call is a vibrating, chirping sound, surprisingly strong for so small an animal. It has been likened to that made by a metallic clicker or by running a finger over the teeth of a pocket comb. It has been described as raucous and grating; a low-pitched, somewhat musical rattle (Pope, 1944:93); and as a loud stridulating sound of ascending pitch (Logier, 1937:11). It has been represented by Seton (1918:83) as a piercing "prreep, preep." Individuals heard widely over the range of the species suggested to me the following: "ā-ā-ā-āh" or "r-ā-ā-ā-āh," "oo-ā-ā-ā" or "wo-ā-ā-ā-ā," the last two as determined at a distance (50 feet), the first two at close range (15 feet).

Breckenridge (1944:68) estimates the duration of a single call at about 1 second and the number of separate notes as about 9. I have found calls to last ½ second or slightly less but there is without doubt variation with individuals and temperature. It is difficult to determine the number of separate notes or clicks that make up a single call. By using the teeth of a pocket comb to simulate the sound and then counting the number of teeth employed, I estimate that from 4 to 7 separate notes occur. Five or 6 are probably most common.

Data on rate of calls are summarized below.

Locality	*Date*	*Time* (P.M.)	*Number of animals in chorus*	*Calls per minute*	*Temperature, °C.*	
					Water	*Air* (1 inch above water)
Kansas						
4 mi. N of Pittsburg, Crawford Co.	June 2, 1950	9:10	2, sometimes 3	90	20.0	21.0
1 mi. W of Lawrence, Douglas Co.	June 4, 1950	9:30	7	36-40	15.8	12.8
Wyoming						
3 mi. WNW of Old Faithful Geyser, Yellowstone Nat'l Park	June 16, 1950	9:25	3	72	12.3	7.8
Utah						
Holladay, Salt Lake Co.	June 18, 1950	9:10	100+	30-34	20.0	14.4

From these scant data there is a suggestion that rate may be related to number of singers rather than temperature.

In a chorus the calls of individuals come in irregular fashion but at times they may come into phase and then seem to be in unison. At a distance of ¼ mile or more the quality of sound is surprisingly different from that at close range. Uninitiated, one might suspect a different species of amphibian. A colleague has suggested that it is a "continuously discontinuous" sound, less erratic than when heard at close range. At a distance the sounds suggest to me *Acris gryllus*. They seem, however, to be slower, perhaps more regular, with less rattle, and of higher pitch than in *Acris*.

I estimated the pitch of frogs in Yellowstone Park as about the second A above middle C. The call commonly has a slightly rising inflection. At Holladay, Utah, Dr. Max Crittenden and I determined that pitch varied with size of individuals, the smaller animals having the weaker, higher voices.

This species, except at the height of a breeding congress, may be rather difficult to capture. The animals are often disturbed by a light and by one's movements. Their small size and their habit of calling from the base of clumps of sedge and grass in the water make them difficult to see and puts them in a position for quick retreat below the surface into a favorable hiding place. Fortunately, the animals often can be stimulated to call by an imitation of the voice which can be accomplished, as mentioned earlier, by scraping a pocket comb. When one or two males are captured, their calls from the collecting receptacle may help to keep a chorus alive.

In the large chorus at Holladay, Utah, Dr. Crittenden and I found the animals difficult to locate although they called all about us, within a foot or two of our feet. It was the expanding yellowish vocal pouch that usually was seen first. We found that by cupping our hands behind our ears and leaning forward from side to side, within 2 to 3 feet of the water, we could triangulate and thereby pretty well single out calls and locate individuals.

In choruses observed by me, individuals have been spaced 6 inches to 20 feet apart, depending on the numbers involved. A calling animal typically sits erect with his forelimbs against grass stems or other support in the water and his body immersed at varying depths—the water line striking him anywhere between the sacral hump and axilla. The ventral surface of the vocal sac, when expanded, is commonly above or at the surface of the water. The inflated sac is round in lateral aspect but may be slightly flattened or depressed dorsally when viewed from the front. In a flashlight beam it may appear pale greenish yellow.

Food.—The following items have been recorded: spiders; insects—a Mayfly naiad, a mirid, aphids, a caddisfly larva, a small moth larva, dipterans, beetles (carabids, a large grub, and an *Aphodius*), ants; and algae (Tanner, 1931:184-85; Cragin, 1881:118; Hartman, 1906:228).

Reproduction.—The southern form (southeastern United States) breeds as early as December and January. Those farther north usually breed later. In Florida the breeding period may last until August. Breckenridge (1944:69, Minnesota) says this species is one of the first amphibians to become active in the spring, the earliest calls usually coming in the latter part of March. They probably breed through April and May. Eight to 10 weeks may be required for passage of the egg and tadpole stages at this latitude. Livezey and Wright (1947) give the season for *triseriata* as March 20 to May 20 and *septentrionalis* as May to early June. Evenden (1946: 257) in Elmore County, Idaho, on April 6, 1944, heard the evening chorus of these frogs and the next day found a ditch well-stocked with the species but no eggs. By October 14, 1944, there were swarms of adults as well as metamorphosing tadpoles in the transformation stage, in the same ditch. In Ontario, Canada, adults congregate for breeding in April, mostly in temporary ponds (Logier, 1937:11).

Harper (1931b:68) reports on choruses of this frog [under *P. septentrionalis*] in the northern part of its range. The castanet-like trilling of this species was heard at Edmonton on May 15 and 16, 1914, and on the former date some eggs were collected in a muddy pool on a wooded slope beside the Saskatchewan. Individuals were found on May 17 in a vegetation-filled pool in a wet, bush-bordered meadow in the outskirts of the city.

Choruses were heard especially during the evening and night at a number of points along the Athabaska River from Athabaska Landing northward, May 18 to 31. It was quite abundant on the Athabaska Delta despite the fact that during this period (late May and early June) there were frequently close to freezing temperatures and once or twice thin ice formed on quiet water overnight. The species was heard commonly at Chipewyan, June 10 to 19.

At La Saline in 1920 it was recorded commonly and almost daily for 6 weeks from May 11. From May 14 to 24, when the species was heard every day, the minimum temperature recorded was 31°F. and the maximum was 68.5°F. (along the Athabaska River).

On April 2, 1907, Wright and Allen (1908:41) watched a confined pair from Buffalo, New York, lay from 500 to 600 eggs in 2½ hours. In laying, the female ordinarily grasped the branch with her forelimbs. When about to deposit she brought one heel up to the stem and near the vent. Farther back the other foot held the stem with the toes. Each time, just before the voidance of the eggs, the female raised her anus and the male stretched to bring his vent near hers. The process required about 90 fertilizations and emissions. Clusters containing from 20 to 70 eggs were laid in lots of 2 to 10 (emitted in small strings) during each of 16 periods of activity. Duration of these laying periods varied from 2 to 7 minutes. The pair rose to the surface between periods. These intervals of rest varied from 2 to 17 minutes (average 4 minutes).

EGGS. Egg masses often less than 1 inch in diameter, deposited commonly in clear pools attached to vegetation. Eggs laid in loose irregular cluster; envelope surrounding masses weak and watery, masses suggestive of those of *Hyla regilla;* single indistinct gelatinous envelope (sometimes 2 in *triseriata*) averaging 6.4 mm., range 5.0 to 7.8 mm., rarely 3.0 mm. (*triseriata*) or 7.0 mm., range 6.0 to 8.5 mm. (*septentrionalis*); when 2 envelopes in *triseriata*, outer 3.0 mm., inner 2.1 mm. (observed by Smith, 1934:467, Kansas); ovum 0.9 to 1.2 mm. (*triseriata*) or 1.2 to 1.4 mm. (*septentrionalis*), black or brown above and white below; 15 to 300 eggs per mass, usually less than 100 (*triseriata*); complement 500 to 1,459± per female (*triseriata*) (Livezey and Wright, 1947). It is possible the difference in number of eggs per cluster may be correlated geographically, with the larger clusters occurring in the West.

Pack (1920:7) reports on size of egg clusters in the southern part of Logan, Utah, found on May 15, 1919. "The number of eggs in the twenty-two egg masses taken were as follows: 66, 45, 53, 33, 65, 46, 88, 38, 40, 67, 32, 50, 64, 87, 77, 15, 65, 51, 73, 45, 130, and 190." The number of eggs was much greater than that typical for the species as given by Dickerson (5 to 20 eggs). Ruthven, Thompson, and Gaige (1928:42, Michigan) say that the eggs hatch in about 2 weeks. Likewise, Logier (1937:11) reports that eggs hatch in this time, with transformation occurring in June in Ontario, Canada. According to Dickerson (1920:159-60) eggs deposited March 22 hatched April 5. By April 20 the legs were budded. Hatchlings in the West may be from 3/16 of an inch (4.5 mm.) to approximately 5/16 of an inch (7.5 mm.) (Pope, 1944:93). Ellis and Henderson (1915:257) found eggs and adults in temporary pools formed by melting snow near Boulder, Colorado, during the first 10 days of May, 1914. Larvae were very black and about 8 mm. long at hatching. The equivalent of about 2 months is required for complete development from eggs to transformation (Gloyd, 1928).

LARVA. Tadpole small, maximum total length before metamorphosis 30 to 32 mm.; tail tip obtuse, rounded; tail slightly attenuated toward tip; dorsal fin extended to about vertical of spiracle; spiracle sinistral, below lateral axis, directed backward and slightly upward; spiracle opening round, inner edge slightly free from body; eye slightly dorsal to lateral axis; anus dextral, opening about on level of ventral fin. (Pl. 31.)

Labial teeth 2/3; entire mouth, except a median dorsal space about 1/2 length of first upper row of teeth, surrounded by continuous papillary fringe, which is doubled around angles of mouth; this doubled papillary fringe extends downward somewhat medial to lateral edges of last (outer) row of lower labial teeth, and above to lateral edges of upper labial teeth; a few extra papillae inside fringe at angles of mouth; second (inner) row of upper labial teeth divided medially, the 2 halves separated from each other by about 1/2 length of either half; lateral edges of inner row on upper labium medial to those of outer row; upper mandible broadly U-shaped, its external edge finely denticulated; length of upper mandible contained in first upper row of teeth about 1½ times; lower mandible V-shaped, its external edge finely denticulated; first (inner) row of lower labial teeth slightly indented medially; and very slightly shorter than second row; last (outer) row approximately ½ length of second row, and broadly concave toward mandible; lateral edges of 2 inner rows of lower labium more or less coincide with lateral edges of upper labial rows. (Pl. 32.)

Body dark above, uniformly and closely stippled with iridescent bronze; metallic copper beneath (Ruthven, Thompson, and Gaige, 1928:41); tadpole nearly black at hatching (Dickerson, 1920:159); eyes closely stippled with bronze; body quite transparent; dorsal and ventral tail fins with finely scattered pigment areas, dark brown in color (preserved material); dorsal musculature of tail heavily pigmented, ventral musculature slightly less (foregoing larval description from Youngstrom and Smith, 1936:629-30, Kansas, unless otherwise indicated).

Larvae 20 to 43 mm. in total length, obtained by the author, 13.6 miles north-northwest of Heber, U.S. Highway 40, Summit County, Utah, on June 25, 1949, agree closely with the description by Youngstrom and Smith. Differences noted were greater size range, tip of tail pointed in some, lateral edges of inner row of upper labium in some specimens were little if at all medial to edges of outer row; in several, upper mandible contained 2 times in upper row of teeth; outer lower row ⅓ length of second lower row in several specimens. They were colored in life as follows: dorsal surface and sides of head and body olive with sooty spots; copper and golden sheen on sides; iris copper, with horizontal dusky area; venter silver with coppery highlights centrally; area beneath gill chambers golden; tail musculature olivaceous; tail fins translucent, dorsal fin becoming greenish olive at juncture with body.

Pope (1944:93) writing in the Chicago area, gives 1 to 1¼ inches (25 to 30 mm.) as the size of the mature tadpole, and larval life as 40 to 90 days. Transformation occurs at a larval length of less than ½ inch in British Columbia, according to Carl (1943:46). Length of newly metamorphosed individuals in Kansas was about 7.5 mm. from snout to tip of tail remnant (Youngstrom and Smith). In Minnesota, Breckenridge (1944:67) says: "The tadpoles metamorphose at a little over an inch (29 to 32 mm.) into frogs with a body length of about half an inch (12 mm.)." Ruthven, Thompson, and Gaige (1928:42) state that in Michigan ". . . metamorphosis is completed early in June." Dickerson (1920:160) writing of the frog in northeastern United States says transformations take place from May 26 to June 12 at a tadpole length of slightly over an inch. The stripes on the back do not appear until the creatures are actually on the point of leaving the water.

SUBSPECIES

1*a*. Hind limbs shorter, particularly in female. *Range*. From Minnesota to Montana northward into the Mackenzie region of Canada ...... *P. n. septentrionalis* Boulenger

1*b*. Hind limbs longer. *Range*. Oswego, New York, westward along the southern shore of Lake Ontario, to northeastern Arizona, Utah, and Idaho, and south to Arkansas and Louisiana .... *P. n. triseriata* Wied

CANYON TREE-TOAD

Hyla arenicolor Cope
Plate 19

Range.—Southern California as far north as central San Luis Obispo County, south into Mexico to Guadalajara and Toluca, and well into Lower California; in Arizona, southern Utah, southern Colorado, and throughout New Mexico, into western Texas to Del Rio. Smith and Taylor (1948:89) report the species in Mexico in Distrito Federal, and the states of Baja California, Chihuahua, Coahuila, Durango, Guanajuato, Guerrero, Hidalgo, Jalisco, Mexico, Michoacán, Morelos, Nayarit, San Luis Potosí, Sinaloa, Sonora, and Zacatecas. Sporadic in occurrence. So far as I can learn, no specimens have been taken in the lower part of the Colorado Desert, in southeastern California, and extreme western Arizona. (Pl. 59.)

Type locality.—Northern Sonora, Mexico (Cope, 1866:84). The original description of this species was made by Baird (1854:61) under the name "*Hyla affinis*." The name was changed by Cope (1866:84) to *H. arenicolor*, because of the preoccupation of the name *affinis*.

Description.—STRUCTURE. Adult to slightly over 2 inches; resembles *H. regilla* (p. 322), but differs in following ways: toes with larger, more transversely expanded tips; web between toes of hind foot often more fully developed, at least in animals from California—in many, webbing connecting fourth and fifth toes leaves fifth toe near tip and at nearly right angle when toes spread (in *H. regilla*, this web extends proximally at about 45° angle); animals from areas outside California seem more often to have reduced webbing; skin generally more rugose; no well-defined eye stripe; tympanum 1/5 to slightly over 1/2 size of eye opening; thenar tubercle elongate, ovoid; palmar tubercle represented by 1 to 3 tubercles, totaling size of thenar; inner metatarsal tubercle oval, round-surfaced, outer one absent or to ⅕ size of inner tubercle; tarsal fold present. COLOR. Ground color above varies from whitish gray through brown, gray olive, to dusky, rarely is almost black; scattered spots and blotches of darker color usually present dorsally; eyelids commonly crossed centrally with dark marking; eyelid markings may or may not meet to form transverse bar or broad triangle on head; legs barred with dark markings; below whitish or cream, usually with considerable yellow or orange color in femoral region (particularly on posterior surface), groin, posterior surface of tibia, and in axilla; iris with metallic yellow or cream markings often giving over-all effect of grayish. JUVENILE. Headquarters Santa Rita Experimental Range, Santa Rita Mountains, Pima County, Arizona, July 21, 1949, WJR 351 (recently metamorphosed): Above grayish olive; tympanum not evident; yellow of hind limbs present but weak; venter cream, iris deep gold. SEXUAL DIFFERENCES. In life male may have purplish-brown suffusion on throat; throat of female unmarked or sometimes speckled with brownish; in preserved males gular pouch may be partly distended or when contracted loose skin may be folded in 5 or 6 longitudinal pleats.

Adult, RCS 3249, obtained July 16, 1949, 1 mile northeast of Peña Blanca Springs, Santa Cruz County, Arizona: Ground color above medium gray with lavender tinge; spots sooty; tympanum with pinkish tinge; below white on throat and chest, belly cream, seat patch light brown; groin, anterior, and posterior surfaces of femur, inner surface of tibia, upper surface of foot, yellow with greenish cast; axilla with touch of pale greenish yellow; iris light gray with golden tinge and with fine flecking and tracery of blackish.

Adult male, WJR 304, from the same locality as RCS 3249: Dorsal ground color creamy gray, spots deep olive green; below white between forelimbs, otherwise yellowish cream; concealed areas of hind limbs when limbs flexed, yellow; yellow in groin and somewhat anteriorly; gular area purplish gray; iris greenish gold with speckling and tracery of blackish.

Habitat.—Pools or rapidly flowing streams in rocky canyons. In southern California, found within or in the vicinity of streams which flow from the mountains into the deserts or semiarid regions. Klauber has found it on granite boulders to about 100 feet horizontally and to 50 feet vertically from the nearest stream (Storer, MS). It seems to be principally an inhabitant of the Upper Sonoran Zone in California although elsewhere it may reach the Lower Sonoran Zone as at Grand Canyon (McKee and Bogert, 1934:178). Greater toe-pad development and more extensive webbing in *arenicolor* in California may be related to their occurrence in swifter water and a rockier habitat than that commonly occupied by *H. regilla.* In Arizona, Little (1940:262) found this species common in the pine-fir and chaparral-woodland zones but uncommon in the semidesert.

COLORATION OF ADULTS FROM THE SANTA RITA EXPERIMENTAL RANGE HEADQUARTERS, SANTA RITA MOUNTAINS, PIMA COUNTY, ARIZONA
July 21, 1949

Specimen (WJR No.)	*Dorsal ground color*	*Dorsal blotches*	*Tympanum*	*Concealed portions of hind limbs and groin*	*Ventral surfaces*	*Iris*
342	Olive with yellow	Deep green with olive	Gold	Lemon yellow	Milk	Pale gold
343	Lavender gray	Dark green olive with gray	Gold	Lemon yellow	Milk	Pale gold
344	Lavender pink with gray	Greenish gray	Gold limited to postero-ventral portion; remainder dark gray	Lemon yellow	Milk	Pale gold
345	Yellowish tan	Dark olive green	Gold	Weak yellow	Milk	Pale gold above, almost whitish below
346	Golden tan	Greenish gray	Gold	Lemon yellow	Milk	Pale gold
347	Tannish gray	Tannish olive	Gold	Weak yellow	Milk (gular area light purple)	Pale gold
348	Lavender tan	Yellowish sooty	Gold	Lemon yellow	Milk	Pale gold
349	Buffy cream with yellow	Dark olive gray	Gold	Lemon yellow	Milk (gular area light purplish black)	Pale gold
350	Yellowish tan with gray	Olive with dark gray			Milk (gular area light purplish black)	

Taylor (1936a:478) obtained 11 individuals from the immediate vicinity of a spring, about 2 miles north of La Posa, Sonora, Mexico. The spring was in a small basin in a cleft in a low mountain range. There was a luxuriant growth of palm and fig trees. The frogs emerged at twilight from among the dead palm leaves, which hung suspended about the trunk of the palms. The frogs approached the pools below the spring. Here they were captured as they sat in the edge of the water or on the banks. All appeared to be half grown. They were marked with distinct round spots on a lighter, grayish ground color.

Near Peña Blanca Springs, Santa Cruz County, Arizona, on July 16, 1949, between 9:00 and 10:00 P.M., William Riemer, Ernest Stebbins, and I explored a narrow water-scoured rocky ravine along which were several natural "tanks" of standing water. The first pool was about 8 by 6 feet and 1 foot or so in greatest depth. There was an accumulation of coarse sand at the downstream side. The rock surfaces were rough, but aside from the deposit of sand there was very little loose material. Vegetation was scanty, consisting principally of bunchgrass and ocotillo on the hillsides above the ravine. An adult *Hyla arenicolor* was found 15 feet from the pool on a dry surface, perched on top of a small rocky prominence. It was in the dark phase; no dorsal spotting was evident. The animal was easily captured by hand. Several other adults were found among rocks and grass in damp places in the bottom of the ravine and on the dry bare rock of the canyon walls. Larvae, many of large size, were present in considerable numbers in the pool. (Pl. 44, fig. 1.)

A second pool, about 50 yards down the canyon, was visited from 9:30 A.M. to 12:10 P.M. on July 17. It measured approximately 12 by 5 feet and was about 1½ feet in greatest depth. Like the first, it was contained in a natural basin in the rock and there was a similar sand deposit at its downstream side. The rocky walls of the ravine partly overhung it. There were many pits but few fissures in the irregular rock surfaces surrounding the pool. The rock was generally ash gray (whitish) with a buffy cast here and there, and with scattered patches of grayish-green, rust, and sooty lichens. The water was greenish brown, the bottom of the pool not visible beyond a depth of 6 or 8 inches. There were no plants growing in the pool or at its edges except algae which formed a greenish tinge on the rocks in sheltered places near the water. Six adults were found in shaded niches in the rock, from 3 to 4 feet above the water. The slopes to the north of the ravine were covered with clumps of grass, and a scattering of ocotillo and chilicote, those to the south with oaks.

Near the Santa Rita Experimental Range Headquarters, Santa Rita Mountains, Pima County, Arizona, on July 21, 1949, I found a single adult in short grass 12 feet from the edge of a pool in the canyon above headquarters. The pool had been formed by damming of the intermittent stream course. It measured approximately 30 by 45 feet and was possibly 6 feet deep. The concrete dam was 50 to 60 feet along its upper surface, 1½ feet wide at the top, and about 9 feet high at the mid-point. The water was moderately clear, with some growth of an aquatic plant on the bottom, evident near shore. There was an extensive growth of ocotillo and prickly pear cactus on the rocky granitic slope to the southwest. Oaks, ocotillo, chilicote, mesquite, and prickly pear were present on the northeast slope of the canyon. Sycamores and ash were in the canyon bottom. Recently metamorphosed canyon tree-toads were found near the water's edge on the inner face of the dam, and there were many large larvae in the pool. Riemer found 10 adults, from 3 to 8 feet from the ground, on the exposed, nearly vertical face of the dam.

On June 28, 1950, accompanied by Charles Lowe, I visited Millard Canyon, Los Angeles County, California, to search for this species. The canyon was rather narrow and deep, running northeast and southwest on the south slope of the San Gabriel Mountains. There were many water-worn granitic boulders along the bottom and a considerable growth of willows, *Mimulus,* and other plants near the stream. In places the riparian growth was too dense to get through easily and was shoulder or head high. In other locations, however, there was practically no vegetation. The stream was small, only 2 to 6 feet wide and 3 to 4 inches deep except where there were pools. In places it disappeared underground.

Oaks, chaparral, and a few big cone spruce were observed on the sides of the canyon. Judging from the character of the stream bed, the canyon had been subject to torrential currents, although the present vegetation suggested that this had not occurred in recent years.

All the hylas were found in depressions in large water-worn granitic boulders, 6 to 10 feet in greatest measurement. They were situated in exposed places where there was little or no sheltering vegetation. Water was usually within 2 or 3 feet, although one animal was 6 feet from the stream and would have required several jumps to reach it. The frogs avoided the south side of the rocks. One, however, was on a southeastern exposure but was shaded by the canyon wall. The animals were generally 2 to 3 feet above the surface of the stream. All blended remarkably with the rock surfaces upon which they rested, apparently, like the flounder, approximating the pattern of their backgrounds. Perhaps by coincidence, but I doubt it, an individual on a rock with much dark blotching and streaking was prominently dark-blotched; another on a surface with small dark flecks had much smaller markings.

Behavior.—In the daytime this species may be found perched in niches in rocks along stream courses, usually close to water. In May, 1915, Slevin

(1928:112) found the species congregated in crevices of the largest granite boulders strewn along the bed of the Tujunga River, Los Angeles County, California. In some instances as many as 10 or 15 were taken from a single crevice. They were so compact in places that 6 or 7 individuals could be picked up at once. When approached, these toads commonly squat close to the substratum, or if quiet will remain so, relying on their protective form and color for concealment. One may sometimes succeed in slipping the bulb of a slender thermometer under them, and some individuals will tolerate attempts at insertion of the thermometer into the cloaca.

In California, according to Storer (1925:207) the female is more aquatic than the male. On two occasions at Peña Blanca Springs, Arizona (between July 5 and 25), Campbell (1934:6) observed adults foraging in the daytime in exposed and dry situations. One individual was about 15 feet from a stream, the other nearly 100 yards away. As in *regilla,* the adhesive toes facilitate climbing.

Near Peña Blanca Springs, on July 16, 1949, 6 adult individuals were observed at one of the "tanks" described earlier under "habitat." Four animals were on the south wall of the ravine, nearly in a row, spaced about a foot apart and about 4 feet above the water. They were situated where well shaded and where they would be protected from the sun throughout the day. The other 2 were on the north bank, at nearly the same height above the water, in pockets in the rock where they were likewise sheltered from the sun. The air temperature near the toads at 12:00 M. was 34.2°C.; the water of the pool 32.5°C. During our visit of nearly 3 hours, the animals were immobile except for pulsations of their throats or occasional slight shuffling movements of the limbs. They rested close to the rock with their limbs tucked in at their sides and their heads lowered on their forefeet. The pose was catlike. They matched the rock so perfectly in color, contour, and texture that at first, before their locations were well in mind, some difficulty was experienced in relocating them when one looked away. Their eyes were conspicuous. These organs were often partly concealed, however, by the nictitating membrane.

We were able to work close to them, coming many times within 1/4 inch or nearer, yet they did not move, apparently relying on their cryptic form and color for protection. All, however, were facing the pool and were so situated that a single jump would put them in the water. I tried to count the gular pulsations of one animal but the movement was too fast to record. The nostrils and eardrums, the latter brown and conspicuous, moved in time with the throat movements. We induced individuals to leap into the water by touching them lightly. Of 3 so stimulated, 2 quickly left the water, making their way in several hops up the nearly vertical walls in the direction of their niches. The third went to the opposite side of the pool, probably because I stood near his niche. The first two animals remained in the water for only a few seconds, the third for less than a minute. The latter emerged noticeably darker than when he entered the water. A few minutes later, as he sought a rock niche, ash-gray spots were beginning to appear in the dark gray ground color.

All 6 animals were marked by removal of toes and their niches were numbered. We hoped to determine whether the same niche was repeatedly used. No tree-toads were found July 18, two days later. There had been a heavy rain and the water in the pool was a foot higher. Many new pools had formed in the ravine. The next day, however, one animal was discovered in his niche; none of the others could be found.

Near the Santa Rita Experimental Range Headquarters on July 21, 1949, 10 adults were found by Riemer on the exposed, nearly vertical face of a dam 9 feet high, in a rocky canyon above headquarters (see "habitat," p. 316). Although the surface upon which the toads rested faced northwest; except for an overcast, sunlight would have reached them during midday. The colors of the animals, before disturbed, ranged from purplish red to olive gray and, although not matching the rock surface closely, the animals were well camouflaged by pattern, skin texture, and general tone of the colors.

The unnatural uniformity of the surface rendered them more conspicuous than they would have been on most natural backgrounds. Only one individual appeared nervous during the observations. It moved about over the face of the rock clinging with the body at an angle of about 45° from the perpendicular. The direction of the movement apparently made little difference as to position of the body. When picked up or just before, each animal eliminated a rather large quantity of water through the anus. Does this mean that the body tissues are saturated with water prior to the animals taking up daytime posts, and that these toads rely on such [illegible]tion to maintain a suitable body water level and

THERMAL DATA

[illegible]os Angeles County, California, June 28, 1950, [illegible] perched in niches on granite boulders

Temperature °C.		
Body	Substratum	Air
19.1	18.8 (stream nearby 16.1)	19.3
21.0	20.0 (between frog and rock)	22.5
23.0		

temperature throughout the day? They appear to be largely hydrophobic animals, at least in the daytime, when not breeding.

Voice.—Storer (1925:208) compares the note of the species in California with that of *H. regilla*. It differs in being lower in pitch, somewhat weaker in volume, and without any tendency toward a two-syllable sound as is heard often from *regilla*. Two individuals, timed, croaked at 1-second intervals. A chorus at Tahquitz Creek began about 4:00 P.M., soon after the sun had disappeared behind the San Jacinto Range; was strongest just after dark, from about 7:30 to 8:30 P.M.; and continued into the night at least until 2 A.M.

The voice has been described as like the "ba-a-a" of a slightly hoarse lamb (Eaton, 1935:7) or like that of a goat (Dugès in Mexico, according to Cope, 1887:14). It has also been likened to the quack of a duck, though not so blatant as that of a mallard (Storer, 1925:208). Campbell (1934:5) describes the call of the male as a low "r-r-r-r." During the courtship of these amphibians, he noted a female answering a male in the same style but in a much higher pitch. The male then called "too-eet, too-eet" in a very low pitch. Following this, 2 females that had been attracted entered the water. When they neared the male, he leaped toward them and clasped one of them. The female tried to escape. During Campbell's observation, the females always managed to get away. The male did not follow them more than an inch from the pool. They started hopping away, but as soon as the male began to croak (the "r-r-r-r" call) they stopped and slowly approached. As they neared they answered in high voices, he again called "too-eet, too-eet," and the whole performance was repeated. Apparently identity of the sexes of the individuals discussed was inferred from their behavior.

The male commonly faces the stream or pool when croaking, often with a rock at his back. According to Storer (1925:207) the rock may serve as a shelter against the approach of enemies from the shore and also to some extent as a sound reflector.

Food.—Twelve individuals from Saint George and Zion Park in southwestern Utah were examined by Tanner (1931:187). Seven had empty stomachs, the other 5 contained the following: a dytiscid, an ant, a large caterpillar, beetles (Dryopidae), small gryllids (*Ceuthophilus*), a giant water bug (belostomatid), centipedes, and spiders.

Reproduction.—Breeds from early March to July. Atsatt (Storer, 1925: 209) found eggs of this species in Snow Creek on the south side of San Gorgonio Pass, Riverside County, California, April 15, 1923. The breeding season was at its height.

EGGS. Usually deposited in quieter water of rocky streams. Deposited singly; single gelatinous envelope, 3.87 to 5.0 mm., average 4.40 mm.;

ovum 1.8 to 2.4 mm., average 2.07 mm.; eggs usually attached to leaves, sticks, debris, and rocks on or near bottom of rocky pools; may sometimes be floating, and in small potholes eggs may be clumped; several hundred in complement (essentially from Livezey and Wright, 1947:189). Storer (1925:214) suggests that single eggs are more able to withstand the buffeting of the stream during periods of sudden increase in water than an egg cluster.

LARVA. Resembles *H. regilla* in form; to 2 inches in length; spiracle sinistral, just below lateral axis, aperture directed backward; center of aperture slightly behind mid-point of body; anus dextral. (Pl. 31.)

Labial teeth 2/3; upper labium fringed with continuous row of teeth; papillae extend above and inward beyond end of first upper labial tooth row for about 1/4 to 1/7 of length of first row; end of second row usually even with end of first upper row of teeth; horny beak contained 1.8 to 2.0 times in first upper row; median space of second upper row short, 8 to 10 times in length of either half; inner papillae poorly developed, 2 to 3 rows at end of the 3 rows of lower teeth; beneath third lower labial row no inner papillae or very scarce; third lower labial row equal to or slightly shorter than first lower row; first and second rows of lower teeth about equal or second row longer and 1.5-2.0 greater than horny beak (largely from Wright, 1929:64). (Pl. 32.)

General coloration at first black, later olivaceous to gray, sometimes with reddish or orange suffusion on tail; tail may be crossbanded, marbled, or spotted with dark and yellowish marks; below iridescent light gray; iris olivaceous with golden markings above and below pupil.

Larva 1/2 inch in body length, with hind limbs moderately well developed, obtained July 16, 1949, 1 mile northeast of Peña Blanca Springs, Santa Cruz County, Arizona: Body above olive with greenish and yellow, under magnification seen to consist of blackish ground color overlaid with pale gold and copper pigment flecks; these flecks are closely set, providing rather uniform color but lines and flecks of black ground color appear here and there; tail musculature similarly marked with pale gold flecks but with larger gaps among them, resulting in a dark blotched and spotted appearance; tail membranes whitish, translucent, with spots of melanic color and with few scattered, pale yellow chromatophores, especially on ventral fin; tail musculature like dorsum, coppery basally and with dark and light mottling; appearance of copper color seems to depend in large part on intensity of illumination, as it appears almost anywhere on body in highlighted areas; two cream spots on snout in front of nostrils; iris with orange-yellow rings, one around pupil, another more peripherally situated. Smaller larvae, about 1/4 inch in body length, possess heavier melanic ground color and fewer golden chromatophores but otherwise are similar to larger larvae, including cream spots on snout. In bright sunlight tadpoles have streak of copper on either side of tail fin extending well onto body, when animals swimming slightly downward; when rising to surface, anterior part of body and upper eyelids assume this color, due to highlighting of these areas.

Forty to 75 days may be spent as a tadpole; transformation, at about 15 mm., may occur in early June to mid-August. King (1932:176) found larvae in White House Canyon (Madera Canyon) in the Santa Rita Mountains, Arizona. Some were transforming at 18 mm. body length. On August 26, 1933, Campbell (1934) found a stream in the Peña Blanca area, Santa Cruz County, Arizona, full of tadpoles. They were beginning to hatch and several newly metamorphosed young were taken. From eggs collected on April 14 and 15 at Snow Creek, Riverside County, California, 3 larvae were hatched on or about April 20. These measured 8.1 mm. in total length (Storer, 1925:211). A nearly metamorphosed young individual, with a mere stub of a tail remaining, was taken at La Puerta, San Diego County, June 5, 1909. It measured 17 mm. in head-and-body length, indicating that larval life is probably short (Storer *loc. cit.*).

Remarks.—It appears that at least two subspecies of *Hyla arenicolor* should be recognized. The California form seems to differ in character of the dorsal spotting, skin texture, foot tubercles, tarsal fold, webbing of the toes, and in behavior from the canyon tree-toad of Arizona and New Mexico.

PACIFIC TREE-TOAD

Hyla regilla Baird and Girard
Plate 19

Range.—From British Columbia (mainland and Vancouver Island), south through Washington, Oregon, California, and Lower California; on Catalina, Santa Rosa, and Santa Cruz islands off the coast of southern California and Cedros Island off the west coast of Lower California; also in Idaho, western Montana, and Nevada. Old records for the vicinity of Flagstaff, Arizona, are probably of *Hyla wrightorum.* I have seen specimens in the collection of Brigham Young University, upon which Utah records have been based. They appear to be *Pseudacris nigrita.* The species may, however, be present in northwestern Utah. This is the only salientian known from the islands off the coast of California. (Pl. 59.)

Type locality.—Sacramento River, in Oregon and Puget Sound (Baird and Girard, 1852b:174). Type from Sacramento River, California.

Description.—STRUCTURE. Adult approximately 1¼ to, but usually under, 2 inches; digits with enlarged terminal discs, slightly less transversely expanded than in *arenicolor;* hind toes webbed, with margin of web between successive toes, when spread, usually curving distinctly inward, leaving fifth toe at approximately 45° angle (margin of web commonly leaves fifth toe at nearly 90° in *arenicolor* from California); skin usually smooth or with a few inconspicuous tubercles but occasionally quite rough; tympanum round, 1/4 to slightly over 1/2 size of eye opening, located in eye stripe; thenar tubercle elongate, ovoid; palmar tubercle represented by 3 small, closely associated, tubercles totaling size of thenar; metatarsal tubercles as in *arenicolor;* tarsal fold present. COLOR. Ground color highly variable: green, various shades of brown, occasionally reddish, light gray, to almost black; capable of marked color change (from dark brown to bright green); conspicuous blackish eye stripe extending from nostril to well behind eye, often beyond axilla; eye stripe occasionally faint in preserved specimens or, in life, in dark phase; stripe broadest behind eye, narrow anteriorly, bordered below by light stripe; often with triangular or T- or Y-shaped dark brown or blackish mark on head, with arms of Y extending anteriorly to eyelids; back with several longitudinal stripes of dusky color, often variously broken to form spots, bars, and blotches; almost endless variety in shape and arrangement of dorsal markings; limbs crossbanded or blotched with dark color; below unspotted whitish or pale yellow, occasionally dusky; yellow or orange color becoming pronounced posteriorly, especially on under surfaces of limbs, rear of femur, and in groin; iris rust to bronze, lightest above pupil. SEXUAL DIFFERENCES. Male with olivaceous to dusky gular area. When vocal sac deflated often 8 to 12 longitudinal folds present.

Animals from the Lake Como region, Ravalli County, Montana, reported by Rodgers and Jellison (1942:10-11) exhibit a tendency toward numerous rather small spots, bars, and blotches dorsally. Several have small spots and flecks of dark color on their chests. The animals from Montana resemble in pattern individuals from Washington, Oregon, and California, more than they do the boldly marked animals of the Great Basin. Rodgers and Jellison (1942:11) state, "This evidence tends to confirm what might be expected, namely, that the population of the Bitterroot Valley is related to that of the Pacific coast through past or present connection along the Columbia River drainage."

Habitat.—This species is highly adaptable, occurring from the Lower Sonoran to the Boreal Life-zone, from sea level to over 11,000 feet. It seeks cover in a variety of places such as rock fissures, under bark, in vegetation along streams, in rodent and other burrows, in nooks and crannies in buildings, and in culverts. It frequents ponds, springs, streams, irrigation canals, and other bodies of water, but has been found as far as 1/2 mile from water (Storer, 1925:219). (Pl. 43, fig. 2.)

Behavior.—Largely nocturnal, but active also in the daytime. In some localities, at lower elevations, it is active throughout the year. It is not especially attracted to trees but, rather, is usually found on or near the ground. The capacity for color change is great. The dorsal pattern appears as the frog lightens but may fade as extreme lightening occurs. Change from an unspotted dark coloration through a medium light-colored phase with spots, to an unspotted light phase, may take place in 8 to 10 minutes. The dark eye stripe is only obscure when in the dark phase. Throughout the color change it is constant in appearance. (Based in part on Dickerson, 1920:136.)

Tadpoles of this species were found in rather saline water, at 33.4°C. at Paraiso Hot Springs [west of Soledad, Santa Lucia Mountains], California (Brues, 1932:283). In an exposed tule-bordered pool along the Mohave River, 3 miles north of Victorville, San Bernardino County, California, on June 19, 1949, I found mature and metamorphosing larvae in water 18.7°C., where the pool was shaded by the tules. The water was 22.3°C. where exposed to the sun.

Voice.—Well developed in the male. The volume of the voice is out of proportion to the size of the frog. Storer (1925:221) describes the call of an individual chorusing frog as "krĕck-ĕk," uttered over and over again in rapid sequence, about one a second, the last syllable with rising inflection (11, 12, and 15 notes in 15-second intervals, 28 in 30 seconds, another at the rate of 80 a minute, and exceptionally even faster). When one is near a chorusing assembly of these frogs, the volume of the sound is so great as to exclude most other sounds. When singing, the male may float with his limbs outstretched and his globular pouch extended to or beyond his chin. Full choruses in California may begin in December or January. Chorusing may extend over a long period from November or December to April, occasionally May, and even early June. At any season of the year, a single prolonged note, "kr-r-r-ĕck," lower in pitch than the song note, may be heard (Storer, 1925:222).

Food.—Needham (1924:3) examined the stomachs of 18 individuals obtained in ponds at the head of Laguna Canyon, Orange County, August 24, 1922. Three had empty stomachs. The remainder had eaten a variety of minute, mostly nonaquatic insects. About 80 per cent of the food consisted about equally of small leaf-hoppers (jassids) and small dipterans. The leaf-hoppers were such as abound in shore vegetation. The dipterans were midges, small crane flies, and a variety of small muscoid flies many of which had doubtless developed as larvae in the mud of the pond. The remainder of the food consisted of myrmecine ants (perhaps 10 per cent), a few parasitic hymenopterans (ichneumonids and braconids), a few very small beetles, a number of spiders (*Erigone* and a related genus), and a single terrestrial isopod crustacean. The insects were all very small, the largest being an ortalid fly, *Anacampta latiuscula*.

Reproduction.—Considering the species over its entire range, it spawns over a long period, from January to the middle of May (Livezey and Wright, 1947:200) and probably in June and July in interior British Columbia (Carl, 1943:45). May be found in large aggregations during the breeding season.

Smith (1940:379-80) has described mating and oviposition. The beginning of the breeding season is marked by congregation of large numbers of vociferous males at transient rain pools and more permanent bodies of water. The females do not enter the water until ready to lay. They ordinarily enter in late afternoon or early evening, and mating and egg-laying is commonly completed by the following morning. Since the females enter singly or in small groups, the superior numbers of males make probable immediate mating. There is usually a preliminary period of clasping lasting from 4 to 24 hours under laboratory conditions (probably 4 to 9 or 10 hours in nature). Amplexus is pectoral. The male grips the female tightly with his forelimbs but ordinarily does not contact her with his body behind his pectoral region except when inseminating eggs. The legs of the male are flexed in a sitting pose. Insemination occurs at the moment of extrusion of the eggs. The male brings his cloacal aperture close to that of the female, discharging a quantity of transparent semen, and with a quick firm extension slides his feet posteriorly over the sides and hips of the female, then deftly retracts to his previous position.

Simultaneously with the foot action of the male, the female extrudes a clutch of eggs into the cloud of sperm. Sometimes before releasing a mass of eggs, the female scratches at the substratum on which the eggs are to be deposited. As the eggs are extruded, the cloaca of the female is brought close to this surface and their attachment is effected. Adhering eggs may be removed from her cloaca by her tarsi through a precise flexor-extensor reflex. Intervals between layings are from 2 to 10 minutes or longer. The behavior of the female is characterized by bursts of activity. Shortly after oviposition the pair separate. Amplexus may last from 8 to 40 hours or more. The total number of eggs observed by Smith was from 500 to 750, but Storer (1925:225) records a female that deposited 1,250 eggs, in a period of nearly 24 hours. The number of eggs per clutch is usually about 16, but varies from 5 to 60. There is a tendency toward the close of laying for clutches to taper off to 3 or 4 or even single eggs. There is indication that the embrace of the male may be necessary for proper extrusion of the eggs.

EGGS. Clusters deposited in shallow water of any sort of quiet pond, commonly at depths above 4 inches; attached to sticks, leaves, vegetation, and other objects in the water or found floating, usually attached to objects, at the surface. Several masses may be laid close together, one against another, or separated less than 1 inch. Eggs usually laid in loose cluster commonly of irregular shape; 2 gelatinous envelopes, outer one sticky, 4.7 to 6.7 mm.; inner one 1.88 to 2.70 mm., average 2.0 mm., distinct; ovum 1.23 to 1.35 mm., average 1.30 mm., brown above and yellow below; 9 to 70 eggs per packet, usually about 22 to 25 (largely from Livezey and Wright, 1947:199-200). Probably the number of eggs per mass reflects in a general way the degree of solitude experienced by a pair when the eggs are deposited (Storer, 1925:224).

LARVA. Tadpole medium (45 mm.), full, and deep-bodied; tail medium or fairly long (1½ to 2 times head-body length), tip acute or obtuse; no flagellum; dorsal fin not exceeding, slightly less, same as, or slightly greater than musculature in depth, sometimes extending onto body to as far as a line connecting posterior margins of eyes; tail in general quite deep [often deeper than body]; spiracle sinistral, more directed backward than upward, opening round or elliptical, plainly visible; spiracle below lateral axis; eye just above lateral axis, in dorsal aspect often extending to lateral outline, just visible from venter; anus dextral, opening just above level of lower edge of ventral fin; muciferous crypts not distinct. (Pl. 31.)

Labial teeth ⅔; upper labium fringed with continuous row of teeth; papillae extend above and inward beyond end of first upper row of teeth ⅐ to ⅕ length of upper row; end of second upper labial row may extend beyond end of first upper row or be even with it; horny beak may be contained in first upper labial row 1¼ to 1¾ times; median space in second upper row contained about 2 times in one of lateral segments; usually well-formed inner row of papillae on side of labium down almost to end of lower labial tooth row; third row of lower labial teeth with only single row of papillae below it and usually contained about 2 to 3 times in length of first or second lower labial rows; first and second lower rows of labial teeth about same length as upper rows (partly from Wright 1929:60. Deviations from Wright, in foregoing account, are based on 6 larvae, 23.5 to 38.2 mm. in total length, hind limbs absent to well developed, obtained 2 miles south of Beatty, Nye County, Nevada, on June 21, 1949). (Pl. 32.)

General color blackish, yellowish brown to dark brown, heavily spotted with black; below whitish, iridescent, with bronze or coppery tinges; tail mottled with black; iris golden, with dark area anterior and posterior to pupil.

In the laboratory, larvae may hatch in less than one week (Pickwell, 1947:75). Development to the stage of hatching, at Berkeley, is accomplished in about 2 weeks (Storer, 1925:225). Newly hatched larvae were 6.0 to 7.5 mm. in total length. At metamorphosis the head-and-body length varies from 11.2 to 16.5 mm. In 1922, at Thornhill Pond, Berkeley,

California, individuals still in the process of change were seen as late as August 10 (Storer, 1925:226). According to Carl (1943:45), in coastal British Columbia young are ready to leave the water by mid-July. According to Pickwell (1947:77) approximately 2 years are required for maturation.

SONORAN TREE-TOAD

Hyla wrightorum Taylor
Plate 19

Range.—Forested plateau of north-central Arizona and the Huachuca Mountains of the southeastern part; northern New Mexico and possibly western Texas; Chihuahua and probably Sonora in northern Mexico. (Pl. 59.)

Type locality.—11 miles south of Springerville, Apache County, Arizona (Taylor, 1938:436).

Other localities. ARIZONA.—1½ mi. NW of Miller's Peak (Taylor, 1938:436) and Peterson Ranch, at 6,100 ft. (MVZ), Huachuca Mts., Cochise Co.; vicinity of Williams; McNary; Hart Canyon, about 50 mi. S of Winslow; Pinetop (Chapel, 1939); Lake-O-the-Woods (Wright and Wright, 1949:365). NEW MEXICO.—Santa Fe (Taylor, *loc. cit.*).

Description.—STRUCTURE. Adult usually under 2 inches; closely resembles *H. regilla;* differs in following ways: Taylor (1938:439) ". . . in having a smooth rather than pustular skin, and in having a longer leg, the tibiotarsal joint reaching the tip of the snout or beyond, instead of to the region of the eye. The webbing of the toes is somewhat less and the diameter of the tympanum is greater than half the diameter of the eye; the toes and fingers are wider with somewhat wider pads." With our few specimens of *wrightorum,* I have been unable to confirm Taylor's statement that the legs are longer than in *regilla.* Animals from near the extremes of the range of the latter (Montana and Lower California) and 3 adult *wrightorum* from Arizona were tested. Perhaps with more specimens of *wrightorum* greater leg length would be shown. Metacarpal and metatarsal tubercles essentially as in *H. arenicolor;* tarsal fold present. COLOR. Eye stripe long, extending well back along sides posterior to shoulder where it may break into several segments; usually no dark mark on head between or behind eyes; dark spot may be present on each eyelid; commonly a pair of longitudinal dark bars posteriorly on back, sometimes small pair of spots or bars farther anteriorly, otherwise body largely unmarked above; limbs with spots or bars but less distinctly banded than *regilla*. Like *regilla* may be green above; rear of femur and groin orange or gold with greenish tinge; below light-colored, unspotted, except sometimes few dark flecks on throat. SEXUAL DIFFERENCES. Male with dark throat, dull greenish tan in life; throat of female whitish.

Habitat.—Frequents wooded areas; may be found in trees to considerable heights. Enters relatively quiet water for breeding—grassy pools, ponds, streams, and swamps.

Chapel (1939:225) found this species in Arizona only on the southern forested edge of the Colorado Plateau, around 7,000 feet, from the vicinity of Williams southeast to McNary. The frogs were found in forests consisting of ponderosa pine, with small areas of Douglas fir, white fir, Mexican white pine, and other trees. The pines predominate in a mixture including species of oak, junipers, and piñon pine. The lower limit of distribution in this region seemed to be the rim of the Colorado Plateau, with an elevation of about 5,000 feet.

Before and after the breeding season, the frogs occasionally were found in the forest. Concealing coloration and the ventriloquial character of the voice aid the species in escaping detection. This frog is found on the ground and in damp places in trees. Chapel mentions an individual that fell from the top of a tree 75 feet high, jarred loose when the tree was cut.

Alden Miller found an adult male, MVZ 46632, on August 3, 1948, at an elevation of 5,700 feet, on the Rio Gavilan, 7 miles southwest of Pacheco, Chihuahua, Mexico. At the time, the river was low but flowing. The animal was taken near the stream in a rocky gorge at the base of a slab rock cliff. Sycamores, maples, and oaks grew along the stream.

Behavior.—More arboreal in habit than *regilla*. Chapel (1939:226) mentions hearing them calling on sultry days from the trees.

Voice.—In the male it is a low pitched, harsh, metallic clack, according to Wright and Wright (1942:159); 2 to 10 or 12 or more notes may be given in succession, with acceleration toward the end of the series. The vocal sac is spherical.

Chapel (1939:226) notes, "Fresh rains bring out a renewed chorus. A chorus usually lasts two or three nights and then quickly thins out to a few disconsolate males for two to four more nights. A chorus continues all night, with the greatest volume before midnight. Probably new individuals make up most of each new chorus."

Food.—Seven individuals from near Williams, Arizona, obtained by Chapel (1939:227) in 1937, possessed the following in their stomachs: 7 beetles, 4 *Ips*, 1 fly, 1 spider, 2 small earthworms, and grass particles.

Reproduction.—With the onset of the breeding period, initiated by summer rains, individuals migrate toward rain pools. Large, grassy, shallow ponds appear to be favored but the animals may also be found at permanent lakes, brooks, wells, and in nearly any place where rain water collects in sufficient quantities. The majority of individuals remain along the edges of shallow grassy ponds in parklike areas in the forest.

The breeding season in Arizona is from June to August, but in any year the dates vary. Heavy summer rains, common on the Colorado Plateau in July and August, are the determining factor. These storms delimit the breeding season. The seasons noted by Chapel (1939:226) were:

1933, Pinetop and Hart Canyon,	7,000 feet,	July 2—August 9	—heavy rains
1935, Pinetop	"	July 7— July 28	—normal rains
1937, Williams	"	July 2— July 14	—subnormal rains

Breeding is intermittent within this period. Many choruses and tadpoles were found in rapidly flowing brooks but no eggs. Egg masses are probably either laid in the quiet backwashes or are washed into them to hatch.

EGGS. Livezey and Wright (1947:208) give size of ovarian eggs as 1.0 to 1.4 mm. in diameter; general appearance of eggs and manner of occurrence resemble *Hyla regilla*.

Chapel (1939:226) says that tadpoles gather in shallow, warm, side pools full of decaying vegetable matter. They also gather in great numbers around fresh cow manure and apparently feed on the dissolved and softened material. Larvae transform in late summer, recently metamorphosed frogs measuring 10 to 13 mm. in length. Many still possess stubby tails.

LARVA. Description based on 6 preserved specimens (CU 4548) obtained July 9–10, 1942, by Anna and Albert Wright at Lake-O-the-Woods, Gila County, Arizona. Specimens loaned through the courtesy of W. J. Hamilton, Department of Conservation, Cornell University, Ithaca, New York. All possess hind limbs—the smallest having limbs 2.8 mm. long, the largest having limbs 16.2 mm. Measurements made of straightened limb.

Total length from 34.2 to 44.7 mm.; tail 21.1 to 29.0 mm., 6.8 to 9.8 mm. in greatest height at about mid-point; head-body 7.4 to 8.2 in greatest depth, 8.2 to 10.6 in greatest width at or near mid-point; greatest depth of dorsal and ventral fins about same and each same or slightly less than greatest depth of musculature near juncture with body; tip of tail subacute to obtuse; spiracle on or just below lateral axis, opening vertically elliptical, directed upward and backward; eyes laterally situated, corneal surface on or near lateral outline of head as viewed from above; nostril at or slightly posterior to mid-point between anterior margin of eye and tip of snout; anus dextral, opening at or slightly above edge of ventral fin. (Pl. 31.)

Labial teeth 2/3, first upper row longest; second row with narrow median space, 1/4 to 1/5 length of one of lateral segments, latter about length of upper mandible; first and third lower rows about same length; second lower row slightly longer than others; labial papillae completely fringe mouth except for centrally situated section on upper labium, about 1/4 to 1/3 width of mouth; labial fringe not emarginate laterally; papillae present inside fringe at corners of mouth and extending on lower labium to third lower labial tooth row. (Pl. 32.)

Above dull brownish olive on head-body with slate-colored areas of viscera showing through skin; larger specimens with scattered brown flecks on body, principally laterally situated; under magnification numerous closely set flecks (melanophores) rather uniformly distributed on pale yellowish-gray ground color; below light yellowish gray with dark intestinal mass showing posteriorly; under magnification no melanophores ventrally except few pin-point flecks across throat just posterior to mouth; melanophores of sides thin out and disappear rapidly at and below lateral axis; tail musculature cream, stippled (observed under magnification) with dark brown melanophores; melanic stippling irregular on last 1/2 to 1/3 of tail musculature, resulting in pale yellow and dark blotches; melanophores may be aggregated elsewhere on tail, forming blotches and spots of dark brown scattered anteriorly to base of tail; tail fins translucent, with lines, blotches, and stippling of dark brown, most abundant on posterior 1/2 of tail, scarce or absent on anterior 1/4 (particularly on ventral fin).

TRUE FROGS

Family Ranidae

Structure.—Pectoral girdle firmisternal; vertebrae procoelous; centrum of sacral vertebrae convex anteriorly, with double condyle posteriorly; 7 presacral vertebrae, eighth biconcave; ribs absent; urostyle attached to 2 condyles; sacral diapophyses cylindrical or slightly expanded; teeth in upper jaw; vomerine teeth present or absent; tongue free posteriorly, usually notched behind; pupil horizontally or vertically oval; tympanum distinct or not evident; terminal phalanges various; fingers free, toes webbed; digits not dilated at tips or more or less dilated; when dilated, terminal phalanges may be more or less T-shaped; no intercalary cartilages. North American species are members of genus *Rana,* with relatively smooth skin, varying development of dorsolateral folds, horizontal pupil, no parotoid glands or cranial crests, no well-developed warts, and without dilated digits.

Mature larvae of species considered here medium to large, from about 2 to 6 inches (*Rana catesbeiana*); oral disc usually emarginate laterally; labial teeth often 2/3 but may be $\frac{2\text{-}7}{3\text{-}6}$; dorsal fin highly arched (*Rana sylvatica*) or not (*Rana boylii*), extending well onto body or not; anus dextral; spiracle sinistral near lateral axis.

Habits.—Fossorial, terrestrial, and aquatic. In the genus *Rana* the eggs are commonly laid in relatively large, grapelike clusters, the individual eggs often with 3 jelly envelopes. Amplexus is characteristically pectoral.

Range.—Widely distributed but absent from New Zealand, the West Indies, and the southern part of South America. Absent from Australia except the northern part. Primarily an Old World family. Africa seems to have been the center of differentiation. The single genus *Rana* with 8 species is treated here. Its range is similar to that of the family.

Key to Species
Figure 31

1*a*. With large, well-defined, dark brown to blackish spots on dorsal surface of body, outlined with color lighter than ground (1); spots located between well-developed, light-colored dorsolateral folds, evenly outlined, usually round or oval. . *Rana pipiens*, p. 355

1*b*. Without distinct dorsal spots or, if spots present, not outlined with color lighter than ground (5); spots located between dorsolateral folds, irregular in outline (4, 5); folds usually similar in color to ground color (*Rana sylvatica* excepted) 2

2*a*. (1*b*) Eye mask present, set off by whitish line on upper jaw (7, 8, 9); dorsolateral folds present (4, 5, 6), extending well behind sacral hump. 3

2*b*. Eye mask absent; dorsolateral folds obscure, or absent, or extending only to sacral hump 5

3*a*. (2*a*) No red or yellow on underparts in life; eye stripe usually well defined, blackish, prolonged beyond nostril to, or nearly to, edge of upper lip (3, 6, 9); whitish vertebral stripe present (6) or absent (3); unicolored between dorsolateral folds, or with broad central brownish band darker than ground color, or with much elongate diffuse spots; groin not heavily mottled with blackish; size smaller, 1 1/5 to 3 1/4 inches . . . . *Rana sylvatica*, p. 373

3*b*. Red or yellow underparts in life; eye stripe not prolonged to edge of upper lip and sometimes vague or absent (4, 5); without vertebral stripe; usually with rounded spots of varying size between dorsolateral folds (4); spots well defined (5) or vague (4); seldom unicolored between dorsolateral folds; groin may or may not be heavily mottled with blackish; size larger 1 4/5 to 3 4/5 inches 4

4*a*. (3*b*) Eyes appear turned upward; upper eyelids reduced; hind limb and foot relatively short; groin usually lacks heavy dark mottling (5); limbs commonly spotted, less often barred; above with varied number of inky-black spots, irregular in outline, and of varying size, contrasting sharply with lighter ground color (5); usually distinct whitish stripe on upper jaw, usually long, extending from snout commonly to shoulder (8) .... *Rana pretiosa,* p. 367

4*b*. Eyes appear more lateral in position; upper eyelid largely conceals eye from above; hind limb and foot relatively longer; groin usually contrastingly marked with dark mottlings (4); limbs often barred with dark color; above with dark spots, sometimes with diffuse outline, usually not as sharply defined as in *pretiosa* (*R. aurora cascadae* excepted) (4); whitish stripe on upper jaw usually extending from beneath eye to, or stopping short of, shoulder (7) .... *Rana aurora,* p. 334

5*a*. (2*b*) Eardrum inconspicuous, colored like rest of head (10), usually tuberculate; adult to 4½ inches 6

5*b*. Eardrum conspicuous (11, 12, 15), as large as eye in female (12), usually several times larger than eye in male (11), differing in color from rest of head and not tuberculate; adult to 8 inches 7

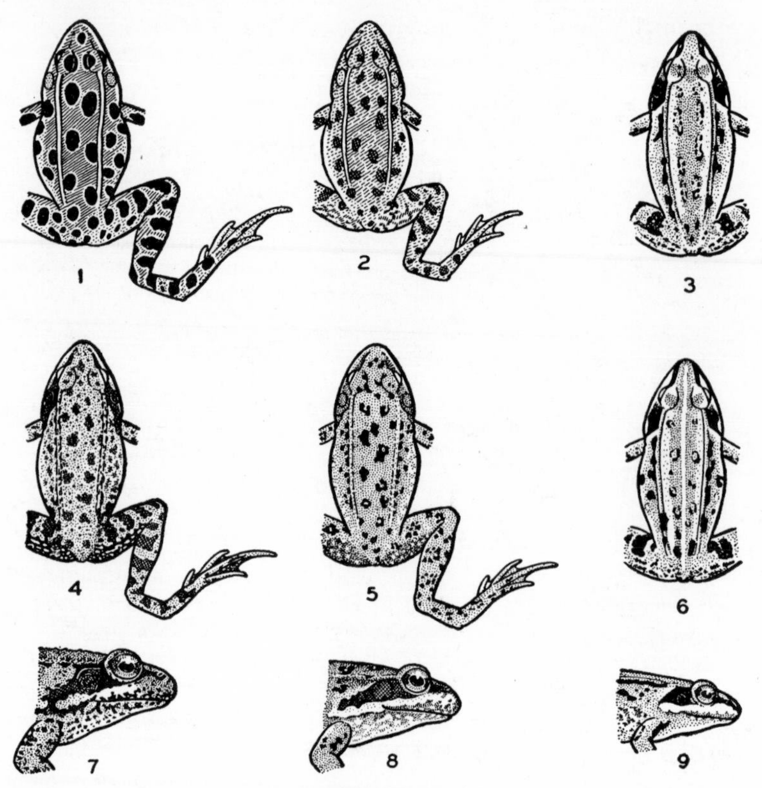

Fig. 31. 1, *Rana pipiens;* 2, *R. pipiens-fisheri* intermediate [*R. onca*]; 3, 6, 9, *R. sylvatica;* 4, 7, *R. aurora;* 5, 8, *R. pretiosa;* 10, 13, *R. tarahumarae;* 11, 12, 18, 19, *R. catesbeiana;* 14, *R. boylii;* 15, 16, 17, *R. clamitans.*

6*a*. (5*a*) Adult often with dark-colored throat and sometimes dark-colored venter (13) (immatures may lack dusky coloration); size large, to 4½ inches, New Mexico, Arizona, and northwestern Mexico .... *Rana tarahumarae,* p. 382

6*b*. Throat not commonly suffused with dark color although frequently spotted (14); size smaller, seldom much over 3 inches; California, western Oregon, and extreme western Nevada .... *Rana boylii,* p. 339

7*a*. (5*b*) No dorsolateral folds (18); only tip (last phalanx) of fourth toe usually free of web (19); no white streak posteriorly on upper jaw ...... *Rana catesbeiana,* p. 345

7*b*. Dorsolateral folds present but usually not extending beyond sacral hump and often stopping short of it (16); 2 phalanges of fourth toe usually free of web (17); edge of upper jaw with white streak extending posteriorly to shoulder (15) .... *Rana clamitans,* p. 351

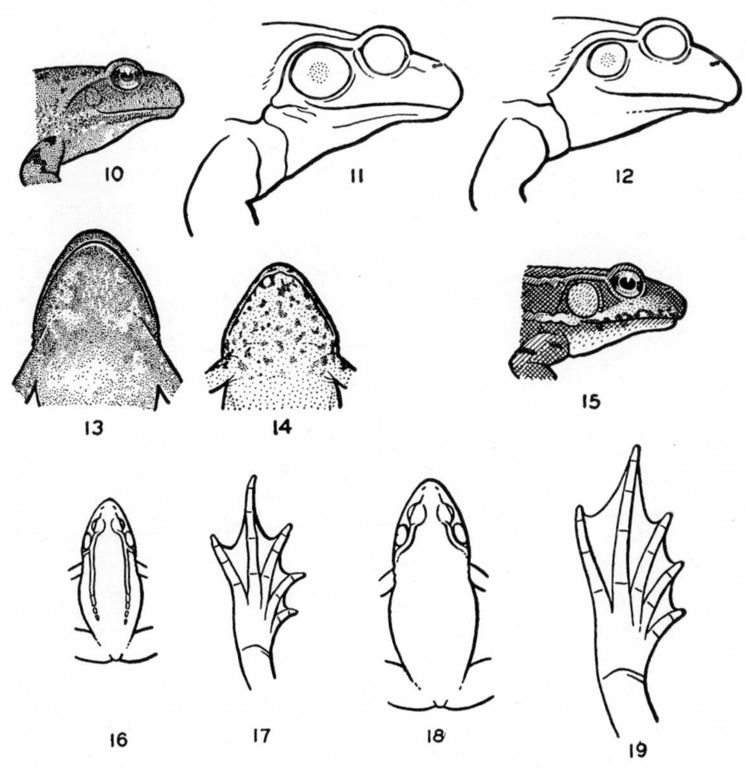

Fig. 31 (continued). Explanation on page 332.

RED-LEGGED FROG

Rana aurora Baird and Girard
Plate 23

Range.—From southwestern British Columbia and Vancouver Island south through Washington, Oregon, and California into northern Lower California at least as far south as the Santo Domingo River. Occurs in coastal areas, including mountainous sections, in Washington and Oregon and extends eastward to Michigan Bluff, Placer County, California. The subspecies *draytonii* has been introduced at Millett, Nye County, Nevada (Linsdale, 1940:208). (Pl. 60.)

So far as I can determine this frog does not now occur naturally on the floor of the Great Valley of California. It is conceivable that under primitive conditions, before water was commandeered for purposes of irrigation, this species occupied overflow pools of streams and rivers in the valley.

Type locality.—Puget Sound (Baird and Girard, 1852b:174).

Description.—STRUCTURE. Adult approximately 2½ to over 5 inches; dorsolateral folds present, occasionally indistinct; skin smooth or roughened with numerous small tubercles; tympanum evident, ⅔ to nearly same size as eye; vomerine teeth large, in 2 clusters between internal nares; 3 elongate oval metacarpal tubercles more or less well defined, arranged in transverse row, thenar largest, other two each may be ½ to ⅔ size of thenar; inner metatarsal tubercle elongate, oval, round-surfaced; outer tubercle absent or to ⅓ size of inner one; no membranous flap of skin on tarsus but sometimes low rounded ridge. COLOR. Blackish to dark brown eye mask usually present, extending from nostril to angle of jaw; mask sometimes poorly defined, represented by mottlings; whitish or yellowish streak above mouth extending from below eye toward and often to shoulder; above brownish to olive with dusky spots, often with fuzzy outline and commonly with light centers, especially in *draytonii;* spots highly variable in size from minute speckling to blotches around 5 or 6 mm. across; limbs blotched and crossbarred with blackish; groin mottled black and yellow or greenish yellow; below light-colored, with varying amounts of dark mottling; in life lower sides, posterior part of ventral surface of body, and ventral surface of hind legs reddish; reddish color varies in intensity and extent both geographically and individually;

some animals from San Diego County, for example, have an almost complete absence of red on the lower surfaces, it being present only on the distal part of the hind limbs; immatures may almost wholly lack red color; iris golden yellow or with coppery or orange color; capable of considerable color change, from dark to light phase. JUVENILE. May be brighter-colored dorsally than adult. SEXUAL DIFFERENCES. Male with greater development of webbing of toes and smaller than female; some males have inconspicuous diagonal groove across middle of swollen base of first finger; first finger of male short, with thick base and "nuptial" excrescence in form of largely medial and dorsomedial pigmented glandular area; female has elongate first digit without markedly enlarged base; forearms of male become massive during breeding period. Dickerson (1920:213) says male of subspecies *draytonii* is less rich in coloring (less red) than female and is more likely to be distinctly spotted.

Habitat.—Frequents permanent bodies of relatively quiet water such as ponds, pools along streams, reservoirs, springs, lakes, and marshes. Occasionally found in running water of streams. In San Diego County, for example, it may occupy small water courses. In the northern part of the range, individuals may be found considerable distances from water, among ferns and other vegetation in damp woods. Grinnell and Camp (1917:149) observe that the subspecies *draytonii* inhabits chiefly the Upper Sonoran Life-zone, but extends into the Transition and Lower Sonoran zones.

Behavior.—Highly aquatic. Usually quite wary. Hibernates in mud at bottoms of ponds and creeks in winter, emerging in January and February in middle California (Dickerson, 1920:215).

Voice.—The voice is a stuttering series of 5 or 6 low, gutteral, grating sounds followed by a low-pitched growl or yowl. The call might be written "r-r-r-r-r-r rowr." It lasts about 3 seconds. The sounds are pitched near the lower register of the human voice and are all near one pitch except the last which rises and falls slightly. Sometimes only the stuttering notes are given. When the frog calls, the throat enlarges centrally and laterally, expanding at the sides of the lower jaw and over the forelimb insertions. Individuals call from the shallow margins of ponds where they may cling to submerged vegetation. The expanding vocal sac touches the water and the surface vibrates with each call.

Food.—Three individuals from near Lobster Creek in the Rogue River Basin, Curry County, Oregon, reported by Fitch (1936:640), contained small isopods, beetles, a caterpillar, and a Douglas fir needle. One from 4 miles east of Gold Beach, Oregon, possessed 4 small isopods and a silverfish (lepismid).

Reproduction.—Breeding season from January to July; January through March (*draytonii*); February to May (*aurora*); May to July (*cascadae*). Spawning may occur at night. (Livezey and Wright, 1947; Slater, 1939; Storer, 1925.)

EGGS. Commonly deposited in clusters in permanent pools; 3 gelatinous envelopes.

COMPARISON OF THE EGGS OF THE SUBSPECIES OF *Rana aurora*
(After Livezey and Wright, 1947: 201)

	aurora	*cascadae*	*draytonii*
Jelly envelopes	Indistinct, particularly middle one	Distinct	Quite distinct
Outer	10.0 to 14.0 mm.	11.3 mm.	8.5 mm. (7.55 to 11.80 mm.)
Middle	6.80 mm. (6.25 to 7.93 mm.)	5.8 mm.	4.4 mm. (3.94 to 6.40 mm.)
Inner	5.70 mm. (4.0 to 6.68 mm.)	4.9 mm.	3.5 mm. (3.10 to 5.0 mm.)
Ovum	3.04 mm. (2.31 to 3.56 mm.)	2.25 mm.	2.1 mm. (2.06 to 2.81 mm.)
Number of eggs	750 to 1,300 eggs	425 eggs	2,000 to 4,000 eggs
Appearance of masses	Flat masses 6 to 10 inches across; ova ¾ inch apart; jelly of mass loose and viscid with bluish cast; individual eggs 1.2 cc. in volume		Soft viscid mass 2⅗ x 4 x 3 to 6 x 4 x 4 inches; outline of individual eggs evident on surface
Where deposited	At surface of water attached to vegetation		In overflow areas of permanent pools, attached to vegetation just below the surface in water 3 to 6 inches deep

Hatching occurs in 8 to 20 days in *cascadae,* according to Slater (1939c:149). Storer (1925:241) reports that eggs of *draytonii* laid on February 19 and 20 contained embryos about 3 mm. long by March 7; these had already hatched out of the jelly by March 14 (Thornhill Pond, near Berkeley, California).

LARVA. Greatest length of head-and-body 28 mm.; of tail 55 mm.; length of body contained 1.2 to 2.2 times in length of tail; external nares about equidistant between end of snout and eyes; distance between nares 1.2 to 1.9 in interorbital space; this space 3.4 to 5.2 in length of head-body; eyes about 25 per cent of head-body length from tip of snout; spiracle sinistral, aperture directed backward and slightly upward, center of aperture slightly behind mid-point of head-and-body; anus dextral; greatest depth of tail contained 2.5 to 3.2 times in its own length. (Pl. 33.)

Labial teeth 2/3; first upper row complete, second divided into two short segments, the two separated by width of lower jaw; first lower row of full width, interrupted medially; second complete but commonly slightly shortened laterally; third shorter than second, about same length as upper mandible; 3 rows of papillae on each side of mouth, one row complete across lower border. (Pl. 34.)

General coloration of upper and lateral surfaces of body dark brownish (not greenish), much mottled and with numerous dark spots 1 to 2 mm. in diameter, these having diffuse edges; middle of belly whitish iridescent, with slight pinkish tinge; chin and throat and sides of under surface finely mottled with light and blackish markings with slight iridescence; tail lighter than body, with blackish markings separating myomeres and with light mottled pattern on caudal crests; iris dull bronzy yellow (essentially from Storer, 1925:234, subspecies *draytonii*).

May be confused with *R. catesbeiana* (p. 350).

In the vicinity of Berkeley larvae, at hatching, were sooty brown in color, and measured 8.8 to 10.3 mm. in total length (Storer, 1925:241). Size at metamorphosis of 2 animals from the Arroyo Seco, Los Angeles, obtained May 15, 1921, was 27 mm. in head-and-body length (Storer, 1925:243). Carl (1943:48) reports tadpoles collected in a lake near Victoria, British Columbia, on May 9, 1941, when about 1 inch in length, transformed in July of the same year. Over a year (15 months) may transpire before metamorphosis, but Slater (1939c:149) gives the larval period of *cascadae* as 80 to 95 days. In *cascadae*, very few individuals live over to the following summer as tadpoles. Most transform at 14 mm. or less. Sexual maturity is probably reached at the end of 3, and possibly 4, years.

Two red-legged frogs lived 12 or 13, and approximately 15 years. Most of this time was spent in captivity.

Key to Subspecies

1*a*. Dorsal spots inky black, with well-defined edges; dorsolateral folds well developed; below straw-colored in life (particularly in region of hind limbs); principally in Boreal Zone (commonly Hudsonian Zone) of Washington and Oregon. Frogs of the higher Cascade Mountains as far south as Manzanita Creek, Lassen Volcanic National Park, California, probably belong to this subspecies (R. Storm, *in litt.*). .... *R. a. cascadae* Slater

1*b*. Dorsal spots duller, ordinarily without well-defined edges, not inky black; dorsolateral folds less prominent; below reddish in life (particularly in region of hind limbs) 2

2a. Size smaller, adult to 3 inches; skin smoother and more delicate; dorsolateral folds less prominent; hind limb longer, most noticeable in tibial portion; foot longer and with broader web; smaller inner sole tubercle; eyes proportionately larger; dark dorsal spots reduced, when present, usually without light centers. *Range.*—From southwestern British Columbia south in coastal regions through Washington and Oregon into northwestern California at least to Eureka, Humboldt County. .... *R. a. aurora* Baird and Girard

2b. Size larger, adult to 5 inches; skin commonly rougher and thicker; dorsolateral folds prominent; hind limb shorter, most noticeable in tibial portion; foot shorter and with narrower web; larger inner sole tubercle; eyes proportionately smaller; dark dorsal spots usually more definite when present, usually with light-colored centers. *Range.*—California from Redding, Tehama County, and Mendocino County south, generally in coastal regions, into northern Lower California at least to the Santo Domingo River; eastward in California to Michigan Bluff, Placer County, and Placerville, Eldorado County. Introduced at Millett, Nye County, Nevada .... *R. a. draytonii* Baird and Girard

Remarks.—*Rana cascadae* was described by Slater (1939c) from specimens obtained from Elysian Fields, Rainier National Park, Washington, at an elevation of 5,700 feet. Professor Slater reports (1939c) that he has specimens from the higher parts of the following counties in Washington: Chelan, Clallam, Kittitas, Lewis, Mason, Pierce, Skagit, Skamania, Snohomish, and Yakima. A record from Potsville, Idaho, was later declared to be erroneous. *Cascadae* is regarded by Slater as an inhabitant of the Boreal Life-zone, commonly the Hudsonian Zone. *Rana aurora* occurs west of the Cascades but, according to Slater, its range overlaps a little that of *cascadae* in the Canadian Zone.

Dunlap and Storm (1951) report that *cascadae* also occurs in the Cascade Mountains of Oregon. The range may extend even farther south, into northern California. Specimens in the Museum of Vertebrate Zoölogy from the Lassen Peak area are tentatively regarded as *cascadae* by Dunlap, of Oregon State College, who is presently engaged in a study of the relationships of this form and *aurora.*

I have treated *Rana cascadae* as a subspecies of *Rana aurora,* following Stejneger and Barbour (1943:54). I am not acquainted with the frog in the field but have seen preserved specimens, through the courtesy of Dr. Slater. These are so similar to spotted individuals of *aurora,* that I question whether *cascadae* should be accorded specific rank. In the absence of a thorough study of variation in these frogs, I believe it best at present to regard *cascadae* as a subspecies of *aurora.*

Rana pretiosa must be considered in attempting to define the relationships of these frogs. There are a number of old records of this species west of the Cascades in Oregon and Washington, in the range of *Rana aurora.* Indeed, the type locality of both *aurora* and *pretiosa* is given by Baird and Girard as "Puget Sound." According to these authors *Rana pretiosa* is distinguished from *Rana aurora* ". . . in having proportionally much shorter legs, especially the hind ones; also by the palmation of the toes, the membrane of which extends to their very tip, whilst in *R. aurora* the tip of the toes extends beyond their membrane. The granulation of the body and inferior surface of the feet is another feature by which both species differ." Further, these frogs differ in the length of the light stripe on the upper jaw (see key, p. 332) and in eye color (Storm and Dunlap, *in litt.*).

YELLOW-LEGGED FROG

Rana boylii Baird
Plate 20

Range.—In Oregon essentially west of the crest of the Cascade Mountains, from Marion County southward; widespread in California, ranging south to San Diego County, but absent from the northeastern part, the southeastern deserts, and most of the Central Valley. This species ranges zonally from the Upper Sonoran to the Hudsonian Life-zone. The subspecies *sierrae* occurs in the high Sierra Nevada of California (7,000 feet or above, according to localities listed by Slevin, 1928:140). (Pl. 61.)

Type locality.—Eldorado County, California (Baird, 1854:62).

Description.—STRUCTURE. Adult from approximately 2 to 3½ inches; skin usually roughened by numerous minute tubercles; tympanum obscure, in surface texture and color like rest of head, ½ to ⅔ size of eye opening; vomerine teeth small, sometimes not evident (*muscosa*), scattered on elongate transverse ridges between internal nares; dorsolateral folds usually obscure; metacarpal and metatarsal tubercles and tarsal fold essentially as in *R. aurora*. COLOR. Above variable in ground color—blackish, dark brown, reddish brown, gray, olivaceous, or greenish with varying amounts and intensity of dusky spotting and mottling, but some individuals relatively uniform in dorsal coloration; subspecies *sierrae* may have light gray spots dorsally; some individuals with light patch in front of dark area on upper eyelid; below whitish to yellowish, grading to yellow on posterior part of body and hind limbs; gular area, pectoral region, sides of body, and anterior surface of femur mottled in varying amounts with dark color; mottling most often present on throat and on anterior face of femur; some individuals essentially unmarked below; iris with metallic yellow. SEXUAL DIFFERENCES. Male with bulbular swelling at base of dorsomedial surface of first finger; surface of swollen area covered with minute, closely set papillae; in female first finger longer than in male and without swollen, roughened area.

Habitat.—Frequents streams, springs, and lakes. Nearly always found within a few feet of water. Creeks with rocky courses appear to be favored. Seeks moving but usually not swiftly flowing water.

Fitch (1936:640) found the species in the Rogue River Basin, Oregon, confined to the immediate vicinity of permanent streams, at least where water holes persisted through the dry season. It was most common along streams with rocky beds but was present also in those having mud bottoms. Most places of occurrence were in the low Transition or Upper Sonoran life-zones.

The habitat of *sierrae* is described by Storer (MS) as the borders of lakes and stream courses where the water flow is moderate or slow; small creeks in meadows and even mere trickles in hillside ravines. A few individuals occur in isolated pools.

Behavior.—Often active in the daytime. May be found sunning along shore or on rocks in streams. When frightened, seeks seclusion beneath stones or in sediment of stream bottom. Subspecies *sierrae* must hibernate during the winter but other races, at lower elevations, may not.

The subspecies *sierrae,* when handled, may give off a distinct odor resembling mink or garlic (Storer, MS).

Voice.—Ten miles west of Winters, Solano County, California, on April 26, 1925, Storer (MS) heard individuals croaking during the afternoon. The several males in a given area tended to join in voice for a few notes but lacked the synchronism common in a Pacific tree-toad chorus. Storer (MS) says the subspecies *sierrae* gives a low croak like the lowland *boylii.* When handled the former may give 4 or 5 mews like a domestic kitten. The sounds can be heard 50 yards.

I have heard *Rana b. boylii* call in the laboratory. The voice is a gutteral, grating sound, on one pitch or with rising inflection. The lower notes are pitched at about G, two octaves below middle C. A simple croak lasts ½ to ¾ second. Sometimes a group of 4 or 5 croaks lasting ½ second each and with about ½ second intervals is followed by a prolonged rattling sound lasting 2½ seconds. The latter may be given on one pitch. When expanded, the throat has an oval-shaped swelling on either side below a line connecting the angle of the jaw and the upper surface of the base of the forelimb. The long axis of the swelling extends diagonally forward and downward. The throat also swells medially.

Food.—Aquatic and terrestrial arthropods, particularly insects. Grasshoppers were found in the stomach of an individual reported by Storer (1925:257). Two individuals from 5 miles east of Gold Beach, Oregon, reported by Fitch (1936:640), contained hornets (*Vespa*), carpenter ants, a crane fly, a small dipteran, and a water strider (*Gerris*). Other stomachs (7) from 11 miles east of Gold Beach, contained small beetles, dipterans (mosquitoes and others), a small moth, a water snail, and a piece of molted skin.

Reproduction.—At lower elevations, as in the vicinity of San Francisco Bay, this species breeds from the latter part of March to the first of May (*boylii*) after the high-water stage in streams is past and less sediment is being transported; and at higher altitudes from June to August (*sierrae*), after the high-mountain lakes are free of ice and snow. *Muscosa* may breed somewhat later than *boylii*. A mated pair was seen in Santa Anita Canyon, near Monrovia, April 11, 1910 (Storer, 1925:263). Campbell on May 5, 1929, saw what were evidently the first eggs of the season along the west fork of the San Gabriel River in Los Angeles County, California. Others were observed on May 12. This suggests that this frog, like *Triturus*, spawns later in southern California than its congener to the north (Storer, MS).

EGGS. Deposited in clusters in streams or lakes; 3 gelatinous envelopes present.

COMPARISON OF THE EGGS OF THE SUBSPECIES OF *Rana boylii*
(After Livezey and Wright, 1947: 200)

	boylii	*sierrae*
Jelly envelopes (all firm and distinct)		
Outer	4.0 mm. (3.88 to 4.47 mm.)	7.19 mm. (6.43 to 7.87 mm.)
Middle	2.8 mm. (2.58 to 3.35 mm.)	4.60 mm. (4.25 to 5.0 mm.)
Inner	2.5 mm. (2.32 to 2.94 mm.)	3.93 mm. (3.75 to 4.81 mm.)
Ovum		
Size	2.2 mm. (1.93 to 2.48 mm.)	2.17 mm. (1.81 to 2.30 mm.)
Color	Black above; white below	Black above; light gray tan below
Number of eggs	919 to 1,037±	100 to 350
Appearance of masses	Like compact cluster of grapes, with eggs often firmly attached to one another and individual eggs on surface distinct; clusters measuring 2 x 2 x 1⅕ to 2 x 4 x 2⅖ inches	Plinthlike, about 28 x 40 mm., with ova ¼ to ½ inch apart
Where deposited	Deposited in shallow water near margins of streams, attached to stones (often on downstream side) in stream bed where they may pick up much sediment	Attached to stems of sedge or other vegetation or to bank itself

LARVA. Greatest length of head-and-body, 18 mm.; of tail 29 mm.; length of head-and-body contained 1.2 to 1.8 times in length of tail; external nares midway between tip of snout and orbit; eyes well up on top of head; interorbital space 5 to 9 times in length of head-and-body; spiracle sinistral, aperture directed backward and upward, center of aperture decidedly behind mid-point of body; anus dextral; greatest depth of tail (over fins) 3.3 to 4.2 in its own length; height of muscular portion of tail 4.2 to 6.0 in head-and-body length. (Pl. 33.)

Labial teeth in 7/6 rows, first complete across entire mouth region, second to seventh inclusive interrupted medially, the successive rows progressively shorter; first lower row shorter than first upper row and interrupted medially, second to fifth complete, nearly same length but successively shorter; papillae in single row on lateral and ventral borders of mouth (Storer, 1925:247, subspecies *boylii*). (Pl. 34.)

Wright (1929:27) has described subspecies *sierrae:* Tadpole fairly large (72 mm.), body flatter than most ranid tadpoles; distinctive in that tail musculature is wide and keeps same width for an inch or an inch and one quarter and then suddenly tapers off; tail long, tip bluntly rounded; fins are broader back near tail tip than nearer insertion on body; rear half of tail might be termed elliptical in outline, or tail tip might tend toward spatulate tail; broadest part of tail comes where musculature finally begins to taper; dorsal fin narrow forward and extends on to body to vertical twice as near buds of hind legs as spiracle; spiracle sinistral, below lateral axis, decidedly upturned and somewhat backward in direction, with prominent round or elliptical pore evident; anus dextral, opening on level with edge of ventral fin; muciferous crypts distinct; in preserved material they look like brown or black pigment spots; on either side of dorsal fin for distance back of its body insertion there extends a row of crypts which goes diagonally forward on body and finally joins main dorsolateral row which starts from mid-lateral insertion of tail musculature on body; this lateral series travels to back of eye where supraorbital branch goes over eye and above nostril on to snout above mouth; this same lateral branch sends off an infraorbital branch which in front of eye swings far downward away from nostril and ends near corner of mouth; just back of eye infraorbital branch sends loop upward and then abruptly downward to venter where it goes forward as mandibular branch to mouth; another lateral series low on body runs evenly forward until it loops over spiracle.

Labial teeth 3/4; occasionally in some of young forms they may be 2/4 or rarely 2/3; upper labium fringed with row of teeth much longer than beak (about 1½ times beak); second row of lateral teeth of medium length, about ¼ to 2/9 length of first upper row; median space between second row of upper teeth 1 to 2 3/10 times length of either lateral row; third upper labial row about 1/2 length upper row; lower labium has 4 rows of teeth, first 2 about equal and sometimes third also equal to other 2 or slightly shorter; first row often subdivided and sometimes second row; fourth row equal to single row of lower labial papillae, 1/3 to 1/2 length of first lower row; inner papillae on side of labium extend to end of fourth lower labial row of teeth. (All but the section on teeth applies as well to larva of subspecies *boylii.*)

The larva of the subspecies *boylii,* with its 12 rows of labial teeth, 7 above and 5 below the mouth, approaches in oral structure *Ascaphus truei,* another stream-dwelling type.

Recently hatched larvae may measure 7.3 to 7.7 mm. (subspecies *boylii*). About 3 to 4 months is required for growth to metamorphosis in the race *boylii.* It is possible, owing to a shorter growing period (around 3 months) and to lower environmental temperatures, that larvae of *sierrae* overwinter. Larvae metamorphose in the middle of July to late August in the San Francisco Bay region and probably most often in late summer in the high Sierra. Fully transformed young frogs of the race *boylii,* obtained at San Pablo Creek, Contra Costa County, California, August 7, 1922, measured 23.2 to 30.0 mm. in head-and-body length (Storer, 1925:255).

Key to Subspecies
Plate 20

1*a*. Hind limb relatively shorter, when brought forward inside angle of bent tarsus and tibia seldom reaches beyond nose; tympanum smooth or slightly roughened; dorsolateral folds more pronounced; intermediate in size between *boylii* and *muscosa;* spotted above. *Range.*—Southern half of the Sierra Nevada from the vicinity of Lake Tahoe and northward on the slopes of Mount Rose, Nevada, south to Walker Pass, Kern County, California. Found largely above 7,000 feet, ranging to over 11,000 feet .... *R. b. sierrae* Camp

1*b*. Hind limb relatively longer, when brought forward inside angle of bent tarsus and tibia extends to nose or beyond; tympanum roughened; dorsolateral folds less pronounced; above uniformly colored or with varying degrees of mottling 2

2*a*. Averages smaller, usually under 70 mm.; generally darker; anterior portion of head, from line bisecting upper eyelids, somewhat lighter than rest of body or only anterior half of lids light-colored, dark posterior half merging with body coloration; skin with more definite and numerous papillae than in other races. *Range.*—From Marion County, Oregon, south in California to Santa Barbara County, eastward in north-central part to the Sierran foothills and thence southward at low elevations in the Sierra* .... *R. b. boylii* Baird

* Specimens in the Museum of Vertebrate Zoölogy from the western Sierra foothills have been identified with some uncertainty as *boylii.*

2*b*. Averages larger, to 81 mm.; general color lighter with contrasting irregular markings of blackish or brown; posterior portions of upper eyelids, when darker color present, rather sharply set off from color of body. *Range.*—Southern California south of Ventura County—in the San Gabriel, San Bernardino, and San Jacinto mountains south to San Diego County. .... *R. b. muscosa* Camp

Geographic variation.—It is impossible at the present time to discuss accurately the morphological variation of the subspecies of this frog or to designate clearly areas of intergradation. Much additional study of the ecology and morphology (particularly pigmentation) of the living animals is required. The geographic limits of the subspecies *sierrae* are particularly obscure.

Rana boylii of the western foothills of the Sierra Nevada of California are generally regarded as of the subspecies *boylii*. The relationship of *sierrae* to the foothill form is not wholly clear, but intergradation between them seems to occur at about 2,000 to 3,500 feet. A similar divergence seems to exist on the east side of the Sierra. Specimens from Farrington's near Mono Lake, Mono County, California, appear intermediate in pigmentation (in alcohol) and limb length between *boylii* and *sierrae.* Animals from Lone Pine and Big Pine, at the eastern foot of the Sierra, farther south, are near *boylii* (Storer, MS). Those from several localities in Sequoia National Park are apparently intergrades between *boylii* and *sierrae* with stronger tendencies toward the latter.

An area of intergradation between *boylii* and *sierrae* also seems to exist in the northern Sierra, northwest of Lake Tahoe. The tendency seems to be greatest in the direction of *sierrae,* with *sierrae*-like individuals known as far north as near Mineral, Tehama County, California.

The relationship between *Rana aurora* and *R. cascadae, Bufo boreas* and *B. canorus,* and *R. b. boylii* and *sierrae* may be of a similar type. *Cascadae, canorus,* and *sierrae,* may be high mountain differentiates of, respectively, *R. aurora, B. boreas,* and *R. boylii,* stocks.

Intermediate populations may exist between *muscosa* and *boylii* or *muscosa* and *sierrae* in the Tehachapi Mountains. Animals from Bodfish, Kern County, in the Museum of Vertebrate Zoölogy, are somewhat different from both *sierrae* and *muscosa* in dark mottling of the posterior part of the femora and posterior sides.

Rana b. boylii occurs along the San Gabriel River in the San Gabriel Mountains, Los Angeles County, California, within the range of the race *muscosa* (Marr, 1943:56). According to Richard Zweifel, who is studying this group of frogs, the *boylii* of the San Gabriel River resemble closely, in morphology and habits, coastal *boylii* at the southern extreme of its range. He believes that the former at one time may have been connected with the coastal stock. Coastal *boylii* now range south to the Santa Clara

River, the subspecies *muscosa* north to the Pacoima River. The ranges of the two frogs are separated by only 25 to 30 miles (air line), in drainages on either side of low mountains. There is at present no evidence for overlap in distribution or merging of characters. The relationship between *boylii* and *muscosa* in the drainage of the San Gabriel River is similar on a smaller scale. The *muscosa* occur in faster water in rockier parts of the upper portions of the stream, whereas the *boylii* are found in the quieter water at lower levels, where the stream bed has fewer large boulders.

BULLFROG

Rana catesbeiana Shaw

Plate 22

Range.—Widely distributed in North America. Native east of the Rocky Mountains chiefly east of longitude 98° W. Introduced at numerous localities in the West and in Cuba and the Hawaiian Islands. Introduced in British Columbia, Canada, and in the western United States: in Washington, Idaho, Nevada, Utah, Colorado, Arizona, New Mexico, and California. Found in northern Mexico in the states of Nuevo León, Tamaulipas, and probably Sonora. (Pl. 62.)

The spread of the bullfrog in California has been dramatic. The earliest presumed occurrence dates back to about 1905. In a little over 30 years (Storer, MS) it had become common over most of the Sacramento and San Joaquin valleys, the lowland waters of southern California, in many of the valleys of the Coast Range, and in scattered localities elsewhere. Since 1935 additional dispersal has no doubt occurred. In occupying the Great Valley of California, it has filled a gap in the distribution of our native frogs. The animals are sufficiently abundant to supply the local demand for frog legs and in so doing relieve pressure on our highly palatable native species, the red-legged frog. The state has set a limit of 24 per day or 48 per week (Chapter 459, California Statutes of 1933) in an effort to discourage undue exploitation.

Type locality.—North America (Shaw, 1802:106), evidently South Carolina.

Description.—STRUCTURE. Adult to 8 inches—largest anuran north of Mexican border; skin relatively smooth but sometimes roughened with small tubercles; dorsolateral folds absent; tympanic membrane nearly as large as, or, in males, to over twice as large as eye; ridge extending posteriorly from behind eye around dorsal and posterior portion of tympanum; similar ridge present in some other species but usually not as well defined; web of fourth toe often extends to terminal phalanx; metacarpal tubercles vaguely evident or absent; inner metatarsal tubercle much elongate, oval, round-surfaced; outer tubercle very small or absent; no tarsal fold. COLOR. General coloration above greenish or greenish brown to almost black (region bordering Gulf of Mexico), with or without spots of brown, grading to blackish at centers of larger marks; hind limbs with crossbars of dusky or spotted in varying degrees; below whitish to cream, often with tinge of yellowish on chin and posterior parts; usually faint spots, blotches, bars, and lines of dusky ventrally, sometimes reduced or absent on belly, rather consistently present in gular area; iris may be golden or reddish bronze. JUVENILE. Dark markings on dorsum may be in form of black specks suggestive of markings of tadpole; venter usually well mottled with dusky. SEXUAL DIFFERENCES. Tympanum of sexually mature male (not true of immatures) much larger than eye—dark brown marginally; about same size as eye and colored like head in female; male often with yellowish throat as in *clamitans;* female more brown and spotted than male—male more nearly uniformly green (Dickerson, 1920: 230); first finger short and swollen basally in breeding male; under magnification its inner surface from swollen basal portion to tip seen to be covered with numerous closely set tubercles that give skin granular appearance.

Adult male, RCS 2915, obtained June 20, 1949, 2 miles south of Beatty, Nye County, Nevada: Generally green dorsally, brightest on head; scattered dusky blotches and reticulations on back; below whitish with pale yellow tinge on either side of gular area; iris pale yellow with coppery highlights.

Habitat.—Ponds, reservoirs, marshes, and other quiet permanent water providing both depths and shallows and abundant cover. Ponds with mud bottoms are often frequented.

Near Beatty, Nye County, Nevada, on June 20–21, 1949, I explored the margins of several pools along the Amargosa River on the east side of U.S. Highway 99, south of Beatty. The river dwindles rapidly south of town. The pools were largely surrounded by a fairly dense growth of sedges, about 3 feet in height. The banks were generally steep, sloping 45° or more but in some places only 10 to 20°. One pool was 30 feet long by 10 to 12 feet across and generally 1 to 2 feet deep, although in one place it was nearly 4 feet in depth. The water was clear and quiet but that between pools was shallow and riffly. The surface, except in the faster water, was in large part covered with mats of algal scum and there was dark green filamentous alga on the bottom in several places. The mud was grayish, blackish, and buff.

Eight large tadpoles were seen in one of the larger pools. Several were just under the surface scum and were revealed when it was moved. In a shallow place at the side of the pool, where there was considerable growth of dark green algae on the bottom, 5 tadpoles swam rapidly toward deeper water when the scum was moved. Adult frogs were found basking between 8:30 and 9:30 A.M. in open places in the sedge border of the pool. All seen were facing the water and upon my approach leaped into the pool, several squawking as they did so.

Behavior.—Closely restricted to water but may leave it in wet weather. Capable of marked color change from almost black through a dark spotted phase to a spotless yellowish green. This frog is a good swimmer and jumper. An adult may cover 4 to 6 feet at a leap. On several occasions I have had individuals "play possum," becoming limp in my grasp. Hibernates in the colder portions of its range. In Richmond County, Georgia, Neill (1948:108) found this species hibernated "Beneath stones, logs, or piles of trash near or in the water; also in tunnels beneath the banks of streams. Occasional specimens are found in winter beneath small stones or bark scraps that scarcely suffice to cover their bulk." During the breeding period, in ponds where their numbers are not excessively great, adult males may establish croaking posts and individuals may be found repeatedly at some favored location.

Raney (1940:744) reports the following on the behavior of this species in New York. Just before and during the spawning season the behavior of males and females is quite different. During daylight hours both sexes are usually to be found along the water's edge under the alders and other shrubs. At night the males move out into the shallow water among emergent grasses, take positions and give their typical bass call notes. The females, however, stay close to the shore line unless they are ripe. When ready to spawn they make their way to the area occupied by the males. After the height of the breeding season is past, the males tend to stay closer to shore both during day and night, although an occasional individual may be found 20 to 30 feet from shore.

Throughout summer there is great variation in the distance individuals of both sexes as well as juveniles will move. Some are relatively stable, moving only 100 feet or less throughout summer, while others move long distances (up to 3,000 feet). These movements did not appear to be correlated with spawning, food-getting, changes in temperature, or other factors. Those frogs which do move usually travel after dark during or after rain. Bullfrogs living in small pools either along stream beds or isolated ponds tend to remain in these pools all summer if the water level is maintained. Little evidence was found of well-developed homing behavior.

Voice.—Well developed: deep-pitched, hoarse, and bellowing, suggesting "jug-o'-rum," "more rum," "br-wum," "better go around," "be drowned," etc.

Smith (1934:484, Kansas) says, "When singing enthusiastically they call about three to four times in about twice as many seconds, are silent for about five minutes, and then repeat."

Pope (1944:116-17) has suggested the voice may be imitated by the shouting of a prolonged "rum" into an empty barrel as deeply and loudly as possible. The female can call like the male but with less force. When the frog is in pain or shock an almost human scream may be uttered. A "yelping snurp" may be given as the frog dives when startled.

The vocal sacs are paired, internal and lateral. Dickerson (1920:231) says males of this species in Wisconsin and adjoining regions have vocal pouches resembling those of the leopard frog.

Food.—The following items have been recorded: earthworms; snails; crustaceans—crayfish and a copepod (latter probably taken by accident); spiders; insects—grasshoppers, dragonflies (the adults, so far as could be determined, were all females and might have been obtained while ovipositing), an ephemerid (single nymph of *Siphlurus alternatus,* probably taken under water), hemipterans (water striders—*Gerris*), neuropterans, trichopterans (caddisflies—with a single exception all teneral imagos, captured probably as they came to the surface in transformation), lepidopterans (moth larvae), dipterans (tipulids, chironomids [single adult and 11 pupae], stratiomyids, syrphids, tabanids [single adult], and tachinids), beetles (scarabaeids, chrysomelids, curculionids [single adult], carabids, and a single larval elaterid), hymenopterans (ants [*Camponotus* and others], *Bombus,* a wasp [*Vespa*], a saw-fly larva); vertebrates—small fish, frogs, and their larvae (including larvae of own species), snakes (garter snakes and a coral snake [*Micrurus fulvius tenere*] 17 inches in length [Minton, 1949:288]), turtles (probably uncommonly), a young alligator, birds (ducklings, sparrows, a swallow, a brown towhee [*Pipilo fuscus*], and a yellow-throat [*Geothlypis*]), mammals (meadow mice and others). (Frost, 1935; Minton, 1949:288; Needham, 1905; Munz, 1920:55.)

Frost (1935:17) states, "The bullfrog has a singular method of accepting its food, preferring to take it under water. Sometimes it snatches a morsel of food on the bank of a stream or pond but invariably jumps into the water and submerges to swallow. This has been observed a number of times in nature and in captivity."

The larva feeds on diatoms and algae but also shows scavenging tendencies and will take some animal food.

Reproduction.—Season from February to July (Livezey and Wright, 1947:190), with breeding occurring in June and July in northern areas and as early as mid-February in the south (as in Texas). Generally viewed as a late breeder. Employs pectoral embrace.

EGGS. Deposited as surface film, mass 144 to 675 square inches (2.5′ by 0.5′ to 3′ by 5′), in form of disc; 10,000 to 20,000 eggs per complement; deposited among water plants or brush; egg with single gelatinous envelope, 6.4 to 10.4 mm., average 7.6 mm., loose and merges into mass; ovum 1.2 to 1.7 mm., average 1.3 mm., black above and white or cream below (Livezey and Wright, 1947:190).

LARVA. Total length 113 to 135 mm.; head-and-body 41-50 mm.; greatest width of body 22.0-30.3 mm.; internarial width 5.3-6.0 mm.; interorbital width 8.0-12.5 mm.; spiracle sinistral, aperture directed backward and slightly upward, center of aperture about midway on body, on or near lateral axis; greatest height over tail fins 25 mm.; height of muscular part of tail 12-17 mm.; greatest width across mouth region 7.8 mm. (Pl. 33.)

Labial teeth in 2/3 or 3/3 rows, first upper row complete, next divided, represented by segment on either side of mouth, third row (if present) including only few teeth on either side; first lower row divided in midline, second complete across entire mouth region, third undivided but shorter than second; papillae at sides of mouth in 3 rows, extending in part along lower border; one row of papillae bordering mouth region mid-ventrally. (Pl. 34.)

Coloration in life: dorsal surface of body greenish olive to dark olive, with many minute specks of black; sides of tail with spots (up to 2 mm. in diameter) of yellow; ventral surface of body yellow to white, sometimes mottled with dusky, not iridescent; iris golden yellow. (Larval description largely from Storer, 1925:277, based on second-year tadpoles from Sonoma Creek, Sonoma County, and Standard, Tuolumne County, California.)

Eggs usually hatch in 4 to 5 days, or sometimes less according to temperatures (Smith, 1934:485, Kansas). Transformation in New York (Wright, 1914:85-86) usually takes place in July or later, 2 years after deposition of the eggs. Rarely a third winter may be spent in the tadpole stage. Klimstra (1949:231) found that only one winter was spent in the tadpole stage in Davis County, southeastern Iowa, where the frogs entered and bred in an artificial pond. Great range in size may exist at transformation, for example from 43 to 59 mm., with 53 mm., average. This variation is probably related to the lengthy larval period, inequalities in

Comparison of Larvae of *Rana aurora draytonii* and *Rana catesbeiana*
(From Storer, 1925:244)

	Rana aurora draytonii	*Rana catesbeiana*
	Larva from pond in marshes at south end of Tomales Bay, Marin County, California	Larva from creek pool near Farmington, San Joaquin County, California
Snout	More pointed in outline as viewed from above	More rounded in outline
Eyes	Rather close together	Farther separated
Body	Broadest posterior to spiracle, ended behind abruptly	Broadest anterior to spiracle, tapering behind gradually into tail
Tail	Greatest height posterior to midpoint, bluntly tapered toward end Broader at base as viewed from above	Greatest height anterior to midpoint, sharply tapered toward end Narrower at base as viewed from above
Dorsal ground color	Dark browns and yellows	Olive green of light or dark tone
Spots on body	Diffuse-margined, more than 1 mm. in diameter	Sharp-margined, not over 1 mm. in diameter
Ventral surface	Center of belly with *pinkish iridescence*, margins mixed iridescent and blackish in fine pattern	Center of belly whitish, *not iridescent*, margins mottled with dark pattern of large size
Tail	Mottled with light spots	With small dark dots as on dorsal surface of body

For a comparison with the larvae of *Rana clamitans* see page 354.

growth occurring due to varying conditions during this period. Smith (1934:485, Kansas) observes that recently transformed individuals are common and even numerous about pools early in the spring, much earlier than the adults appear.

Remarks.—Raney and Ingram (1941:203) report on growth in this species in New York. The study was based on observation of marked individuals. Frogs which transformed July 16 to August 28, 1940, did so at an average length of 45 mm. (range 27 to 53 mm.). An average-sized bullfrog which transformed during the last 2 weeks in July would reach maturity in late August of the following year at a size ranging from 85 to 105 mm. It would be capable of spawning the following July, 2 years from the time of transformation. Some slower-growing individuals may not reach maturity until 3 years have elapsed, not spawning until 4 years after transformation. Very close to maximum length may be reached by the average adult in 2 to 3 years after transformation. One individual lived 15 years, 8 months in the London Zoölogical Gardens. Two others lived over 7 years and 4 others lived from over 4 to over 6 years (Flower, 1925:272).

GREEN FROG

Rana clamitans Latreille
Plate 22

Range.—Eastern North America from Canada, south to Florida (absent from the southern half) and Louisiana, west to eastern Minnesota, Iowa, extreme eastern Kansas, southeastern Oklahoma, and southeastern Texas. Introduced into western Washington and southwestern British Columbia. (Pl. 62.)

Slater (1939a:4) reports, "On May 10, 1930, while hunting around Toad Lake, Whatcom County, I found some young *Rana clamitans* and on two visits to that lake since then, we have also taken specimens of this green frog. . . . It was supposedly introduced along with some bullfrog tadpoles from Michigan about twenty years ago. It seems to be on the increase along with the bullfrog. . . ."

Type locality.—Charleston, South Carolina (Latreille, 1802:157-58; see Sonnini and Latreille, 1802).

Description.—Adult usually under 4 inches, rarely to 5; said to be smaller in southern part of range; resembles *R. catesbeiana* but differs in having well-defined dorsolateral folds (seldom extending much posterior to sacral hump), webbing of hind foot slightly less developed, not reaching tip of fourth toe (commonly joining toe at base of second phalanx from tip of toe), and yellowish-white streak along edge of upper jaw extending posteriorly to shoulder (most evident in life). Other characteristics: above brown, greenish brown, or dusky olive, sometimes with black spots, usually posteriorly; head and shoulders bright green; below white, sometimes with faint dusky mottlings in gular area, on chest and undersides of femora; legs above have dusky bars or spots; hind part of femur has spots and blotches of dusky; iris golden. JUVENILE. Eyes and head relatively larger in relation to size of body than in adult; dorsolateral folds may be evident even in recently metamorphosed young; dorsal pattern of scattered small dark spots; limbs speckled and blotched with dark color; below whitish, gular area faintly flecked with dusky. SEXUAL DIFFERENCES. Male with yellow or orange-yellow throat and with eardrum much larger than eye, with greenish-yellow spot or ring at its center.

Female lacks yellow color on throat, has considerably smaller tympanum, narrower head, and may be more smooth-skinned and larger than male. In male during breeding period enlargement of thumbs (first finger) and webs occurs similar to that in other species of *Rana.*

Habitat.—Similar to that of *R. catesbeiana* but requires less cover and is less restricted. The species is decidedly aquatic, inhabiting lakes, large ponds (swamps), rivers, and cold springs (Logier, 1937:13). It also occurs in smaller pools and ponds, not inhabited by *R. catesbeiana.* Ranges to 4,200 feet in North Carolina (Pope, 1944:127).

Behavior.—Solitary, except during the breeding period. Hibernates in winter.

Voice.—Logier (1937:13) describes the note as an explosive bass "bung" or "plung," sounding much like the plucking of an elastic cord stretched not too tightly over an empty box. It is often repeated several times or may be followed by several croaking notes. Francis Harper says ". . . its twanging bass note is heard at considerable and probably irregular intervals, of, say, half a minute or more." Ordinarily a single "clung" or "c'tung" is given; but sometimes there is a rather rapid series of several notes: "clung-clung-clung-clung" or "c'tung." The note is not loud nor does it carry far (Wright, 1932:357).

A nasal "ch-u-n-ng" or "k-tun-n-ng" of low pitch is given by the older frogs when they jump for water. Their croaking is different. It is explosive, prolonged, low-pitched and is likely to be repeated 5 or 6 times in succession. When given with less than usual force, it may sound like the drumming of a woodpecker. It can be imitated by the cutting of some kind of coarse, resisting cloth on a table with heavy shears. This frog is known as the "screaming frog" because of a short, high-pitched cry given when an individual is frightened. It is commonly given when the frog leaps into the air and dives to safety. It is given particularly by young animals (after Dickerson, 1920:199).

Vocal sacs paired and lateral, the throat appearing as a flattened pouch when inflated.

Food.—Principally insects and other arthropods. Frost (1935:16) mentions that crayfish and small frogs were taken from the stomachs of large individuals.

Hamilton (1948b:204, 206) found the following food items in the stomachs of 434 individuals of various sizes (27 to 97 mm.) obtained from May to October over several years in New York State (figures are percentages of frequency of occurrence): coleopterans (41.9), dipterans (25.8), orthopterans (13.4), caterpillars (17.9), hymenopterans (4.6), arachnids (12.0), cast skin (*Rana clamitans*) (4.6), hemipterans (8.7), amphibians (frogs) (3.7), mollusks (4.6), crustaceans (2.8), millipedes (3.2), lepidopterans (adults) (2.8), earthworms (1.4), fishes (0.9), odonatans (1.6), mecopterans (1.4), ephemerids (1.4), centipedes (1.4), mites (1.8), undetermined insects (2.8). The presence of small fishes, tadpoles, and aquatic insect larvae strongly suggested that some food is captured beneath the surface of the water.

Munz (1920:55, Ithaca, New York) found that the green frog, although a form remaining close to the water, lives very largely on nonaquatic insects.

Reproduction.—Breeds from May to mid-August in the eastern United States (Wright, 1932:359). Logier (1937:13) states that most of the egg-laying probably occurs in late May and early June in southern Ontario, Canada.

"After a male has successfully attached himself to a receptive female, the latter lowers the head, often enough to submerge it, bows the back downward so that her cloaca is raised just out of the water, and extends her hind limbs, spreading them well apart. The male then shifts himself far forward, moving his hind limbs so that their shanks rest on his laterally projecting thighs. . . . Now, as the female's abdomen contracts, the male moves his feet still farther forward, bringing them almost together and placing his heels anterior to the two cloacas. About the same time, the female expels a batch of thirty to fifty eggs that spread out between the male's feet, come near to or actually touch his cloaca, and (presumably) are suffused with seminal fluid emitted by him. . . . Next, he pushes the eggs away so they spread out at the surface a short distance behind the pair. . . . New abdominal contractions initiate a second cycle of these characteristic movements, which continue rhythmically until the female is spent, from ten to twenty-five minutes later." (Pope, 1944:122-23.)

EGGS. Deposited as surface film, less than 1 square foot in extent (5 to 7 inches by 12 inches); usually deposited around margins of permanent ponds, either attached to vegetation or free; usually 1,000 to 5,000 eggs per mass, in single layer sharply outlined on surface; eggs with 2 gelatinous envelopes, inner one 2.8 to 4.0 mm., average 3.3 mm., circular, elliptical, or pyriform, always distinct; outer one 5.0 to 6.0 mm., average 5.7 mm., indistinct, merges into jelly film; ovum 1.2 to 1.8 mm., average 1.5 mm., black above and white below; capsule may be rather remote from ovum (Livezey and Wright, 1947:190). In New York eggs hatch in 3 to 6 days according to Wright (1914:75).

LARVA. Resembles that of *R. catesbeiana:* tadpole large, not deep-bodied; length of body, 12.2 to 27.8 mm., tail, 18.4 to 57.0 mm.; tail fairly elongate, tip acute; dorsal fin not as wide as musculature, extending forward on body slightly ahead of vertical of buds of hind legs; spiracle sinistral, just visible from dorsal aspect, directed obliquely upward and backward; spiracle below lateral axis; spiracular opening elliptical; muciferous crypts distinct in life, indistinct in most preserved specimens; eye on or above lateral axis and nearer lateral outline in dorsal aspect than mid-dorsal line; anus dextral, opening on level with edge of ventral fin. (Pl. 33.)

Labial teeth ⅔ or ⅓; edge of upper labium fringed with teeth and about equal to upper horny beak in length; in either corner beneath this fringe, a short row (sometimes absent) from $2/15$ to $1/15$ upper row; ends of lateral rows not extending beyond end of upper row; median space between lateral rows 6 to 11 times length of either row; first lower labial row slightly longer or equal to horny beaks in length, and sometimes divided in middle; second row almost equal to first; third row quite short, not nearly as long as in *R. catesbeiana,* usually almost ½ of first row, not ¾ or ⅘ as in *R. catesbeiana,* contained 1½ times in horny beak and much shorter than single row of lower labial papillae; on side of labium inner papillae (inside outer row) extend mesially beyond and beneath second lower labial tooth row, but not to third row. (Pl. 34.)

Background of back dark and covered with fine yellow spots, the whole consequently having an olive green color with numerous distinct dark spots; belly deep cream without decided iridescence; throat and sides mottled with dark green; slight coppery iridescence on venter, more de-

Comparison of Larvae of *Rana clamitans* and *Rana catesbeiana*
(From Orton, 1951, based on larvae from
Camp Crowder, Newton County, Missouri)

	Rana clamitans	*Rana catesbeiana*
Size	Smaller, reaching total length of about 60-100 mm.	Larger, reaching total length of about 75-160 mm.
Labial teeth	Second upper tooth row often very short, sometimes absent	Second upper tooth row well developed and a third upper row often present in large larvae
Dorsal background color	Browner	Greener
Dorsal pattern	Mottled or blotched, sometimes tending to be black dotted	Surface of head, body, and tail heavily peppered with sharply defined black dots
Tail pattern	Distal portion not modified by pigmented internal blood vessels	Young larvae (to about 40 mm. total length) with heavily pigmented blood vessel showing through translucent distal third of tail muscle, forming conspicuous but obviously internal (rather than dermal) dark line

cided on sides and on tail; tail appears green, mottled with brown, covered with fine yellow spots like back (Wright, 1929:45).

In New York, according to Wright (1914:76), the larval period appears to be from 370 to 400 days. Usually by the first of August, transformation is largely but not wholly completed; size at transformation (41 specimens) varies from 28 to 38 mm., average 32 mm.

Ting (1951) reports that in the laboratory transformation occurred as early as 92 days after insemination of the eggs but the majority of larvae transformed 113 days after insemination. The eggs in this study were obtained from a female procured at Columbus, Ohio. He thinks that early breeders produce larvae that should be able to transform the same year the eggs are laid. Larvae from late breeders possibly do not transform until the next year.

A transformed individual lived over 10 years in the London Zoölogical Gardens; 2 others over 7 years; and 3 others lived over 4 to over 5 years (Flower, 1925:273).

LEOPARD FROG

Rana pipiens Schreber
Plate 23

Range.—From southern Canada throughout the United States, although sparingly represented in the Pacific states, south to Nicaragua. In the West it ranges into southeastern British Columbia, eastern Washington, eastern Oregon, northeastern, east-central, and southeastern California. As regards the Californian records for this species, it has possibly been introduced artificially at Lake City and Alturas, Modoc County, and is known to have been introduced at Lake Tahoe (Bryant, *California Fish and Game,* 1917:90). It also has been introduced at Fallen Leaf Lake, California (Storer, MS). As to the Imperial Valley occurrence, Storer (MS) suggests that it may have lived in the Colorado overflow lakes—Blue, Mesquite, Badger, Pelican, etc.—or it has come in with irrigation. In Mexico it occurs on the plateau and in the lowlands. It has been recorded from every state and territory except Quintana Roo (Smith and Taylor, 1948:98). (Pl. 63.)

Type locality.—North America: Raccoon, Gloucester County, New Jersey (Schreber, 1782:185).

Description.—STRUCTURE. Adult 2¼ to slightly over 4 inches; skin smooth or somewhat tubercular; dorsolateral folds present; 3 rather vaguely defined metatarsal tubercles, sometimes not evident, arranged in transverse row; elongate oval, round-edged, inner metatarsal tubercle; outer tubercle very small or absent; tarsal fold more or less well developed. COLOR. Above greenish, brownish, or gray, with conspicuous oval and rounded olive-green, dark brown, or black spots outlined with color lighter than ground color; spots between dorsolateral folds commonly in 2 or 3 irregular rows, but number, size, and arrangement of spots subject to considerable variation; when in extreme light or dark phases, spots may be obscure; spots may occasionally be entirely lacking as in form *burnsi,* recognized by some as a subspecies; light line along upper jaw extending toward shoulder; dorsolateral folds usually light-colored, bronze or yellowish in life; below cream to whitish, usually grading to yellow posteriorly, including ventral surfaces of hind limbs; ventral surfaces generally unspotted, but sometimes throat, chest, and upper abdomen variegated with dusky; hind limbs above with crossbands and spots of dark brown to blackish, outlined with whitish; iris bronze to dusky. JUVENILE. Sometimes unspotted and in some populations, at least, with less yellow color ventrally. SEXUAL DIFFERENCES. Male with lateral external or internal vocal sacs between shoulder and tympanum; tympanum not enlarged or rarely so; male at breeding season with much enlarged first finger with pad on inner side (present throughout year) and convex webs on hind feet; male may become darker than female.

Combined description of 4 adults, RCS 3004-7, obtained June 27, 1949, 1 mile west of Provo, shore of Utah Lake, Utah County, Utah: Two are light green above, the others gray and brown; spots on dorsum of darker individuals suffused with brown centrally, grading peripherally to narrow margin of black; greenish animals have greenish suffusion in center of sooty spots; dorsolateral folds cream to ashy white in all individuals; ground color of sides gray; below white except for dull yellow on undersides of feet; light greenish-yellow suffusion in groin; gray and brown individuals with greenish color on upper surface of femora; iris with horizontal bar of gold, lower side coinciding with pupil; pale gold patch in lower iris, broken by thin vertical line of blackish, extending to pupil; light marks above and below pupil connected by golden pupillary margin.

Adult, RCS 3168, obtained July 11, 1949, 0.6 miles west-southwest of Imperial Diversion Dam, Imperial County, California: Ground color above light olive gray; spots sooty brown, not edged with white; dorsolateral folds about same as ground color; dull orange yellow in groin, on anterior and posterior surface of femur, and posterior surface of tibia; below white anteriorly but flecked laterally in gular region and on chest and abdomen with light orange yellow; underside of hind limbs, lower abdomen and forelimbs, particularly distally, uniformly orange yellow; iris about as RCS 3004-7 but somewhat less light color.

Adult, RCS 3228, obtained July 15, 1949, 4 miles north-northwest of Nogales, Santa Cruz County, Arizona: Olive green above; dorsal spots small and numerous, black with greenish suffusion centrally; tympanum brownish; yellow on posterior and anterior surfaces of femora; below white with yellow color about as RCS 3168; iris as in first description.

Adult, RCS 3384, obtained August 1, 1949, 1 mile above XSX Ranch, East Fork of the Gila River, Grant County, New Mexico: Snout, side of muzzle to below eye, upper surface of head, and upper back yellowish green; ground color of upper surface of hind limbs and lower back brownish gray with olive cast; spots and bars light brownish olive, grading to sooty peripherally, edged with yellow green; dorsolateral folds slightly lighter than ground color of hind limbs; below whitish with dull yellow in groin and extending out onto anterior surface of femur and short distance anteriorly on sides; iris as described earlier.

Adult, RCS 3465, obtained August 22, 1949, 10.9 miles by road west of Hebron, Jackson County, Colorado: Ground color above ash gray with brownish cast; spots inky black edged with ashy; ventral surfaces whitish, without yellow; groin with pale greenish-yellow cast; iris essentially as above.

Habitat.—The leopard frog is a highly adaptable species. It occurs in a great variety of environmental situations. As Burt and Burt (1929:433) point out, it may occur in either clear or muddy water; in shallow ponds or deep ones; in springs, in creeks, or in rivers; and in mountains or lowlands. Its distribution in the typical part of its range seems to be limited only by its ability to reach permanent bodies of water. The species prefers cattail swamps, marshy expanses of other types, grassy overflows, and shallow dead streams. It may frequent irrigation canals. It is usually closely confined to the vicinity of water but may occur considerable distances from water. It possibly has entered extreme southeastern California, with the development of irrigation. (Pl. 45, fig. 1.)

"In the desert areas which this frog inhabits it is generally found along irrigation ditches and the banks of rivers. In the mountain districts it inhabits the grassy meadows, ponds, lakes, and streams. It travels long distances overland and may be found in wet grassy areas a mile or more from the nearest water." (Slevin, 1928:125.)

I have found this species in almost every conceivable situation. The following list will illustrate this variety: (1) a grassy meadow with a clear meandering stream; willow-cottonwood association with water cress and an elodea-like plant in the stream; (2) sedge- and tule-bordered pond on a high plateau covered with basin sagebrush; (3) a grassy field near the tule and sedge-fringe of a lake margin; (4) an irrigation canal with a grass-mat border and with algal scum on the water; (5) tule- and weed-bordered reservoir in mesquite woodland; (6) muddy cattle wallow of a drying water hole in oak woodland; (7) sycamore- and willow-bordered stream in piñon-juniper country; (8) meadow and lake border in yellow pine-oak country; (9) warm mineral springs; (10) temporary rain pool.

Behavior.—This frog is an active, agile species, an excellent jumper and swimmer. Sunning or foraging individuals may often be found some distance from water, but usually close enough so that it can be reached in several jumps. A pursued animal may jump 6 feet or more, especially when aided by a gentle slope, often leaping in a zigzag course. Upon their jumping, fluid, principally water, may be released from the vent. It is often disagreeable in odor. These frogs may hibernate in mud beneath stones and other objects in aquatic situations. Breckenridge (1944:85) in Minnesota reports hundreds of closely crowded individuals in unfrozen water below a dam. The frogs were in water 18 to 24 inches deep, resting on the sand bottom, several yards below the dam. They were not entirely dormant.

At Lakeside, Navajo County, Arizona, on July 29, 1949, I looked for *Hyla wrightorum*. There were several large bodies of water with many clumps of green filamentous algae and submerged waterweeds. As we walked about the pond margins, many *R. pipiens* leaped into the water. In grassy places where concealment was afforded, individuals would almost allow us to step on them before they took to the water. This they could do in most instances in a single leap but a number required 3 or 4 jumps to reach safety. One adult was found on a sunny slope 15 feet from the pond. Upon reaching the water, they would swim rapidly, darting about in a zigzag fashion, coming to rest in a cloud of sediment kicked up as they buried themselves in mud at the bottom or beneath a mass of algae. I heard none make a sound upon being startled. In one small pond about a dozen were seen. Duckweed formed a carpet of green over the surface. The frogs were difficult to see, for when their heads and foreparts emerged, the duckweed clung to their bodies, effectively concealing them. Most individuals were light green in color and when sitting on an algal mat offshore or when in the grass on the bank, they blended well with their surroundings.

Voice.—Wright (1914:53) describes the voice as a long, low, guttural note, 3 or more seconds long, followed by 3 to 6 short notes each a second or less in length. At other times the short notes may precede, or the long and short notes be interspersed in innumerable ways, or the song may be composed entirely of either short or long notes. May croak from below the surface of the water.

Smith (1934:497) says, "In Kansas the song is typically a low chuckling of varied frequency not exceeding 2 or 3 chuckles a second. The sound is scarcely audible, even in a large chorus, more than 150–200 feet away."

Dickerson (1920:176) says moaning or grunting sounds, low-pitched, throaty, and vibrant are given by the males and females during the breeding period.

Noble and Aronson (1942:128-29) have studied sexual behavior in this

THERMAL DATA

Locality	*Date* (1949)	*Time*	*Size*	*Temperature, °C.*			*Condition of occurrence*
				Body	*Substratum*	*Air*	
Utah							
1 mi. E of Murray, Salt Lake Co.	June 24	5:15 P.M.	large larvae and adults		20.8 (water)	22.6 (3″ above ground)	Animals in stream
1 mi. E of Murray, Salt Lake Co.	June 24	4:40 P.M.	adult		18.8 (water)	25.5 (3″ above ground)	Riffly area in stream
1 mi. E of Murray, Salt Lake Co.	June 24	5:30 P.M.	larvae		29.4 (water)		Quiet pool
1 mi. W of Provo, shore Utah Lake, Utah Co.	June 27	10:40 A.M.	adult	23.5	33.0 (damp soil in sun)	20.0 (3″ above ground)	50 feet from water, hopping in open grassy area
Bloomington, Wash. Co.	July 2	11:30 A.M.	larvae		19.4 (water)		In cooler water from spring. Water 34.6°C. available but not used
New Mexico							
1 mi. above XSX Ranch, E Fork of Gila River, Grant Co.	Aug. 1	2:00 P.M.	nearly adult		42.0 (mud)	40.3°	Dove into mud at bottom of hot spring and remained 2–3 minutes
Colorado							
10.9 mi. (by road) W of Hebron, Jackson Co.	Aug. 22	4:30 P.M.	adults		25.5 (water)		Animals frequently took refuge in stream with this temperature
4.3 mi. SE of Colorado Springs, El Paso Co.	Aug. 18	11:15 A.M.	young		24.6 (water)		At edge of creek in moderate flow of water

species. The male emits two kinds of croaks: "a sex call and a warning croak." The female gives only the warning croak but more softly than the male. The sex call of the male is represented phonetically as an "ir-a-a-a ——a-a-h" lasting about 3 seconds. The sound is quavering, starting softly and growing louder as the vocal sacs become completely inflated. Often 3 or more short "rah-rah-rah's" follow the initial vocalization. The call is most often heard during the breeding period. The warning croak is described as "ir-a-a-a-h—ir-a-a-h——ir-a-a-h," etc. It is given when the back or sides of the male are touched. There is also a cry of pain like that of a young chicken. A chorus may be so subdued it may go unnoticed. The females give only a weak warning croak.

At Fort Huachuca, Cochise County, Arizona, on July 21, 1949, from 11:00 to 11:45 P.M., we heard a chorus of *Rana pipiens*. It was composed of from perhaps 30 to 50 calling individuals, situated in shallow water among tules on one side of a large pond, 100 yards long by 40 yards wide. The voicings of an adult male were timed as follows: (½) 16 (½) 26 (½) 10 (½) 10 (1) 7 (1¼) 4 (1) 10 (1½) 8 (1¼) 12 (1) 13 (1¼) 6 (1¼) 8 (1¼) 10 (¾) 15 (¾) 12 (1) 8 (1¼) 18 (1) 4 (1) 14 (1¼) 9 (¾) 5 (1) 10 (1) 7 (1½). The numbers in parentheses are the lengths of the calls in seconds, the others the intervals. The chorus fluctuated in intensity, building up and dying out. The individual calls came faster with crescendo of the chorus. The call suggested a distant, slow, motorboat sound or a snore. There was variation in rate and pitch of the vibrations among the singers. The rate of the separate sounds, in a given call, changed but little, if at all. The call started and ended weakly and, when the call was long, was strongest at the mid-point. Short calls terminated abruptly, did not lower in pitch as did the longer ones. Grunts or owllike hoots were also heard. These sounds were pitched at D above middle C or ½ to 1 note lower. They are not indicated in the foregoing record. They were most often given during the longer intervals.

A croaking male observed by Wm. Riemer was found in about 4 to 6 inches of water, supporting himself with his forelimbs against a tuft of emergent grass. His head was out of the water. The vocal sacs expanded laterally over the limb insertions. They inflated slowly and reached their fullest extent only at the end of the call. When distended they were about ¾ inch long, ½ inch high, and extended laterally ½ inch. They were half submerged when inflated. At the end of the call the gular area was expanded suddenly. Interspersed between the long "motorboat" calls were short grunts. The vocal pouches expanded ⅓ to ½ their capacity when the frog grunted. The animal responded well to imitation.

Food.—The following food items have been recorded for the species in the western part of its range: A leech; snails; sowbugs; spiders; insects

—orthopterans (short-horned [nymphal and adult] and long-horned grasshoppers), field crickets; a stonefly adult; naiads and mature damselflies; a Mayfly naiad; hemipterans (injurious plant bugs [*Lygus elisus, L. hesperus*], pentatomids, water striders, a back swimmer, and saldids), trichopterans, lepidopterans (adults and larvae, including sugar-beet webworms, cutworms, and a zebra caterpillar), dipterans (a house fly, blow flies, mosquitoes [including their eggs], midges, dolichopodids, and a deer fly [*Chrysops discalis*]), homopterans (adult and nymphal leaf-hoppers, pea and English grain aphids), beetles (click-beetles, a leaf beetle, scarabaeids, carabids, cicindelids, alfalfa and other weevils, ground beetles [*Eleodes,* etc.], ladybird beetles [*Hippodamia convergens* and thirteen-spotted ladybirds], silphids, staphylinids, dermestids, hydrophilids, adult and larval dytiscids), hymenopterans (ants, wasps [a vespid, sphecids, and a chrysidid], bees [a honey bee, a bumble bee, and a halictid bee], an ichneumonid); vertebrates—small fish, amphibians (tadpoles, recently shed frog skin, smaller individuals of the same and other species), reptiles (small garter snake); birds (ruby-throated hummingbirds and a yellow warbler). (Knowlton, 1944:119; Tanner, 1931:192; Breckenridge, 1944:85.) Authors who have written of the food habits of the species in other parts of its range are, Drake (1914:263-69), Klugh (1922:14-15), Kirn (1949:84), and Kilby (1945).

Reproduction.—Season over entire range February to December with crests from April to August.

Noble and Aronson (1942:129-30) studied the sexual behavior of this species. Amplexus is normally pectoral. The male arches his back convexly with his ventral surface close against the back of the female and his hind legs tightly flexed. After a few minutes to a full day of clasping, the female begins "backward shuffling" movements, moving her hind legs in such a manner as to cause her to move backward. The movements alternate with periods of rest and normal swimming. Finally the female assumes the posture for oviposition with her legs extended backward, her knees bent outward and her feet together to form a diamond-shaped enclosure. At this time the male shifts slightly forward. The female starts oviposition by a sharp contraction of her abdominal walls followed by a concave arching of her back. The male responds to the female's abdominal contraction by spreading his hind legs slightly and arching his back convexly, thus drawing his cloaca forward (upstroke). He responds to the female's arching back by straightening out the arch of the upstroke which brought his cloaca caudally past the female's and by pressing his legs against the female's abdominal wall (downstroke).

This complex of movements is called by Noble and Aronson, the "ejaculatory pump." Following each pump, a cluster of eggs is ejected from the female's cloaca, and sperm is emitted from the male's. Pumps average 16 (10 to 23) per egg laying. Length of time in the egg-laying posture varied from 2 to 8 minutes (average 4 minutes). The male normally releases the female at or shortly after movement out of the oviposition posture.

Noble and Aronson (1942:140-41) conclude the following in regard to the normal mating pattern of *Rana pipiens:*

"a. The male shows no ability to discriminate between a male, female, or pair at a distance.

"b. Sex recognition in *Rana pipiens* occurs only after the male has attempted to clasp the sex object and depends upon the girth and warning voice of the female. Small girth plus the warning croak cause the clasping male to release. Large girth and absence of the warning croak (silence) cause the male to maintain his clasp.

"c. Oviposition reflexes of the female never occur normally without the initial stimulus of a clapsing male. It is possible to elicit these reflexes experimentally by the use of mechanical devices which simulate the male's clasp.

"d. Ejaculatory pumps of the male follow the egg-laying movements of the female. The ventral surface of the male's body, particularly the pectoral region and ventral surface of the forelimbs, is presumably sensitive to the female's oviposition movements.

"e. Pseudo-oviposition (egg-laying reflexes) can be induced in gravid, nonovulated females which have been given intraperitoneal injections of physiological saline solution. Pseudo-oviposition includes all elements of normal egg-laying (with the exception of egg extrusion) although some phases are quantitatively reduced.

"f. A fundamental clasp pattern is common to both male and female and is subject to seasonal modifications in the male."

Eggs may be laid at any time of day but most often spawning occurs at night. Eggs are typically deposited in a flattened spherical mass, in a firm regular cluster, 3 to 6 by 2 to 3 inches. They are found in open marshy expanses near the surface, usually attached to grasses or other vegetation but sometimes free.

EGGS. Two envelopes present,[11] outer one distinct, 2.5 to 5.6 mm., average 5.0 mm. (seldom as small as 2.5 mm. except immediately after deposition); inner one, also distinct, 1.5 to 3.4 mm., average 2.25 mm.; ovum 1.0 to 2.0 mm., average 1.7 mm., black above and white below; 3,500 to 6,500 eggs per cluster (Livezey and Wright, 1947:198).

[11] Storer (1925:269) mentions 3 distinct jelly coats in eggs found March 28, 1923, between Seeley and Dixieland, Imperial Valley, California. Livezey and Wright (1947:209) state for *R. p. pipiens,* that the gradation in density of the jelly between the inner and outer envelopes at times suggests the presence of a third, middle envelope.

Moore (1944:364) says of the species east of the Rockies that individuals from the north have larger eggs than those from the south. For the northern states he records 1.8 mm. for the average diameter of the uncleaved egg; Louisiana, 1.6 mm.; northern Florida, 1.4 mm.; and southern Florida, 1.3 mm. There are differences in temperature tolerances of the eggs. The upper limit of tolerance for eggs from northern localities is 28° to 29°C., and in Louisiana and northern Florida, 32° to 33°C., and southern Florida 34°C. Eggs from northern and southern Florida were killed at 6°C. but those from Louisiana and to the north can develop. Developmental rates differ between north and south at a given temperature.

Bragg (1944b:13) says the common leopard frog of Oklahoma sometimes produces small masses of eggs. Of over 200 egg masses observed at natural breeding sites during the past 6 years, approximately 10 per cent have been small (200 eggs or fewer in each mass).

In the field at Ithaca, New York, 13 to 20 days were required for hatching (Wright, 1914:58). Dickerson (1920) says eggs from Providence, Rhode Island, laid on April 9, hatched in 9 days. The hatchlings were about 7.5 mm. (5/16 inch), had well-developed gills, and could swim. Growth of these eggs, however, probably was at room temperature.

LARVA. Tadpole large (86 mm.),[12] full, and deep-bodied; length of body (19.6 to 28.2 mm.) 1.3 to 2.2 times in tail length, average 1.7 times; venter not strongly pigmented so that viscera clearly show through in life or preserved specimens [not always true of larvae obtained widely over western North America]; tail medium in length and acute; dorsal fin not equal in width to musculature and extending onto body somewhat ahead of vertical of buds of hind limbs; spiracle sinistral, directed upward and backward, below lateral axis of body; spiracular opening elliptical or round; eye on lateral axis and nearer lateral outline in dorsal aspect than mid-dorsal line; anus dextral, opening on level of edge of ventral fin; muciferous crypts indistinct. (Pl. 33.)

Labial teeth 2/3; edge of upper labium longer than beak and fringed with teeth; on either side, a rather long row of teeth about 1/3 to 1/4 length of first upper row; outer ends of lateral rows about even with ends of upper row; median space between lateral rows 1 to 1 1/2 times either lateral row; third row of lower labial teeth shorter than single row of lower labial papillae, slightly larger, same size or 1/4 to 1/5 shorter than horny beak, and about 2/9 shorter than first lower labial row which is somewhat longer than beak and often subdivided; third lower row relatively not as short as in *R. clamitans*. (Pl. 34.)

Background of back dark brown, covered with fine gold spots and many aggregate ones on sides, general appearance somewhat similar to that of

[12] To 95 mm. in larvae from Santa Cruz County, Arizona.

R. clamitans but darker; background on front of head rather orange; belly deep cream, covered with bronzelike iridescence; gill region pigmented with dark toward sides, covered all over with gold spots, and iridescent; throat area translucent; tail conspicuously lighter than body, fins translucent and marked with scattered fine spots and pencilings; gold spots occur toward base of tail; eye bronze (larval description after Wright, 1929:34—larvae from eastern United States).

Larvae, RCS 3069, 3/4 inch in head-and-body length, obtained July 2, 1949, at Bloomington, Washington County, Utah: Above olive brown, becoming lighter, more yellowish brown from eyes anteriorly; tail light olive, spotted and blotched extensively with pale yellow or cream (clusters of closely set xanthophores [?]); tail musculature stippled with melanophores; tail fins semitranslucent, pale olive to buff; melanophores clustered in irregular manner on tail membranes giving dark-flecked appearance; tail also with pale yellow spots; body below white (guanistic layer) with pinkish tinge; iris pale copper with dusky blotches above, below, anterior, and posterior to pupil (based on larvae considered intermediate between *R. p. fisheri* and *R. p. pipiens*).

Larvae, 3/4 inch in head-and-body length, obtained July 11, 1949, 0.6 mile west-southwest of Imperial Diversion Dam, Imperial County, California: Ground color of upper surface of body dark olive, lightened with numerous, closely set flecks of greenish olive with gray cast; tail fins dull yellowish olive flecked and spotted with buff (xanthophores [?]); tail musculature similarly marked with spots and flecks of closely set, pale buff chromatophores; ventral surface of body white (guanistic) with coppery highlights; pupil dull pale gold with dark blotches as in animals from Bloomington, Utah.

Campbell (1934:7-8) found large larvae in pools in the Peña Blanca Springs area of Santa Cruz County, Arizona, June 30, 1933. A short time later they were metamorphosing. Larvae metamorphose in this area at the beginning of the rainy season. Mosauer (1932:5) reported numerous tadpoles in various stages of development in Dark Canyon, Guadalupe Mountains, New Mexico, between July 5 and July 25; most of them had only the hind limbs showing.

Wright (1914:59-60) gives the larval period for the species in New York as 60 to 80 days. The majority of larvae transform in July but a few individuals transform well into August. The size at metamorphosis may be 18 to 31 mm., average 24 mm. (175 specimens from New York).

Force (1933:131) gives the following information on postmetamorphic growth in the species in northern Michigan: they grow 10 to 11 mm. in the first year after transformation; increase about 7 mm. in the next year; sexual maturity appears to be attained at the age of 3 years (after hatching) or at the beginning of the fourth season of growth. An individual in the London Zoölogical Gardens was probably at least 9 years old at its death (Flower, 1925:273).

SUBSPECIES

(Characters largely from Linsdale, 1940)

1*a*. Spots reduced (fewer or smaller), especially on head; enlarged tympanum in male; reduced hind limbs; to about 3 inches in snout-vent length. *Range*. Known only from the vicinity of Las Vegas, Vegas Valley, Clark County, Nevada, where it is restricted to springs and seepage areas from springs. The surrounding country is largely uninhabitable because of its aridity .... *R. p. fisheri* Stejneger

1*b*. Spots generally not reduced; tympanum of male rarely enlarged; hind limbs longer; to 4½ inches in snout-vent length. *Range*. As given for the species (p. 355) exclusive of the range of *R. p. fisheri* .... *R. p. pipiens* Schreber

Remarks.—A number of subspecies of this frog have been recognized but, in general, they have not been taxonomically well defined. Some, if not all of them, may be based on varying local populations, hence may not represent accurately broader aspects of variation in the species. Moore (1944) studied the taxonomic characters commonly employed in separating *R. pipiens, R. sphenocephala,* and *R. brachycephala* (also considered by some authors as subspecies of *R. pipiens*). The characters were found invalid when samples from many localities were studied. According to Moore it does not appear possible to recognize three species or subspecies of meadow frogs on the basis of differences in body proportions or pigmentation. Therefore he believes the meadow frogs of eastern North America should be known as *Rana pipiens* Schreber. Wright and Wright (1949:498-520) are not wholly in accord with this view. See these authors for a comprehensive discussion of the *Rana pipiens* complex.

The frogs in southern Nevada, southwestern Utah, and northwestern Arizona need study. Linsdale (1940:210) points out that those of Vegas Valley in extreme southern Nevada (which he calls *Rana fisheri*—Stejneger, 1893:227), are sharply isolated from closely related ones in the Colorado and Virgin river valleys. Although other colonies of *Rana* are isolated in eastern and southern Nevada, they have become less markedly differentiated from the common type of southwestern *Rana pipiens.* He further notes, "Whether the frogs of southern Utah and Nevada need separate recognition under the name *onca* as a species or subspecies cannot be determined without a study of the whole species throughout its range, but it seems plain to me that the Vegas Valley ones should be recognized as distinct. Although entered here as a species, this form is obviously closely related to *Rana pipiens* and it might well be known as a race of that species. It contrasts most sharply with that frog in its peculiar shade of ground color, the reduction of dorsal spots, especially on the head, the enlarged tympanum, and in the reduced hind legs."

In view of the intermediacy of the characters and the geographic position of the populations ascribed to *Rana onca,* I do not believe it essential to accord them nomenclatural recognition.

Evidently the last specimens of *Rana pipiens fisheri* to be collected were those taken by Adrian Vanderhorst at Tule Springs, about 16 miles north of Las Vegas, January 13, 1942 (UNMB 364-365). Prior to this, on July 15, 1938, a party from Stanford University consisting of Alex Calhoun, Carl Hubbs and Robert Miller had obtained specimens there. Although the Albert Wrights attempted to get the species, May 16 and 17, 1942, they failed. The springs where they had obtained the frog in August, 1925, were gone. They remark (Wright and Wright, 1949:457), "Our *R. fisheri* may go with the old springs gone, the creek a mess."

On July 5, 1949, I looked for this frog. There have been further restrictions in suitable habitat for the species since the Wrights' visit. Northwest of town, where I presume there were open springs at one time, we found a group of about 10 artesian wells. All were capped. There were several large covered reservoirs. The only permanent water available for frogs in the vicinity of these wells was at the northernmost one. Here in an old excavation about 10 to 12 feet deep by 30 feet across, were tules and other aquatic or semiaquatic plants. Cottonwoods grew about the basin. The tules were so dense it was difficult to find water. At one pool the water was 10 to 18 inches deep and 4 to 6 feet across. Several bullfrogs were heard and seen there. Walking southeast in the direction of town, I found a few other pools for a distance of about 75 yards. Only bullfrogs were seen. It is doubtful if *fisheri* can maintain itself where these large voracious frogs occur.

Below another well was a pool 50 feet across but it appeared to be of recent origin. There was a sparse young growth of tules about it. No frogs were seen.

The Wrights (1949:457) remark concerning their visit, May 16, 1942, "Took us most of the day to locate where the old artesian well and springs were. At the U.S. Fish Hatchery found bullfrogs. The municipal golf course and possibly the hatcheries are where the springs were."

I explored the golf course area and found vague remnants of a small stream bed, possibly the site of the water to which the Wrights refer, as having been followed from the golf course to the Tonopah road. I followed this stream course but found only dead tules and old hummocks held by tule roots. There was no water except at the edge of the golf course where there was a stand of tules about 40 feet across with their bases in water 1 to 2 inches deep. I saw several crayfish but no frogs. There is now evidently little runoff from the golf course. The U.S. Fish Hatchery is gone. A man at Twin Lakes swimming pool said the hatchery had run out of water, hence had to be moved. I searched the banks of 2 large artificial pools at Twin Lakes. The pools were about 250 feet across and about as long, and were perhaps 1 to 3 feet deep. The water was clear and water plants were moderately abundant on the bottom. The pools were concrete and steep-sided, bordered by grass and scattered patches of tules. Again I saw bullfrogs. Residents said these frogs were common but no one had observed any other kinds. There is trout fishing in these pools. The presence of trout and bullfrogs would militate against *fisheri*.

I drove north of Las Vegas on the Tonopah road to Tule Springs where the Stanford group got the frog in 1938 and talked with Cliff M. DeVaney, manager of a dude ranch that now occupies the spring area. DeVaney knew of the frog and its rarity. He described it well. He said he last saw it in the summer of 1942. They had tried to save the animal but when they began "improving" the area on a large scale, the frog disappeared. Thus it appears that one of the last, if not the last, outpost of this species is gone. DeVaney suggested I look at Indian Springs, about 30 miles northwest on U.S. Highway 95. At the Springs there was abundant cool water but again bullfrogs and fish. An elderly lady told me small frogs had been introduced from Las Vegas in 1907 because "she liked to hear them croak at night." These were probably *Hyla regilla*. She said the bullfrogs soon cleaned them out.

Thus it appears that if not already extinct *Rana pipiens fisheri* is existing under most tenuous conditions in the Las Vegas area. Despite the obliteration of its main habitat owing to the growth of a city, one wonders if by a happy chance it may still be present in some other unknown nearby area. Search should be made in the springy, swampy Ash Meadows area west of the Charleston Mountains.

SPOTTED FROG

Rana pretiosa Baird and Girard
Plate 23

Range.—From southeastern Alaska (Sergrief Island) south through British Columbia, Washington and Oregon, eastward through Idaho into western Montana and Wyoming, and in Canada into Saskatchewan (to Lake Waskesin), south into northern Nevada and northern Utah. The ranges of this species and *Rana aurora* are largely complementary. They are said to occur together, however, at some localities in western Oregon and Washington. Robert Storm informs me that *pretiosa* occurs in western Oregon at Portland, Multnomah County; 12 miles south of Corvallis, Benton County; and 6 miles south-southwest of Albany, Linn County. Other localities in western Oregon and localities in northern California, shown on the distribution map for this species, require confirmation. The localities in California are probably based on *Rana aurora cascadae.* (Pl. 63.)

Carl and Cowan (1945b:53) say the two species occupy geographically complementary areas in southern British Columbia. *Pretiosa* is recorded from many localities east of the Coast Range and reaches the coast north of Prince Rupert, while *aurora* is known only from the coast of extreme southwestern British Columbia and the adjacent islands. A record for *pretiosa* on Sumas Prairie (Logier, 1932:323) in the center of the area occupied by *aurora,* and 2 specimens of *pretiosa* from Nicomen Island, in the Fraser River some 50 miles east of Vancouver, indicates the occurrence of these two species in the same general territory. *Pretiosa* may occasionally be carried coastally by high water of the Fraser River.

Type locality.—Puget Sound, Washington (Baird and Girard, 1853: 378).

Description.—STRUCTURE. Adult approximately 2 to 4 inches; dorsolateral folds usually evident; skin often smooth but dorsum usually covered with small rounded tubercles; eyes directed upward, more so than in *Rana pipiens* and others; tympanum ½ to ¾ size of eye opening, in color and texture like surrounding skin of head; 3 metacarpal tubercles arranged in transverse row, central one rounded, outer ones usually elongate oval in shape; metatarsal tubercles as in *R. pipiens;* sometimes a tarsal ridge but not a tarsal fold. COLOR. Above yellowish or reddish brown to dark brown, with few to many irregular inky black spots which sometimes have light centers but ordinarily are not margined with light color; "ink" spots commonly concentrated between dorsolateral folds; brownish eye mask present (sometimes obscure), extending almost to insertion of forelimb; light stripe from snout to shoulder, stripe often faint anterior to eye; below reddish-orange or yellow, best developed in adults (immatures may lack such color); throat and sometimes entire ventral surface spotted and mottled, occasionally largely unmarked ventrally; limbs blotched and spotted with dark color, with markings sometimes forming bands; iris pale metallic yellow. Logier (1932:323) describes living animals from British Columbia thus: ground color above on head, body, and limbs light yellowish brown to medium dark brown; body and head spotted above with black, spots on body often grouped together, either separate or more or less fused, forming irregular, roundish marks resembling ink splashes; hind limbs barred with brown and frequently spotted with black; front limbs spotted or blotched; under surfaces yellowish white, with or without mottling, often richly colored with salmon on belly and limbs, especially in large individuals. JUVENILE. Salmon or yellow color of ventral surfaces absent in newly transformed young; color increases in extent and brilliancy with size. SEXUAL DIFFERENCES. Male smaller than female, with enlarged first finger and with tendency toward convex webbing of hind feet.

See account of *Rana aurora* (p. 339) for comparison with that species.

Adult, RCS 4707, 3¼ inches in snout-vent length, obtained June 17, 1950, at Targhee Pass, 7,000 feet elevation, Fremont County, Idaho: Above brown with black spots on body and sooty brown ones on hind limbs; forelimbs spotted with black; upper half of rear of femur sooty, spotted with cream; rust-colored bar runs length of posterior surface of femur; lower back with tinge of tan; beige stripe from over limb-insertion to just in front of eye; edge of lower jaw rust; below white (guanistic layer) on throat, chest, and upper abdomen; orange-pink lipoid color overlying guanistic color on underside of fore and hind limbs and ventrolaterally on body; lipoid color somewhat blotchy in distribution; undersides of feet purplish sooty; foot tubercles ash gray; pupil margined above with gold crescent and flecked along ventral margin with gold; blotchy transverse band of dull gold across iris just above pupil; lower iris densely flecked with dull gold and nictitating membrane edged with this color.

Adult, RCS 4731, 2¼ inches in snout-vent length, obtained June 20, 1950, 6 miles south-southeast of Salt Lake, Salt Lake County, Utah: Above dark olive brown on body; limbs yellowish olive; under magnification closely set gold chromatophores seen to form layer over all dorsal surfaces; darker area centrally on back may be due to more melanic pigment reaching surface in this area than elsewhere; spots on back black, those on hind limbs sooty; forelimbs unspotted; upper surface of forefoot dull lemon yellow; tympanum colored like surrounding skin of head; dorsolateral folds not evident; cream guanistic layer over all ventral surfaces, overlaid with mottled yellow-orange lipoid color except on underside of head and centrally on chest; lipoid color blotchy, heaviest on underside of limbs and laterally on chest; posterior surface of femur with mottled, diagonal yellow-orange band from near vent to knee joint; throat near margin of jaw suffused with sooty brown; underside of feet sooty; iris heavily flecked with ash white to cream chromatophores, especially above and below pupil.

Habitat.—Frequent streams, springs, ponds, sloughs, and marshy places; about lakes in mountainous areas. Fitch (1936:641) reported the species at Whiskey Creek, 4,510 feet, in the headwaters of the Rogue River, Oregon. The creek was cold, deep, and well shaded, with mossy banks. The locality was in the Canadian Life-zone in an association of lodgepole pine, white pine, and Sitka spruce. (Observation perhaps based on *Rana aurora cascadae*.)

Six miles south-southeast of Salt Lake, Utah, on June 20, 1950, Herndon Dowling and I sought this frog in spring-fed pools in a meadow. The area lies some miles west of the foot of the Wasatch Mountains. We worked from 9:00 to about 9:45 P.M., obtaining 17 adult and immature frogs. The animals varied from about 1¼ to 3 inches in length. Upon our arrival we spent considerable time getting only 2 individuals, but later the animals were discovered more easily. I believe this may have been due in part to our developing skill in detecting the eye shine, but more to increasing abundance of the frogs with the disappearance of twilight. The animals were nonvocal and were usually found resting near the water's edge, often on or partly in floating masses of algae. Several were found with just their heads protruding through the algae. None was observed swimming. Most were easily caught by hand.

There were a half-dozen or so pools variously connected by channels 2 to 8 feet wide. The pools were of varying shape but averaged perhaps 12 to 15 feet across and perhaps a foot or so in depth. The water was clear and could be seen welling up slowly from the bottom of some of the pools. Between several of the ponds, water was moving in the connecting channels. The bottoms were of dark gray mud. The banks were commonly abrupt, the ground level 6 to 8 inches above the water, but often there was a sill of soil and grasses at or near the surface of the water. In places the ground shook slightly as one walked about. Grasses and, what appeared to be, a round-stemmed sedge grew 4 to 6 inches high. A yellow *Mimulus* and water cress grew in some of the connecting channels. The temperature of the water in one of the pools at 9:20 P.M. was 15.2°C.; the air temperature was 14.3°C.

Behavior.—Highly aquatic; resembles *R. aurora* in habits. May hibernate in northern part of range. It has been found buried in mud under a foot or more of water in marshy situations along lake margins (Dickerson, 1920:218-19). Not a strong swimmer or jumper; often rather easily captured. May dive to the bottom of a pond, only half burying itself in the mud.

Voice.—The voice of the subspecies *pretiosa* has been described by Svihla (1935:119-20) as consisting of short, deep bass calls that can be heard at least a quarter of a mile. Vocal sacs internal and lateral. Call may be given under water.

Food.—The following food items have been recorded: mollusks—a slug (*Agriolimax*) and snails (*Physa* and *Lymnaea*); crustaceans—a crayfish and sowbugs; millipedes; a centipede; spiders; insects—grasshoppers, a dragonfly and nymphs, Mayfly nymphs, hemipterans (marsh treaders, a belostomid, water striders, a squash, and other bugs), an aphid, a caddisfly, lepidopterans (moths [noctuids], etc.), dipterans (bluebottle flies, mosquito larvae, a horsefly, crane flies, gnats, a syrphid), beetles (a scarabaeid, hydrophilids, staphylinids, carabids, a weevil, tumblebugs, ladybirds, a grub, dytiscids, and tiger beetles), hymenopterans (ants, wasps, and sweat bees); miscellaneous plant material probably taken incidentally (Thompson, 1913:55; Schonberger, 1945:121; Tanner, 1931: 194).

Reproduction.—Season last of February (time of appearance in the Puget Sound area, Dickerson, 1920:219) to July (*pretiosa*); March to an undetermined time (*luteiventris*) (Livezey and Wright, 1947:195). Logier (1932:323) suggests that spawning in interior British Columbia may occur in June and July. Dickerson (1906:219) gives March as the spawning season for the species at Puget Sound.

COMPARISON OF THE EGGS OF THE SUBSPECIES OF *Rana pretiosa*
(After Livezey and Wright, 1947:195,197-98)

	pretiosa	*luteiventris*
Jelly envelopes	2	1
Inner	5.0 to 6.0 mm. (indistinct)	6.33 mm.
Outer	10.0 to 15.0 mm. (distinct)	(5.0 to 7.12 mm.) (fairly distinct)
Ovum		
Size	2.0 to 2.8 mm.	1.97 mm. (1.81 to 2.12 mm.)
Color	black above; white below	black above; light tan below
Number of eggs	1,100 to 1,500	2,400
Appearance of masses	Lumps, 8″ x 6″; eggs far apart	Mass (with bluish cast), 3″ x 3″ to 8″ x 6″; eggs ¼ to ¾″ apart
Manner of deposition	In shallow water unattached among grasses at edges of ponds with top layer of eggs at surface of water; eggs may gather much debris.	

Carl (1943:50) states that eggs hatch in about 4 days in British Columbia.

LARVA. Sooty brown at hatching, 7.3 to 8.7 mm. in length, adhesive discs and external gills evident; after about 30 days, hind-limb buds appeared and total length had increased from about 8 to 36 mm.; head-and-body 15 mm., tail 20 mm.; depth of body about 10 mm. and greatest width 7 mm.; tail 1.4 to 1.6 times combined length of head-and-body; eyes dorsal, well up on head, rather close together; interorbital distance about 2 mm.; external nares situated almost midway between eyes and tip of snout but slightly closer to eyes; interorbital distance contained 7.5 times in length of head-and-body; anus dextral; spiracle sinistral, directed upward and backward; greatest depth of tail (over fins) contained 2.5 times in length; greatest depth of muscular portion of tail contained approximately 7 times in length.

Four rows of labial teeth, 1 on upper labium divided medially into 2 very short sets situated near ends of upper jaw and 3 lower rows, second or middle one longest, first and third about equal in length; (*luteiventris*, according to Thompson [1913: plate III], has 5 rows of teeth, 2 long upper ones, the second interrupted in the middle, and 3 lower rows, first lower row longer than in *pretiosa*); single row of labial papillae along sides and lower portion of oral disc (Svihla, 1935:121, based on larvae from vicinity of Pullman, Washington).

Subspecies *luteiventris*—length of body 34 mm.; width 22 mm.; length of tail 67 mm.; height 13 mm.; external nares nearer orbits than tip of snout; internarial distance half of interorbital space. Labial teeth in 2/3 rows, second row broadly interrupted medially, fifth row short, about as wide as lower horny jaw. Color in alcohol brownish gray above, with lateral folds a little lighter; belly grayish white; muscular part of tail yellowish white with small gray spots; caudal crests gray with darker spots (from Thompson, 1913:54). Tadpoles metamorphose by the middle of June in eastern Washington.

Logier (1932:323-24) took 19 tadpoles in Brent's Lake, British Columbia, July 1, 1928. They ranged in length from 43 to 76 mm. From this material he concludes: "There would seem to be little doubt that the mature and transforming tadpoles . . . with an average body length for all of 21.98 mm.; and for the eleven larger specimens of 27.63 mm., belonged to the brood of the preceding year and had wintered over as tadpoles, and consequently were ready to begin transformation earlier in the summer than those nearer the coast (Puget Sound) which go through their metamorphosis in the same year in which they are hatched." Recently transformed frogs measure 60 mm., with a head-body length of 26 mm. They lack reddish color on under surface of thighs and on abdomen. At least 2 years seems to be required to reach maturity (Svihla, 1935:121).

Subspecies

1*a*. Below commonly reddish (salmon) in color, sometimes yellowish; red usually of deeper tone than in *luteiventris;* dorsal markings more abundant, larger, and better defined; tubercle at base of fourth toe present and usually 2 well-developed palmar tubercles in mature frog (Thompson, 1913:54). *Range.* Southeastern Alaska south through British Columbia, Washington, Oregon; also in northern Idaho, western Montana, Wyoming, and Utah . . . . *R. p. pretiosa* Baird and Girard

1*b*. Below averages more yellowish or orange than *pretiosa;* in general tends toward paler coloration dorsally and more yellowish ventrally (orange yellow); fewer, smaller, and duller dark spots on dorsum; tubercle at base of fourth toe absent and more commonly one of palmar tubercles poorly developed or absent in mature frog. *Range.* Eureka and Elko counties, northern Nevada; central and southern Idaho, eastern Oregon; possibly also extreme northeastern California and southeastern Washington. Area of intergradation has not been accurately determined . . . . *R. p. luteiventris* Thompson

Remarks.—Storer (MS) regards the validity of the subspecies *luteiventris* as questionable, a view I share. It appears to be no more than a slightly differentiated subspecies of possibly very local occurrence.

WOOD FROG

Rana sylvatica Le Conte
Plate 20

Range.—From Labrador and Nova Scotia to Maryland and, via the Appalachians, to northwestern South Carolina, west to Alaska and British Columbia and in the United States into Minnesota, Illinois, and northwestern Arkansas. A Rocky Mountain population has recently been reported in northern Colorado (Maslin, 1947) and southeastern Wyoming (Baxter, 1947:32). The species probably occurs in western Montana. (Pl. 64.)

Type locality.—Not stated (Le Conte, 1825:282.)

Other localities.—COLORADO. 8 mi. W of Coalmont, 2 mi. N of Sawmill Creek, 8,800 ft.; 8 mi. W of Coalmont, 1 mi. N of Sawmill Creek, 8,500 ft.; Rand, 8,700 ft.; 2½ mi. SE of Rabbit Ears Peak, 9,000 ft. (Maslin, 1947:159).

Description.—STRUCTURE. Adult from approximately 1½ to slightly over 3 inches; dorsolateral folds present; tympanum round, ½ to about same size as eye opening; metacarpal and metatarsal tubercles essentially as in *R. pipiens,* except inner metatarsal tubercle larger, projecting farther from surface of foot; no tarsal fold. COLOR. Above dark brown to reddish brown, greenish, yellowish gray, or gray; two light-colored stripes involving dorsolateral folds and median-light line often present from snout to vent, sometimes stopping short of vent; black or dark brown spots may be present on back and sides; occasionally spots elongate and with light centers; below whitish, sometimes yellowish but not red; with or without dark mottlings on throat and breast; dark bar at anterior base of upper arm; well-defined blackish or dark brown eye mask, narrow between eye and nostril, often extending beyond nostril halfway to edge of upper jaw, broad behind eye, extending to above anterior base of forelimb (sometimes indistinct behind eye); contrasting white stripe on upper jaw below eye mask; hind limbs commonly more or less crossbanded and spotted with dusky; iris golden with lower portion darkened.

JUVENILE. Based on about 2 dozen recently metamorphosed young from 5 miles east-southeast of Rabbit Ears Peak, Jackson County, Colorado, obtained on August 23, 1949: Vertebral stripe, present in all, creamy gold and margined by broad stripe of golden olive, less commonly olive brown or golden brown; just medial to dorsolateral fold is stripe of from golden gray to golden buff, latter most common; medial side of dorsolateral folds same color as latter stripe but often with more gold; lateral surface of fold usually with blackish but such color broken and irregular; lateral to folds is gray-gold or grayish-buff area with black specks; eye mask margined above and posteriorly with deep brown or black, ventrally with area of greenish gold, brown, or olive gold; light stripe on upper lip, extending below eye mask, silvery or gold with tinges of from pale orange to pale green; venter cream with golden tinge; seat patch dull yellowish orange, almost yellowish tan; iris with gold markings (largely from field notes of Wm. Riemer). SEXUAL DIFFERENCES. In male webs of hind feet become convex and first finger becomes swollen basally during breeding season. Male usually darker-colored and more active than female during this period. Female averages larger than male.

Adult, RCS 3479, obtained August 23, 1949, 5 miles east-southeast of Rabbit Ears Peak, Jackson County, Colorado: Dorsal stripe ash gray to cream, bordered by sooty brown; dorsolateral folds yellowish brown; mask blackish brown; upper sides and upper surface of hind limbs sooty brown with purplish cast; several cream to whitish spots anterior to groin; below white (guanistic) with pale purplish spots; seat patch rose; underside of feet purplish or pinkish brown; forelimbs cream anteriorly, bronze dorsally, purplish gray posteriorly, with black bar at base of each; iris with extensive patches of pale orange to pale yellow, above and below pupil; patch posterior and anterior to pupil sooty brown.

Adult, RCS 3480, from same locality as RCS 3479: Vertebral stripe ash white bordered by brown with rusty cast; ash-white area immediately medial to dorsolateral folds; folds coppery tan; glossy black markings bordering dorsolateral folds; spots of cream on upper sides; mask blackish brown, almost black; flecks of pale yellow over tympanum; margin of upper jaw white; below cream to white; forefeet yellowish tan; seat patch pinkish tan; underside of hind feet light pinkish gray with faint orange cast; black patch on shoulder at insertion of forelimb; pale yellow or cream streak on tibia bordered anteriorly with rusty brown; iris with transverse pale yellowish-tan bar above, but with lower edge coinciding with, pupil; dull coppery flecks on brown ground color in lower iris.

Habitat.—Most common in damp shady woods but may be found in rather dry, but shaded situations. Enters ponds and transient pools to breed. May sometimes be found considerable distances from water. Maslin (1947:160) found the species in Jackson County, Colorado ". . . among grass and herbaceous annuals in a dense willow thicket surrounding a small beaver pond. . . . All the specimens captured were found close to clean flowing water, usually in the form of ground seepages or in fresh-water swampy meadows. . . . No frogs of this species were found near creeks or streams or in the vicinity of lakes. The log-choked forest ponds so peculiarly favored by *Rana pipiens* yielded no specimens of *R. s. cantabrigensis,* nor were any found in the stagnant swampy areas. Fourteen specimens were collected in the aspen-coniferous forests of mountainous areas, and 3 in an irrigated meadow near Rand, which lies at the southern end of an extensive plateau, the North Park."

Wright (1914:90) states that in New York, ". . . this species usually chooses still water, rarely the backwaters or bayous of streams. It prefers the leaf-laden ponds and transient pools of wooded districts, though not wholly restricted to such localities. Occasionally we have seen the frogs migrating to swampy cattail stretches for spawning and have both observed and heard them in such situations." Pools no more than 1½ by 4 feet may be used.

Hildebrand (1949:170) describes a pond, referred to as "Frog-pond," where animals were collected in the vicinity of Fort Chimo, Quebec. It was a permanent pond, approximately 100 by 50 yards and 3 to 4 feet deep. The bottom was composed of a mucky, peaty soil, which made wading extremely difficult. The pond was located about 10 miles from the northern limit of the trees along the Koksoak, and was one of hundreds of ponds and lakes that pockmark the region. East of the pond was a swampy area covered with sedges, mosses, and in places larch, dwarf birch, alders, and willows. Black spruce, once abundant, had been nearly eliminated by extensive cutting. The west edge of the pond fronted on an almost barren gneissic ridge, which is so typical of this part of the Canadian shield, and an outlet cut across the southern part of the ridge and dropped precipitously to the Koksoak River. Only a trickle of water ran through this outlet in 1948, due to a light snowfall the previous winter.

The presence of buck bean, *Menyanthes* sp., along the western part of the pond was the chief distinguishing feature of Frog-pond as compared to many other ponds of the area, although *Menyanthes* is not a rare weed in the area. Solid gneissic rocks were visible along part of the north edge of the pond. The east and south edge consisted of mucky peat with borders of sedge and sphagnum moss. The pond was not shaded by tree or willow growth nor was there evidence that such growth had been removed by human agency. Snails (*Lymnaea palustris*), were extremely common in the pond. Caddis flies and dragonfly larvae were not uncommon. No fish were found.

On a visit to the Rabbit Ears Peak locality, on August 23, 1949, I made the following observations: the country was characterized by low relief—mountains with gentle slopes, many with rounded or flattened tops, and some with rocky erosion remnants, as Rabbit Ears Peak. In the broad valleys, where not cultivated, were extensive tracts of basin sagebrush.

There were many hayfields, most of them recently cut. Meandering willow-bordered streams were present with many willow-bordered creeks and seeps leading out from the aspen-coniferous cover of the hills to the main drainages. The aspens, in particular, formed mosaics on the lower parts of the hills. These trees stopped abruptly and irregularly. Among the aspen groves lay areas of basin sagebrush or rather dry grassland. At lower elevations conifers were scattered sparingly among the aspens but higher they gave the horizon a ragged outline. (Pl. 45, fig. 2.)

We looked for *Rana sylvatica* along one of the willow-bordered gullies and in the aspen grove at its head. Among the willows the gully bottom was dry, but in the aspen stand we found water in small amounts, clear and flowing slowly. There was extensive herbaceous cover, rank and green. The trickle was almost completely concealed by vegetation. A few rocks and aspen logs were scattered about. Wm. Riemer found an adult *R. sylvatica* near a leafy, shallow pool.

Along a grassy trickle 8 to 10 inches wide and ½ to 1½ inches deep, I found an adult. The small stream was bordered by willows and ran through the sagebrush to the main stream of the valley. The frog rested in a sunny patch in the grass among willows 3 feet high. *Bufo boreas, Rana pipiens,* and *Pseudacris nigrita* were also obtained along this watercourse. Several adults and young were found along the main stream in the valley. They were discovered on the grassy, sedgy banks or on rocky beaches along the stream. Low-growing willows were abundant. The stream was characterized by riffles and relatively quiet pools. The bottom was pebbly in many places, the water turbid. There were a number of beaver dams that provided additional quiet water. The banks were undercut or steep in many places with openings among roots that afforded concealment for the frogs.

Many larvae and metamorphosing young were found in a small pond completely overgrown with a grasslike sedge, 24 to 36 inches high. The pond was surrounded by scrubby willows and there were aspens on two sides. It was situated at the lower end of an aspen grove in a hollow in the hillside. Basin sagebrush occurred between it and the willow-bordered river at the bottom of the slope. *Pseudacris* and *R. pipiens* larvae were also abundant as well as metamorphosing *Pseudacris.* The terrestrial individuals were found most abundantly on grass where well trampled by sheep or in the sparser grass at the edges of the pool. Such areas were exposed to the sun, yet were damp.

Behavior.—Hibernates in logs, stumps, and possibly beneath stones and leaf litter in terrestrial situations. Schmidt observes in Wisconsin that it gathers in autumn in roadside ditches where he believes it may hibernate under water. Emerges early from hibernation; abundant in spring ponds by the first week in April in Michigan (Ruthven, *et al.*, 1928:50). A terrestrial species, inhabiting damp forests. Solitary and shy except during the breeding season.

Wright (1914:93) found that to capture mated pairs it is best to watch the vicinity of the first bunch of eggs deposited. Pairs are often under cover near the egg area or at times directly beneath the masses. On April 6, 1908, under and above the sedge area which 2 days later had 37 clumps of eggs, 6 pairs of mated frogs were captured.

Maslin (1947:160) describes the behavior of individuals collected in Jackson County, Colorado. They jumped without exceptional agility into the pond, where, upon reaching the bottom, they remained quiet. No effort was made to kick up mud or to seek cover. They could be seen clearly beneath the water and were easily captured. Near Buffalo Pass, in making their escape the frogs would take several short leaps toward the cover of willow bushes, but once beneath their sheltering branches the frogs remained quiescent, allowing the branches to be carefully parted without making any further movements. They seemed to rely for protection more on their amazing color pattern than on physical agility. This species is capable of rather quick color change through shades of brown.

Near Rabbit Ears Peak, Jackson County, Colorado, on August 23, 1949, an adult was found resting in a sunny patch of grass. Its body temperature at 10:00 A.M. was 16°C. Two juveniles were on a rocky section of the shore of a stream, sunning—air temperature ½ inch above the substratum in the shade, 24.6°C.; substratum, 24.4°C. (in the sun); water, a few inches from shore, 19.4°C.; time 11:25 A.M.

Voice.—A hoarse, grating, clacking sound not unlike the clucking of domestic ducks. Logier (1937:15) describes the males at the breeding ponds as very noisy, ". . . uttering an incessant high-pitched croaking."

Wright (1914:88, New York) describes the voice of this species in considerable detail. The croak of *Rana sylvatica* is higher-pitched than that of *Rana clamitans* and not so strong in volume or carrying quality. It can be heard only a short distance from the pond whence it comes. In chorus it is more of a rattle than in any of the other frogs. When held in the hand and squeezed, the male may make a grating noise. The croak would be confused only with that of *Rana pipiens,* for at this season no other *Rana* would make itself heard. The wood frog's note is shorter, less sustained, and not as loud or as deep as that of *R. pipiens.* The meadow frog's note may be several short croaks followed by 2 or more longer ones, or the reverse, or the shorts and longs may be interspersed in other fashions; while the wood frog's note is short, not always a succession of croaks—a sharp and snappy clack. At times, however, 2 to 4 or 6 notes may be given in rapid succession; and when close at hand they sound high and grating. The croak of the meadow frog may take 6 seconds if the succession is given, or less than 1 second if only one croak is sounded; but that of the wood frog never extends more than a second. Wright (*loc. cit.*) states that anywhere from 50 to 200 males have been observed floating at the surface during a breeding congress. Individuals may croak from beneath the surface of the water. Females can call weakly and they may emit a "yeow" when molested. The vocal sacs of the male are paired, lateral and internal, but the throat and chest inflates markedly with the production of the call.

Food.—Newly transformed frogs have been found to take 13 per cent aquatic forms, adults 98 per cent nonaquatic. These frogs are chiefly insectivorous but they also eat small millipedes, snails, and various other invertebrates of moderate size. They may creep after their prey before making a capture (Pope, 1944:109).

Reproduction.—Season March to July (*cantabrigensis*) and last half of March through April (*sylvatica*). Concerning time of activity of *Rana sylvatica* in the northern part of its range, Hildebrand (1949:169) learned that the frogs were common when melting snow forms large pools. At Fort Chimo on the Labrador peninsula they were not uncommon in May and June, but during July and August they disappeared, according to the natives. Mating occurs most often at night but also in the daytime. The embrace is pectoral. Eggs may be deposited soon after ice leaves the ponds. Woodland ponds and less commonly swamps and quiet water of streams serve as breeding sites.

Noble and Farris (1929:16) studied sex recognition in this species. The males sprawl at the surface of the water. They seize any object of appropriate size moving near them. Sex recognition is first accomplished after the embrace. If the object seized has the right qualities, it is retained. For the wood frog these qualities are (1) wide girth and resistance to compression (males injected with water are accepted and retained) and (2) silence; females are released when they are spent for the same reason males are rejected—they are of small girth and lack the required firmness. Seized males give warning notes which foster release. Receptive females are silent. Other factors modifying the embrace are fatigue, degree of sexual ardor, and retreat of the pair under the surface.

Expulsion of the eggs is rapid, requiring only 5 or 10 minutes. A number of females may lay in the same general area. The laying period is short; the bulk of the eggs may be deposited in a week.

EGGS. Dickerson (1920) mentions the occurrence of a green alga in the egg jelly of the eastern form, *sylvatica,* and speculates on its function. "The jelly about the egg becomes green in colour, and thus the egg-

Comparison of Eggs of Subspecies of *Rana sylvatica*
(After Livezey and Wright, 1947:197)

	sylvatica	*cantabrigensis*
Two jelly envelopes		
Inner (indistinct)	3.8 mm. (3.6 to 5.8 mm.)	3.48 mm. (3.06 to 4.06 mm.)
Outer (distinct)	6.4 mm. (5.2 to 9.4 mm., usually 5.8 to 7.0 mm.)	5.08 mm. (4.25 to 5.43 mm.)
Ovum Size	1.9 mm. (1.8 to 2.4 mm.)	1.67 mm. (1.50 to 1.81 mm.)
Color	←Black above; white below→	
Number of eggs per cluster	1,000 to 3,000 (sometimes as few as 500)	
Appearance of masses	Firm and spherical, rarely to 6 inches (*sylvatica*); numerous masses deposited in a small area, often in contact	
Where deposited	In shallow ponds near surface to 6 inches, occasionally to 2 to 3 feet; attached to vegetation in any part of pond	

masses bear a close resemblance in position and appearance to the floating masses of green pond-scum. The green colour of the jelly about the eggs is due to the presence of innumerable miscroscopically small green plants. The relation between these plants and the developing egg is one of mutual advantage. The plants feed on the large amount of carbon dioxide breathed out by the young tadpoles, and the tadpoles get, as their share in the partnership, the free oxygen that the plants give out as a waste product from their starch-forming process. This oxygen must be of infinite value, produced everywhere in the midst of the egg-mass, because it supplies sufficient pure air for breathing, in spite of the crowded condition of the two thousand or more growing tadpoles."

Spawning occurs in April in southern Ontario, and the eggs hatch in from 2 to 3 weeks (Logier, 1937:15). Wright (1914:96) states for the species in New York, "It would appear that with average water-temperatures of 44 to 50 degrees the eggs usually hatch in 24 to 17 days; with temperature of 50 to 60, in 17 to 7 days; with temperatures of 60 to 70, in 7 to 4½ days."

Hatchlings are about 7 mm. in length. The external gills are poorly developed and the larvae are barely able to swim, but 64 hours later they are able to swim actively.

LARVA. Tadpole medium (49.8 mm.),[13] full, and deep-bodied; length of body (14.4 to 17.2 mm.) contained 1.5 to 2.2 times in tail (23.8 to 33.2 mm.), average 1.8; venter not strongly pigmented; tail quite long, tip decidedly acuminate or attenuate; dorsal fin high, sometimes greater than width of musculature and extending onto body to vertical through spiracle or shorter distance, more in this respect like *Hyla* tadpoles; ventral fin as well developed as dorsal; spiracle sinistral and directed upward and backward, below lateral axis; eye above (or on, according to Wright, 1929) lateral axis, almost on lateral outline in dorsal aspect; eyes sometimes just visible from venter; anus dextral, opening on level of edge of ventral fin; muciferous crypts indistinct. (Pl. 33.)

Labial teeth 2/3 (2 animals from Rabbit Ears Peak) or 3/4; upper labium with labial tooth row on its upper edge, this row as long as or much longer than beak (about 1½ times beak); second row of lateral upper labial teeth long, about 2/5 of upper row; median space usually 2/5 to 4/5 length of one of lateral rows; outer ends of lateral rows often extend beyond ends of upper row; third upper labial row, when present, usually about ½ length of second row or ¼ or 2/9 of length of first upper row; lower labium has 3 or 4 rows of teeth; first 3 of about equal length, and these longer than beak; fourth row of labial teeth about equal to single row of lower labial papillae; fourth row 6/11 to 7/11 of first row of lower labial teeth; labium on either side with inner papillae to end of the fourth lower labial row. (Pl. 34.)

Background of back and sides greenish black marked with fine gold and with few orange spots; also with iridescent areas, particularly on sides, giving whole a greenish-brown appearance; cream line extends along upper jaw (not observed in our larvae from Colorado); venter with cream ground color; belly slightly pigmented at sides; gill region quite heavily pigmented, but overlaid with silver spots; throat region lavender gray with fine dark and silver spots, whole venter iridescent, giving belly distinct pinkish-bronze appearance; iris bronze; tail somewhat lighter than body, pigment graded evenly over muscular portion and fins, but as a whole darker above; small gold spots scattered over surface, some of which become iridescent (based on material from eastern United States [Wright, 1929:26]).

Mature larva, RCS 3492, obtained August 23, 1949, 5 miles east-southeast of Rabbit Ears Peak, Jackson County, Colorado: Above with blackish and olive gray markings; tail musculature, at lower portion of base, cream; remainder of tail musculature light gray suffused with melanophores; tail fins spotted and blotched with sooty; venter ash gray (guanistic layer over viscera); pale gold pigment flecks in area of throat; base of

[13] To 51.5 mm. in larvae from near Rabbit Ears Peak, Jackson County, Colorado, collected by the author.

limbs ventrally and posterior portion of abdomen, yellowish; iris with pale orange, or coppery flecks forming patches above and below pupil.

Developmental period (from eggs to transformation) for the species in New York is given by Wright (1914:97) as lasting about 90 days. In larvae, developmental periods range from 44 to 85 days, average 67 days. Size at metamorphosis (Wright, *loc. cit.*) as from 12 to 21 mm., rarely over 19 mm., average 16 mm. (139 specimens).

Hildebrand (1949:170-71) presents data on reproduction of this species in the vicinity of Fort Chimo, Labrador. On June 21, 1948, when wading along the waterward edge of *Menyanthes* in Frog-pond (see habitat section, p. 375), 11 globular balls of eggs were found attached to plants about 4 inches below the surface with 1 to 2 feet of water beneath the clusters. One cluster was attached to deadwood, a small larch tree in the water. Larvae were about to hatch, and when the clusters were shaken some escaped and swam away. One cluster contained 540 7 mm. tadpoles, and an estimated 100 escaped in handling.

On July 22, tadpoles were found quite numerous over the rocky bottom on the north edge of the pond in about 1 foot of water; none was seen among the *Menyanthes*. Eight tadpoles measured 21 to 28 mm. On September 2, one tadpole (27 mm. in total length) was found with all 4 legs developed. On September 20, small frogs and tadpoles were numerous. Measurements were as follows: 2 small frogs with only a trace of tail 17 and 19 mm., respectively; 1 frog 22 mm. total length, tail 6 mm.; 1 tadpole 31 mm. total length, tail 17 mm. and the hind and forelegs well developed; 1 tadpole with no foreleg development, 38 mm. total length, tail 19 mm. Hildebrand (1949:172) says that unfavorable summer temperatures might result in the entire yearly tadpole population not metamorphosing in its first summer.

Subspecies [14]

(Characters from Maslin, 1947)

1*a*. Relatively stocky, with tibia-body proportion ranging from .45 or less to .55; leg to heel measurement equal to or shorter than body length; 2 or 3 phalanges free of web; light-colored vertebral stripe present. *Range*. From Alaska and British Columbia to Michigan, northeastward to a line between the Great Lakes drainage and Hudson Bay to the Gaspé Peninsula; south in the Rocky Mountains to Colorado and southwestern Kansas, largely in the coniferous forest area (see map of biotic communities, Pitelka [1941:114]) .... *R. s. cantabrigensis* Baird

[14] Delineation of these ranges is uncertain. Further study of variation in relation to distribution is needed for this species. I follow Wright and Wright (1949) in recognizing only 2 subspecies.

1*b*. Less stocky, with tibia-body proportion of more than .55; leg length greater than body length; web more often less extensive, 3 phalanges free of web; vertebral stripe absent. *Range*. Quebec and Nova Scotia to Maryland and the Appalachians, to western South Carolina, westward to the Great Plains, largely in the deciduous forest biome. .... *R. s. sylvatica* Le Conte

MEXICAN FROG

Rana tarahumarae Boulenger
Plate 21

Range.—Chihuahua, Sonora, and Jalisco, Mexico. Ranges into the United States in the mountains of southern Arizona and possibly New Mexico. Smith and Taylor (1948:100) include western Texas in the range of this species. (Pl. 61.)

I have seen 2 of the specimens (USNM 100876-7) upon which Little and Keller's (1937:221) record for Mesilla Dam, New Mexico, is based. The others are not at the National Museum. Those examined by me were 68 and 42 mm. in snout-vent length. These appear to me to be young bullfrogs. When I visited the dam area March 13, 1950, two young men told me that there were 3 kinds of frogs there—the toad frog (*Scaphiopus*?), striped frog (*Rana pipiens*?) and the bullfrog (*Rana catesbeiana*). They also said there were toads. One of the men had lived in the area for 20 years. I saw bullfrogs but did not obtain any other anurans. I believe the Little and Keller record requires confirmation.

Likewise, Little's (1940:262) record of the species at Rose Creek near Roosevelt Reservoir, Gila County, Arizona, seems dubious although there are environmental situations in this area where one would expect this frog. I examined USNM 105186-93, part of the lot of 22 frogs taken of about 100 observed by Little in pools shaded by alders and sycamores along Rose Creek. These appear to me to be young bullfrogs.

Type locality.—Ioquiro [=Yoquivo] and Barranca del Cobre, Sierra Tarahumaré, Chihuahua, Mexico (Boulenger, 1917:416).

Description.—STRUCTURE. Adult to 4½ inches; closely resembles *R. boylii* but averages larger and hind limbs are shorter, close to *R. b. sierrae* in limb length. COLOR. Above usually deep grayish olive to blackish brown in preservative; vaguely outlined, sometimes light-centered dark markings on body; limbs crossbanded and blotched with blackish; no stripe on upper jaw as may be present in *R. boylii;* rarely faint lightening in jaw-stripe area; ventral surfaces light-colored, unmarked, or with throat and sometimes venter dusky. SEXUAL DIFFERENCES. Male with swollen first finger and with tendency toward median, diagonal depression across swollen base of digit; no diagnostic differences in throat color; female reaches larger size than male.

Adult, RCS 3282, 4½ inches in snout-vent length, obtained July 18, 1949, ½ mile southwest of Yanks Spring, Sycamore Canyon, Santa Cruz County, Arizona: Dorsal surfaces olive with underlying suffusion of tan; dorsal spots sooty, obscured by olive green, under magnification seen to consist of fine stippling; tan of dorsum grades on sides into pale greenish yellow with orange cast; upper surface of thighs tan with yellow in light-colored areas posteriorly and like sides anteriorly; upper surface of tibia essentially like thigh; ventral surface whitish to cream; upper surface of foot medially and posterior surface of tibia colored like sides; anterior and posterior surfaces of forelimbs similarly colored; upper surface of forelimbs like dorsal surface of thigh; ventral surfaces of forefeet sooty with purplish between the darker areas; web of hind foot streaked with dull yellow and sooty; ventral surfaces of hind feet sooty with markings of dull yellowish tan and purplish along sides of toes; tympanum colored like surrounding skin of head; iris pale orange with lighter orange pupillary ring and many flecks of dusky.

Habitat.—On June 18, 1931, Campbell (1931b:164) found about 20 individuals of this species near Peña Blanca Springs, at about 4,000 feet, Santa Cruz County, Arizona, clustered about potholes in a canyon. There was no running water at this season. A number were also found in an old tumbled-in mine which had filled with water.

In July and August 1933, Campbell again visited the Peña Blanca locality. He writes (1934:8-9), "This frog . . . seems to be of rather common occurrence in the permanent water holes of the region, though it is not as abundant as *Rana pipiens*. *R. tarahumarae* is more dependent upon the water supply than is *pipiens*, and does not stray far from the streams. Before the rainy season began we found a number of specimens under a very big rock at the edge of a large, permanent pool; they had retreated far out of sight under the edge of the rock; when poked with a stick they came out with a squawk and leaped into the water. Others at the same pool were in niches in a perpendicular rock wall, within one jump of the water. A few were found at the reservoir at Peña Blanca; they came out of the water at night and sat on the concrete edge until the sunlight reached them the next morning.

"There were large larvae in the cattle trough into which the reservoir drained. Later in the season, August 20, we found several half-grown specimens in the stream in the canyon above Peña Blanca Springs, where the water was not permanent. These . . . frogs resembled *Rana boylii* in their habit of stationing themselves in the midst of the riffles of the stream. We did not hear them croak, nor did we find any eggs, hence it is probable that they breed during the spring."

Near Yanks Spring, Santa Cruz County, Arizona, on July 18, 1949, I hiked southwest down Sycamore Canyon which drains into Sonora, Mexico. This is one of several canyons that provide an avenue for dispersal of Mexican species into the United States. There were scattered pools of water and in one place, about 1 mile down the canyon from Yanks Spring, a small stream a few feet wide and an inch or so in average depth, connected 2 rather large pools. This was the only place where water was flowing. The bottom of the canyon was coarse sand, gravel, and boulders with occasional stretches of water-scoured rock. The canyon walls were rocky with a number of seeps on the southeast side. There were cottonwoods, mulefat, and walnuts in and near the canyon bottom. Oaks were scattered over the surrounding hills. Many *Rana pipiens* larvae were seen in the pools but no *Rana tarahumarae* tadpoles. Water of one pool where *pipiens* larvae were abundant was 24.3°C.; air 1 inch above the ground in the shade was 28.2°C. at 1:25 P.M. About one rocky pool we obtained 3 adult *R. tarahumarae.* These had a distinctly rusty cast in the dorsal coloration. *Rana pipiens* adults were fairly common in the canyon, and a *Microhyla* was heard. (Pl. 46.)

Food.—An adult female (RZ 1281), about 4 inches in snout-vent length, obtained on August 24, 1950, in Sycamore Canyon, Santa Cruz County, Arizona, by Richard Zweifel, contained a turtle, *Kinosternon sonoriense,* with a carapace length of 1⅜ inches, and a fish, *Gila ditaenia,* approximately 3½ inches long.

Reproduction.—The breeding season evidently follows the heavy summer rains which begin in July (Campbell, 1931b:164).

EGGS. I include here a description of eggs, presumably of this species, found by Richard Zweifel on August 23, 1950, in Alamo Canyon, 2½ miles southwest of Peña Blanca Springs, in the Pajarito Mountains, Santa Cruz County, Arizona. Mr. Zweifel has kindly allowed me to examine and report this material.

The eggs were in a rounded cluster, measuring about 2½ by 3 inches, attached at the center of a rock-bottom pool, about 3½ feet across and 8 feet long. The pool was situated in an intermittent stream bed. The eggs were in water about 7 inches deep. They were covered with a layer of sediment which caused them to resemble the color of the bottom of the pool. Six adults (an additional one seen) (4 males and 2 females), 3 immatures, and 2 metamorphosing individuals, with tails not yet resorbed, were procured. Many mature tadpoles were present. The ovaries of the females appeared to be in a postbreeding condition. The basal portion of the first digit in the males was swollen and darkened. Leopard frogs (*R. pipiens*) were present in considerable numbers.

The eggs may be characterized as follows: two envelopes present, both distinct; outer envelope 3.7 to 5.0 mm.; inner one 2.9 to 3.4 mm.; ovum

2.0 to 2.2 mm. (in neural crest stage), black above, whitish below; estimated 2,200, or more, eggs in cluster.

The eggs were firmly attached to one another, individual eggs anchored at 1 to 4 points to adjacent eggs. Considerable effort was required to separate attached eggs. When pulled apart, the connecting strand of jelly exhibited a median, transverse partition, but the eggs did not separate there. The jelly strand pulled off next to the surface of one or the other egg, leaving a shallow pit, while the egg retaining the strand exhibited a low hummock of jelly, the contracted, connecting material. Eggs of *R. boylii* and *R. pipiens* were similarly connected and it may be that most anuran eggs that are deposited in clusters, and that adhere firmly to one another, have a similar type of jelly connection.

Most of the eggs were uniformly sooty or nearly black and in the neural tube stage; others, however, seemed to be in the blastula stage and were whitish over the lower (vegetal) half of the egg.

I compared the eggs with those of *R. pipiens* from Sycamore Canyon, Santa Cruz Country, Arizona, and with those of *R. boylii* from Frank Valley, Marin County, California. I am certain of the identity of both of these lots of eggs.

The *R. pipiens* eggs from Sycamore Canyon, on the average, measured 6 mm. to the surface of the outer jelly envelope, 1.8 mm. to the outer surface of the inner envelope, and 2.2 mm. across the ovum. The outer jelly capsule, thus, was larger in relation to the size of the ovum than in the presumed *R. tarahumarae* eggs and the ova of the cluster appeared less closely associated than in the Alamo Springs material. The inner jelly capsule, however, had a smaller diameter than that found in the Alamo Springs eggs. Ovum size was similar in the two lots. In the *R. pipiens* eggs there was a weakly differentiated zone, suggesting a third capsule, between the ovum and the outer surface of the inner capsule.

It is, of course, impossible to say to what extent these differences may be due to the stage of expansion of the jelly capsules (due to water absorption following laying), manner of preservation, or individual variation in clutch form and structure. Nevertheless, both lots possessed eggs that appeared to be in similar developmental stages and the methods of preservation were similar.

I also compared the eggs with those of *Rana boylii,* obtained directly from an individual in captivity. Although all dimensions were smaller in *R. boylii,* the proportions were similar. Smaller size may be due partly to preservation but also perhaps may be related to the size difference between adults of *R. tarahumarae* and *R. boylii.* The *boylii* eggs, on the average, measured 3.3 mm. to the surface of the outer envelope, 2.6 mm. to the outer surface of the inner envelope, and 1.8 mm. across the ovum.

The eggs were firmly adherent to one another in a rather compact cluster.

LARVA. Head-body 23 mm., depth 13.2 mm.; body widest well behind eyes; estimated tail length 32 mm. (tip malformed and much of fins missing), depth 8.8 mm.; tail musculature stout, tail same depth for a distance ⅔ of body length from its base and nearly half of width of body in depth; tip of tail acute (usually rounded in *R. boylii*); dorsal fin originating on vertical at limb buds; mature larvae may reach 80 to 100 mm. in total length; spiracle directed backward and slightly upward, opening vertically oval; spiracle midway on body on lateral axis; anus dextral, opening at edge of base of ventral fin; eye about same distance from midline as from outline of head; nostril about midway between eye and tip of snout. (Pl. 33.)

Labial teeth 5/3 (sometimes 4/3), first row about 1½ times upper mandible; second row of 2 segments, with each part contained in first row about 2½ times; segments separated by space about ⅔ length of one segment; lateral segment of third row about half lateral segment of second; so progressively shorter to fifth row; first lower row slightly shorter than second upper one, with narrow interspace; third lower row undivided, slightly longer than upper mandible; second lower row similar in length to first lower row; papillary fringe extends short distance medially on either side above first upper row of labial teeth; single row of papillae surrounds remainder of mouth except for few additional papillae at corners of mouth. (Pl. 34.)

Dorsal surfaces dark brown, everywhere finely stippled with silvery to pale gold; dorsolaterally on body, gaps in stippling result in dark spotting; silvery stippling becomes denser, finally forming solid layer on ventral surface of body, obscuring viscera; tail musculature pale yellow to cream with spots and blotches of dark brown, most abundant dorsally; tail fins spotted with dark brown; light color of tail musculature extends well forward on body (foregoing description largely based on a preserved specimen from Santa Cruz County, Arizona, provided by Joseph Slevin).

Campbell (1931b:164) found larvae transforming June 18, 1931. Tadpoles were also found June 30, 1933, in the Peña Blanca Springs area (Campbell, 1934:8).

Remarks.—This species is close to *R. boylii*. In structure, pigmentation, and behavior of adults and larvae there are many points of similarity. There is also resemblance between the habitats of the two forms. *Tarahumarae* and *boylii* may well be differentiates of a common stock.

There is some question regarding the validity of the record for the species, 1½ miles above the XSX Ranch, Socorro County, New Mexico (Linsdale, 1933:222). This specimen was presented to the Museum of Vertebrate Zoölogy along with 20 reptiles and 9 other amphibians from

California, by J. E. Law. The New Mexican frog was the only one from out of state. Of the California material, all the amphibians were from southern California. Six are *Triturus torosus* from 1½ miles north of Sierra Madre. This is the habitat of *Rana boylii muscosa*. I find the frog labeled XSX Ranch indistinguishable from specimens of *muscosa* in our collection and quite different from our *Rana tarahumarae*. Linsdale (*loc. cit.*) had earlier noted the marked similarity between the frog received from Law and specimens of *Rana boylii*. On August 1, 1949, we visited the XSX Ranch area. We found many *Rana pipiens* but no *R. tarahumarae*. The river flows through a deep gorge. There are cottonwoods along the river bottom. Piñon-juniper sparsely covers the surrounding hills. The county line has been changed. The locality is now in Grant County, New Mexico.

MICROHYLIDS

Family Microhylidae

Structure.—Size of adults from about ⅓ to about 4 inches; greater range in skeletal modification than in any other family; pectoral girdle firmisternal, more specialized representatives with ventral elements absent except coracoids; vertebrae diaplasiocoelous or procoelous; ribs absent; urostyle usually attached by 2 condyles but in 2 genera fused to sacrum; sacral diapophyses more or less dilated; premaxillary and maxillary teeth present or absent, more specialized with teeth absent; prevomerine teeth present or absent; tongue oval, thin, with posterior half free or, on other hand, subcircular, thick, and not free behind; tongue with longitudinal furrow in some; palate ridged transversely (few genera excepted), one ridge commonly bounding oesophagus, other more anteriorly situated on palate (occasionally third fold and sometimes only posterior fold present); terminal phalanges simple, **T**- or rarely **Y**-shaped; subarticular tubercles absent or sometimes present (*Phrynella*); intercalary cartilages absent; tympanum concealed or exposed although majority of genera have middle ear fully developed; pupil horizontal (sometimes erect).

Habits.—Arboreal, terrestrial, and fossorial. The arboreal forms usually possess adhesive discs on their toes or subarticular tubercles. The fossorial species commonly have pointed heads and slender toes.

The majority of the species either pass their larval stages within the egg capsule or hatch out to form a distinctive tadpole with a median spiracle, toothless and expansible mouth, and no external nares until just before transformation. Many of these species are microphagous. Those species that undergo metamorphosis within the egg lack adhesive organs, external gills, branchial clefts, internal gills, operculum, spiracle or mouth armature; nourishment is entirely derived from the yolk, and respiration is accomplished through a leaflike, vascular, nonmuscular tail which is apposed to the inner surface of the egg capsule.

Parker (1934) has monographed this family.

Range.—The family is found in the Americas, southern Africa, Madagascar, southern and eastern Asia and adjacent islands, the whole of the Indo-Australian Archipelago; and Cape York Peninsula, Australia. Only the genus *Microhyla* is considered here. It ranges in southeastern Asia and adjoining islands and in the New World in South America (through Brazil), Central America, and the southern part of North America; in the United States it occurs in the southeastern and southern parts (from Parker, 1934:12-13).

NARROW MOUTH TOAD

Microhyla carolinensis (Holbrook)
Plate 19

Range.—On the Atlantic coast from Maryland to the Florida Keys, west to southeastern Nebraska, central Kansas, southwestern Oklahoma, western Texas, and southern Arizona, southward well into Mexico. In Mexico in the states of Tamaulipas, Coahuila, Chihuahua, Sonora, Sinaloa, and Durango. The subspecies *mazatlanensis* occurs within the area covered by this book. (Pl. 62.)

Type locality.—Charleston, South Carolina (Holbrook, 1836:83).

Description.—STRUCTURE. Size small, 4/5 to 1½ inches; subspecies *mazatlanensis* from Santa Cruz County, Arizona—20 males (25.2 to 29.6 mm.) and 3 females (30.0 to 31.5 mm.) head small with pointed snout; eye small and beadlike; tympanum not evident; fold of skin extending from arm insertion to eye on either side and sometimes completely across head immediately behind eyes (not evident in some preserved specimens); skin of shoulder and of back of head loose; skin tough (although it appears delicate), smooth, or with scattered minute tubercles; body depressed; waist broad; legs short; 3 oval-shaped metacarpal tubercles arranged in transverse row; oval or rounded inner metatarsal tubercle present, outer one lacking; fingers and toes slender without webbing; subarticular tubercles present; teeth absent; tongue broad, only posterior portion free; 2

transverse ridges in palatine region; upper jaw projecting well beyond lower. COLOR. Hecht and Matalas (1946:2) contrast the coloration of the 3 subspecies of *M. carolinensis* as follows. *Carolinensis:* ventral surface mottled; dorsum dark (brown, silvery gray) and blotched above or markings obscured by dark background, sometimes with dorsolateral stripe, indistinct or if distinct bordered by a dark margin. *Olivacea:* ventral surface immaculate or with scattered melanophores; dorsum light (usually tan), not blotched, rarely with dark spots, a faint bar sometimes present on femur and tibia. *Mazatlanensis* (race treated here): ventral surface with scattered melanophores; dorsum light tan (dark brown) or grayish with at least some spots, a distinct bar (or group of blotches) on femur and tibia. SEXUAL DIFFERENCES. Male with dark throat patch and generally somewhat smaller than female. Breeding male with minute tubercles ventrally, most abundant on margins of lower jaw, on chest, lower abdomen, and hind legs; not evident on females.

Adult male, RCS 3247, obtained July 16, 1949, 1 mile northeast of Peña Blanca Springs, Santa Cruz County, Arizona: Above deep olive brown; markings on legs blackish brown; scattering of few minute cream-tipped tubercles dorsally; below whitish with pale lavender cast; whitish to cream spots on sides; sooty throat patch; iris deep brown with pale gold flecks.

Habitat.—After one of the first heavy rains of the season at Peña Blanca Springs, Santa Cruz County, Arizona, Campbell (1934:6) found individuals in a boggy spot at the overflow of the reservoir. They were squatting in the half inch or so of water between the hillocks of grass and were calling.

Campbell (1934:7) writes, "On the evening of July 20, we went up the canyon to investigate a chorus of *Hyla arenicolor* which we had heard for several nights. A number of *Gastrophryne* [=*Microhyla*] were found in the pools, croaking. Curiously enough, they seemed to be limited to the pools at the bases of trees; possibly they remained among the roots in the daytime."

Wright and Wright (1942:230) mention that *olivacea* is found under logs or stumps sunk in the ground and to the south under fallen trunks of Spanish bayonet. The species breeds in ponds, roadside ditches, and temporary rain pools. At Beeville, Texas, March 24, 1925, individuals were found croaking at the edge of a roadside ditch, above water. When a light was shone on an individual it crawled, mouselike, quickly up the bank and through the grass (Wright and Wright, 1942:231).

Wood (1948:226) mentions a specimen ". . . collected [after the mating season] by F. D. Hole on May 24, 1946, from beneath a flat rock on the border of the spillway of Laurel Lake, Blount County, Tenn. The habitat consisted of a large, active ant nest, in the center of which was the toad. Ants were not attempting to molest the toad, and it is presumed that this can be accounted for only by some noxious secretion. In captivity this specimen ate ants readily, which indicates that this species can become an ectoparasite on an ant colony."

Neill (1948:109) states that in Richmond County, Georgia, this species "Overwinters in rotten logs, and is sometimes found beneath the bark of a decaying pine stump three or four feet above the ground; always very active when uncovered."

Dice (1923:46, 52) found this species on rocky ground and in the hillside forests of Riley County, indicating that it is more characteristic of terrestrial than aquatic habitats in Kansas. The usual cover is rocks.

Near Peña Blanca Springs, Santa Cruz County, Arizona, July 16-18, 1949, 3 adults were found on damp soil under rocks in bunch grass on the sandy bottom of a water-scoured rocky gully. There were several pools in basins in the rock. Many mature larvae were found in one of these. *Hyla arenicolor* were found on the rocky walls surrounding the pool. Ocotillo and bunch grass were present on one side of the canyon, oaks and walnuts on the other.

At another place, about 2 miles west of Peña Blanca Springs, numbers of these little toads were found moving toward a muddy cattle "tank," a small pool of water held in check by a concrete dam across a gully. There was a sparse short growth of green grass about the pool where the soil was not churned by the hoofs of cattle. The country was oak woodland. The microhylas were calling from the margin of the pool. Several were discovered in shallow water that had collected in hoof marks. The assembling of this chorus occurred the night following an afternoon of heavy rain, one of the first of the season.

Near Yanks Spring, Sycamore Canyon, Santa Cruz County, Arizona, on July 18, 1949, a single individual was heard giving its baaing note about 11:30 A.M. on a bright day. It was in or near a pool in a coarse sandy, gravelly, and rocky, intermittent stream bed. Cottonwoods and walnuts were in the canyon bottom and oaks were scattered over the rocky slopes. The pool was covered with a duckweed-like plant and there were many clumps of green algae in the water and about the pool margin.

Behavior.—Nocturnal. Spends most of its time concealed under the bark of fallen and decaying trees, emerging only toward evening and after heavy rains. Proceeds by short jumps in rapid succession.

At Peña Blanca Springs, Arizona, on July 16, 1949, we found these little toads very active and agile, despite their chunky bodies and short limbs. One individual, 3/4 inch long, jumped 8 to 10 inches at a leap. He swam effectively, kicking his hind legs simultaneously and with his forelimbs back along the sides of his body.

Cope (1889:386) states, "The animals are extremely shy, and become silent on the approach of human footsteps; and as only the tip of their nose projects above the water-level, they disappear beneath it without leaving a ripple."

At Peña Blanca Springs, Arizona, Campbell (1934:6) observed individuals calling at intervals of approximately 12 seconds, mostly in unison. On July 20, 1933, these toads were found in pools, croaking. Several pairs were found in amplexus, both in the pools and just out of the water. The male has a round, blackish vocal pouch that swells in croaking, to the size of a small marble. Some males were sprawled out on the water after the manner of *Scaphiopus,* but most were standing upright in the water next to the roots of trees or near the bases of large rocks, with their heads emerging. About 7 miles east and somewhat north of Patagonia, at a little station named Vaughan, Campbell (1934:7) heard them croaking on the evening of August 23.

Voice.—The voice has been described (Smith, 1934:503, Kansas) as ". . . a high, shrill buzz of some 2 to 3 seconds duration, and of such slight volume that a single call cannot be heard more than fifty to a hundred feet away. A full chorus sounds like a band saw in operation." The note has been likened to a shrill long-drawn "quaw quaw," repeated at intervals of several seconds' duration. Wright and Wright (1942:231) state that *olivacea* starts its call with a little whistle (something like "whee"), following it with its beat. The voice of *carolinensis* has been described as a bleating baa. These toads usually call from water with their hindquarters submerged and their forefeet on the bank or some other support but occasionally they may be out on the bank of the pool. The call lasts 1.5 to 2.0 seconds, with perhaps 20 calls in 30 seconds. Dickerson (1920:167) suggests that an isolated call sounds like an electric buzzer—short, unmusical, and vibrated rapidly; a buzz, harsh and metallic in quality.

At a muddy cattle "tank" in an oak woodland 2 miles west of Peña Blanca Springs, Santa Cruz County, Arizona, on July 17, 1949, we made observations on the voice of this species. It had rained hard during the afternoon. At 8:30 P.M., while at this pool, we heard a faint sheeplike baaing. At first we thought it came from a considerable distance up the hillside, but we finally located it, only 20 feet away, by triangulation. The little fellow sat upright, nearly vertically, in shallow water in a hoof mark. With each bleat his vocal sac expanded to about the size of a pea. His calls were timed while he was illuminated with a flashlight. This probably disturbed him somewhat. The calls (in parentheses) and intervals in seconds were as follows: (1) 10 (1) 11½ (2) 45 (1) 69 (3) 40 (2½) 32 (3). During the interval of 45 seconds the toad moved about. The vocal sac was out of the water as the animal called. Several other individuals were calling intermittently from the same pool. The calls were pitched about at A above middle C. As we left the area about 9:15 P.M. we encountered many individuals making their way toward the water. A large female was picked up 250 feet from the pool. When the light was shone on her she crouched, placing her head against the ground. It rained shortly after we left.

On July 18, at Peña Blanca Springs, we heard the first microhylid call at 7:30 P.M. It was still somewhat light. There was a good chorus by 9:10 P.M. The individual call began with a lisping whistle, suggesting to me the "wist" or "whit" of an Audubon warbler. This was followed by a prolonged buzzing note. Sometimes 3 or 4 animals called more or less together but they seldom started simultaneously. Occasionally a lone call was heard. Once in a while many voices would be heard at once followed by an interval of silence and then again in unison, but this performance was erratic. We estimated that there were 6 or 8 males in the chorus. At close range, the voices suggested a hive of honeybees but the individual sounds ended too abruptly for a bee. Wm. Riemer thought they sounded like bees at close range but more like sheep at a distance. At close range some individuals were observed to have a quaver in their voices. This added to the honeybee quality of the sound. Occasional individuals gave a ragged, hoarse, poorly defined note. It had rained the day before, starting the seep below the covered spring. Tonight was the first time a microhylid was heard since we arrived July 16. Line riders told us that it had not rained for 2 weeks previously and prior to that only enough to start the grass growing. This may have been the first activity of the species since the early summer dry period.

Food.—The food apparently consists almost entirely of ants. A number of specimens from numerous, widely scattered localities in Kansas contained nothing in their stomachs aside from large numbers of small ants (Smith, 1934:503, *olivacea*). Tanner (1950), near Lawrence, Douglas County, Kansas, found a small female under a flattened rock that covered the main entrance to a colony of small ants. The frog had apparently worked itself into the loose soil, for it was surrounded with soil except for its back which was in contact with the underside of the rock. The animal's head was free and only a few inches away from one of the ant burrows. This individual and others taken the same day defecated remains of ants.

Reproduction.—Livezey and Wright (1947:190) give the season as May to September for the subspecies *carolinensis;* mid-March to September for *olivacea.* Amplexus is axillary. The species commonly breeds after heavy rains.

EGGS. The eggs of *mazatlanensis,* the form occurring in the area of this book, have not been reported, hence my observations are included in some detail. On July 19, 1949, in a seep 200 feet north of the covered spring at Peña Blanca Springs, Arizona, I found the eggs of this species. There had been a microhylid chorus there the night before. The eggs formed surface films on the water in the hoofprints of cattle. The water in the marks was 28.6°C. at 10.30 A.M., while that at the source of the seep, 60 feet away, was 26.7°C. This water, at its source, was moving slowly. Eggs in 2 of 5 clusters were counted, 175 in one, about 200 in the other. Although nearly touching one another, the eggs did not adhere but seemed to be held in a group by the surface tension of the water. When touched they usually sank, adhering to the bottom of the container with the vegetal pole uppermost. The single jelly envelope, flattened on one side, measured 4 mm., the ovum 1.2 to 1.4 mm. The latter was intense black (dark brown when preserved) above and on the sides, the pigment extending well laterally and downward toward the vegetal pole. The eggs are thus protected from excessive radiation from the sides as well as from above, perhaps of importance in eggs deposited as a surface film in well-illuminated surroundings.

LARVA. Tadpole small (26.4 mm.) (to 38 mm. in Louisiana specimens [Orton, 1946] and to 31 mm. in my specimens from Santa Cruz County, Arizona), length of body (9.2 to 10.8 mm.) in tail (9.8 to 16.4 mm.) 1.06 to 1.77, average 1.37 times; body flat, wide, elliptical, snout sometimes somewhat truncate; tail medium, obtuse or rounded (acute in all my specimens from Santa Cruz County, Arizona), sometimes with black tip; dorsal and ventral fins not equal to depth of musculature at its base; dorsal fin scarcely extends onto body, reaching vertical somewhat ahead of developing hind legs; spiracle median, closely associated with anus, just ahead of it, not very apparent until hind legs begin to appear, when it becomes separated from anus; eye distinctly lateral in position; from one eye to snout and around to other eye tadpole has prominent canthus made by flat ventral and dorsal sides of head; external nares not apparent until near metamorphosis, when they open very close together on top of snout; anus median at end of edge of ventral fin; muciferous crypts indistinct. (Pl. 27.)

Teeth 0/0; no horny mandibles; no papillae; upper labial edge dark and emarginate in middle, sometimes with traces of papilla-like processes on margins of upper jaw flaps; just below emargination is a lower light-colored (or dark as in some *mazatlanensis*), median, beaklike prolongation on margin of lower labium. (Pl. 28.)

General color black, overlaid with fine yellow, light purplish-gray, Quaker drab, or hair-brown dots; transverse stripe of belly divided in middle and apricot yellow or buff yellow in color; along either side of belly a light buff stripe; another such stripe on either side of gill region; sometimes whole venter with small, light buff or pale orange-yellow spots, heaviest on belly and sides and lightest on throat; interspaces are purplish gray, violet gray, or plumbeous; (in *mazatlanensis* there is mid-ventral light stripe and one ventrolaterally on either side converging somewhat anteriorly; additionally there is a scattering of light spots and blotches ventrally); tail with light buff or white stripe along middle of muscular part, reduced to few scattered blotches (most abundant basally in *mazatlanensis*); after first ½ inch, stripe breaks up into spots, which finally disappear caudally; above and below this continuous stripe is clear black; above this black is light purplish gray or there are Quaker drab dots; Quaker drab not present in ventral fin; ventral and dorsal fins on caudal half including muscular part heavily blotched with black or rather light purplish gray or hair brown giving tail tip almost black appearance; scattered spots most abundant in dorsal fin (anteriorly on tail in *mazatlanensis*) (largely from Wright, 1929:15, *carolinensis,* southeastern United States).

Combined description of 4 mature larvae, RCS 3246, obtained July 16-18, 1949, 1 mile northeast of Peña Blanca Springs, Santa Cruz County, Arizona: Above brown, speckled irregularly and somewhat vaguely with black on body and tail musculature; few cream spots extending into dorsal area laterally, especially behind eyes; tail musculature with black and light buffy-brown blotches laterally; similar markings on upper sides of body; tail fins translucent, with faint yellowish tinge; below light gray with cream-colored markings; this coloration extending on lower sides of body and onto tail base; scattering of pale, dull gold spots and blotches along lower margin of ventral fin and toward base of dorsal fin; iris pale copper.

Campbell (1934:7-8) found larvae on August 2, 1933, at Peña Blanca Springs, Arizona.

Transformation occurs the first season.

An individual lived 6 years 1 month in the Philadelphia Zoölogical Garden (Conant and Hudson, 1949:3).

Remarks.—I have followed Hecht and Matalas (1946) in regarding the form *olivacea* as a subspecies of *Microhyla carolinensis.* These authors found apparent intergrades between *M. carolinensis* and *M. olivacea* at several localities, including Latimer County, Oklahoma, and reduced the two forms to subspecific status. Smith (1934), under *Gastrophryne olivacea,* Wright and Wright (1949), and others have considered *olivacea* as a species distinct from *carolinensis.* Recently Blair (1950:152) has presented findings pertinent to an understanding of the relationship of these frogs.

A comparison of specimens of *olivacea* from the vicinity of Locust Grove, Mayes County, with specimens of *carolinensis* from near Oaks, Cherokee County, Oklahoma, reveals no indication of intergradation, yet the two localities in question are but 15 miles apart. Differences in ecological requirements would not seem to be important in separating the two forms in the region of contact.

None of the specimens from the first locality can possibly be confused with any of those from the second locality. In the specimens of *olivacea* the dorsum is olive, in the *carolinensis* it is brown; in the former the venter is immaculate, in the latter it is mottled. It is also to be noted that the specimens of *carolinensis* average considerably larger than those of *olivacea.*

Blair (1950:152) believes that the relationship of *carolinensis* and *olivacea* may be similar to that of *Bufo woodhousii* and *B. fowleri* (Blair, 1941), in which hybridization apparently takes place at some points of contact and not at others. The reluctance of males of *carolinensis* to clasp smaller females of *olivacea* would seem to constitute an incomplete isolating mechanism. Another such rudimentary isolating mechanism is the fact that *olivacea* is more dependent upon rainfall for breeding activity than is *carolinensis.*

Whether the relationship between *olivacea* and *mazatlanensis* (the form occurring in the area of this book) is like that between *olivacea* and *carolinensis* is unknown. In size and pigmentation *mazatlanensis* from Peña Blanca Springs, Arizona, more closely resembles *olivacea* than *carolinensis. Mazatlanensis* and *olivacea* probably intergrade.

I prefer to regard *olivaceous* and *carolinensis* as in the same species until their specific character, if it exists, can be shown more conclusively.

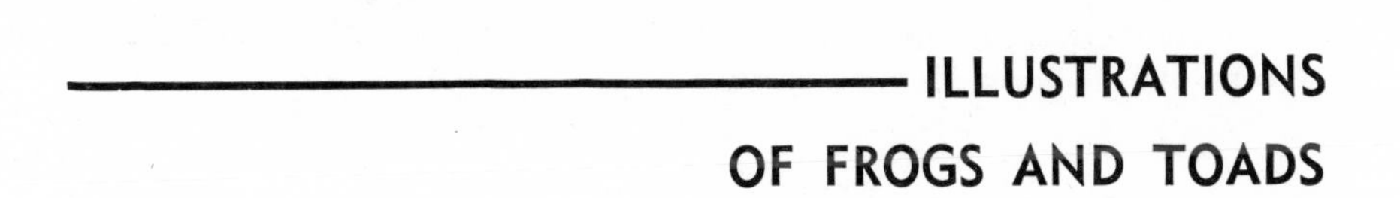
ILLUSTRATIONS
OF FROGS AND TOADS

Plate 14

Couch Spadefoot *Scaphiopus couchii,* Jornada del Muerto, 8.7 miles west and 22.8 miles south of New Bingham Post Office, Socorro County, New Mexico. × 2/3

Central Plains Spadefoot *Scaphiopus bombifrons,* Jornada del Muerto, 8.7 miles west and 22.8 miles south of New Bingham Post Office, Socorro County, New Mexico. × 2/3

Hammond Spadefoot *Scaphiopus hammondii,* MVZ 34979, 11½ miles east and 22 miles north of Gerlach, 4,200 feet, Pershing County, Nevada. × 5/6

Barking Frog *Eleutherodactylus latrans* (?), MVZ 28778, 2 miles east of Guirocoba, Sonora, Mexico. × 4/5

SCAPHIOPUS COUCHII

SCAPHIOPUS BOMBIFRONS

SCAPHIOPUS HAMMONDII

ELEUTHERODACTYLUS LATRANS

Plate 15

Colorado River Toad *Bufo alvarius.* Form based on MVZ 44715, Highway 92, 8 miles south of Fry, Cochise County, Arizona; color, MVZ 44716, Tres de Mayo Mine, 14 miles northeast of Nogales, Santa Cruz County, Arizona. × 5/6

Little Green Toad *Bufo debilis,* Jornada del Muerto, 8.7 miles west and 22.8 miles south of New Bingham Post Office, Socorro County, New Mexico. × 1

Hammond Spadefoot *Scaphiopus hammondii,* RCS 4724, Holladay, Salt Lake County, Utah. × 5/6

BUFO ALVARIUS

BUFO DEBILIS

SCAPHIOPUS HAMMONDII

Plate 16

Western Toad *Bufo boreas.*

Subspecies

Halophilus, turbid pool south of Westwood Village, West Los Angeles, Los Angeles County, California. × ¾

Exsul, MVZ 31426, Deep Springs Valley, 5,000 feet, Inyo County, California. × ¾

Yosemite Toad *Bufo canorus,* male, MVZ 31948, Tioga Pass, 9,950 feet, Tuolumne County, California; female, MVZ 16060, Tamarack Flat, 6,300 feet, Yosemite National Park, California. × ⅘

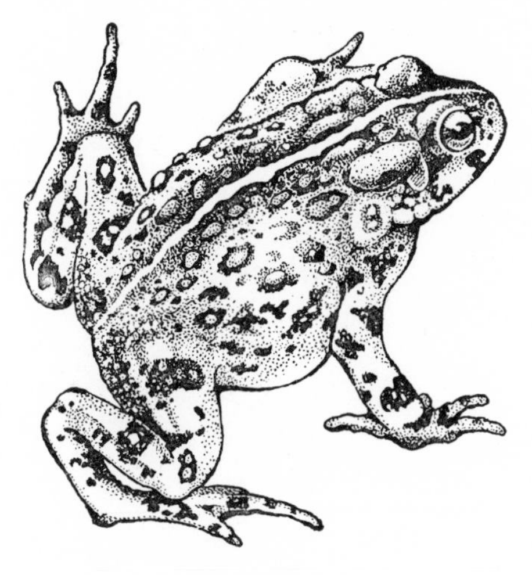

HALOPHILUS

EXSUL

BUFO BOREAS

MALE

FEMALE

BUFO CANORUS

Plate 17

Great Plains Toad *Bufo cognatus,* MVZ 14085, Crystal Spring, Pahrauagat Valley, Lincoln County, Nevada. × 3/4

Desert Toad *Bufo punctatus,* Joshua Tree National Monument, Riverside County, California. × 1

Sonoran Toad *Bufo compactilis,* MVZ 49374, Carlsbad, Eddy County, New Mexico. × 2/3

BUFO COGNATUS

BUFO PUNCTATUS

BUFO COMPACTILIS

Plate 18

Cope Toad *Bufo microscaphus.*

Subspecies

Microscaphus, MVZ 12899, Meadow Valley Wash, 7 miles south of Caliente, 4,000 feet, Lincoln County, Nevada. × 3/5

Californicus, MVZ 42337, Mohave River, 2 miles north of Victorville, San Bernardino County, California. × 3/5

Canadian Toad *Bufo hemiophrys,* AMNH 17869, Saskatchewan, Canada. × 2/3

Woodhouse Toad *Bufo woodhousii,* MVZ 29089, Paterson, 250 feet, Benton County, Washington. × 2/3

MICROSCAPHUS

CALIFORNICUS

BUFO MICROSCAPHUS

BUFO HEMIOPHRYS

BUFO WOODHOUSII

Plate 19

American Bell Toad *Ascaphus truei,* MVZ 17162, north side of Rogue River, 11 miles above its mouth, Curry County, Oregon. × 5/6

Sonoran Tree-toad *Hyla wrightorum,* MVZ 13835, Peterson Ranch, 6,100 feet, Huachuca Mountains, Cochise County, Arizona. × 5/6

Pacific Tree-toad *Hyla regilla,* O'Neals, Madera County, California. × 5/6

Canyon Tree-toad *Hyla arenicolor,* coastal southern California. × 5/6

Cricket-frog *Acris gryllus,* MVZ 41529, 5 miles east of Little Rock, Pulaski County, Arkansas. × 5/6

Swamp Cricket-frog *Pseudacris nigrita,* MVZ 29914, Paradise Park Reservoir, 15 miles north of Whiterocks, Uintah County, Utah. × 1

Narrow Mouth Toad *Microhyla carolinensis,* AMNH A53032, Trincheras, Sonora, Mexico. × 5/6

ASCAPHUS TRUEI

HYLA WRIGHTORUM

HYLA REGILLA

HYLA ARENICOLOR

ACRIS GRYLLUS

PSEUDACRIS NIGRITA

MICROHYLA CAROLINENSIS

BOYLII

MUSCOSA

RANA BOYLII SIERRAE

RANA SYLVATICA

Plate 20

Yellow-legged Frog *Rana boylii.*

Subspecies

Boylii, MVZ 35524, Waddell Creek, 100 feet, Santa Cruz County, California. × 5/6

Muscosa, MVZ 4856, trail up Mount Wilson, below half-way house, Los Angeles County, California. × 5/6

Sierrae, MVZ 31969, Elizabeth Lake, 9,500 feet, Tuolumne Meadows, Tuolumne County, California. × 5/6

Wood Frog *Rana sylvatica,* MVZ 8462, Kispiox Valley, 23 miles north of Hazelton, British Columbia, Canada. × 5/6

RANA TARAHUMARAE
Plate 21

Mexican Frog *Rana tarahumarae,* CAS 81453, Alamo Spring, Pajarito Mountains, Pima County, Arizona. × 5/6

Plate 22

Bullfrog *Rana catesbeiana,* MVZ 14669, Waterford, Stanislaus County, California (reared in Berkeley). × ½

Green Frog *Rana clamitans,* MVZ 29987, near Douglasville, Douglas County, Georgia. × ⅔

RANA CATESBEIANA

RANA CLAMITANS

Plate 23

Red-legged Frog *Rana aurora.*

Subspecies

Aurora, MVZ 40984, Strawberry Canyon, Berkeley, Alameda County, California. × ½

Cascadae, MVZ 41238, Manzanita Creek, 250 yards west of outlet of Manzanita Lake, 5,900 feet, Shasta County, California. Color pattern based mainly on MVZ 42724, Deer Creek, 11 miles west-southwest of Lake Almanor, Tehama County, California. × ⅔

Spotted Frog *Rana pretiosa,* OSCMNH 5827, McFadden's Marsh, 12 miles south of Corvallis, Benton County, Oregon. × ⅔

Leopard Frog *Rana pipiens,* MVZ 49439, 13 miles northeast of Provo, Utah County, Utah. × ⅔

RANA AURORA

RANA PRETIOSA

RANA PIPIENS

Eggs and Larvae

EGGS

Drawings of anuran eggs have been adapted largely from Livezey and Wright (1947). Those of salamanders have been made from fresh material unless otherwise indicated. (Pls. 24, 25, pp. 431, 433.)

Pigmented eggs are represented in black, unpigmented ones in white. When pigmented, the melanic material is situated near the surface of the ovum and is heaviest at the animal pole, thinning laterally and often disappearing ventrally.

There is considerable variation in the intensity of pigment, the color of eggs varying from tan or olive to black. The pigment probably helps to protect eggs laid in illuminated situations from deleterious radiation. This idea has been supported by experiment. Two lots of eggs from a single batch have been radiated from the vegetal and from the animal poles. Survival was considerably lower in the former. In line with this explanation for the pigment, it is of interest that unpigmented eggs are laid in situations where light is absent or weak. In our area, such eggs are deposited by salamanders such as *Rhyacotriton, Dicamptodon,* and the plethodontids; and among anurans, by *Ascaphus truei*. Size of egg shows little correlation with size of species.

Following fertilization, the zygote becomes movable within the egg capsule by liquefaction of the innermost layer of jelly. It thus comes to lie with the animal pole uppermost, in a fluid-filled chamber, the capsular cavity. The result is that the animal pole, the area of most intense embryonic activity, at least in the earlier stages of development, maintains a constant orientation with respect to gravity and, in exposed eggs, to light. At an early stage of development cilia form and the embryo rotates. The egg may nearly fill the capsular chamber (as in most anurans) or may be considerably smaller (as in the newts).

There may be 1 to 4 transparent gelatinous envelopes. The jelly is deposited about the eggs as they pass through the oviducts. When the eggs are laid, the gelatinous material absorbs water and the capsules thicken.

Eggs may be laid singly or in a mass, in the form of a cylinder, sphere, plate, or in files or strings. The individual eggs may be free or variously connected. When attached they may be broadly adherent, connected by strands of jelly, or attached individually to a common base.

The eggs of our salamanders are laid in aquatic or terrestrial situations, the latter by plethodontids. The frogs and toads all deposit their eggs in the water with the exception of *Eleutherodactylus latrans.*

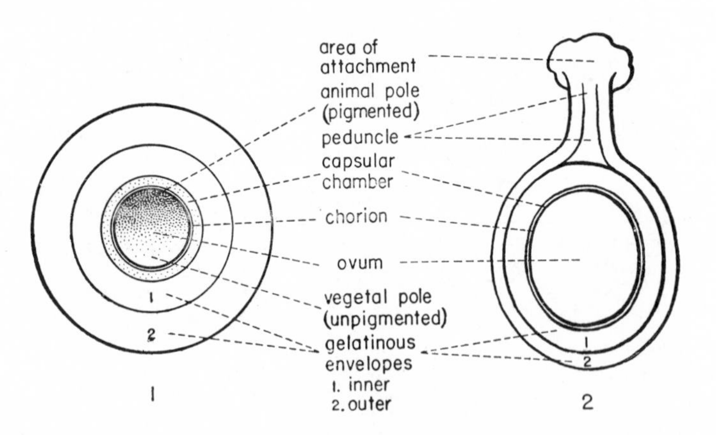

Fig. 32. Structural characteristics of amphibian eggs. Diagram 2 is the egg of a plethodontid salamander.

Key to Amphibian Eggs

(Section on anurans largely adapted from Livezey and Wright, 1947)

1*a*. Eggs unpigmented 2

1*b*. Eggs pigmented 13

2*a*. (1*a*) Deposited in terrestrial situations[15] (damp places in logs, under bark, beneath rocks, in rock crevices, or pockets in the ground) 3

2*b*. Deposited in truly aquatic situations (floating or submerged in water) 11

3*a*. (2*a*) Eggs with peduncles or connected by slender strand of jelly and arranged like a string of beads; eggs disconnected from string may have slender strand of varying length at either end; 2 jelly envelopes (not readily discerned unless envelopes swollen with water)[16] 4

3*b*. Eggs without peduncles, unattached or broadly attached to substratum or each other; 2 or 3 jelly envelopes 8

4*a*. (3*a*) Eggs commonly pendant, suspended by peduncle of variable length; 2 transparent jelly layers present, outer one usually with low, rounded, nipple-like projection opposite peduncle 5

4*b*. Eggs usually not suspended—arranged in rosary-like string or if separated, peduncles adherent to substratum. Two transparent jelly envelopes present, outer one without nipple-like projection although fragment of jelly strand may be present 7

5*a*. (4*a*) Peduncle short, around 3 to 6 mm. in length. Eggs apparently commonly deposited in cavities in ground. Season, probably May to August .... *Aneides flavipunctatus*, p. 134

5*b*. Peduncle longer, approximately 8 to 20 mm. in length 6

6*a*. (5*b*) Eggs larger, laid in hollows in trees or logs and in cavities in ground. Ovum 6.9 by 7.4 mm. Season, probably from June to September .... *Aneides lugubris*, p. 144

6*b*. Eggs smaller, probably most commonly laid in hollows in trees or rotten logs. Ovum 4.1 by 5.1 mm. Season, probably June to September ..*Aneides ferreus*, p. 129

7*a*. (4*b*) Egg smaller, ovum approximately 3 to 4 mm., 4 to 6 mm. to outer capsule. Season, November to March .... *Batrachoseps attenuatus*, p. 113

7*b*. Egg larger, ovum approximately 4 mm., 9 to 10 mm. to outer capsule. Season, April to ? .... *Batrachoseps wrighti*, p. 123

8*a*. (3*b*) Egg surrounded by 2 layers of jelly. Eggs usually adherent to one another and to substratum, forming grapelike mass. Deposited in cavities in ground in damp soil or in rotten logs. Range, southwestern mainland and Vancouver Island, British Columbia, south in coastal areas to extreme southern San Diego County, California. Ranges inland in California through the Siskiyou and southern Cascade Mountains southward through the Sierra Nevada and thence into the mountains of southern California. Season, April to September .... *Ensatina eschscholtzii*, p. 100

[15] *Dicamptodon*, *Rhyacotriton*, and *Plethodon dunni* are included here with uncertainty. One clutch of *Dicamptodon* eggs was found attached to a submerged timber, another lot was washed out of a subterranean spring, with drilling operations. The mode of occurrence is hence not well known. Eggs of *Rhyacotriton* presumably were found by Phillips Putnam but were not certainly identified. They occurred in a spray-drenched situation along a well-shaded mountain stream. The manner of deposition of *P. dunni* eggs is inferred from the habits of the adults.

[16] Number of jelly layers of eggs of western plethodontid salamanders readily determined only in freshly laid eggs. Later in development the egg capsule becomes thin and membranous and the gelatinous layers are not easily discerned.

8*b*. Egg surrounded by 2 or 3 layers of jelly and attached to substratum or deposited in a cluster (as based on eggs deposited in captivity) 9

9*a*. (8*b*) Eggs probably to be found in water-soaked situations, attached to under surfaces or sides of rocks 10

9*b*. Eggs probably to be found in less soaked situations, judging from behavior of adults, probably beneath bark and in rotten logs and beneath rocks and other surface objects or in cavities in the ground; 2 envelopes. Range, southwestern British Columbia including Vancouver Island, south, west of crest of the Cascades, through Washington into northwestern Oregon, at least as far south as vicinity of Coquille, Coos County. Season, May to ? .... *Plethodon vehiculum*, p. 87

10*a*. (9*a*) Apparently 2 envelopes; ovum, 4.5 mm. in diameter; inner jelly layer, 0.4 mm.; second layer, 0.08 mm.; and outer layer, 1.0 mm. in thickness (measurements based on recently laid eggs deposited in captivity). Eggs broadly attached to substratum and tending to adhere to one another. Thirteen eggs constituted clutch. Eggs laid in captivity on May 25 and 26. Range, western Oregon from the Rogue River Basin, Curry County, in the southwestern part of the state, north to immediately north of the Columbia River in Wahkiakum and Cowlitz counties, Washington. Not known east of the crest of the Cascade Range. Season, May to ? .... *Plethodon dunni*, p. 71

10*b*. Three envelopes; ovum, 3.8 to 4.0 mm. in diameter; inner jelly layer, 0.7 mm.; second layer, 0.3 mm.; and outer layer, 7.7 mm. in thickness (calculated from figure of Noble and Richards, 1932:21). Eggs per female number 7 to 15, average 9. Range, middle Humboldt County, California, north into the Olympic Peninsula of Washington. Not known east of the Cascades. Season, June to ? .... *Rhyacotriton olympicus*, p. 59

11*a*. (2*b*) Eggs in rosary-like strings attached to underside of stones in cold mountain streams; to outer surface of single envelope, 8 mm. in diameter. Season, May to September .... *Ascaphus truei*, p. 191

11*b*. Eggs laid separately, not in a rosary-like string 12

12*a*. (11*b*) Eggs attached singly beneath or on sides of stones in running water; ovum 3.8 to 4.0 mm. in diameter; middle layer much thinner than other coats; egg, with membranes, measuring about 7.5 mm. in diameter. Season, probably April through July .... *Rhyacotriton olympicus*, p. 59

12*b*. Eggs attached by short peduncles, about 70 present in single clutch described; ovum about 5.5 to 6.0 mm. in diameter. Eggs in subterranean springs or in streams. Season, March to ? .... *Dicamptodon ensatus*, p. 52

13*a*. (1*b*) Eggs largely deposited singly 14

13*b*. Eggs largely deposited in masses 20

14*a*. (13*a*) Two or more gelatinous envelopes 15

14*b*. One gelatinous envelope (capsular cavity in which ovum may move as egg is rotated, not regarded here as a jelly layer) 16

15*a*. (14*a*) Eggs with 3 jelly layers. Eggs attached to twigs, weeds, and other objects at rather shallow depths in quiet water. Ovum pigmented, 1.9 to 4.0 mm. in diameter; 2 inner jelly layers somewhat thinner and denser than outer coat; egg, with membranes, measuring about 4.5 to 10.0 mm. in diameter. Season, December (*californiense*) through March, or perhaps later .... *Ambystoma tigrinum*, p. 45

15*b*. Eggs with 2 jelly layers 15c

15*c*. (15*b*) Ovum 2.5 mm. in diameter; outer envelope 12 to 17 mm., depending on amount of water absorption by capsules. Season, February to April (?) .... *Ambystoma macrodactylum,* p. 39

15*d*. Ovum 1.06 to 1.17 mm. in diameter; outer envelope 2.98 to 3.70 mm. Season, generally February to October. In area covered by book, only in extreme eastern Colorado and New Mexico .... *Acris gryllus crepitans,* p. 300

16*a*. (14*b*) Eggs with large capsular cavity in which ovum moves freely when eggs inverted 17

16*b*. Eggs without conspicuous capsular cavity, not extensively movable within capsules 18

17*a*. (16*a*) Eggs smaller, ovum measuring about 1.8 mm. in diameter; diameter of capsular cavity approximately 2.7 mm.; outer jelly capsule 0.7 to 0.8 mm. in thickness; eggs commonly laid singly. Season, December to June ...... *Triturus granulosus,* p. 19

17*b*. Eggs larger, usually laid in compact clusters, only incidentally singly; ovum about 2 mm. in diameter; diameter of capsular cavity approximately 5 mm.; outer jelly capsule 0.5 to 1.0 mm. in thickness. Season, December to April or perhaps later .... *Triturus torosus,* p. 27

18*a*. (16*b*) Ovum 1.8 to 2.4 mm., average 2.07 mm.; envelope 3.87 to 5.0 mm., average 4.4 mm. Eggs usually attached to leaves, sticks, debris, and rocks on or near the bottom; may sometimes be floating, and in small potholes may be clumped. Season, first of March to July .... *Hyla arenicolor,* p. 320

18*b*. Ovum 1.3 mm. or less (0.9 to 1.3 mm.) 19

19*a*. (18*b*) Ovum 1.0 to 1.3 mm.; black above and white below; envelope 3.2 to 3.6 mm. Eggs stuck to bottom of streams, pools, etc.; may appear in short strings (files) or sometimes as a loose bottom film; sometimes occur as surface film. Season, April to June .... *Bufo punctatus,* p. 284

19*b*. Ovum 1.06 to 1.17 mm. (average 1.13 mm.) in diameter; dark brown to black above and tan below. Outer envelope 2.98 to 3.70 mm.; firm and definite in outline. Eggs deposited in shallow water, strewn on the bottom, or attached to stems of grass or other vegetation. Complement may be 315 to 340 eggs. Season, extensive, any month of year in parts of Texas; February to October elsewhere ...... *Acris gryllus crepitans,* p. 300

20*a*. (13*b*) Mass consists of surface film or submerged layer, often single egg in thickness 21

20*b*. Mass consists of submerged strings, or clusters 24

21*a*. (20*a*) Mass consists of surface film deposited in relatively quiet water 22

21*b*. Mass consists of submerged layer, deposited usually on stones in moderately fast to rapidly flowing water. Ovum around 2.75 mm.; freely movable in large fluid-filled capsular cavity; firm jelly capsule surrounds capsular cavity. Range, known from Sonoma, Mendocino, and Humboldt counties, California. Probably also in Del Norte County, California. Apparently restricted to coastal California north of San Francisco Bay. Season, April and probably extending over longer period .... *Triturus rivularis,* p. 22

22*a*. (21*a*) Size of film large; 35 square inches (5 inches by 7 inches) or larger; 1 or 2 gelatinous envelopes, 5.6 to 10.4 mm. to outer surface of outer jelly layer 23

22*b*. Size of film smaller; 28 square inches (4 inches by 7 inches) or less; 1 gelatinous envelope, measuring 2.8 to 4.0 mm. Deposited in any depression containing water, temporary or permanent. Season, July and perhaps earlier and later .... *Microhyla carolinensis mazatlanensis*, p. 393

23*a*. (22*a*) One gelatinous envelope, 6.4 to 10.4 mm., average 7.6 mm., loose and merges into mass; size of film large, 35 square inches (5 inches by 7 inches) or larger. Deposited among water plants or brush. Species introduced at scattered localities in western United States. Season, February to July .... *Rana catesbeiana*, p. 349

23*b*. Two gelatinous envelopes. Mass less than one square foot in extent (5-7 inches by 12 inches). Usually deposited around margins of permanent ponds, either attached to vegetation or free. Species introduced in western Washington and southwestern British Columbia. Season, last of March to mid-August .... *Rana clamitans*, p. 353

24*a*. (20*b*) Eggs in loose, irregular cylinders or bands and files or strings 41

24*b*. Eggs in lumps; not as above 25

25*a*. (24*b*) Each egg with only 1 gelatinous envelope (fluid-filled capsular cavity, conspicuous in some eggs, and thin layer on inner side of envelope, next to capsular cavity [in *Triturus*], not considered as jelly layers) 26

25*b*. Each egg with 2 or 3 gelatinous envelopes 31

26*a*. (25*a*) Ovum in large fluid-filled capsular cavity; moves conspicuously when egg inverted 27

26*b*. Ovum in restricted capsular cavity 30

27*a*. (26*a*) Smaller masses, not more than 25 cc. in volume, outside diameter of mass not more than 30 mm.; outer jelly coat around individual eggs about 8 mm. in diameter 28

27*b*. Larger masses, 150 cc. or more in volume, outside dimensions 60 by 70 by 80 mm. or more; individual jelly capsules about 10 mm. in diameter. Deposited in ponds or pools along stream courses attached to vegetation beneath surface. Season, January to July .... *Ambystoma gracile*, p. 34

28*a*. (27*a*) Egg mass flattened, usually single egg in thickness. Season, April to ? .... *Triturus rivularis*, p. 22

28*b*. Egg mass spherical 29

29*a*. (28*b*) Egg larger, ovum about 2.8 mm. in diameter. Season, March and April or perhaps later .... *Triturus t. sierrae*, p. 27

29*b*. Egg smaller, ovum about 2.06 to 2.35 mm. in diameter. Deposited in ponds or at sides of streams down to 150 mm. below surface of water, attached to vegetation or other objects. Season, December to April or perhaps later .... *Triturus t. torosus*, p. 27

30*a*. (26*b*) Mass plinthlike or globular, relatively firm. Envelope fairly distinct; ovum 1.81 to 2.12 mm., average 1.97 mm. Number of eggs per mass large, 2,400; eggs 1/4 to 3/4 inch apart. Mass 3 inches by 3 inches to 8 inches by 6 inches, with bluish cast. Deposited in shallow water near margins of ponds. Season, March to ? .... *Rana pretiosa luteiventris*, p. 370

30*b*. Mass loose, irregular cluster. Envelope indistinct; ovum 0.9 to 1.2. mm. Fifteen to 300 eggs per mass, usually less than 100; complement 500 to 1,459± per female. Mass usually less than one inch in diameter and deposited in clear pools attached to vegetation. Season, about March 20 to May 20 .... *Pseudacris nigrita triseriata,* p. 310

31*a*. (25*b*) Two envelopes present 32

31*b*. Three envelopes present 34

32*a*. (31*a*) Mass is a firm regular cluster 33

32*b*. Mass is a loose cluster, usually one inch or less in diameter 38

33*a*. (32*a*) Mass is a sphere 2½ to 4 inches in diameter, containing 2,000 to 3,000 eggs. Deposited in ponds in woods or fields, attached to vegetation. Season, March to July .... *Rana sylvatica cantabrigensis,* p. 379

33*b*. Mass is a plinth 1 to 4 by 2 to 6 by 2 to 12 inches in size, containing 1,000 to 7,000 eggs 40

34*a*. (31*b*) Outer envelope 3.88 to 4.47 mm., average 4.0 mm. Deposited in shallow water near margins of streams, attached to stones in stream bed. Pick up much sediment. Season, latter part of March to first of May .. *Rana boylii boylii,* p. 341

34*b*. Outer envelope 6.43 to 14.0 mm. 35

35*a*. (34*b*) Number of eggs per mass 425 or less 36

35*b*. Number of eggs per mass 750 to 4,000 37

36*a*. (35*a*) Outer envelope 6.43 to 7.87 mm., average 7.19 mm.; middle envelope 4.25 to 5.0 mm., average 4.60 mm.; inner envelope 3.75 to 4.81 mm., average 3.93 mm. Mass of 100 to 350 eggs deposited near banks of small streams, attached to stems of sedge, etc. or to bank itself. Season, June to August .... *Rana boylii sierrae,* p. 341

36*b*. Outer envelope 11.3± mm.; middle envelope 5.8 mm.; inner envelope 4.9 mm. Season, last half of May to first half of July .... *Rana aurora cascadae,* p. 336

37*a*. (35*b*) All gelatinous envelopes indistinct, particularly middle one. Outer envelope 10 to 14 mm.; middle envelope 6.25 to 7.93 mm., average 6.80 mm.; inner envelope 4.0 to 6.68 mm., average 5.70 mm.; ovum 2.31 to 3.56 mm., average 3.04 mm. Seven hundred and fifty to 1,300 eggs in flat masses 6 to 10 inches across. Masses deposited at surface of water attached to vegetation. Season, March to July .... *Rana aurora aurora,* p. 336

37*b*. All gelatinous envelopes quite distinct, middle one particularly dense and distinct. Outer envelope 7.55 to 11.80 mm., average 8.5 mm.; middle envelope 3.94 to 6.40 mm., average 4.40 mm.; inner envelope 3.1 to 5.0 mm., average 3.5 mm.; ovum 2.06 to 2.81 mm., average 2.1 mm. Two thousand to 4,000 eggs in soft viscid mass 2¾ by 4 by 3 to 6 by 4 by 4 inches. Masses deposited in overflow areas of permanent pools, attached to vegetation just below surface in water 3 to 6 inches deep. Season, January to March; crest January and February .... *Rana aurora draytonii,* p. 336

38*a*. (32*b*) Cluster elliptical. Eggs sometimes attached to objects by stalk of jelly. Deposited in muddy or clear pools of all sorts near bottom; attached to vegetation or objects projecting from bottom at edge of water; masses close together. Season, last of May to August .... *Scaphiopus bombifrons,* p. 206

38*b*. Cluster irregular 39

39*a*. (38*b*) Outer envelope 4.7 to 6.7 mm., sticky; ovum 1.23 to 1.35 mm., average 1.3 mm.; 9 to 70 eggs per packet, usually about 22 to 25. Packets deposited in shallow water of any sort of quiet pond, attached to vegetation. Season, January to mid-May .... *Hyla regilla,* p. 325

39*b*. Outer envelope 2.98 to 3.70 mm. 39c

39*c*. (39*b*) Fifteen to 300 eggs per mass, usually less than 100; ovum 0.9 to 1.2 mm. Mass usually less than 1 inch in diameter and deposited in clear pools attached to vegetation. Season, about March 20 to late June .... *Pseudacris nigrita triseriata,* p. 310

39*d*. Two to 7 eggs per mass; ovum 1.06 to 1.17 mm., average 1.13 mm. Season, February to October .... *Acris gryllus crepitans,* p. 300

40*a*. (33*b*) Outer envelope large, 10 to 15 mm.; inner envelope 5 to 6 mm., indistinct; 1,100 to 1,500 eggs in mass 8 by 6 inches. Deposited in shallow water unattached among grasses at edges of ponds; top layer of eggs at surface of water. Season, February to July .... *Rana pretiosa pretiosa,* p. 370

40*b*. Outer envelope smaller, average 5 mm., range 2.5 to 5.6 mm. (seldom as small as 2.5 mm., except immediately after deposition); inner envelope 1.5 to 3.4 mm., average 2.25 mm., distinct. Thirty-five hundred to 6,500 eggs deposited in open marshy expanses near surface, usually attached to grasses or other vegetation but sometimes free. Season, March to mid-May .... *Rana pipiens,* p. 362

41*a*. (24*a*) Mass loose, irregular cylinder or band, attached along plant stems, blades of grass, or between 2 adjacent plants 42

41*b*. Mass consisting of files or strings 43

42*a*. (41*a*) Two gelatinous envelopes present. Cylindrical mass containing 10 to 42 eggs. Masses deposited in temporary pools attached to plant stems, grass, or upper surface of small rocks. Eggs occasionally attached to vegetation by stalk 5 to 10 mm. long. Season, mid-February to August. .*Scaphiopus hammondii hammondii,* p. 214

42*b*. One gelatinous envelope present. Forty-five to 125 eggs close together in rather firm cylinder. Attached to vegetation in water usually less than 6 inches in depth. Season, April to August .... *Scaphiopus couchii,* p. 200

43*a*. (41*b*) Files or strings without continuous gelatinous encasing, like string of beads 44

43*b*. Files or strings with continuous gelatinous encasing 45

44*a*. (43*a*) Two gelatinous envelopes present. File of 10 to 42 eggs deposited in temporary pools attached to vegetation or to upper surface of small rocks. Season, mid-February to August .... *Scaphiopus hammondii hammondii,* p. 214

44*b*. One gelatinous envelope present, 3.2 to 3.6 mm. Files short, commonly deposited on bottom of small, shallow often rock-bound pools. Season, April to September, with May commonest month .... *Bufo punctatus,* p. 284

45*a*. (43*b*) One envelope present 46

45*b*. Two envelopes present 49

46*a*. (45*a*) Envelope more than 5 mm. in diameter, 5.62 to 6.12 mm., average 5.77 mm. Eggs deposited in tangled strings on bottom of pool among leaves, sticks, gravel, mud, etc. Season, May and June .... *Bufo microscaphus californicus,* p. 273

46*b*. Envelope less than 5 mm. in diameter (1.8 to 4.6 mm.) 47

47*a*. (46*b*) Envelope 2.6 to 4.6 mm., average about 3.5 mm. Long strings, 8 to 10 feet, deposited in tangled mass around vegetation or debris in practically any type of pool or stream. Season, March to July .... *Bufo woodhousii,* p. 292

47*b*. Envelope 2.4 mm. or less (1.8 to 2.4 mm.) 48

48*a*. (47*b*) Envelope slightly scalloped in appearance. Long coils deposited in temporary pools. Season, first of May to mid-July .... *Bufo compactilis,* p. 256

48*b*. Envelope not scalloped. Long (400 inches) ropelike strings of 7,500 to 8,000 eggs deposited in temporary pools or shallow streams in water 12 to 18 inches deep, usually after first heavy summer showers. Season, May to July.................... ....*Bufo alvarius,* p. 233

49*a*. (45*b*) Partitions separating individual eggs. Envelopes decidedly scalloped, almost beadlike, appear laminated. Eggs deposited after heavy rains in temporary pools, permanent springs, and small streams, attached to debris near bottom. Season, April to September .... *Bufo cognatus,* p. 252

49*b*. No partitions separating individual eggs 50

50*a*. (49*b*) Ovum 1.65 to 1.75 mm. Masses of 16,500 eggs deposited in long strings along margins of ponds and streams in shallow water, not deeper than 300 mm., usually in water less than 150 mm. Range, from Mendocino and Butte counties south into northern Lower California. Season, January to July .... *Bufo boreas halophilus,* p. 241

50*b*. Ovum 1.50 to 1.75 mm. Range, from northeastern California to Colorado, thence north and west through western Montana to Puget Sound. Also to British Columbia and southwestern Alaska to Prince William Sound. Season, March to September, crest during June and July .... *Bufo boreas boreas,* p. 241

ILLUSTRATIONS OF AMPHIBIAN EGGS

Plate 24

Eggs of salamanders. × $1\frac{3}{5}$

(Pigmented eggs are shown in black, unpigmented ones in white.)

1. *Triturus granulosus*
2. *T. rivularis*
3. *T. torosus sierrae*
4. *T. torosus torosus* (Storer, 1925)
5. *Dicamptodon ensatus* (Thickness of jelly capsule and size of pedicel estimated.)
6. *Rhyacotriton olympicus*
7. *Ambystoma gracile* (Storer, 1925)
8. *Ambystoma macrodactylum*
9. *Ambystoma tigrinum* (*californiense*) (Storer, 1925)
10. *Plethodon dunni*
11. *P. vehiculum*
12. *Ensatina eschscholtzii*
13. *Batrachoseps attenuatus*
14. *B. wrighti*
15. *Aneides ferreus*
16. *A. lugubris*
17. *A. flavipunctatus* (subspecies *niger*, Saratoga, California)
18. *A. flavipunctatus* (subspecies *flavipunctatus*, Hayden Flat, Trinity County, California)

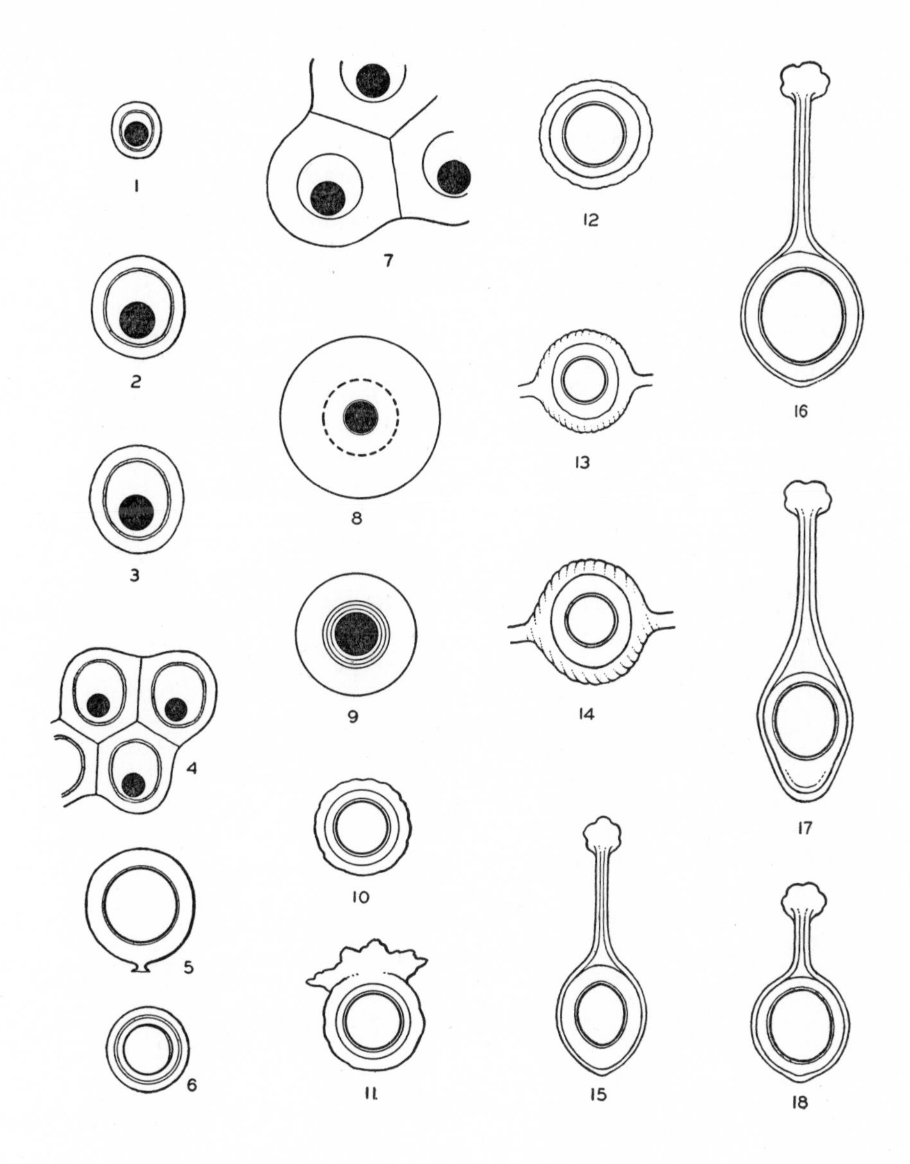
1
2
3
4
5
6
7
8
9
10
11
12
13
14
15
16
17
18

Plate 25

Eggs of anurans (largely adapted from Livezey and Wright, 1947). × 1⅘
(Jelly layers of indistinct outline are indicated by broken lines)

1. *Ascaphus truei*
2. *Scaphiophus couchii*
3. *S. hammondii hammondii*
4a. *Bufo alvarius*
4b. " "
5a. *B. boreas halophilus*
5b. " " "
6. *B. microscaphus californicus*
7. *B. cognatus*
8. *B. compactilis*
9. *B. punctatus*
10a. *B. woodhousii*
10b. " "
11. *Hyla arenicolor*
12. *H. regilla*
13a. *Acris gryllus*
13b. " "
14a. *Pseudacris nigrita triseriata*
14b. " " "
14c. " " "
15a. *Rana tarahumarae* (Some uncertainty in identification. See p. 384.)
15b. *Rana boylii boylii*
16. *R. boylii sierrae*
17. *R. aurora aurora*
18. *R. a. draytonii*
19. *R. a. cascadae*
20. *R. clamitans*
21. *R. catesbeiana*
22. *R. pipiens*
23. *R. pretiosa pretiosa*
24. *R. p. luteiventris*
25. *R. sylvatica cantabrigensis*
26. *Microhyla carolinensis mazatlanensis*

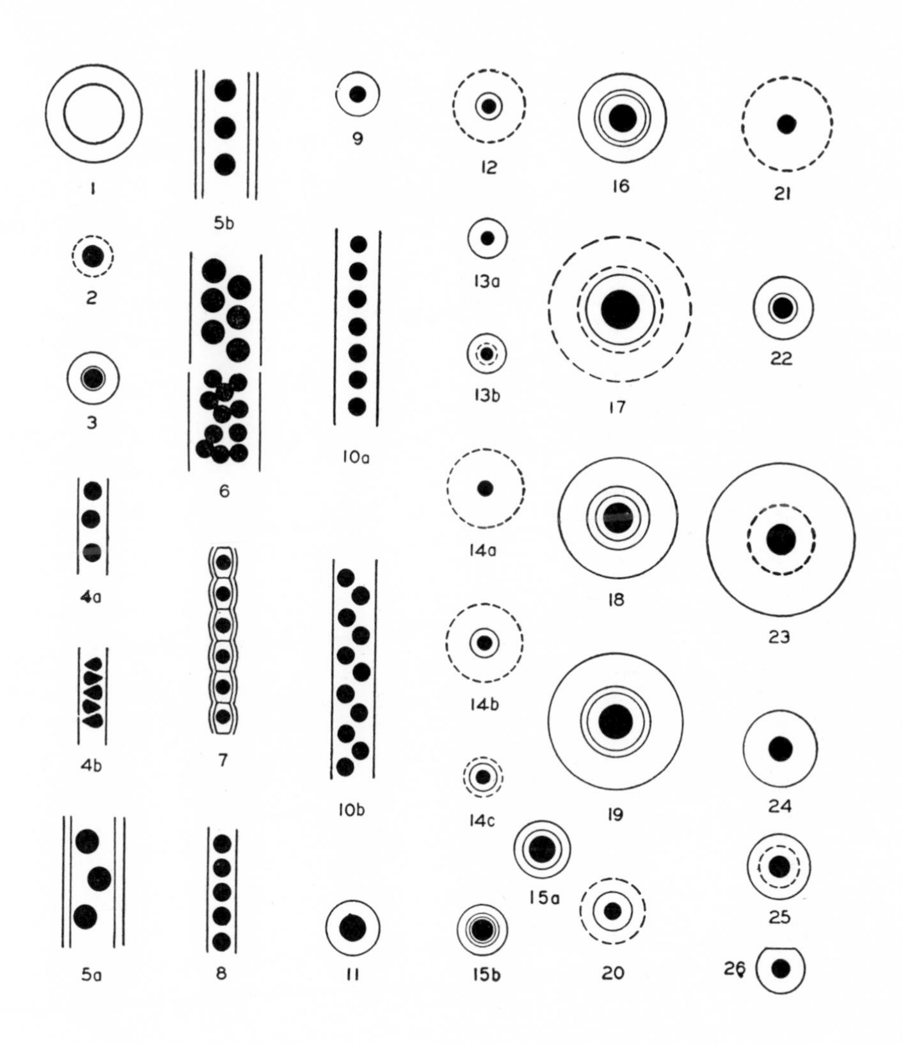
1
5b
9
12
16
21
2
13a
22
3
13b
17
10a
6
14a
4a
18
23
14b
4b
7
19
24
10b
14c
15a
25
5a
8
11
15b
20
26

LARVAE

Salamanders.—Plate 26, page 447, shows aquatic salamander larvae in dorsal and lateral views. Relative size is not shown. Two structural types are recognized (Fig. 33), the (1) pond and (2) mountain brook (or stream) types. The former is characterized by large tail fins, the high dorsal fin extending forward to the insertion of the forelimbs; the gills are long and plumelike; the toes are long; and a pair of balancers is usually present in young larvae (fig. 34, 4, p. 437). The balancers are thought to function in aiding the newly hatched larva, when resting on the bottom, in keeping its gills free from bottom muck. They are lost, as the limbs become more fully formed. The stream type larva is specialized for life in moving water. The broad fins of the pond type larva have given way to a more streamlined tail with reduced fins; the toes are shorter; and the gills are reduced, possibly related to the increased oxygen content of turbulent water. A third type (Fig. 33), the terrestrial larva of plethodontid salamanders, exhibits further specializations—the tail fins are gone; the gills are commonly large, leaflike, and highly vascular, lying just below the egg capsule, and functioning in respiration.

Upon metamorphosis the aquatic larvae lose their gills and tail fins, develop eyelids, and undergo changes in dentition and tongue structure. The larvae of some species, however (*Ambystoma tigrinum, A. gracile,*

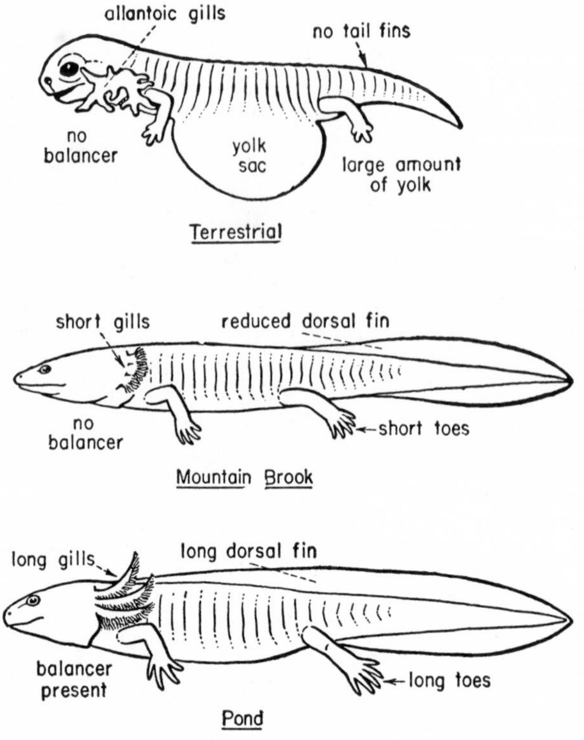

Fig. 33. Salamander larval types. The species upon which the drawings were based are, from top to bottom, *Batrachoseps wrighti, Dicamptodon ensatus,* and *Ambystoma macrodactylum.*

etc.), may remain as larvae and some may breed in the larval state (pedogenesis). Young of our terrestrial species emerge from the egg, fully formed.

Anurans.—Plates 27 to 34, pages 449 to 463, depict form and pigmentation of tadpoles and their mouth parts. Relative size (with a few exceptions noted) is shown. For the most part pigmentation is shown as it appears in preserved specimens, hence eyes appear black with white pupils, visceral masses dark, etc. Identification of western tadpoles as to family is not difficult, with perhaps the exception of the Hylidae and Ranidae, which are much alike. Recognition of species within a family such as the Ranidae is more difficult. Information on tadpole variation is largely lacking; some species are known only from scant material, hence statements in the key, for such species, may not be adequate.

Illustrations are of tadpoles well along in development, at or beyond the third stage of Dugès (time of appearance of the hind-limb buds).

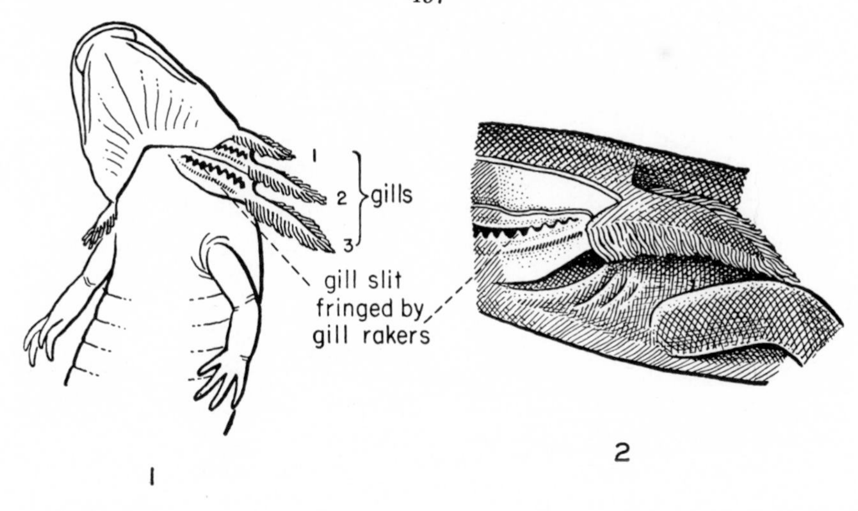

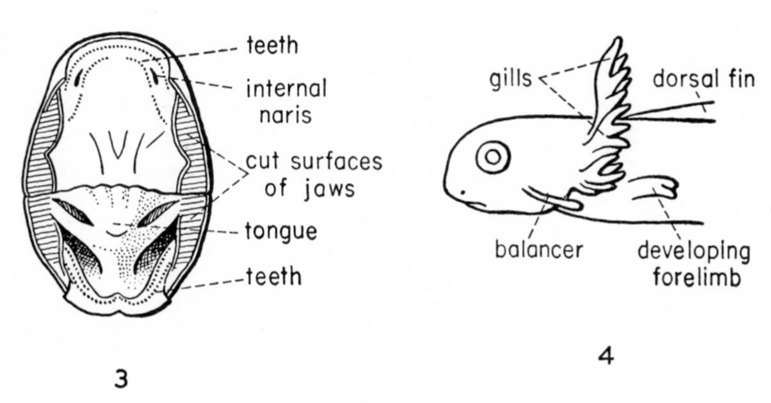

Fig. 34. Larval structures in salamanders. 1. Gills spread to show gill rakers. 2. Gill rakers on the anterior surface of the third gill arch. 3. Widely opened mouth of an aquatic larval salamander to show the arrangement of the teeth. 4. Early stage pond-type larva showing the balancer.

Mouth parts are represented semidiagrammatically. The mouth typically consists of an oral disc fringed by one or more rows of oral or labial papillae (probably sensory in function), several rows of labial teeth, and a pair of horny mandibles. The dental equipment functions in scraping detritic and plant material from rocks, sticks, and other objects in the water. The mandibles may be used by some species (spadefoot toads and others) in capturing and dismembering animal prey. The labial teeth, under magnification, are seen to consist of numerous short, horny spines arranged in a row like the teeth of a comb. The dental formula $\frac{2}{3}$ refers to the number of labial tooth rows on the upper and lower labia. Range in number of tooth rows is shown in the following manner: $\frac{2\text{-}5}{3\text{-}6}$ (fig. 35, p. 439).

Newly hatched tadpoles possess external gills and generally a pair of ventral suckers which serve as a holdfast. With further development, folds of skin grow posteriorly in the head region. External gills are succeeded by internal ones that come to lie within the overgrowing opercular folds. The ventral suckers disappear. Eventually the operculum encloses the gills except for the spiracular opening. Water taken in through the mouth is passed over the gills and out the spiraculum (spiracle).

Most anuran larvae are herbivorous and scavenging in their feeding habits. They possess a long intestine, coiled, watchspring-like. Hind-limb buds appear at the base of the tail and the forelimbs develop, concealed in the gill chambers. With the approach of metamorphosis, the forelimbs are passed through the opercular covering. In those species (the majority) with the spiracle on the left side, the left limb is passed through the spiracular opening usually somewhat before the appearance of the right limb. The right limb is thrust through the opercular covering, the tissues of which are probably broken down by chemical and mechanical forces. With metamorphosis, the larval mouth parts are modified—the labial tooth rows and papillae are lost, the gape of the mouth increases, the horny covering of the mandibles disappears, and, depending on the species, conical teeth develop. During, or shortly before metamorphosis, the tadpole mouth parts may be so modified as to be unreliable in identification. Ultimately, the tail is resorbed and the coiled intestine shortens, assuming the carnivorous form of the adult.

Key to Amphibian Larvae[17]

Plates 26 to 34

1*a*. Head broader than and distinct from body; both forelimbs and hind limbs developed at an early stage; external gills present on neck, not covered; mouth parts adapted for handling animal food (figs. 33 and 34) ...... Salamanders. Urodela 2

1*b*. Head not distinguishable from body—two fused into common ovoid mass; gills covered soon after hatching by thin opercular membrane; limbs not in evidence until late in development; mouth parts adapted for rasping, but not for handling large particles (fig. 35) .... Frogs and toads. Anura .. 10

[17] Adapted in part from Storer (1925).

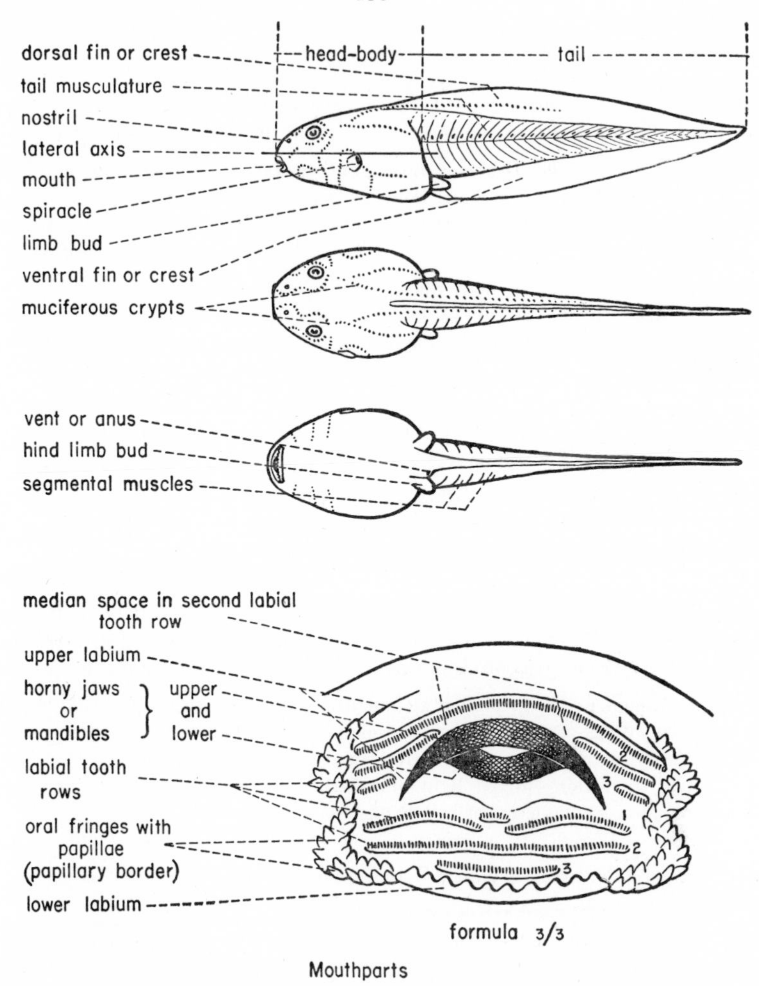

Fig. 35. Structural characteristics of tadpoles.

2a. (*1a*) Mountain-brook type larva (fig. 33)—dorsal fin originating above hind limbs or at base of tail; gills relatively short; gill slits and rakers reduced (5 to 7 rakers on anterior face of third arch) (fig. 34, 1 and 2); balancers typically lacking on very young larvae 3

2b. Pond type larva (fig. 33)—dorsal fin extending well forward, at least to middle of back, and usually to region above forelimbs; gills long;[18] gill slits and rakers not reduced (9 to 22 rakers on anterior face of third arch); balancers typically present on very young larvae (*Ambystoma tigrinum* excepted) (fig. 34, 4) 4

[18] Since the gills shorten and the tail fin becomes reduced as the time for transformation to the terrestrial stage approaches, these characters cannot be relied upon to distinguish individuals closely approaching or in the process of metamorphosis.

3*a*. (2*a*) Dorsal fin usually with prominent smoky light and dark marbling; body brownish above with numerous small flecks of whitish that may unite to form small blotches; usually whitish streak runs diagonally ventroposteriorly from eye; no shallow groove running upward and backward from each nostril; 5 to 7 gill rakers on anterior face of third arch; to 8 or more inches .... *Dicamptodon ensatus,* p. 53

3*b*. Dorsal fin not marked as above; body above usually with speckling of irregular black dots on brownish ground color; light eye streak absent; shallow groove running upward and backward from each nostril; no gill rakers on anterior face of third arch; usually under 3 inches .... *Rhyacotriton olympicus,* p. 60

4*a*. (2*b*) Ground color of body above light-colored, plain yellowish in life, with 2 conspicuous, usually continuous, longitudinal stripes of blackish, one along either side of body near base of dorsal fin and scattering of black spots of irregular size on the sides 5

4*b*. Above mottled light and dark or uniformly dark-colored; no well-marked longitudinal stripes of blackish or, if stripes present, margins diffuse and stripes may be interrupted with whitish or yellowish patches 6

5*a*. (4*a*) Margins of dorsal, longitudinal blackish stripes less evenly formed and many black spots present farther ventrally on sides; young larvae with more yellow in ground color; in streams, reservoirs, and lakes of Sierra Nevada of California ....
.... *Triturus torosus sierrae,* p. 27

5*b*. Margins of dorsal, longitudinal blackish stripes more even; less dark spotting ventrally on lower sides; less yellow in ground color in younger larvae; in streams, ponds, and reservoirs of coastal areas of California .... *Triturus torosus torosus,* p. 27

6*a*. (4*b*) Roughened strip present at juncture of tail fin with tail musculature, produced by openings of granular (poison) glands; similar roughened zone in parotoid regions; milky secretion may exude from these areas in larger larvae with preservation; body coloration—mixed light and dark brown with numerous round dots (about 0.5 mm. in diameter) of yellow on lateral and ventral surfaces ....
.... *Ambystoma gracile,* p. 34

6*b*. No glandular areas as indicated above; body usually not colored as above ....
.... 7

7*a*. (6*b*) Tail fin reduced, not extending as far anteriorly on trunk as in typical pond-type larva; balancers absent or rudimentary in recently hatched individuals; dark pigment uniformly distributed over back and sides; in fairly rapid streams principally in coastal redwood belt of California north of San Francisco Bay......................
.... *Triturus rivularis,* p. 23

7*b*. Tail fin typically extending well anteriorly to region of forelimbs or neck; balancers present in recently hatched individuals; body generally with mottled style of coloration; usually in ponds, lakes, or quiet streams 8

8*a*. (7*b*) Five to 7 gill rakers on anterior face of third arch (based on 4 animals, 3 from Latah County, Idaho, and 1 from Alameda County, California); trunk with 2 longitudinal rows of light spots which in older individuals may form light stripe
.... *Triturus granulosus,* p. 19

8*b*. Nine to 22 gill rakers on anterior face of third arch; trunk without rows of light markings or light stripe 9

9*a*. (8*b*) Nine to 13 gill rakers on anterior face of third arch; rather uniformly light greenish gray to brownish gray, flecked and mottled with dark brown and black; below dirty white; length to approximately 3 inches .. *Ambystoma macrodactylum*, p. 39

9*b*. Seventeen to 22 gill rakers (6 animals, counting smallest nubbins as gill rakers) on anterior face of third arch; coloration various—uniformly colored, with dark spotting, with blackish and yellow markings, or rather uniformly greenish; length to 10 inches .... *Ambystoma tigrinum*, p. 46

10*a*. (1*b*) No oral disc; no horny mandibles or labial tooth rows; flaplike upper labium, notched medially, overhanging lower labium; no labial papillae; eyes lateral, on canthus; spiracle median, situated well posteriorly on body .... Microhylidae. *Microhyla carolinensis*, p. 393

10*b*. Oral disc and horny mandibles present (lower one reduced or absent in *Ascaphus*); labial teeth present; upper labium not flaplike; labial papillae present; eyes may be lateral but not on canthus 11

11*a*. (10*b*) Oral disc large, suctorial, occupying about ½ area of ventral surface of body; lower horny mandible reduced to minute crescent of horn or absent; labial teeth $\frac{2\text{-}3}{7\text{-}12}$; spiracle median, posterior to mid-point of head-body .... Ascaphidae. *Ascaphus truei*, p. 192

11*b*. Oral disc occupying considerably less than ¼ area of ventral surface of body; 2 well-developed horny mandibles; labial teeth $\frac{1\text{-}7}{2\text{-}6}$; spiracle sinistral (on left side) 12

12*a*. (11*b*) Lower labium without oral papillae; papillae confined to sides of mouth .... Bufonidae 13

12*b*. Lower labium, as well as sides of mouth, with oral papillae 20

13*a*. (12*a*) Head-body above uniformly black or deep brown; tail musculature similarly dark-colored; ventral color but slightly lighter than dorsal; in life, intestine usually shows through skin of abdomen (*Bufo canorus* sometimes excepted) 14

13*b*. Head-body olive, gray, or tan above, commonly spotted or mottled with blackish to brown (very young and sometimes preserved tadpoles may be dark brown or blackish); tail musculature colored about like body, marked with spots and blotches of dark brown to blackish (preserved specimens may have scattered black spots on cream ground color); venter light-colored, contrasting with dorsum; in life, intestine not showing or only slightly visible through skin of abdomen (intestine may be visible in very young larvae) 18

14*a*. (13*a*) Upper labium and its tooth rows extended ventrolaterally; oral fringes reduced, largely occupying lower half of sides of oral disc .. *Bufo punctatus*, p. 284

14*b*. Upper labium and upper labial tooth rows not extended ventrolaterally; oral fringes longer, extending full length of sides of oral disc 15

15*a*. (14*b*) Sides of body, as viewed from above, emarginate (indented) behind eyes; North Dakota; northwestern Minnesota; and Canada in Manitoba, Saskatchewan, Alberta, and Northwest Territory .... *Bufo hemiophrys*, p. 264

15*b*. Sides slightly if at all emarginate behind eyes; range not as above 16

16*a*. (15*b*) Ventral surface of tail without melanic (black to dark brown) pigment (immaculate in preservative); in life, ventral surface of tail may be blotched with whitish to pale yellow; dorsal fin with few scattered flecks of melanic pigment; maximum total length, about 23 mm.; principally from Idaho, Utah, and central Arizona, eastward into the Great Plains .... *Bufo woodhousii,* p. 292

16*b*. Ventral surface of tail with melanic pigmentation; dorsal fin with weak (*B. canorus*) to heavy (*B. boreas*) stippling of melanophores in dorsal fin; maximum total length to 56 mm.; principally from the Rockies, west 17

17*a*. (16*b*) Darker ventrally, intestine scarcely, or not at all, visible even in preserved specimens; dorsal fin with relatively few, large, branched melanophores; snout shorter; generally above 6,500 feet in the Sierra Nevada of California .... *Bufo canorus,* p. 247

17*b*. Lighter ventrally, intestine visible; dorsal fin closely stippled with minute melanophores; snout longer; widespread in Pacific coast region; at lower elevations in Sierra Nevada than *canorus* .... *Bufo boreas,* p. 241

18*a*. (13*b*) Tail musculature marked with irregularly outlined, often broken, purplish-brown to dark brown lateral stripe running midway full length of tail or tail musculature light-colored with scattered black spots; dorsum of head-body olivaceous in life; southeastern New Mexico, southwestern Kansas, western Oklahoma, Texas south into Mexico 34

18*b*. Tail musculature rather uniformly colored or irregularly spotted and blotched with vague to well-defined dark markings; conversely, caudal dark color may predominate (some *woodhousii*), with light color (pale yellow to whitish) forming blotches; general color of dorsum of head-body olivaceous, gray, to sooty, under magnification dark ground color seen to be overlaid by silvery or pale yellow, metallic pigment flecks forming scattered spots and blotches or rather extensive, but usually somewhat broken, stippling 19

19*a*. (18*b*) In life dorsal surface of body mottled brown and gray; under magnification silvery areas seen to be interwoven with black ones; throat with greenish-yellow iridescence, extending caudally along sides of abdomen, gradually shading into grayish green; central portion of abdomen with reddish iridescence marked with very fine black and golden spots (Bragg, 1936b:18) second lower labial tooth row 2¾ to 4 times longer than third row (based on figures of Bragg, 1936b:19 and Smith, 1946:95) ....
.... *Bufo cognatus,* p. 253

19*b*. In life dorsal surface of body olivaceous to sooty, in lighter individuals (probably depending in part on state of concentration or dispersion of melanic pigment), dark ground color overlaid by stippling of pale gold, continuous or with gaps permitting darker ground to show through as blotches; venter with pale bluish-green iridescence (Colorado Plateau *woodhousii*); second lower labial tooth row about ¼ to ⅓ longer than third row .... *Bufo woodhousii,* p. 292

20*a*. (12*b*) Anus median, opening at edge of ventral fin near its juncture with body; spiracle very low on body, well below lateral axis; head-body, as viewed from above, usually broadest anterior to mid-point (*couchii* perhaps an exception); eyes close together well up on head; oral disc rounded, not emarginate laterally ......
.... Pelobatidae 21

20*b*. Anus dextral (on right side), opening at edge of ventral fin near its juncture with body; spiracle on, or slightly below, lateral axis; head-body, as viewed from above, broadest at, or behind, mid-point; eyes lateral or usually nearer outline of head, as viewed from above, than mid-dorsal line; oral disc with lateral emarginations (Ranidae) or not (Hylidae) 23

21*a*. (20*a*) Size small, mature tadpole 18 to 24 mm. in total length; dark gray, bronze, to nearly black, black when preserved; southern Arizona, southern and eastern New Mexico, southwestern Oklahoma, Texas into Mexico .... *Scaphiopus couchii,* p. 200

21*b*. Size large, mature tadpole about 30 to 70 mm.; light to medium gray or brown, seldom dark except when preserved; from southern British Columbia well south on Mexican Plateau; west to Great Valley of California and east to Mississippi River .. 22

22*a*. (21*b*) Upper mandible typically with beak and lower one with notch; principally west of Rocky Mountains .... *Scaphiopus hammondii,* p. 214

22*b*. Upper mandible without beak and lower one without notch; principally east of Rocky Mountains .... *Scaphiopus bombifrons,* p. 206

23*a*. (20*b*) Oral disc emarginate (indented) laterally; labial teeth 2/3, 3/3, 3/4, 4/3, 6/6, 7/6; size larger, mature tadpoles from about 45 to 145 mm. in total length .... Ranidae 24

23*b*. Oral disc not emarginate laterally; labial teeth 2/2 or 2/3; size smaller, mature tadpoles from about 25 to 50 mm. .... Hylidae 31

24*a*. (23*a*) Labial teeth $\frac{2\text{-}7}{3\text{-}6}$, uncommonly 3/3, rarely 2/4 or 2/3 (some young *Rana boylii sierrae*) 25

24*b*. Labial teeth typically 2/3, sometimes 3/3 27

25*a*. (24*a*) Labial teeth $\frac{2\text{-}4}{3\text{-}4}$; dorsal fin high; tail musculature not contrastingly marked with dark and light color, mature tadpoles to about 50 mm. .... *Rana sylvatica,* p. 380

25*b*. Labial teeth $\frac{3\text{ (rarely 2)-}7}{3\text{-}6}$; dorsal fin not especially high; tail musculature often contrastingly marked with dark and light color; mature tadpoles to about 90 mm. 26

26*a*. (25*b*) Labial teeth 6/6, 7/6 (*boylii*), 3/4, less commonly 2/4 or 2/3 (*sierrae*); size of mature tadpoles smaller, to about 70 mm.; tail not as boldly spotted; usually in streams in mountains of western Oregon and California ...... *Rana boylii,* p. 342

26*b*. Labial teeth 4/3 or 5/3; size of mature tadpoles large, to about 90 mm.; tail, including both fins and musculature, heavily spotted with bold dark markings; streams and springs in central and southern Arizona, southwestern New Mexico, and Mexico in the Sierra Madre .... *Rana tarahumarae,* p. 386

27*a*. (24*b*) Third lower labial tooth row short, about 1/2 length of first lower row; introduced in western Washington and southwestern British Columbia .... *Rana clamitans,* p. 353

27*b*. Third lower labial tooth row 3/4 to nearly same length as first lower labial row 28

28*a*. (27*b*) Dorsal crest highly arched; mature tadpoles to about 50 mm.; coloration more uniformly dark with less tendency toward speckling; northern Colorado, south-central Wyoming, Alaska, and Canada, east to Atlantic Coast . . *Rana sylvatica,* p. 380

28*b*. Dorsal crest not as highly arched; mature tadpoles 80 to about 145 mm.; olivaceous body and tail covered with small spots and flecks of blackish or dark brown and pale yellowish or cream 29

29*a*. (28*b*) Belly heavily pigmented, intestine usually not evident even in preserved specimens; mature tadpoles to about 145 mm. 30

29*b*. Belly may or may not be heavily pigmented in life, intestine evident in preserved specimens; mature tadpoles to about 90 mm. .... *Rana pipiens*, p. 363

30*a*. (29*a*) Ground color of dorsal and lateral surfaces of head-body dark browns and yellows in life; spots on body with diffuse margins, more than 1 mm. in diameter; center of belly with pinkish iridescence in life; Pacific Coast principally in mountainous areas .... *Rana aurora*, p. 336

30*b*. Ground color of dorsal and lateral surfaces of head-body in life olive green of light or dark tone; body spots sharp-margined, rarely over 1 mm. in diameter; center of belly whitish or cream, not iridescent; probably introduced in every state in the United States covered by this book .... *Rana catesbeiana*, p. 349

31*a*. (23*b*) Tip of tail with conspicuous black marking, occasionally not evident; labial teeth 2/2; eastern Colorado and eastern New Mexico, east to Atlantic coast, north to Great Lakes region, and south into northeastern Mexico .... *Acris gryllus*, p. 301

31*b*. Tip of tail without black marking; labial teeth typically 2/3, sometimes 2/2 32

32*a*. (31*b*) Tail deep, dorsal fin highly arched anterior to mid-point; eyes on lateral outline of head, as viewed from above .... *Pseudacris nigrita*, p. 311

32*b*. Tail not as deep, dorsal fin less arched; eyes on lateral outline of head (*Hyla regilla*) or not (*Hyla arenicolor*) 33

33*a*. (32*b*) Eyes on outline of head as viewed from above; southern British Columbia to tip of Lower California, east to eastern Nevada .... *Hyla regilla*, p. 326

33*b*. Eyes not reaching outline of head as viewed from above; coastal southern California and southern Utah and Colorado south to Guerrero, Mexico .... *Hyla arenicolor*, p. 321

34*a*. (18*a*) Tail musculature spotted with black on light-colored background; in life, underside of body white; California and northern Lower California .... *Bufo microscaphus californicus*, p. 273

34*b*. Tail musculature with irregular, dark-colored lateral stripe or blotches tending to form stripe; in life, underside of body light tan to pinkish cinnamon; in area covered by this book, found only in southeastern New Mexico .... *Bufo compactilis*, p. 256

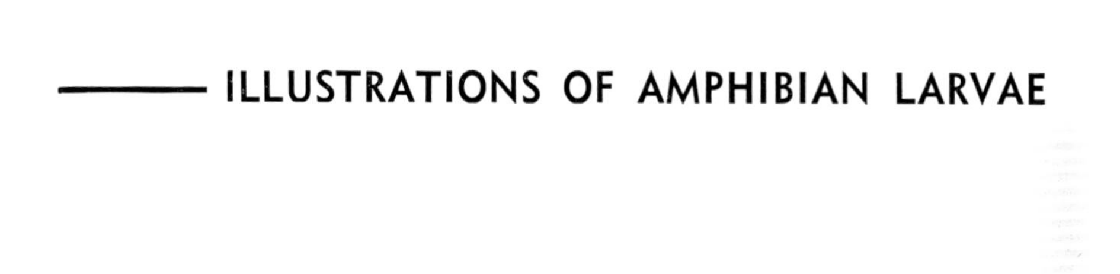

ILLUSTRATIONS OF AMPHIBIAN LARVAE

Plate 26

Triturus torosus, MVZ 24859, 56 mm. in total length, Arroyo Mocho, 1,900 feet, northeast of Cedar Peak, Alameda County, California, September 19, 1937.

Triturus granulosus, RCS 2876, 52 mm., Moscow Mountains, 7 miles northeast of Moscow, Latah County, Idaho, early June, 1949.

Triturus rivularis, MVZ 21769, 42 mm., 5 miles north-northwest of Cazadero, Sonoma County, California, September 19, 1936.

Dicamptodon ensatus, MVZ 4927, 75 mm., Mendocino City, Mendocino County, California, July 13, 1913.

Rhyacotriton olympicus, CAS 81251, 60 mm., Mill Creek Park, Del Norte County, California.

Ambystoma gracile, MVZ 34206, 63 mm., Old Fort Clatsop, Clatsop County, Oregon, August 24, 1940.

Ambystoma tigrinum, MVZ 31854, 65 mm., Madrone, Santa Clara County, California, May 3, 1931.

Ambystoma macrodactylum, MVZ 10035, 67 mm., Lake Helen, 8,500 feet, Shasta County, California, July 14, 1924.

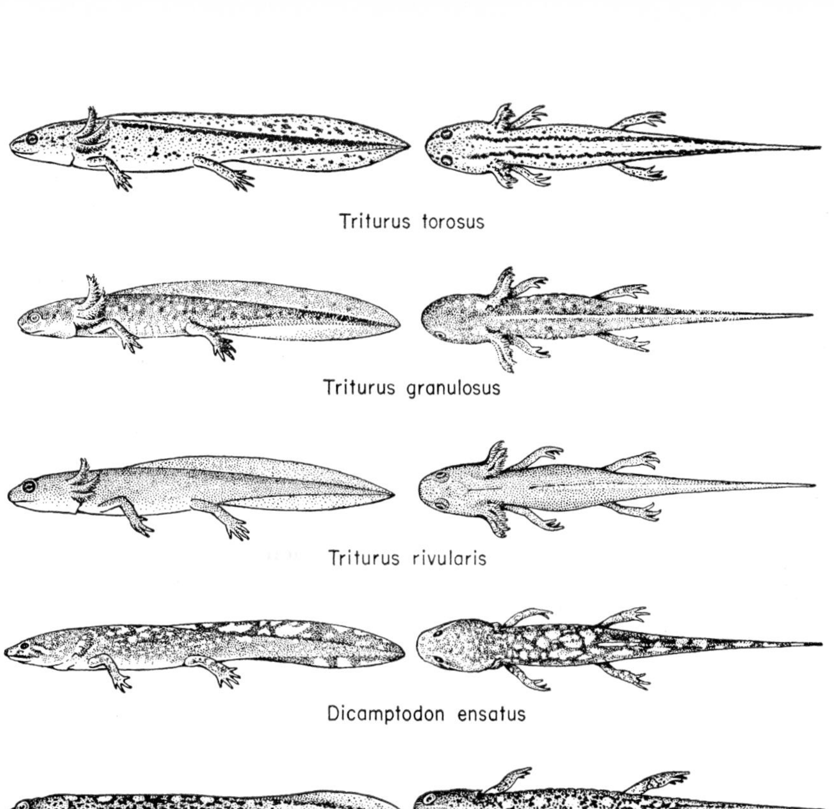

Triturus torosus

Triturus granulosus

Triturus rivularis

Dicamptodon ensatus

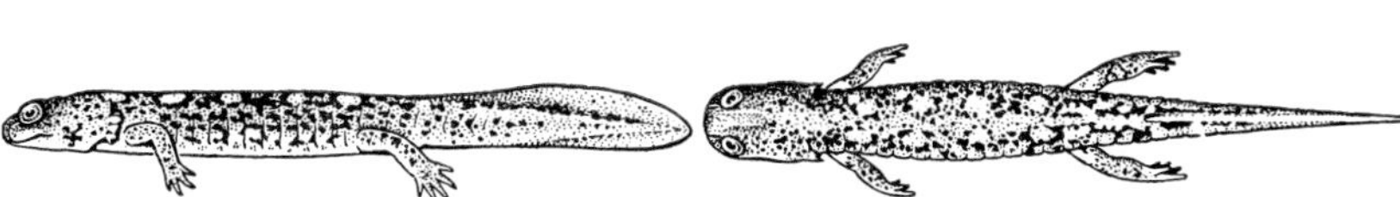

Rhyacotriton olympicus

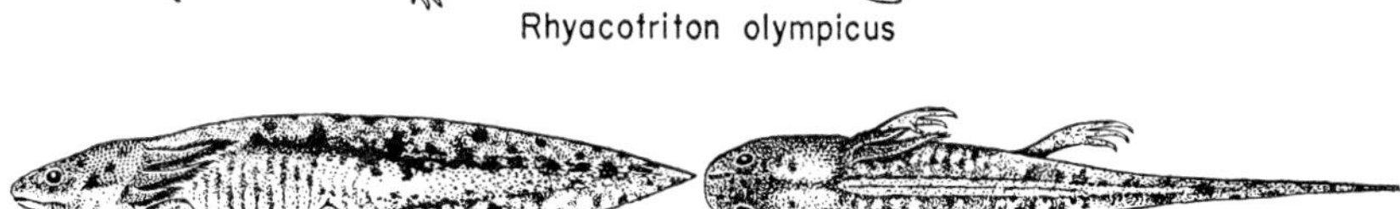

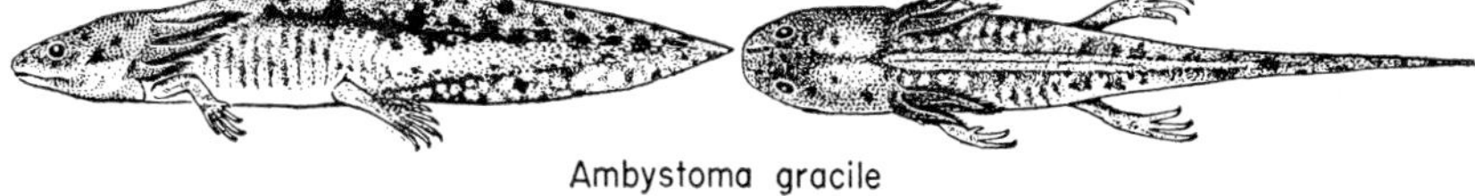

Ambystoma gracile

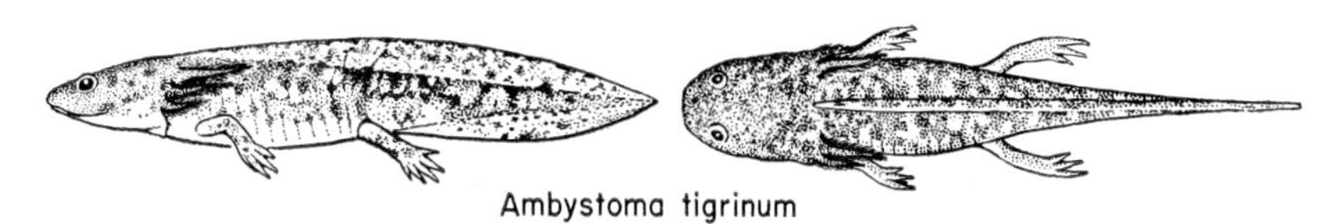

Ambystoma tigrinum

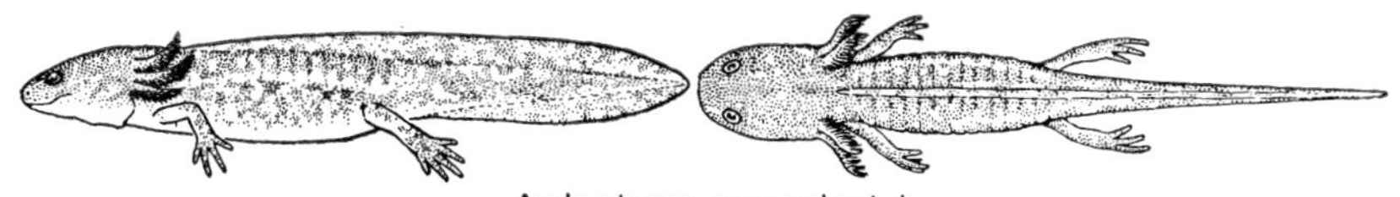

Ambystoma macrodactylum

Plate 27

Ascaphus truei, MVZ 29801, small tributary (first on south side) Wilson Creek, 8 miles ± north of Klamath, Del Norte County, California, August 21, 1939. × 5/6

Microhyla carolinensis, RCS 3246, 1 mile northeast of Peña Blanca Springs, Santa Cruz County, Arizona, July 16, 1949. × 5/6

Scaphiopus hammondii, MVZ 30334, 2½ miles southeast of Vernal, Uintah County, Utah, June 25, 1933. × 5/6

Scaphiopus bombifrons, MVZ 47169, specimen received from A. N. Bragg, 4 to 5 miles southwest of Erick, Beckham County, Oklahoma, June 12, 1946. × 5/6

Scaphiopus couchii, RCS 3323, 10.5 miles north-northeast of Douglas, U.S. Highway 80, Cochise County, Arizona, July 23, 1949. × 5/6

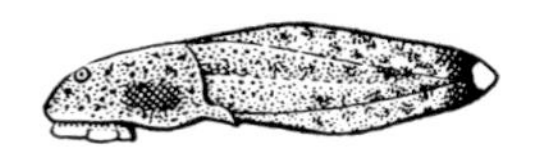

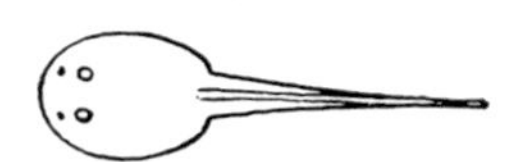

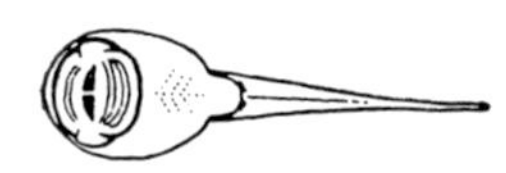

Ascaphus truei

Microhyla carolinensis

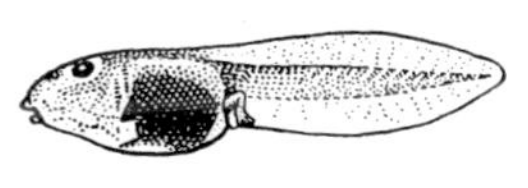

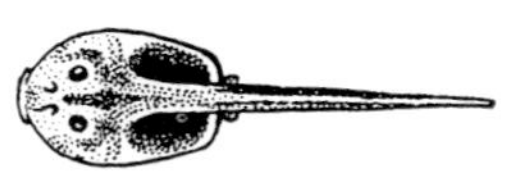

Scaphiopus hammondii

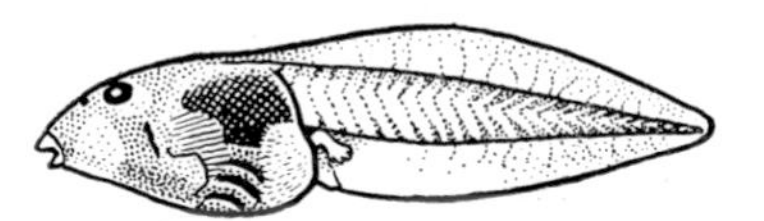

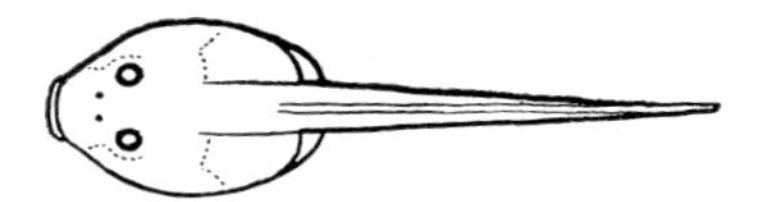

Scaphiopus bombifrons

Scaphiopus couchii

Plate 28

In this and all following plates depicting the mouthparts of tadpoles, when specimen number and locality of collection are omitted, the drawing is based on the same individual as that of the tadpole.

Ascaphus truei, MVZ 8502, 8 mm. across disc; *Microhyla carolinensis,* 3 mm.; *Scaphiopus hammondii,* 3.7 mm.; *Scaphiopus bombifrons,* 4 mm.; *Scaphiopus couchii,* 1.75 mm.

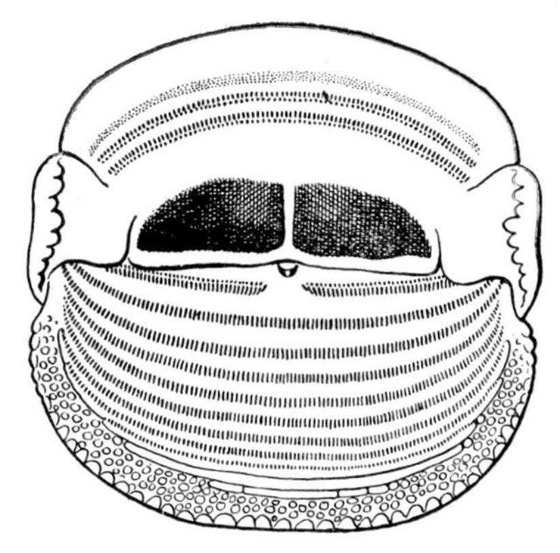

Ascaphus truei

Microhyla carolinensis

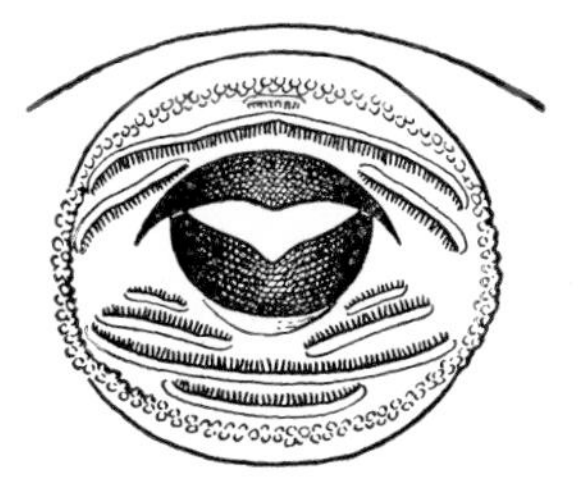

Scaphiopus hammondii

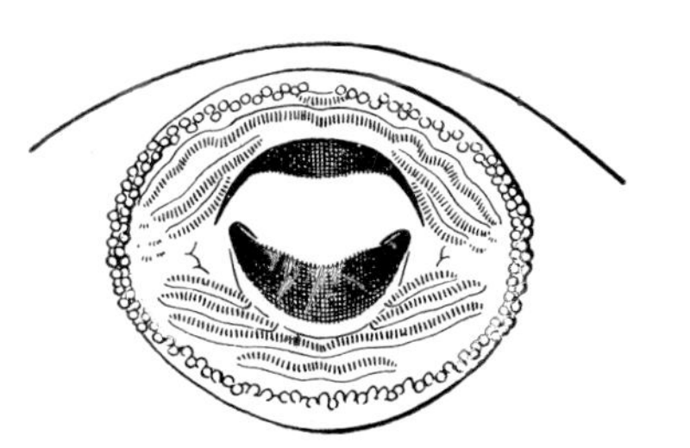

Scaphiopus bombifrons

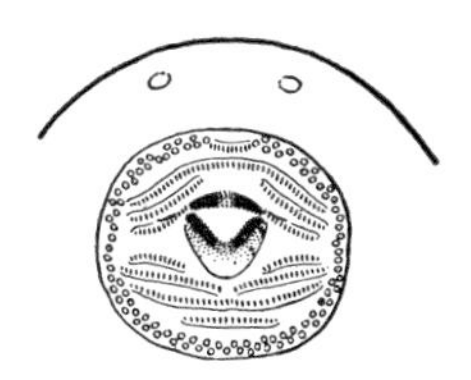

Scaphiopus couchii

Plate 29

Bufo boreas, vicinity of Berkeley, Alameda County, California. × 5/6

Bufo punctatus, MVZ 35623, Pass between Granite and Providence mountains, 4,100 feet, San Bernardino County, California, June 25, 1940. × 5/6

Bufo canorus, SNHM 2936, Peregoy Meadow, Yosemite National Park, Mariposa County, California, June 20, 1928. × 5/6

Bufo woodhousii—woodhousii × microscaphus hybrid (?), RCS 3088, Bloomington, Washington County, Utah, July 3, 1949. × 5/6

Bufo microscaphus, RCS 2889, Mohave River, 3 miles north of Victorville, San Bernardino County, California, June 19, 1949. × 5/6

Bufo hemiophrys, MMNH 1522, Crookston, Polk County, Minnesota, July 3, 1943. × 5/6

Bufo compactilis, UOMZ 24354, 2.7 miles east of railroad at Granite, Greer County, Oklahoma, June 11, 1946. × 5/6

Bufo woodhousii, MVZ 49525, 0.8 miles north-northwest of Lakeside, near State Highway 173, Navajo County, Arizona, July 29, 1949. × 5/6

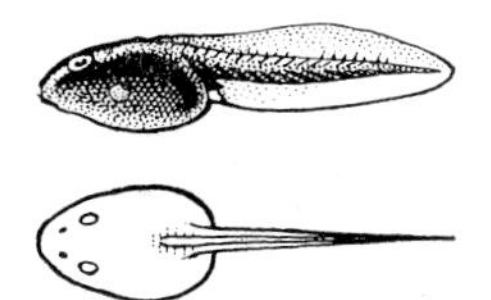

Bufo boreas

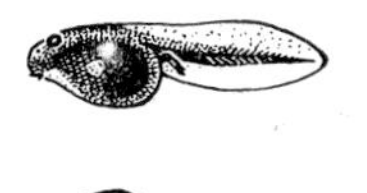

Bufo canorus

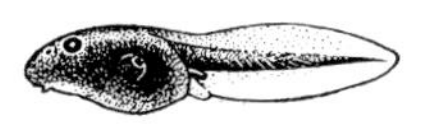

Bufo hemiophrys

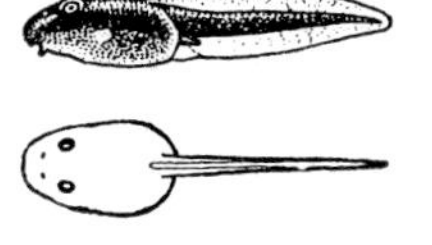

Bufo punctatus

Bufo woodhousii X
microscaphus hybrid (?)

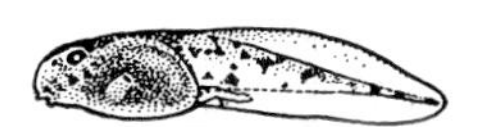

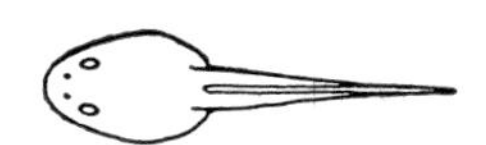

Bufo microscaphus
californicus

Bufo compactilis

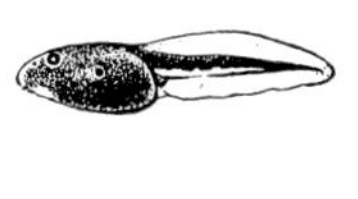

Bufo woodhousii

Plate 30

Bufo boreas, 3 mm. across disc; *Bufo punctatus,* 3.3 mm.; *Bufo canorus,* 2 mm.; *Bufo woodhousii* × *Bufo microscaphus* hybrid (?), 2.1 mm.; *Bufo hemiophrys,* MMNH 1523, 1.7 mm.; *Bufo compactilis,* 3 mm.; *Bufo woodhousii,* 1.8 mm.; *Bufo debilis* × 15, Schwartz Canyon, Comanche County, Kansas, (after Smith, 1934—some doubt as to identity); *Bufo cognatus* × 30, Meade County State Park, Kansas (after Smith, 1946).

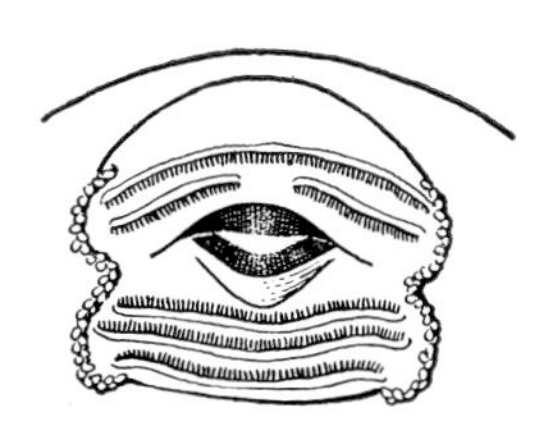

Bufo boreas

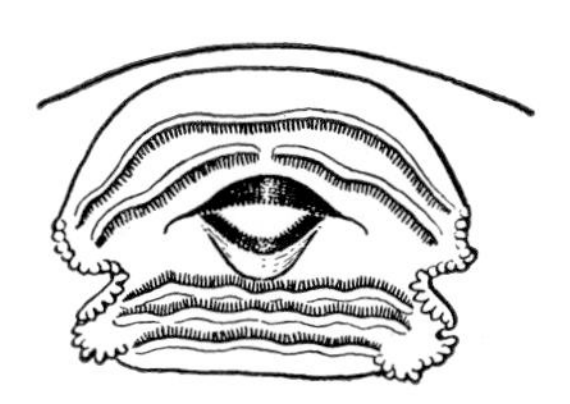

Bufo punctatus

Bufo canorus

Bufo woodhousii X
Bufo microscaphus
hybrid (?)

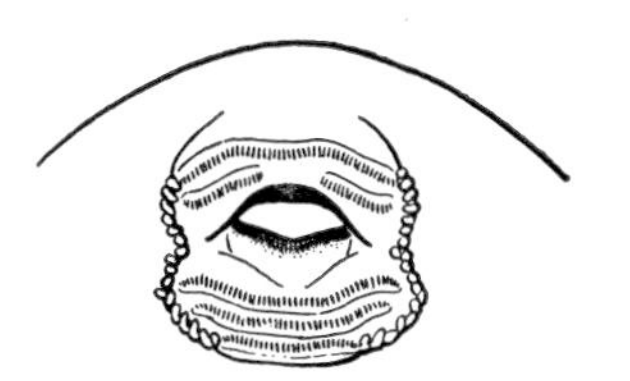

Bufo hemiophrys

Bufo compactilis

Bufo woodhousii

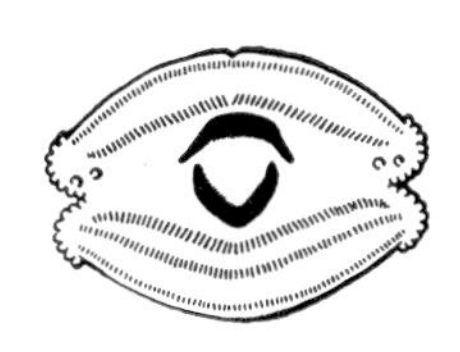

Bufo debilis

Bufo cognatus

Plate 31

Acris gryllus, AMNH specimen, 7 miles west of Cuero, DeWitt County, Texas, July 26, 1947. × 5/6

Pseudacris nigrita, RCS 2969, 13.6 miles north-northwest of Heber along U.S. Highway 40, Summit County, Utah, June 25, 1949. × 5/6

Hyla arenicolor. (a) MVZ 27865, Canyon of Crawford's Ranch, 14 miles northwest of Carrizo Station, San Diego County, California, June 5, 1938; (b) RCS 3343, Rose Creek Lodge, headwaters Rose Creek, 5,300 feet, Gila County, Arizona, July 25, 1949. × 5/6

Hyla regilla, RCS 2918, 2 miles south of Beatty, Nye County, Nevada, June 21, 1949. × 5/6

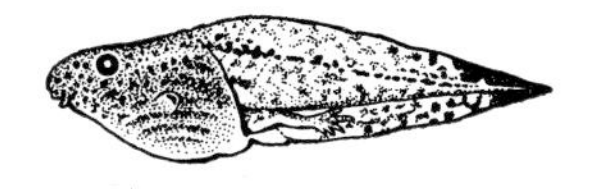

Acris gryllus

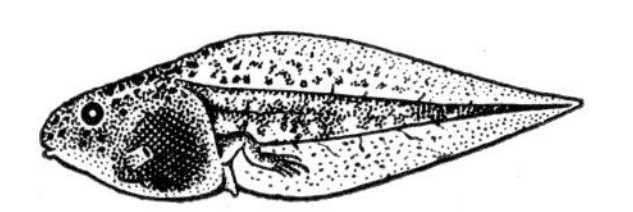

Pseudacris nigrita

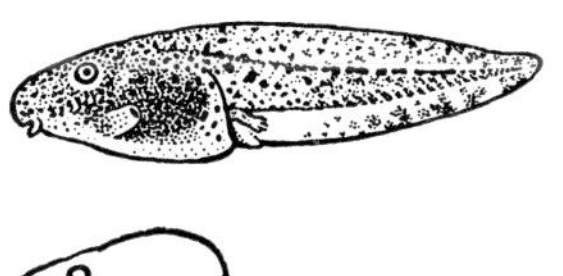

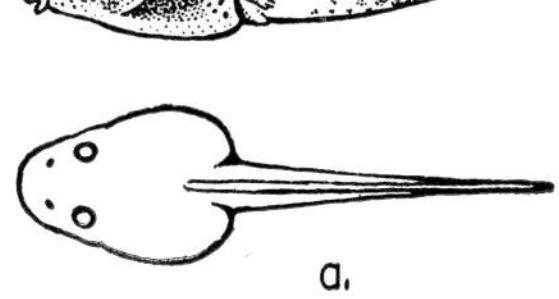

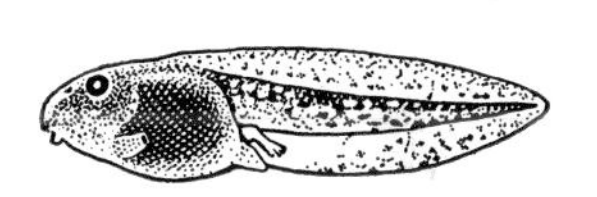

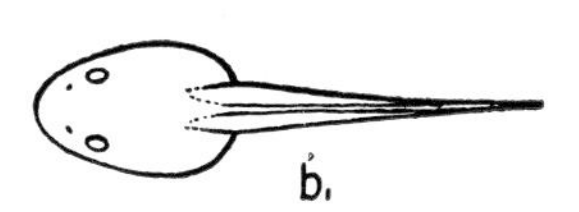

Hyla arenicolor

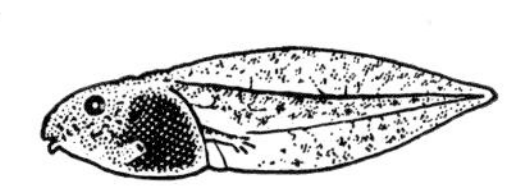

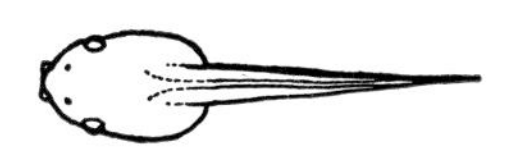

Hyla regilla

Plate 32

Acris gryllus, 2.2 mm. across disc; *Pseudacris nigrita,* 2.75 mm.; *Hyla arenicolor,* 3.3 mm.; *Hyla regilla,* 3 mm.

Acris gryllus

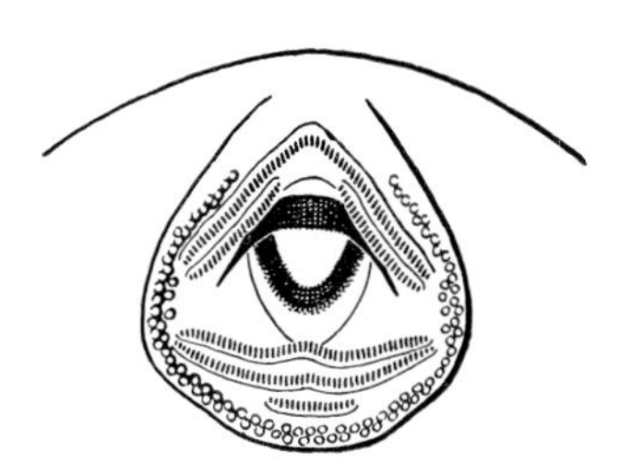

Pseudacris nigrita

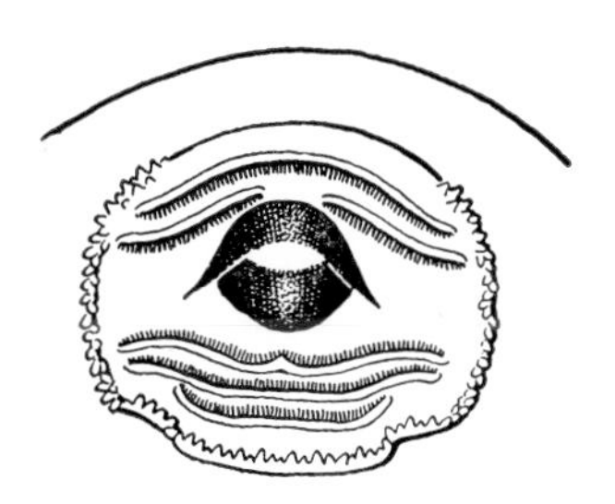

Hyla arenicolor

Hyla regilla

Plate 33

Rana catesbeiana, MVZ 28257, Mohave River, just below bridge north of Victorville, San Bernardino County, California, April 8, 1939. × 2/3

Rana pipiens, RCS 3069, Bloomington, Washington County, Utah, July 2, 1949. × 5/6

Rana clamitans, RCS 3753, 3.9 miles southwest of Irvington, U.S. Highway 90, Mobile County, Alabama, March 31, 1950. × 5/6

Rana boylii, MVZ 40621, 1 mile southeast of San Benito Peak, 4,400 feet, San Benito County, California, August 11, 1944. × 5/6

Rana aurora, 3 miles southeast of Berkeley, Alameda County, California, June 9, 1922. × 3/4

Rana tarahumarae, CAS 81444, Alamo Springs, Pajarito Mountains, Pima County, Arizona, May 18, 1946. × 5/6

Rana sylvatica, RCS 3492, 5 miles east-southeast of Rabbit Ears Peak, Jackson County, Colorado, August 23, 1949. × 5/6

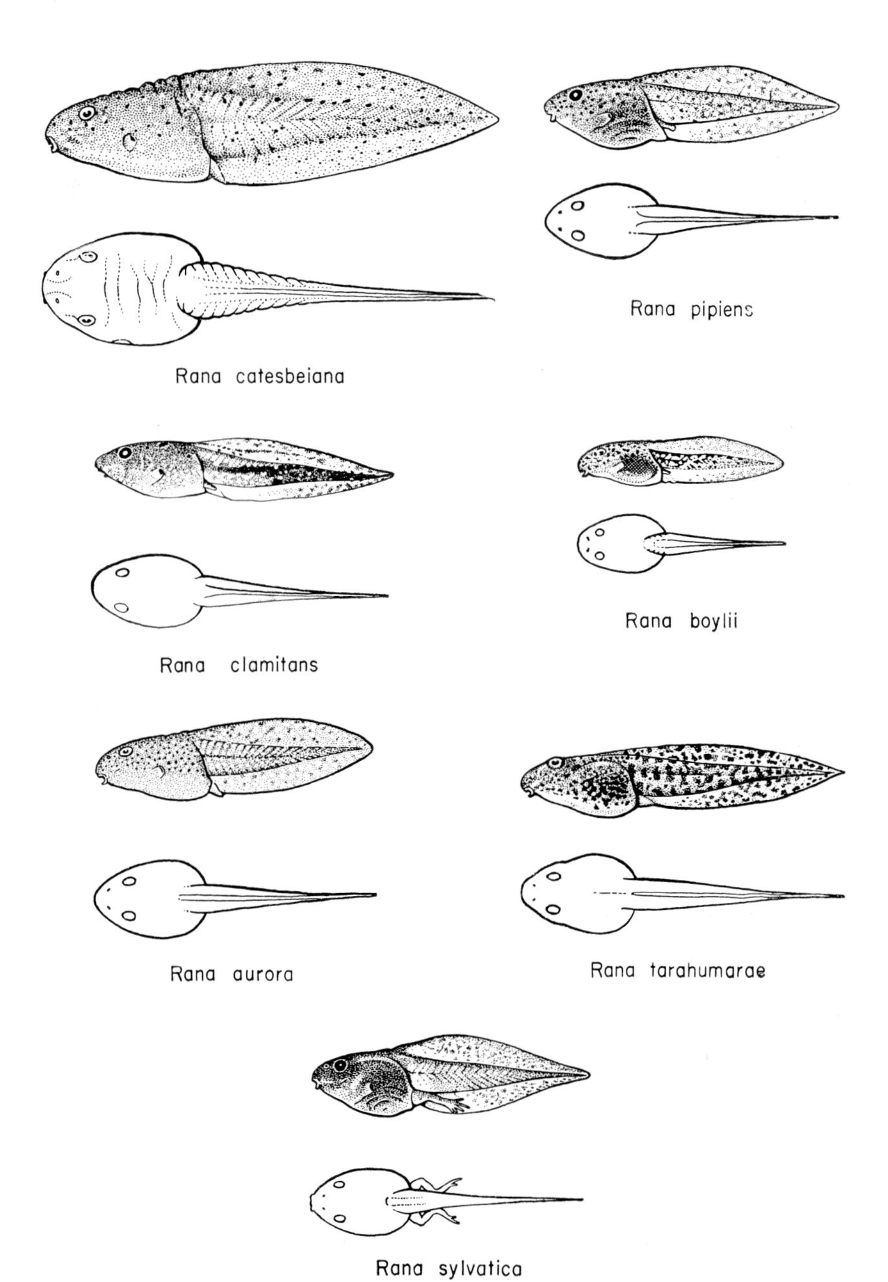
Rana catesbeiana
Rana pipiens
Rana clamitans
Rana boylii
Rana aurora
Rana tarahumarae
Rana sylvatica

Plate 34

Rana catesbeiana, 8 mm. across disc; *Rana pipiens,* MVZ 28065, pond about 3 miles northeast of Wellsville, Montgomery County, Missouri, September 5, 1932, 2.5 mm.; *Rana clamitans,* 3.9 mm.; *Rana boylii,* 3.6 mm.; *Rana aurora,* 4.5 mm.; *Rana tarahumarae,* 4.5 mm.; *Rana sylvatica,* 3.3 mm.

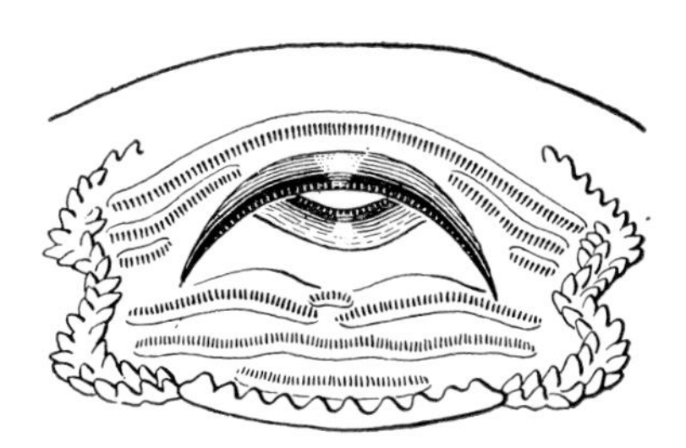
Rana catesbeiana

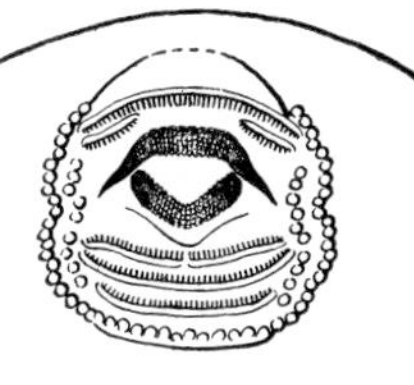
Rana pipiens

Rana clamitans

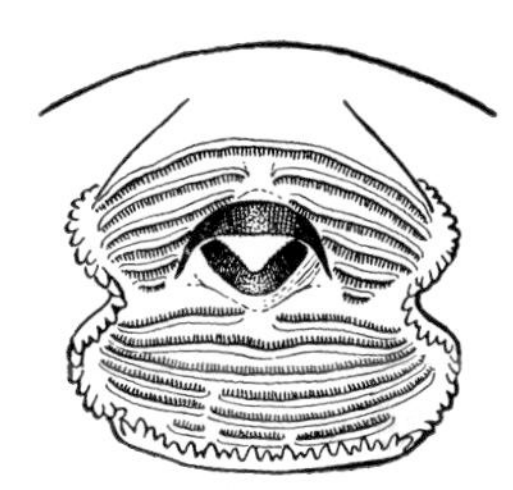
Rana boylii

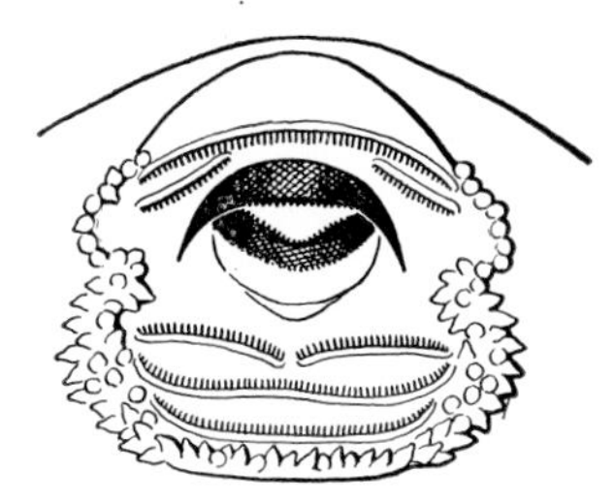
Rana aurora

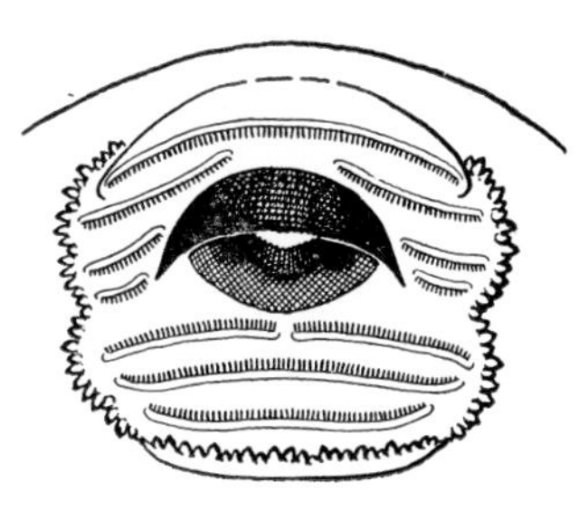
Rana tarahumarae

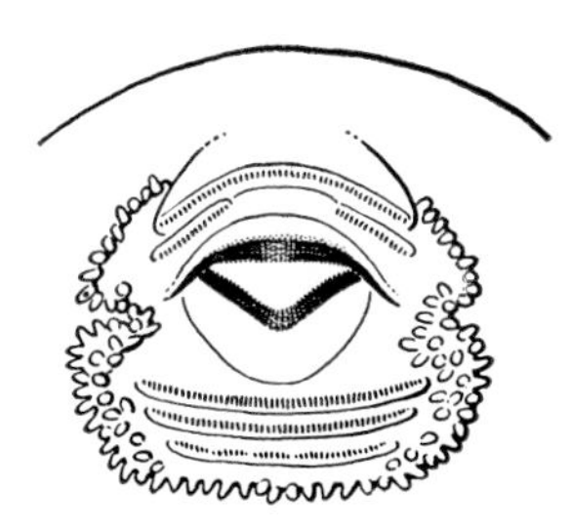
Rana sylvatica

Habitats

Plate 35

1. Cascading stream habitat of the Olympic salamander (*Rhyacotriton olympicus*) at or near the type locality at the south end of Lake Cushman, Mason County, Washington. Salamanders were collected under rocks along the edges and on higher ground in the center of the stream. The bell toad (*Ascaphus truei*) also occurs in such streams. Photograph April 16, 1948.

2. Douglas fir (*Pseudostuga taxifolia*), aspen (*populus tremuloides*) habitat of the New Mexican salamander (*Plethodon neomexicanus*) in the Jemez Mountains, 8,750 feet, 12 miles west and 4 miles south of Los Alamos, Sandoval County, New Mexico. An individual was found under the bark of the log in the left foreground. Photograph of the type locality August 14, 1949.

1

2

Plate 36

1. Type locality of *Plethodon vandykei idahoensis* (=*Plethodon idahoensis* Slater and Slipp) on the south shore of Wolf Lodge Bay, Coeur d'Alene Lake, Kootenai County, Idaho. The forest is principally Douglas fir (*Pseudostuga taxifolia*) with scattered yellow pines (*Pinus ponderosa*). Salamanders were found beneath moss-covered rocks on top the ridge, about 35 feet above the road, in the center foreground and in talus along the base of the road cut to the right. Photograph April 19, 1948.

2. Niche of *Plethodon vandykei idahoensis* in stabilized rock rubble. The salamanders were found where the rocks were moss-covered and gave evidence of having been in repose for some time. Photograph April 19, 1948.

1

2

Plate 37

1. Habitat of Eschscholtz salamander (*Ensatina eschscholtzii*) 1½ miles west and 5 miles north of Piute Peak, 7,000 feet, in the vicinity of Saddle Spring Camp, Kern County, California. Intergrades between the subspecies *croceater* and *platensis* occur here. The young trees are white fir (*Abies concolor*) and Jeffrey pine (*Pinus ponderosa jeffreyi*). Salamanders were found under logs and in rotten wood such as in the center of the picture. Note the small stream in the foreground. Photograph April 16, 1947.

1

Plate 38

1. Habitat of the Sacramento Mountains salamander (*Aneides hardii*), near the type locality, about 1½ miles east of Cloudcroft, 8,600 feet, Otero County, New Mexico. The trees are principally Douglas fir (*Pseudostuga taxifolia*) and spruce (*Picea*). On August 4, 1949, when the photograph was taken, grass was green and wild flowers were blooming in profusion. Salamanders were found under rocks and beneath the bark of Douglas fir logs.

2. Vicinity of the type locality of the clouded salamander (*Aneides ferreus*), 4.8 miles by road northwest of Umpqua, Douglas County, Oregon. This salamander is almost invariably found under bark of downed or standing dead trees, most commonly Douglas fir. Photograph April 9, 1948 by C. Lowe, Jr. and R. Stebbins.

1

2

Plate 39

1. Type locality of the Lyell salamander (*Hydromantes platycephalus*), head of Lyell Canyon near Donohue Pass Trail, 10,800 feet, Tuolumne County, California. The locality is at timberline as evidenced by the scattered, stunted white-bark pines (*Pinus albicaulis*). The rocks are granite with scattered patches of grass and heather among them. Salamanders were found under rocks in the shallow gully to the right of the large granitic mass in the center foreground. Photograph July 6, 1948.

2. Niche of the Lyell salamander (*Hydromantes platycephalus*). Closeup of the gully referred to in Figure 1. A salamander was found under the rock that rests against the sloping granitic substratum in the lower left hand corner of the picture. Note the seepage from a melting snowbank that was situated just outside the field of the photograph. Photograph July 6, 1948.

3. Habitat of the black salamander (*Aneides flavipunctatus*) 12.5 miles northwest of Shasta, near U.S. Highway 299, Shasta County, California. Salamanders were found in water-soaked soil among the rocks in the lower right hand portion of the photograph. Alders (*Alnus rhombifolia*) grow above the waterfall. The area in the foreground is shaded by canyon oaks (*Quercus chrysolepis*). Photograph by C. Lowe, Jr. and R. Stebbins, April 23, 1948.

1

2

3

Plate 40

1. Breeding pond of Couch (*Scaphiopus couchii*) and Hammond (*S. hammondii*) spadefoot toads, 10.5 miles northeast of Douglas, Cochise County, Arizona. Eggs and larvae of the Couch spadefoot were found. A single little green toad (*Bufo debilis*) was discovered about 100 feet from the pool, hopping in its direction. The pool was temporary, formed by summer thundershowers. Yucca, mesquite, and cactus are common plants in the area. Photograph July 23, 1949.

2. Representative mountain valley habitat of the western toad (*Bufo boreas boreas*) in the Rocky Mountains, 2 miles west and 4 miles north of Silverton, San Juan County, Colorado. The forested slopes are composed largely of lodgepole pine (*Pinus contorta*), Douglas fir (*Pseudostuga taxifolia*), and spruce (*Picea pungens*). Photograph August 25, 1949.

1

2

Plate 41

1. Habitat of the western toad (*Bufo boreas exsul*) at Deep Springs, approximately 5,000 feet, 7 miles south of Deep Springs Valley School, Inyo County, California. The subspecies *exsul* is evidently confined to the springs in this arid valley. The valley is surrounded by rather barren mountains, topped with a scattered growth of piñon pines (*Pinus cembroides*) and juniper (*Juniperus californicus*). Bushes along the canal are largely rabbit brush (*Chrysothamnus*). Individuals were extremely abundant on the mud banks of the canal and in the water. The white streak in the distance is an alkaline flat. The Hammond spadefoot toad was also found here. Its larvae were abundant in the canal. Photograph June 20, 1949.

2. Habitat of the desert toad (*Bufo punctatus*) at Cottonwood Spring, 3,000 feet, near the west side of the Eagle Mountains, Riverside County, California. In the Colorado and Mohave deserts this species commonly occurs at spring areas in the mouths of mountain canyons. In the photograph are cottonwoods (*Populus fremontii*), California fan palms (*Washingtonia filifera*), and a low scrubby growth principally of mesquite (*Prosopis chilensis*), vegetation in association with which this toad is often found in the western part of its range. Photograph July, 1946.

1

2

Plate 42

1. Habitat of the Cope toad (*Bufo microscaphus californicus*) along the Mohave River, 3 miles north of Victorville, San Bernardino County, California. Adults were found hopping about on the sandy banks among the cottonwoods and willows. Larvae were obtained in the quieter, shallower parts of the river. Photograph June 19, 1949.

2. Niche of the larvae of *Bufo microscaphus californicus* in the Mohave River near Victorville. Tadpoles were found principally under masses of algae at the margins of the quieter channels of the stream. Their coloration closely matched the sandy bottom. Photograph June 19, 1949.

1

2

Plate 43

1. Breeding pond of the Woodhouse toad (*Bufo woodhousii*) 2 miles southwest of Joseph, near U.S. Highway 89, Sevier County, Utah. A calling male was collected among the emergent grasses near the dead limb in the foreground. Photograph June 28, 1949.

2. Breeding pond of the Pacific tree-toad (*Hyla regilla*) 2 miles west of Hyampom, Trinity County, California. South Fork Mountain, in the background, is covered with a dense coniferous forest dominated by Douglas fir (*Pseudostuga taxifolia*). A mist hangs over the mountain. A large chorus of *Hyla* was observed here February 10 to 13, 1947. The Eschscholtz salamander was found in considerable numbers under rotting logs and beneath bark in the Douglas fir stand beyond the pond. Photograph February 13, 1947.

1

2

Plate 44

1. Natural "tank" 1 mile west of Peña Blanca Springs, approximately 4,000 feet, Santa Cruz County, Arizona, where larvae of the narrow mouth toad (*Microhyla carolinensis mazatlanensis*) were found. Adult canyon tree-toads (*Hyla arenicolor*) were ensconced in niches, principally in the shaded area of rock on the left above the pool. Several adult *Microhyla* were discovered under rocks on damp sand in the bottom of the ravine below the pool. The desert toad (*Bufo punctatus*) also frequented this canyon. Ocotillo, chilecote, bunch grass, and oaks occurred on the surrounding hills. Photograph July 17, 1949.

2. Habitat of the canyon tree-toad (*Hyla arenicolor*) at the headwaters of Rose Creek, 5,300 feet, Gila County, Arizona. Many larvae were collected in the pools along this cold mountain stream. Trees along the stream were sycamores, alders, and walnuts and on the slopes above, oaks and yellow pine. Photograph July 25, 1949.

1

2

Plate 45

1. Marshy area at Bloomington, about 4 miles south of Saint George, Washington County, Utah, where larvae of the leopard frog (*Rana pipiens*) were found. Many adult and metamorphosing *Bufo microscaphus* and *Bufo woodhousii* and a single adult *Rana pipiens* were seen. Sedges and grasses dominate the foreground. The trees in the distance are principally tamarisk (*Tamarix gallica*). Photograph July 4, 1949.

2. Habitat of the wood frog (*Rana sylvatica*) 5 miles east-southeast of Rabbit Ears Peak, Jackson County, Colorado. The frogs were found along the willow-bordered streams of this broad valley. Basin sagebrush (*Artemisia tridentata*) forms extensive tracts. The hills in the distance are covered with conifers and aspen (*Populus tremuloides*). The leopard frog (*Rana pipiens*), western toad (*Bufo boreas*), and swamp cricket frog (*Pseudacris nigrita*) were also found here. Photograph August 23, 1949.

1

2

1

Plate 46

1. Habitat of the Mexican frog (*Rana tarahumarae*) ½ mile southwest of Yanks Spring, Sycamore Canyon, Santa Cruz County, Arizona. Adult frogs were obtained at the pool in front of the large granite boulder in the center foreground. The trees are willows and cottonwoods. Oaks and walnuts were also present. Photograph July 18, 1949.

DISTRIBUTION MAPS

Localities shown in the following maps are based on specimens in the Museum of Vertebrate Zoölogy and records in the literature. It has not been possible for me always to verify the latter. In instances where I am dubious about a record, this is indicated by a question mark. Not all known records appear. I have merely attempted to block out the range.

Plate 47

NATURAL VEGETATION

(Adapted from Shantz, H. L. and R. Zon, 1924, Natural vegetation, U.S. Dept. Agric., Atlas Amer. Agric., sect. E.)

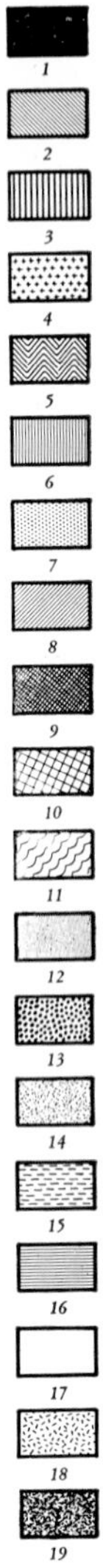

Forest Vegetation (Western)

1. Spruce—Fir (Northern coniferous forest)

Cedar—Hemlock (Northwestern coniferous forest):

2. Western larch—western white pine
3. Pacific Douglas fir
4. Redwood

Yellow Pine—Douglas Fir (Western pine forest):

5. Yellow pine—sugar pine
6. Yellow pine—Douglas fir
7. Lodgepole pine
8. Piñon—Juniper (Southwestern coniferous woodland)
9. Chaparral (Southwestern broad-leaved woodland)

Desert Shrub Vegetation

10. Sagebrush (Northern desert shrub)
11. Creosote bush (Southern desert shrub)
12. Greasewood (Salt desert shrub)

Grass Vegetation

13. Tall grass (Prairie grassland)
14. Short grass (Plains grassland)
15. Mesquite grass (Desert grassland)
16. Bunch grass (Pacific grassland)
17. Alpine meadow (Alpine grassland)
18. Marsh grass (Marsh grassland)

Forest Vegetation (Eastern)

Oak (Southern hardwood forest)

19. Oak-hickory

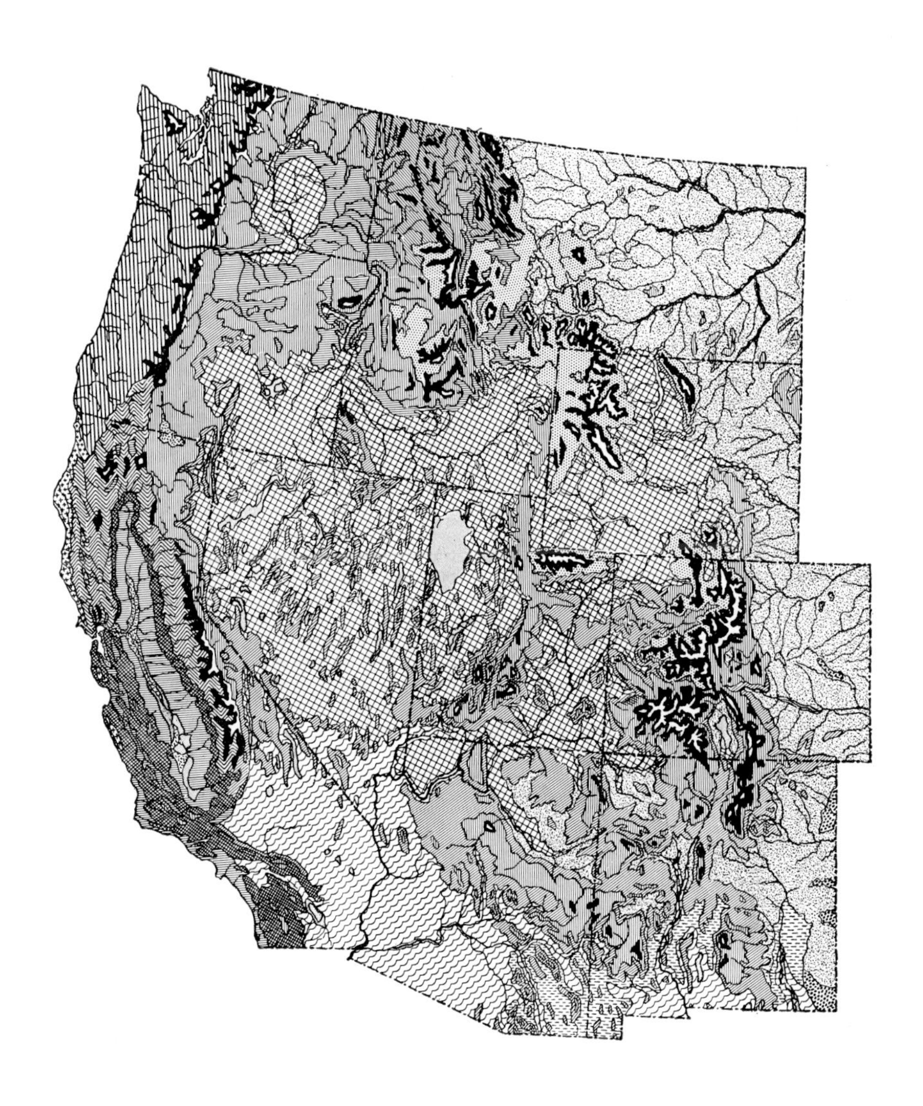

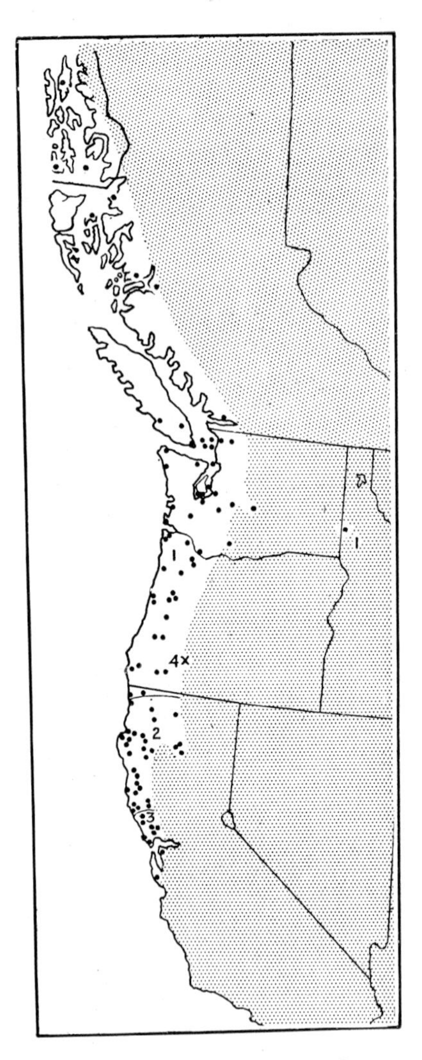

TRITURUS GRANULOSUS
1. GRANULOSUS
2. SIMILANS
3. TWITTYI
4. (X) MAZAMAE

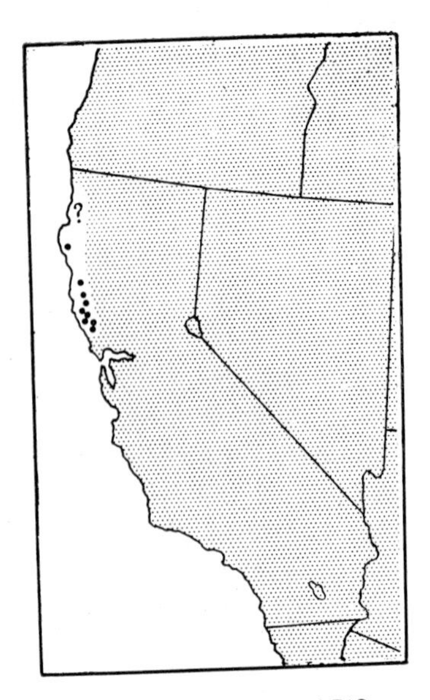

TRITURUS RIVULARIS

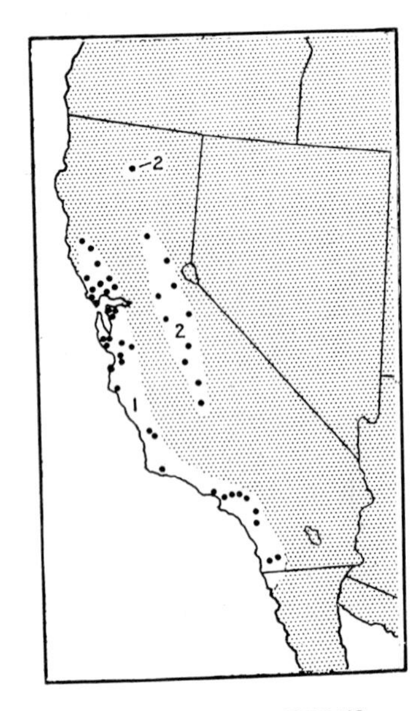

TRITURUS TOROSUS
1. TOROSUS
2. SIERRAE

Plate 48

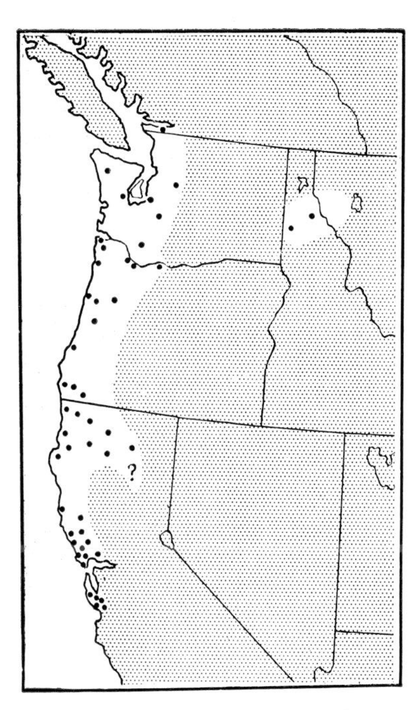

DICAMPTODON ENSATUS

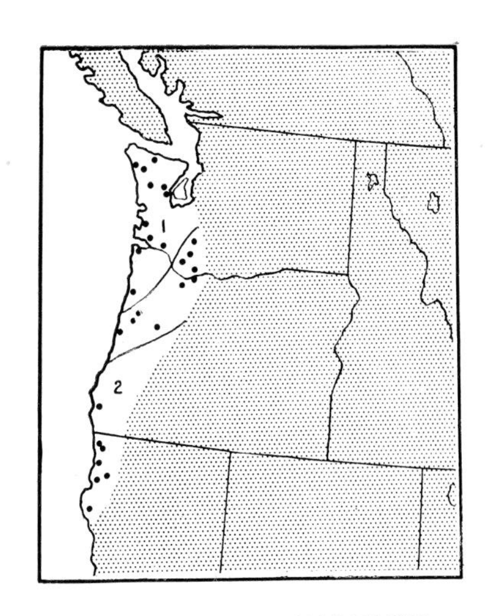

RHYACOTRITON OLYMPICUS
1. OLYMPICUS
2. VARIEGATUS

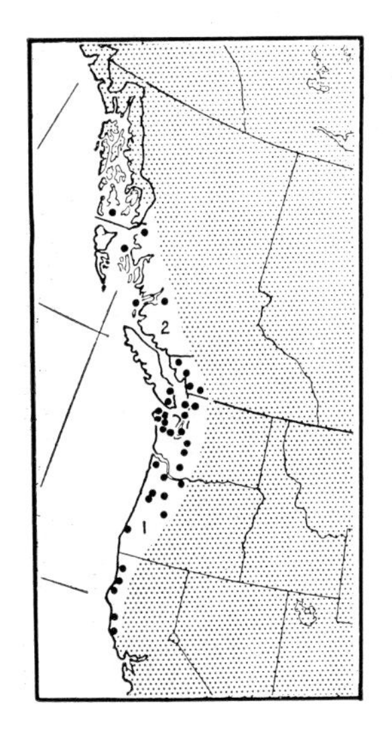

AMBYSTOMA GRACILE
1. GRACILE
2. DECORTICATUM

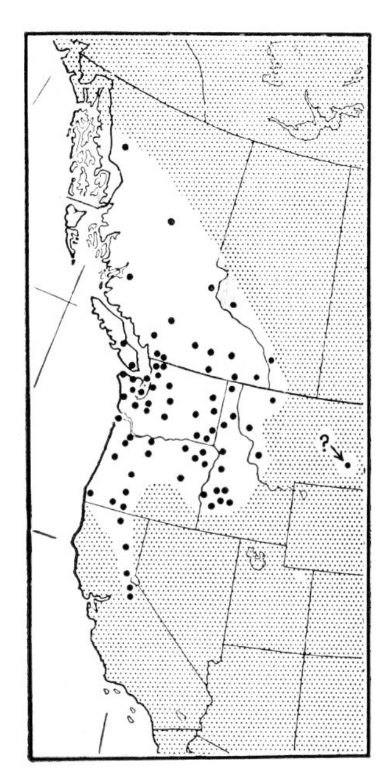

AMBYSTOMA
MACRODACTYLUM

Plate 49

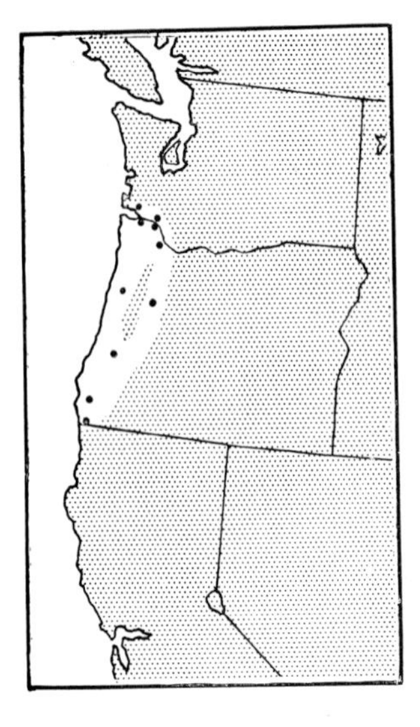

PLETHODON DUNNI

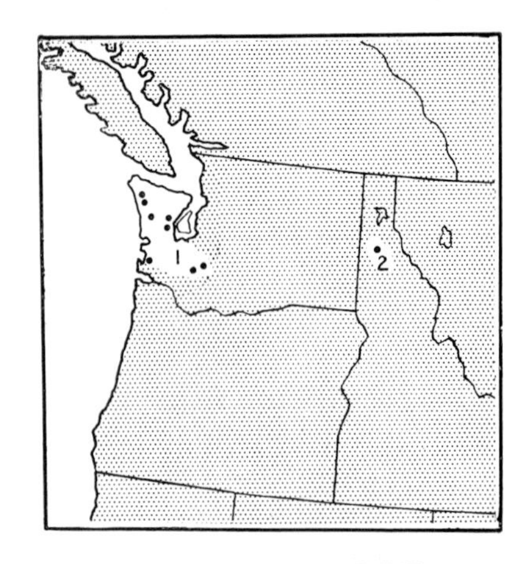

PLETHODON VANDYKEI
1. VANDYKEI
2. IDAHOENSIS

Plate 50

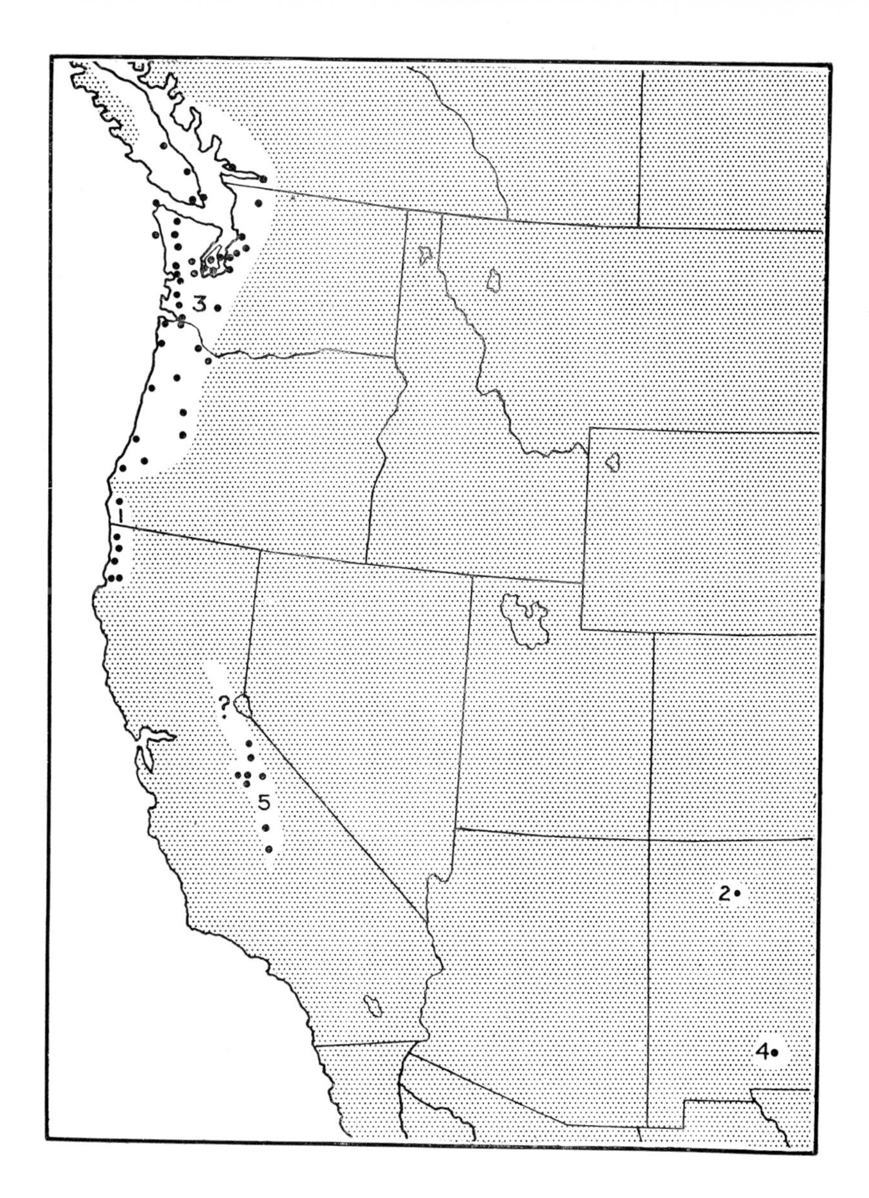

1. PLETHODON ELONGATUS
2. PLETHODON NEOMEXICANUS
3. PLETHODON VEHICULUM
4. ANEIDES HARDII
5. HYDROMANTES PLATYCEPHALUS

Plate 51

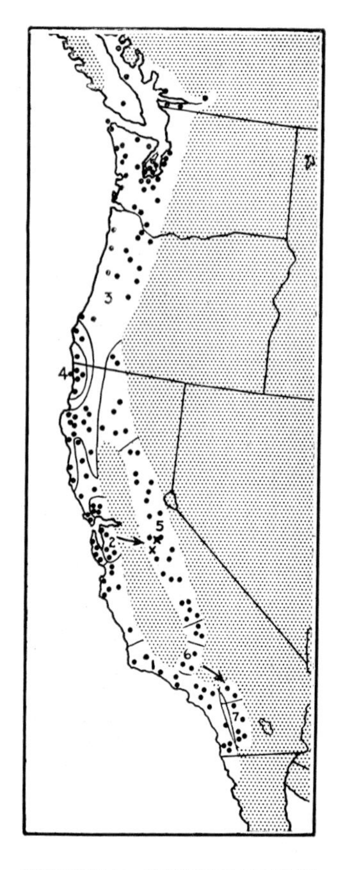

ENSATINA ESCHSCHOLTZII
1. ESCHSCHOLTZII
2. XANTHOPTICA
3. OREGONENSIS
4. PICTA
5. PLATENSIS
6. CROCEATER
7. KLAUBERI
X. XANTHOPTICA IN THE SIERRA NEVADA

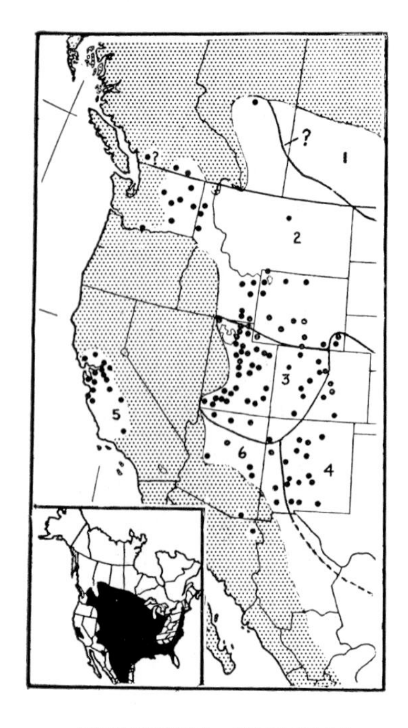

AMBYSTOMA TIGRINUM
1. DIABOLI
2. MELANOSTICTUM
3. NEBULOSUM
4. MAVORTIUM
5. CALIFORIENSE
6. AFFINITY UNCERTAIN

Plate 52

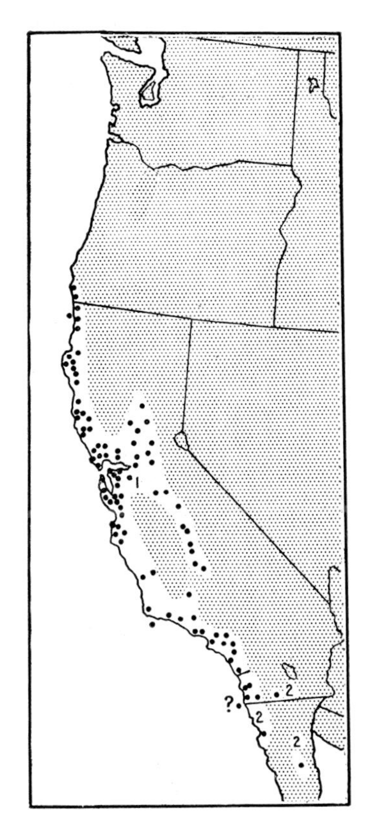

BATRACHOSEPS ATTENUATUS
1. ATTENUATUS
2. LEUCOPUS

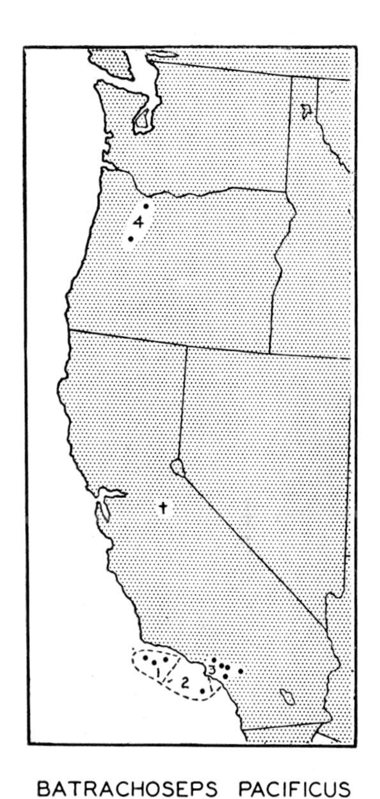

BATRACHOSEPS PACIFICUS
1. PACIFICUS
2. CATALINAE
3. MAJOR

4. BATRACHOSEPS WRIGHTI

† FOSSIL PACIFICUS-LIKE BATRACHOSEPS

Plate 53

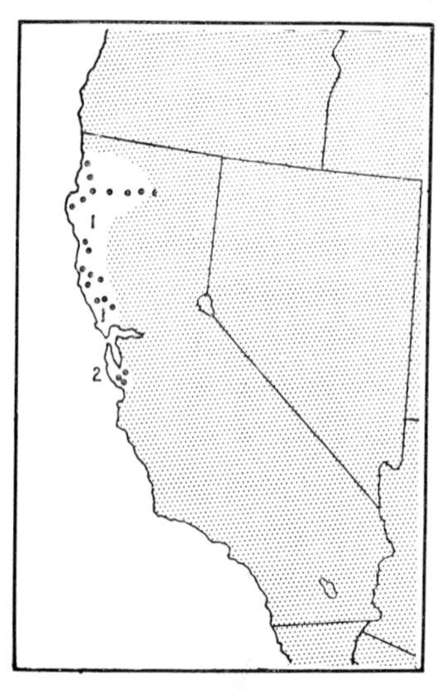

ANEIDES FLAVIPUNCTATUS
1. FLAVIPUNCTATUS
2. NIGER

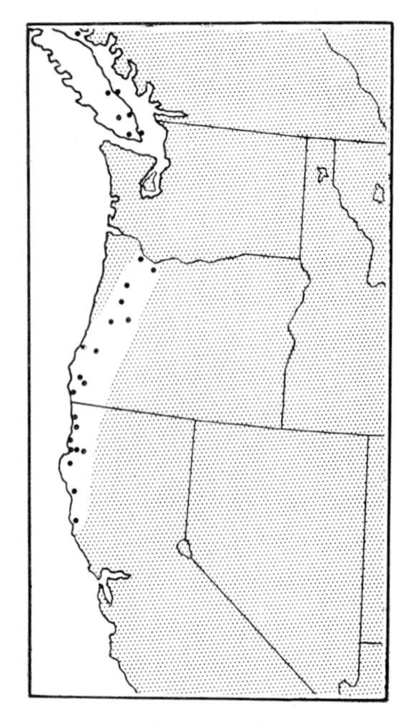

ANEIDES FERREUS

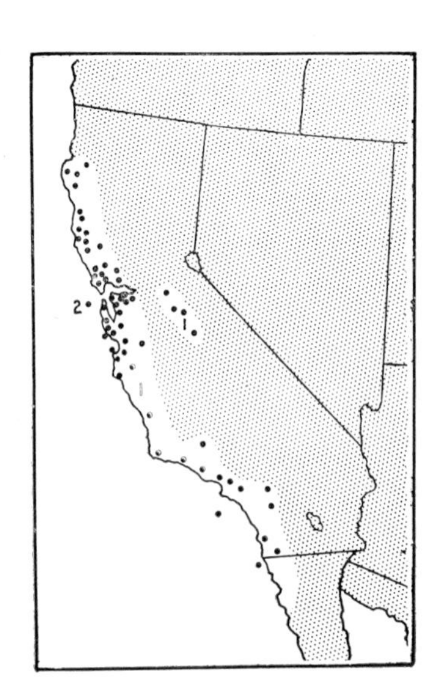

ANEIDES LUGUBRIS
1. LUGUBRIS
2. FARALLONENSIS

Plate 54

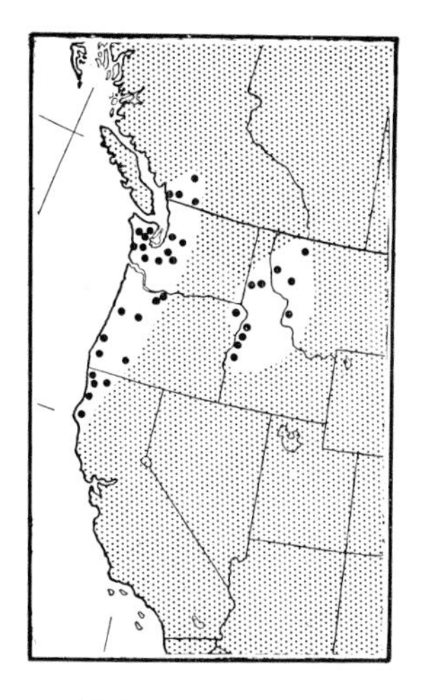

ASCAPHUS TRUEI

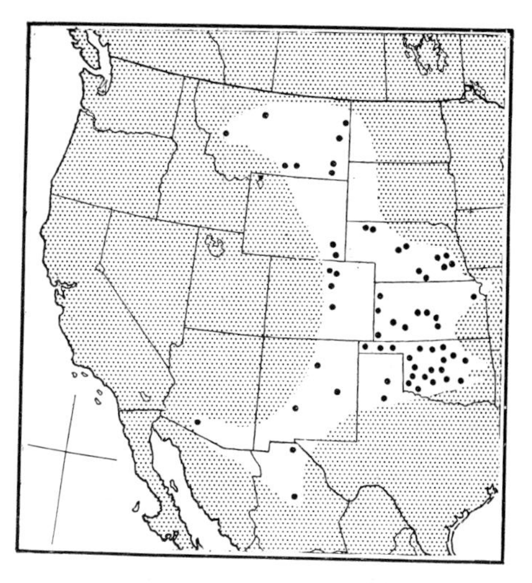

SCAPHIOPUS BOMBIFRONS

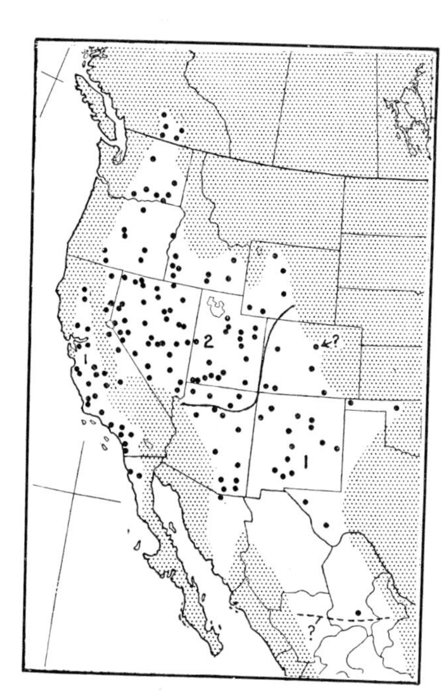

SCAPHIOPUS HAMMONDII
1. HAMMONDII
2. INTERMONTANUS

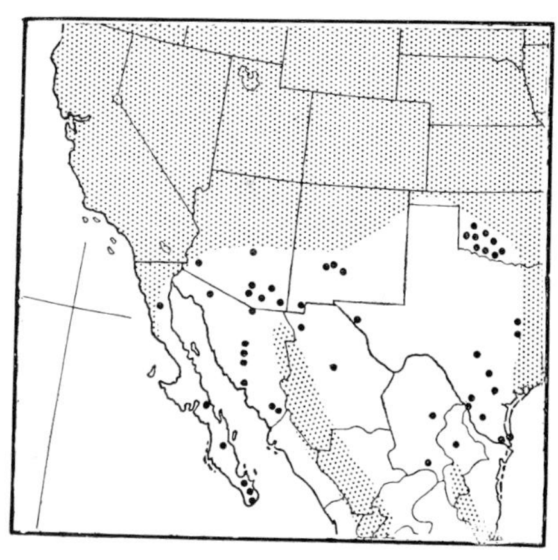

SCAPHIOPUS COUCHII

Plate 55

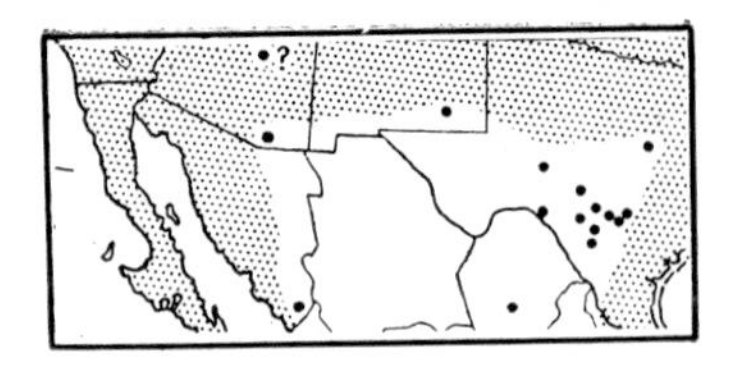

ELEUTHERODACTYLUS
LATRANS

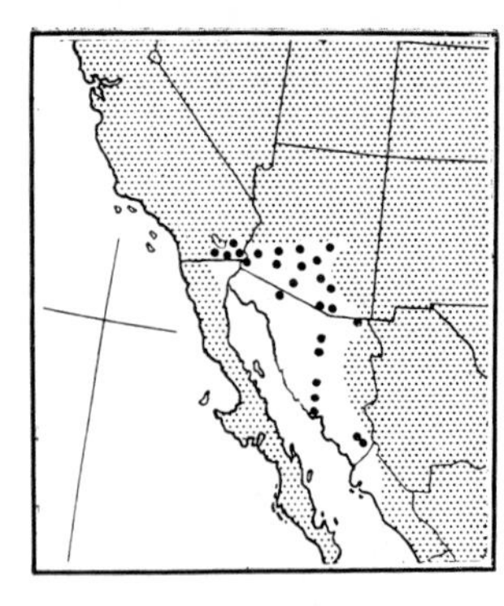

BUFO ALVARIUS

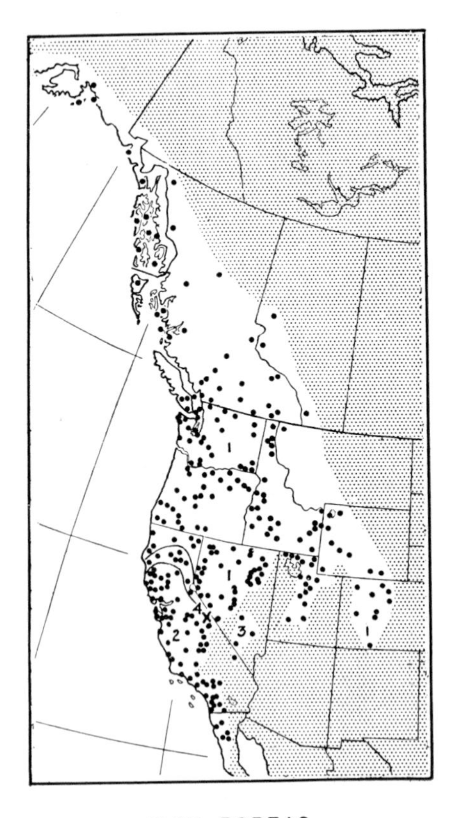

BUFO BOREAS
1. BOREAS
2. HALOPHILUS
3. NELSONI
4. (X) EXSUL

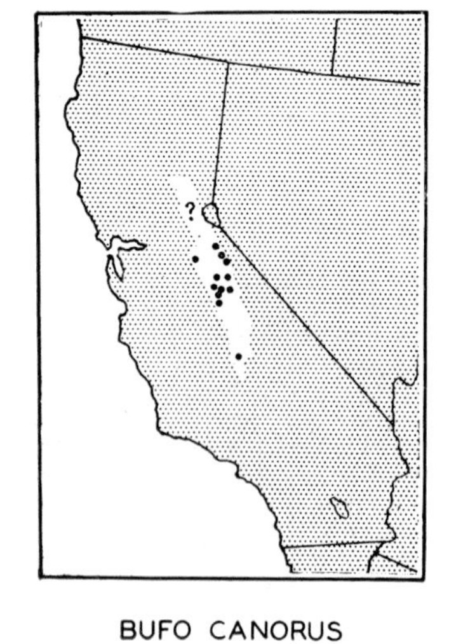

BUFO CANORUS

Plate 56

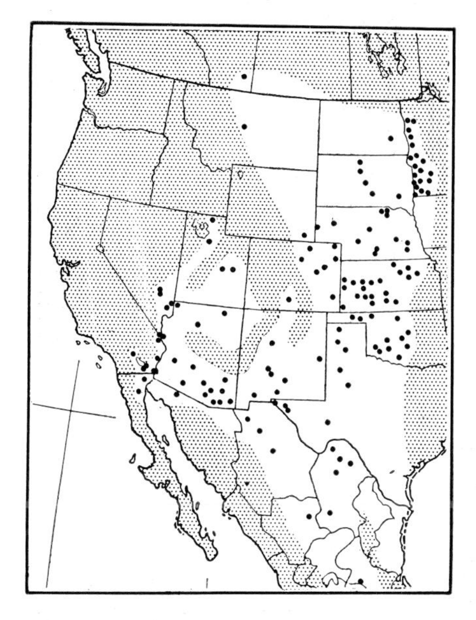

BUFO COGNATUS

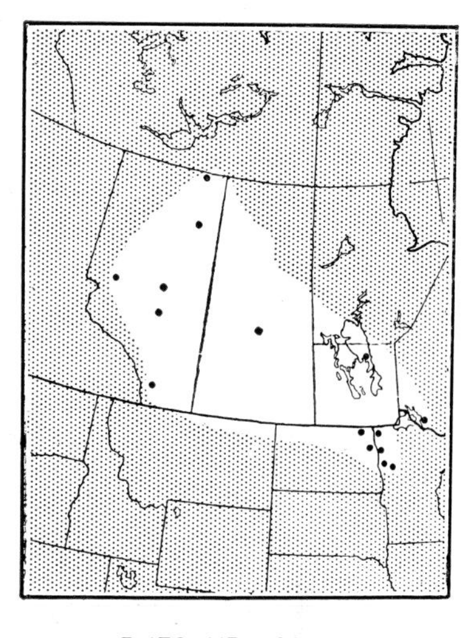

BUFO HEMIOPHRYS

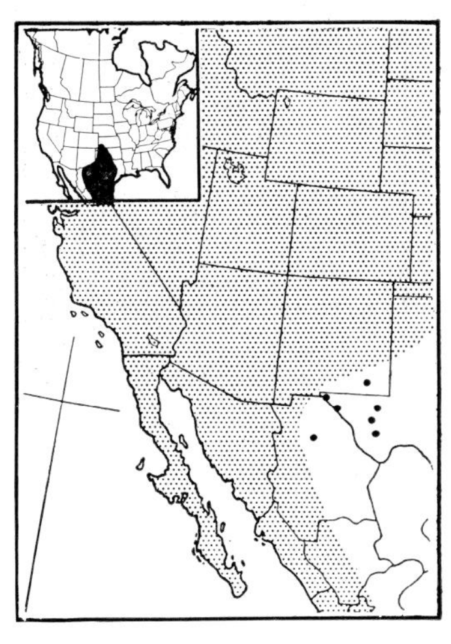

BUFO COMPACTILIS

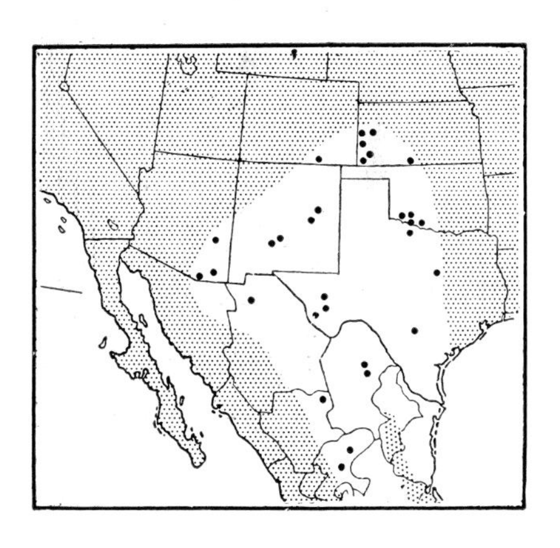

BUFO DEBILIS

Plate 57

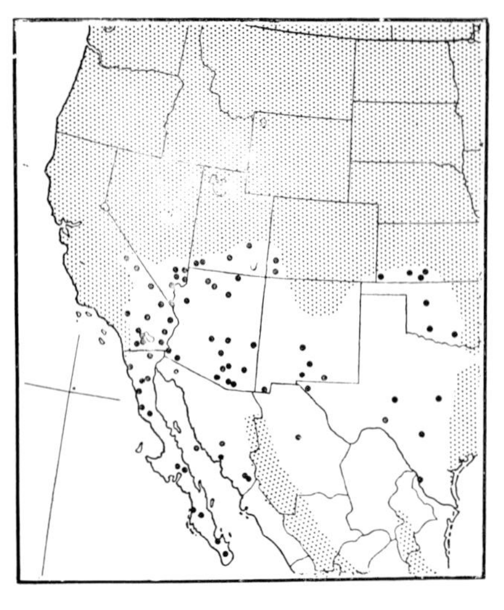

BUFO PUNCTATUS

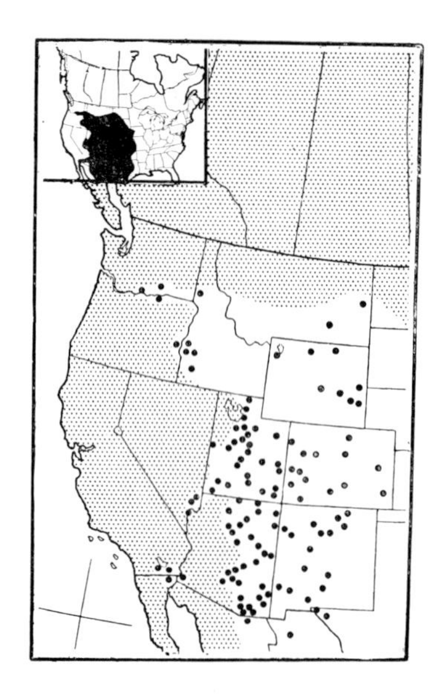

BUFO WOODHOUSII

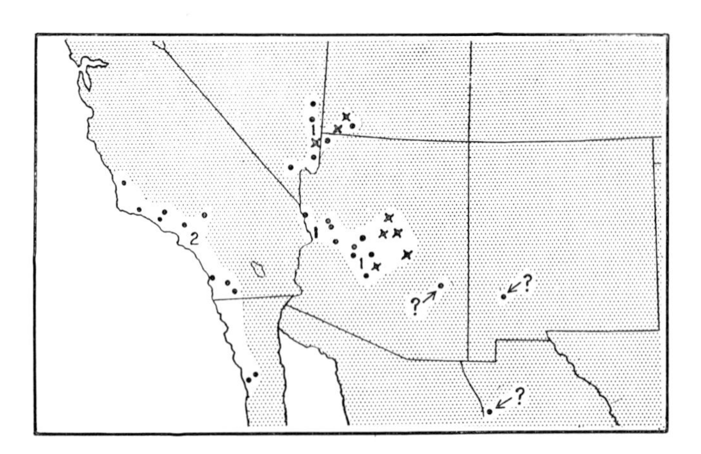

BUFO MICROSCAPHUS
1. MICROSCAPHUS
?↗ UNCERTAIN RELATIONSHIP
2. CALIFORNICUS
× M+W HYBRIDS

Plate 58

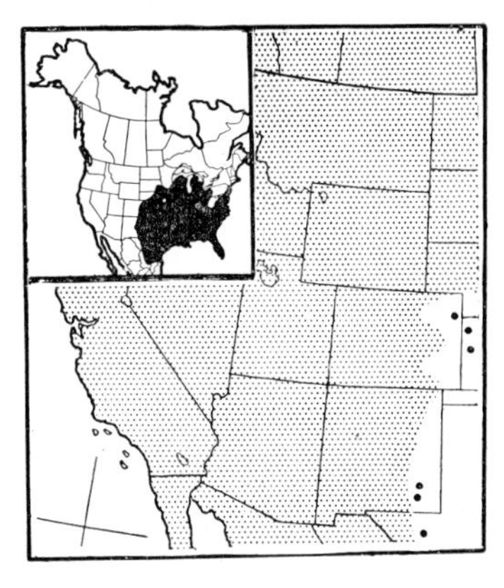

ACRIS GRYLLUS

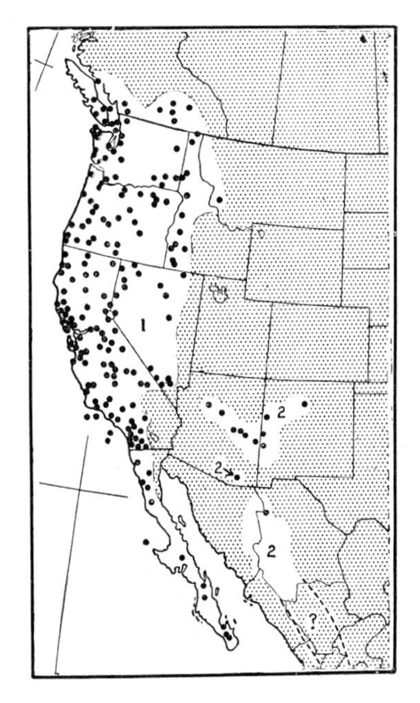

1. HYLA REGILLA
2. HYLA WRIGHTORUM

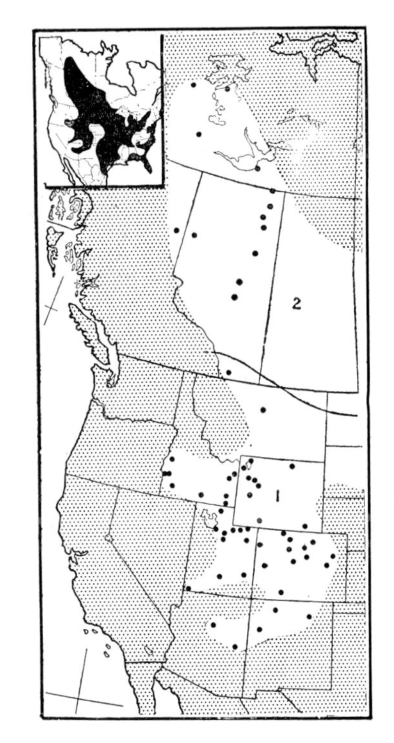

PSEUDACRIS NIGRITA

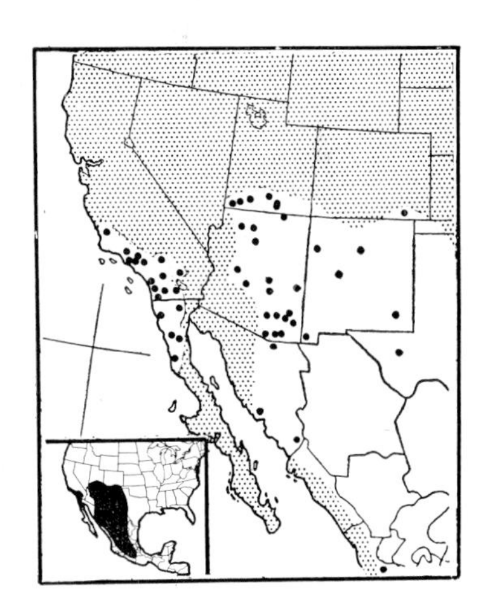

HYLA ARENICOLOR

Plate 59

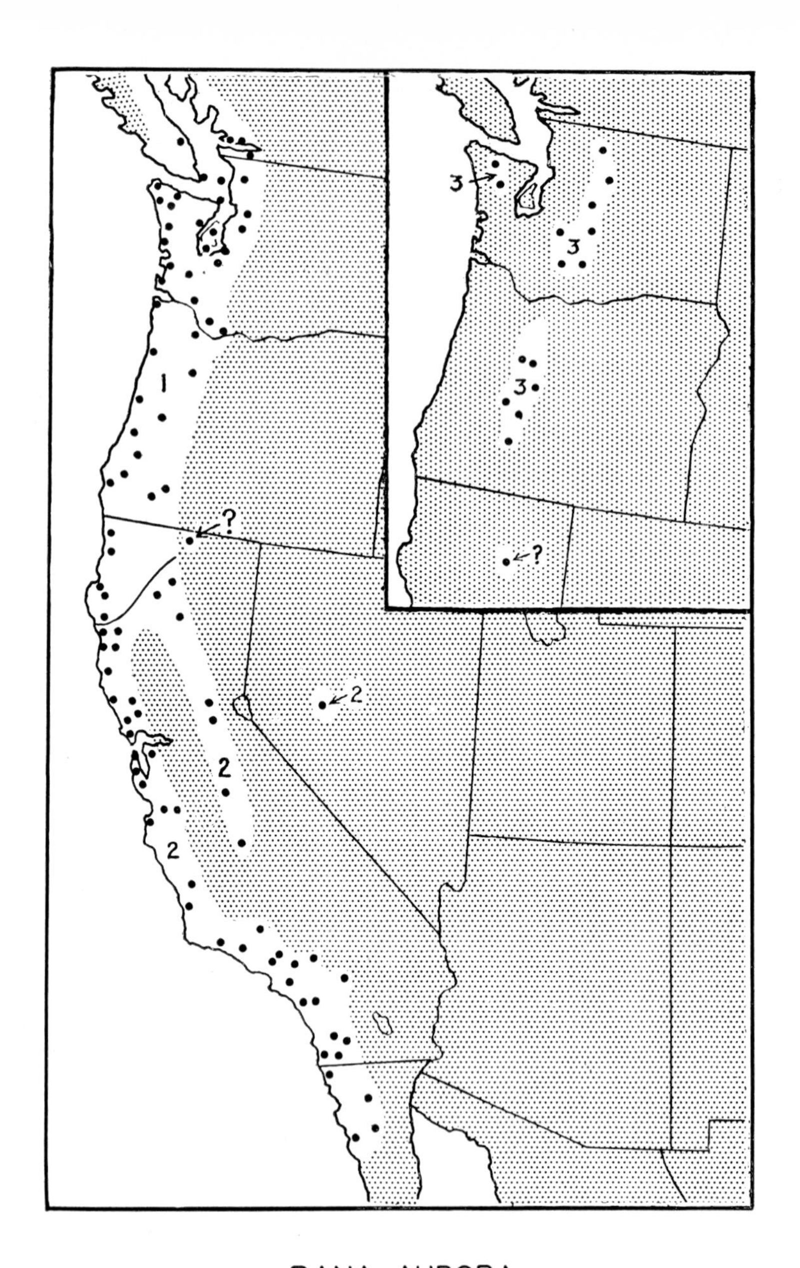

RANA AURORA
1. AURORA
2. DRAYTONII
3. CASCADAE

Plate 60

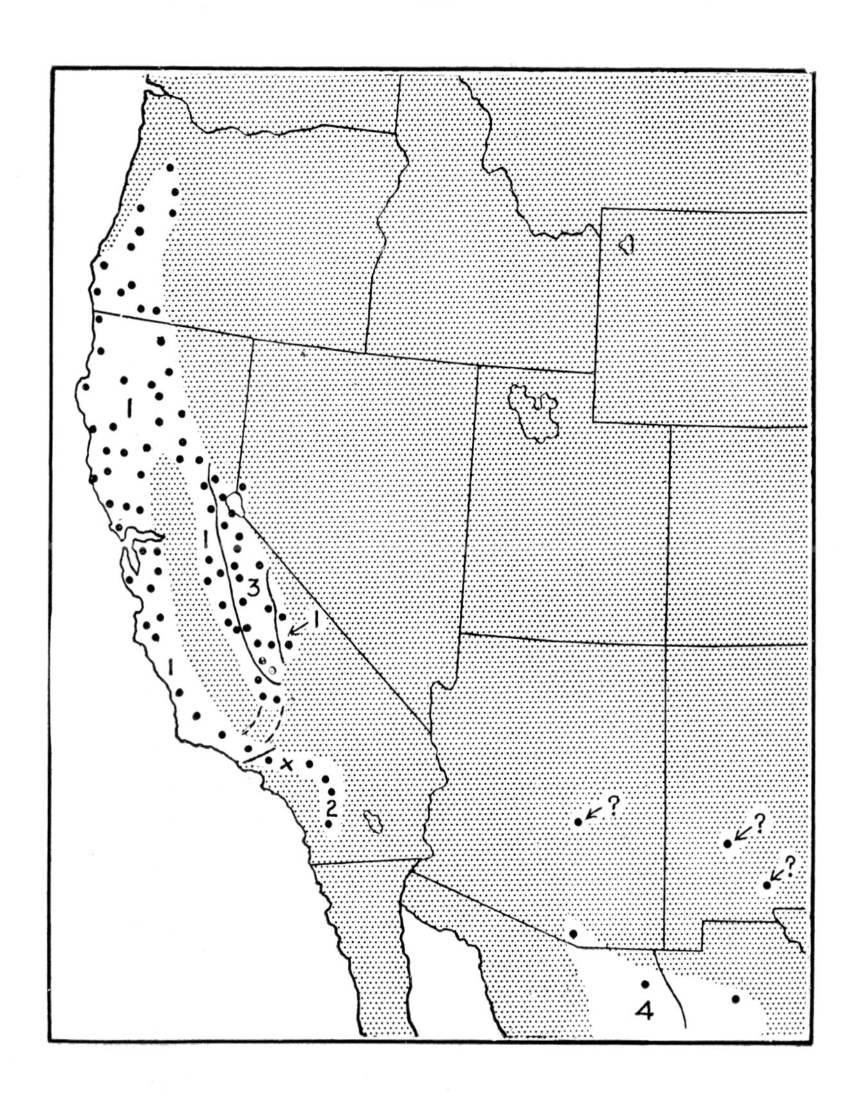

I.-3. RANA BOYLII
  I. BOYLII
  2. MUSCOSA
  3. SIERRAE
  X. BOYLII IN THE RANGE OF MUSCOSA

4. RANA TARAHUMARAE

? RANA TARAHUMARAE

Plate 61

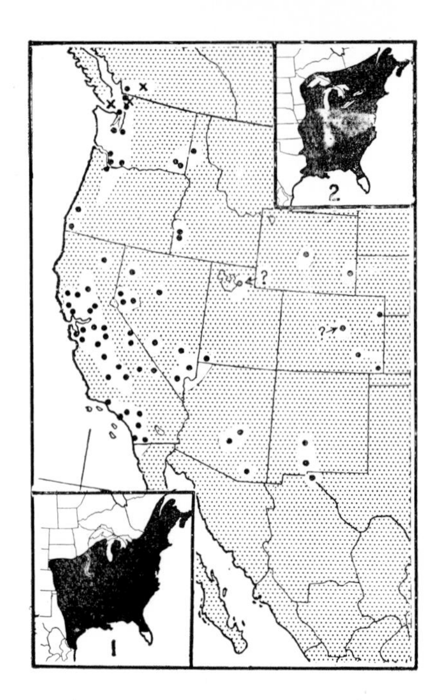

1. RANA CATESBEIANA
2. X. RANA CLAMITANS

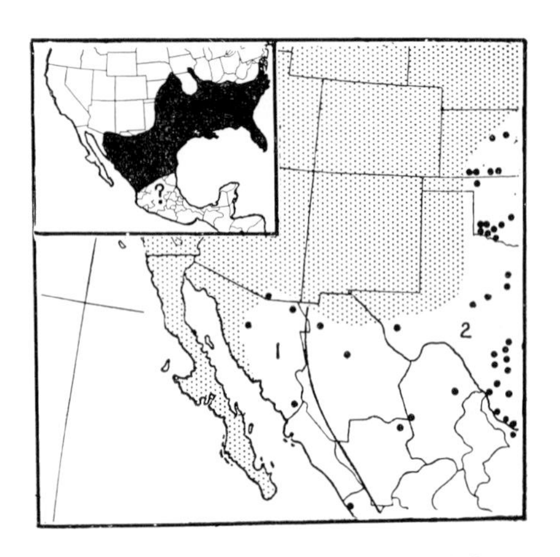

MICROHYLA CAROLINENSIS
1. MAZATLANENSIS
2. OLIVACEA

Plate 62

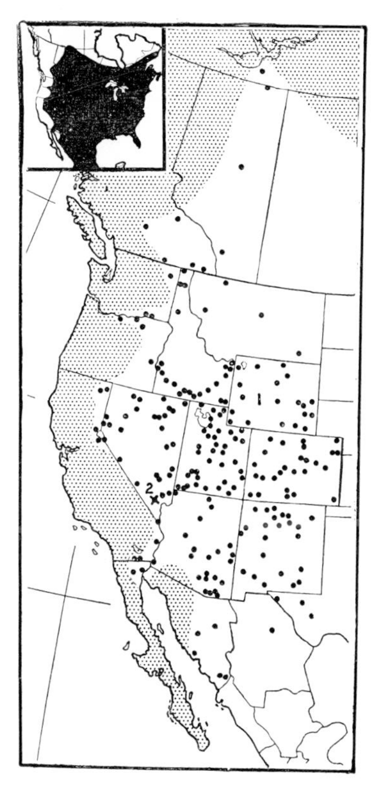

RANA PIPIENS
1. PIPIENS
2. FISHERI (x)

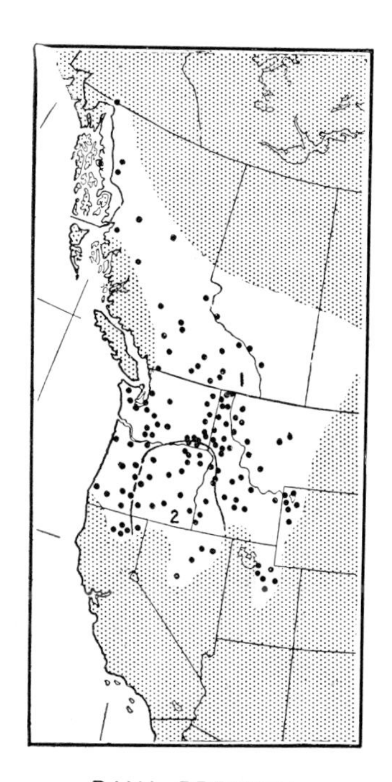

RANA PRETIOSA
1. PRETIOSA
2. LUTEIVENTRIS

Plate 63

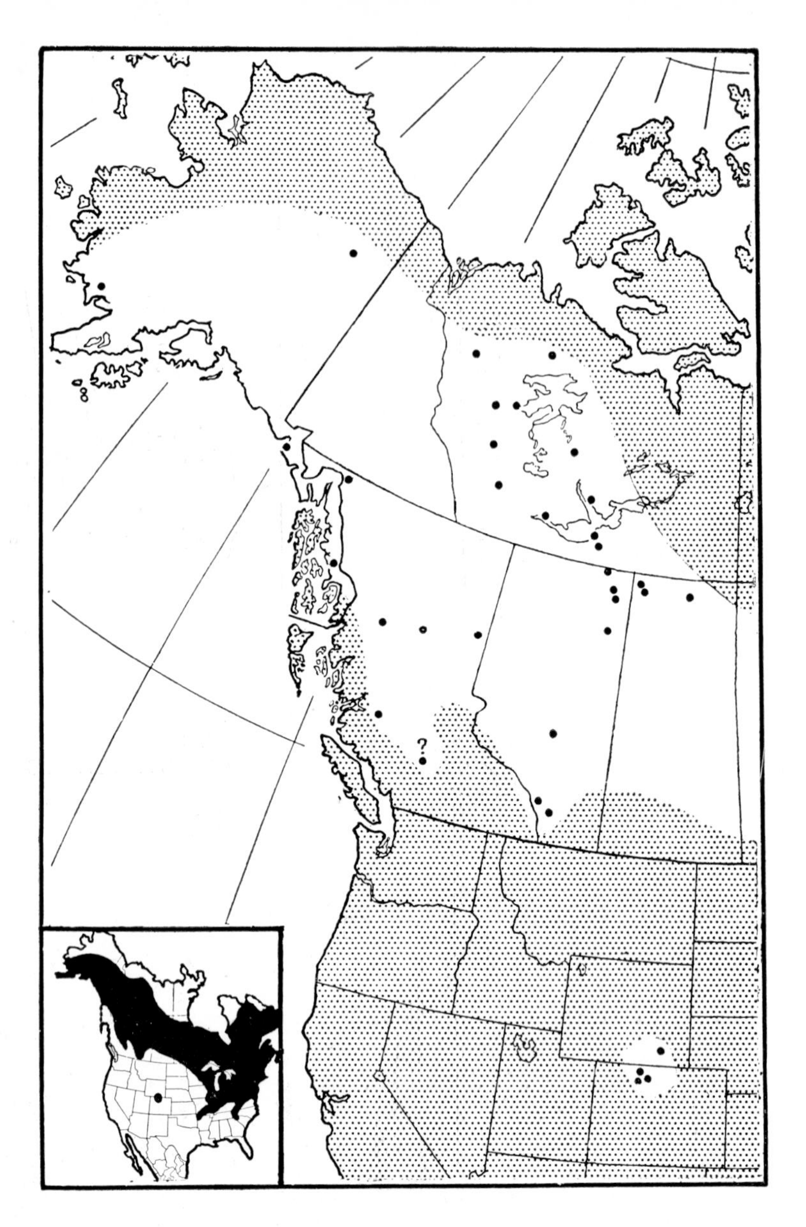

RANA SYLVATICA

Plate 64

GLOSSARY

Allantoic gills. Applied to the embryonic gills of wholly terrestrial plethodontid salamanders. These gills appear and function during the period of development within the egg and normally atrophy at hatching. In some species they are large, flattened, highly vascular, fanlike structures that spread out immediately beneath the egg capsule and function in respiration. In structure and function, they resemble somewhat the allantois of amniotic vertebrates (reptiles, birds, and mammals).

Allopatric distribution. See "geographically complementary races." Applies to species and higher categories as well as races.

Amphicoelous vertebra. A vertebra, the centrum of which possesses a concavity at both ends. In amphibians such vertebrae are considered primitive.

Amplexus. An embrace. The sexual embrace of a male anuran (toad or frog) or salamander.

Anuran. A tailless amphibian. Any member of the order Anura, the group to which the frogs and toads belong.

Axolotl. Any of several larval salamanders of the genus *Ambystoma.* Such larvae may live and breed in the larval condition but are capable of discarding their gills and fins, while beginning to breath air at the surface, and of eventually emerging as adult salamanders.

Bifurcation. Subdivision into two parts.

Buccopharyngeal. Refers to the region of the mouth and throat (pharynx).

Choana (pl. choanae). The opening of the nasal passage into the mouth.

Chromatophore. A pigment-bearing cell, especially one capable of changing its form or the concentration of its pigment, causing changes of color in the skin by exposing surface areas of pigment. Among the amphibians considered in this book, three primary types are recognized: lipophores, guanophores, and melanophores.

Cloaca. The common chamber into which the intestinal, urinary, and generative canals discharge in birds, reptiles, amphibians, and many fishes.

Cloacal papillae. Numerous small hair or nipple-like projections (villosities) from the lateral wall of the vent in male salamanders. Ducts of the cloacal glands open at their ends. The cloacal glands produce the jelly or mucus that forms the base of the spermatophore.

Compressed. Flattened laterally, as the tail of tadpoles and larval and aquatic adult salamanders. Narrow from side to side, and deep in a dorsoventral direction.

Cuneiform. Wedge-shaped.

Cyclostomous. Round-mouthed.

Dermal. Pertains to the skin.

Dextral. On the right side.

Dorsum. The back of an animal; the upper side of an appendage or part.

Erythrocyte. Red blood cell.

Flagellum. A slender filament at the tip of the tail in some tadpoles.

Geographic variation. Pertains to variation in animals or plants that is correlated with distance; morphological or physiological changes that occur with changes in geographic position.

Geographically complementary races. Races or subspecies that replace one another geographically; subspecies connected with, or adjacent to, one another but whose ranges do not overlap. Allopatric distribution.

Granular gland. A gland, commonly of simple alveolar type producing a toxic holocrine secretion (by breakdown of contained cells). Such glands are widespread among amphibians and are called poison or venom glands. Their function is probably primarily protective. The secretion of these glands is commonly whitish, viscous, and astringent.

Guanophore. A pigment cell containing guanin, a product of protein hydrolysis. This substance, as crystalline uric acid, commonly imparts a whitish cast to the cell. Guanophores may appear opaque white, silvery, pale blue, brassy, etc., depending on the shape and arrangement of the contained crystals and on interference phenomena.

Hybridization. Refers to the union, with production of offspring, of the male of one race, variety, species, genus, etc., with the female of another; crossbreeding of animals or plants.

Insemination. Introduction of sperm into the reproductive tract of the female or, among the majority of anurans, release of sperm into the extruded egg mass.

Intercalary cartilage. A cartilaginous element situated between the terminal and post-terminal phalanges in hylid and polypedatid frogs. It probably provides greater mobility of the terminal phalanx, facilitating climbing.

Intergrade. To merge gradually one with another through a series of intermediate forms.

Intermandibular gland. A gland found in certain salamanders, hedonic in function, which is situated between the rami of the lower jaw—in the region immediately behind the chin.

Lipophore. A pigment cell containing lipoid (fatty) substances. Such cells are often responsible for the red, orange, and yellow colors of amphibians. They are commonly branched, but among amphibians seem generally not to be contractile.

Mandibular teeth. Teeth attached to the lower jaw (mandible).

Maxillary bone. A bone on either side of the head forming most of the lateral border of the upper jaw and bearing most of the upper teeth.

Melanophore. A pigment cell, often with numerous branched (dendritic) processes radiating from a central reservoir, that contains granules of melanin, a dark brown to black pigment. These granules may be dispersed in the cell processes or concentrated in the cell reservoir.

Mental gland. A gland situated beneath the skin of the chin (intermandibular area) of certain male salamanders. Its secretion appears to have a hedonic function, inhibiting the female during courtship.

Meroblastic cleavage. Segmentation of the egg involving only partial cleavage due to the impediment of a large amount of yolk. It is observed in extreme form in the large-yolked eggs of birds where, in the early stages of development, a disc of cells appears on the surface of the undivided yolk mass. Among amphibians such cleavage is known in certain plethodontid salamanders, but in less extreme form than in birds.

Metamorphosis. A marked and more or less abrupt change in the form or structure (and usually also in the habits, food, etc.) of an animal during postembryonic development, as when a tadpole changes into a frog.

Microphagous. Feeding on minute plants and animals, often those accumulating on the surface of water.

Monotypic. One type. A monotypic genus, for example, contains a single species.

Nasal bones. Paired bones in the vertebrate skull that lie between the nostrils and behind the premaxillary bones. In amphibians they are situated beneath the skin of the upper surface of the snout.

Neoteny. The condition of having the larval period indefinitely prolonged.

Opisthocoelous vertebra. Vertebra with the centrum concave posteriorly.

Ovarian egg. An egg within the stroma of the ovary.

Oviposition. The act of egg-laying.

Ovoviviparous. Producing eggs that have a well-developed shell or covering (as in oviparous animals) but which hatch within the body of the parent, as in some reptiles and elasmobranch fishes.

Ovum. Egg; female gamete.

Papilla (pl. papillae). Any small nipple-like or pimple-like projection or part.

Pedicel. A slender stalk. The eggs of certain plethodontid salamanders are attached by pedicels. The tongue of some lungless salamanders (*Hydromantes,* etc.) is spoken of as pedicelled. Such a tongue is mushroom-like, attached to the floor of the mouth by a central stalk. The edges of the tongue are free.

Pedogenesis. Reproduction by young or larval animals as in the axolotl.

Phalanx (pl. phalanges). In vertebrates, one of the finger or toe bones.

Plantar tubercle. Tubercle on the sole of the foot.

Pleuroperitoneum. The common lining of the chest and abdominal cavities in lungless salamanders.

Plinthlike. From the Greek word meaning tile. Used in reference to an amphibian egg cluster that forms a flattened, three-dimensional, somewhat rectangular mass.

Postorbital furrow. Refers to a furrow passing from the vicinity of the posterior corner of the eye, a variable distance posteriorly. Among salamanders this furrow typically extends horizontally to meet a lateral vertical furrow that is continuous with the gular fold.

Premaxillary bone. One of a pair of bones (sometimes fused) in the upper jaw, at the front of the mouth that is situated between and anterior to the maxillary bones. It may or may not bear teeth.

Premaxillary teeth. Teeth attached to the premaxillary bone.

Punctate chromatophore. Refers to the appearance of the pigment cell when the pigment is concentrated in the cell reservoir. When in this condition the radiating branched processes of the cell are not visible; the cell appears as a spot, commonly of irregular outline. This terminology is employed by Parker (1948).

Punctostellate chromatophore. Pertains to the appearance of a pigment cell. A condition intermediate between punctate and stellate.

Pyriform. Having the form of a pear.

Race. Used in this book as a synonym of subspecies.

Sinistral. On the left side.

Spermatheca. A chamber for the storage of sperm. Among salamanders, varies in complexity from a number of tubules opening individually on the roof of the cloaca to a group opening by a common duct.

Spermatophore. Male sex product of salamanders, typically consisting of a gelatinous cone capped with a mass of sperm. Deposited in damp situations on land or in the water, depending upon the species. The sperm capsule is removed from the jelly cone by the female, with her cloaca.

Subspecies. A subdivision of a species; a variety or race; a category (usually the lowest category recognized in classification) ranking next below a species. The differences separating subspecies are usually slight and are commonly bridged in zones of intergradation. Some systematists insist that intergradation should be the criterion in deciding whether two adjacent, slightly different animal populations should be considered as subspecies or species. If intergradation (or intermixture of characters) does not exist, they are regarded as species.

Sympatric distribution. Overlapping or, in varying degree, superimposed distribution of two or more subspecies, species, or higher categories. Relates to the coexistence (geographically) of two or more forms. The opposite of allopatric distribution.

Thoracolumbar. Pertains to the region between the forelimbs and hind limbs, the chest and loins.

Tibiofibular. Pertains to the segment of the hind limb between the heel and knee.

Torpid. Having lost motion or the power of exertion or feeling; dormant; numb. Commonly used in reference to hibernating animals or animals stupefied by low temperatures.

Triparted. In three parts as the allantoic gills of certain plethodontid salamanders. Such a gill possesses three primary divisions from a common base.

Tubercle. A small knoblike prominence or excrescence.

Urodele. A salamander. Any amphibian of the order Urodela, the tailed amphibians.

Venter. The belly; the abdomen.

Zygote. The fertilized egg.

ABBREVIATIONS

AHM, Alden H. Miller; AMNH, American Museum of Natural History; CAS, California Academy of Sciences; CPS, College of Puget Sound; CU, Cornell University; HR, Harold Reynolds; JRH, John R. Hendrickson; LT, Lee Talbot; RCS, Robert C. Stebbins; RZ, Richard Zweifel; SDSNH, San Diego Society of Natural History; UCDDZ, University of California at Davis, Division of Zoölogy; UNMB, University of Nevada Museum of Biology; UOMZ, University of Oklahoma Museum of Zoölogy; USNM, United States National Museum; WJR, William J. Riemer; ♂, symbol for male; ♀, symbol for female.

BIBLIOGRAPHY

ADAMS, L. 1942. The natural history and classification of the Mount Lyell Salamander, *Hydromantes platycephalus*. Univ. Calif. Publ. Zoöl., 46(2):179-204.

ANDERSON, P. 1945. New herpetological records for Missouri. Bull. Chicago Acad. Sci., 7(5):271-75.

ARNOLD, L. W. 1943. Notes on two species of desert toads. Copeia, 1943:(2):128.

BAILEY, V. 1913. Life zones and crop zones of New Mexico. N. Amer. Fauna, 35:1-100.

BAIRD, S. F. 1850. Revision of the North American tailed-batrachia, with descriptions of new genera and species. Jour. Acad. Nat. Sci. Phila., 1(4):281-94.

———. 1854. Descriptions of new genera and species of North American frogs. Proc. Acad. Nat. Sci. Phila., 7:59-62.

———. 1859a. Reptiles of the Boundary. United States and Mexican Boundary Survey, 2(2):1-35.

———. 1859b. Report on reptiles collected on the survey. Pacif. R. R. Rep., 10, Williamson's Route, 1859 (4):9-13.

BAIRD, S. F. and C. GIRARD. 1852a. Characteristics of some new reptiles in the Museum of the Smithsonian Institution. Proc. Acad. Nat. Sci. Phila., 6:173.

———. 1852b. Descriptions of new species of reptiles, collected by the U.S. Exploring Expedition under the command of Capt. Charles Wilkes, U.S.N. Proc. Acad. Nat. Sci. Phila., 6:174-77.

———. 1853. Communication [describing *Rana pretiosa* and *Bufo columbiensis*]. Proc. Acad. Nat. Sci. Phila., 6:378-79.

BAUMAN, J. 1950. Migration of salamanders. Yellowstone Nature Notes, 24(1):4-5.

BAXTER, G. T. 1947. The amphibians and reptiles of Wyoming. Wyoming Wild Life, 1947:30-34.

BELLERBY, C. W. 1934. A rapid test for the diagnosis of pregnancy. Nature, 133: 494-95.

BISHOP, S. C. 1934. Description of a new salamander from Oregon, with notes on related species. Proc. Biol. Soc. Wash., 47:169-72.

———. 1937. A remarkable new salamander from Oregon. Herpetologica, 1(3):92-95

———. 1943. Handbook of salamanders (Ithaca, N.Y.: Comstock Publ. Co.), xiv + 555 pp.

BLAIR, A. P. 1941. Variation, isolating mechanisms, and hybridization in certain toads. Genetics, 26:398-417.

———. 1947. Field observations on spadefoot toads. Copeia, 1947(1):67.

———. 1950. Note on Oklahoma microhylid frogs. Copeia, 1950(2):152.

BLANCHARD, F. C. 1932. Length of life in the tiger salamander, *Ambystoma tigrinum* (Green). Copeia, 1932(2):98-99.

BOGERT, C. M. and J. A. OLIVER. 1945. A preliminary analysis of the herpetofauna of Sonora. Bull. Amer. Mus. Nat. Hist., 83(6):297-426.

BOULENGER, G. A. 1882. Catalogue of the Batrachia Gradientia s. Caudata and Batrachia Apoda in the collection of the British Museum (ed. 2; London, printed by order of the trustees), viii + 127 pp.

———. 1917. Descriptions of new frogs of the genus *Rana*. Ann. and Mag. Nat. Hist. 20(120):413-18.

———. 1920. A monograph of the American frogs of the genus *Rana*. Proc. Amer. Acad. Arts and Sci., 55(9):413-80.

BOYER, D. A. and A. A. HEINZE. 1934. An annotated list of the amphibians and reptiles of Jefferson County, Missouri. Trans. Acad. Sci. St. Louis, 28(4):185-200.

BRADY, M. K. and F. HARPER. 1935. A Florida subspecies of *Pseudacris nigrita*. Proc. Biol. Soc. Wash., 48:107-10.

BRAGG, A. N. 1936a. The ecological distribution of some North American Anura. Amer. Nat., 70(730):459-66.

———. 1936b. Notes on the breeding habits, eggs, and embryos of *Bufo cognatus* with a description of the tadpole. Copeia, 1936(1):14-20.

———. 1937a. A note on the metamorphosis of the tadpoles of *Bufo cognatus*. Copeia, 1937(4):227-28.

———. 1937b. Observations on *Bufo cognatus* with special reference to breeding habits and eggs. Amer. Midl. Nat., 18(2):273-84.

———. 1940a. Observations on the ecology and natural history of Anura. VI. Wasmann Collector, 4(1):6-16.

———. 1940b. Observations on the ecology and natural history of Anura. I. Habits, habitat, and breeding of *Bufo cognatus* Say. Amer. Nat., 74:322-49 and 424-38.

———. 1940c. Observations on the ecology and natural history of Anura. II. Habits, habitat, and breeding of *Bufo woodhousii woodhousii* (Girard) in Oklahoma. Amer. Midl. Nat., 24(2):306-21.

———. 1941. Tadpoles of *Scaphiopus bombifrons* and *Scaphiopus hammondii*. Wasmann Collector, 4(3):92-94.

———. 1943. On the economic value of Oklahoma toads. Proc. Okla. Acad. Sci., 23:37-39.

BRAGG, A. N. 1944a. The spadefoot toads in Oklahoma with a summary of our knowledge of the group. Amer. Nat., 78(779):517-33.

———. 1944b. Egg laying in leopard frogs. Proc. Okla. Acad. Sci. [1943], 24:13-14.

———. 1945. The spadefoot toads in Oklahoma with a summary of our knowledge of the group, II. Amer. Nat., 79(780):52-72.

———. 1946. Aggregation with cannibalism in tadpoles of *Scaphiopus bombifrons* with some general remarks on the probable evolutionary significance of such phenomena. Herpetologica, 3(3):89-97.

BRECKENRIDGE, W. J. 1944. Reptiles and amphibians of Minnesota (Minneapolis, Minn.: Univ. Minn. Press), xiii + 202 pp.

BROCCHI, M. P. 1879. Sur divers batraciens anoures de l'Amérique Centrale. Bull. Soc. Philom. Paris, 3(1):19-24.

———. 1882. Étude des batraciens de l'Amérique Centrale. Mission scientifique au Mexique et dans l'Amérique Centrale, 3(2):122 pp.

BROWN, W. C. and J. R. SLATER. 1939. The amphibians and reptiles of the islands of the state of Washington. Occas. Papers Dept. Biol. Coll. Puget Sound, 4:6-31.

BRUES, C. T. 1932. Further studies on the fauna of North American hot springs. Proc. Amer. Acad. Arts and Sci., 67(7):184-303.

BURGER, W. L. JR., and A. N. BRAGG. 1947. Notes on *Bufo boreas* (B. and G.) from the Gothic region of Colorado. Proc. Okla. Acad. Sci., 27:61-65.

BURGER, W. L., P. W. SMITH, and H. M. SMITH. 1949. Notable records of reptiles and amphibians in Oklahoma, Arkansas, and Texas. Jour. Tenn. Acad. Sci., 24(2):130-34.

BURGESS, R. C., JR. 1950. Development of spadefoot toad larvae under laboratory conditions. Copeia, 1950(1):49-51.

BURKE, C. V. 1911. Note on *Batrachoseps attenuatus* Esch. Amer. Nat., 45(535):413-14.

BURNETT, W. L. 1926. Notes on Colorado herpetology. Occ. Papers Mus. Zoöl. and Entomology. State Agric. Coll., Fort Collins, Colo., 1(1):1-4.

BURT, C. E. 1932. Records of amphibians from the eastern and central United States (1931). Amer. Midl. Nat., 13(2):75-85.

———. 1933(1932). Amphibians from the Great Basin of the West and adjacent areas. Amer. Midl. Nat., 14(4):350-54.

BURT, C. E. and M. D. BURT. 1929. Field notes and locality records on a collection of amphibians and reptiles, chiefly from the western half of the United States. I. Amphibians. Jour. Wash. Acad. Sci., 19(19):428-34.

CAMP, C. L. 1915. *Batrachoseps major* and *Bufo cognatus californicus*, new Amphibia from southern California. Univ. Calif. Publ. Zoöl., 12(12):327-34.

———. 1916a. Description of *Bufo canorus*, a new toad from the Yosemite National Park. Univ. Calif. Publ. Zoöl., 17(6):59-62.

———. 1916b. *Spelerpes platycephalus*, a new alpine salamander from the Yosemite National Park, California. Univ. Calif. Publ. Zoöl., 17(3):11-14.

———. 1916c. Notes on the local distribution and habits of the amphibians and reptiles of southeastern California and in the vicinity of the Turtle Mountains. Univ. Calif. Publ. Zoöl., 12(17):503-44.

———. 1917. Notes on the systematic status of the toads and frogs of California. Univ. Calif. Publ. Zoöl., 17:115-25.

CAMPBELL, B. 1931a. Notes on *Batrachoseps*. Copeia, 1931(3):131-34.

———. 1931b. *Rana tarahumarae*, a frog new to the United States. Copeia, 1931(4):164.

———. 1934. Report on a collection of reptiles and amphibians made in Arizona during the summer of 1933. Occas. Papers Mus. Zoöl. Univ. Mich., 289:1-10.

CARL, G. C. 1942. The long-toed salamander on Vancouver Island. Copeia, 1942(1):56.

———. 1943. The amphibians of British Columbia. Brit. Columbia Prov. Mus. Handbook No. 2:1-62.

———. 1944. The natural history of the Forbidden Plateau area, Vancouver Island, British Columbia. Report Prov. Mus. Nat. Hist. and Anthropology for 1943:18-40.

CARL, G. C. and I. M. COWAN. 1945a. Notes on the salamanders of British Columbia. Copeia, 1945(1):43-44.

———. 1945b. Notes on some frogs and toads of British Columbia. Copeia, 1945(1):52-53.

CARY, M. 1917. Life Zone investigations in Wyoming. N. Amer. Fauna, 42:1-95.

CHANDLER, A. C. 1918. The western newt or water-dog, (*Notophthalmus torosus*) a natural enemy of mosquitoes. Ore. Agric. Coll. Exp. Sta., Bull. 152:1-24.

CHAPEL, W. L. 1939. Field notes on *Hyla wrightorum* Taylor. Copeia, 1939(4):225-27.

CLEMENTS, F. E. and V. E. SHELFORD. 1939. Bio-ecology. New York, 423 pp.

COCKERELL, T. D. A. 1927. Zoölogy of Colorado (Boulder, Colo.: Univ. Colo.), vii + 262 pp. Sect. on Amphibia, pp. 111-13.

CONANT, R. and R. G. HUDSON. 1949. Longevity records for reptiles and amphibians in the Philadelphia Zoölogical Garden. Herpetologica, 5(1):1-8.

COOPER, J. G. 1860. No. 4 Report upon the reptiles collected on the survey. Rep. Expl. Surv. Miss. River to Pacific Ocean, 12(2):292-306.

COPE, E. D. 1863. On *Trachycephalus, Scaphiopus* and other American Batrachia. Proc. Acad. Nat. Sci. Phila., 1863:43-54.

———. 1865. Third contribution to the herpetology of tropical America. Proc. Acad. Nat. Sci. Phila., 1865:185-98.

———. 1866. On the structures and distribution of the genera of the arciferous Anura. Jour. Acad. Nat. Sci. Phila., 6(2):67-112.

———. 1867. On the Reptilia and Batrachia of the Sonoran Province of the Nearctic region. Proc. Acad. Nat. Sci. Phila., [1866](18):300-14.

———. 1869. A review of the species of the Plethodontidae and Desmognathidae. Proc. Acad. Nat. Sci. Phila., 1869:93-118.

———. 1878. A Texan cliff frog. Amer. Nat. 12(3):186.

———. 1880. On the zoölogical position of Texas. Bull. U.S. Nat. Mus., 17:1-51.

———. 1884. Notes on the geographical distribution of Batrachia and Reptilia in western North America. Proc. Acad. Nat. Sci. Phila. (1883)35:10-35.

———. 1886. Synonymic list of the North American species of *Bufo* and *Rana*, with descriptions of some new species of Batrachia, from specimens in the National Museum. Proc. Amer. Philos. Soc., 23:514-26.

———. 1887. Catalogue of batrachians and reptiles of Central America and Mexico. Bull. U.S. Nat. Mus., 32:1-98.

———. 1889. The Batrachia of North America. Bull. U.S. Nat. Mus., 34:1-525.

COUES, E., and H. C. YARROW. 1878. Notes on the herpetology of Dakota and Montana. Bull. U.S. Geol. Survey, 4(1):259-91.

Cowan, I. M. 1941. Longevity of the red-legged frog. Copeia, 1941(1):48.

Cragin, F. W. 1881. A preliminary catalogue of Kansas reptiles and batrachians. Trans. Kans. Acad. Sci., 7:112-20.

Danforth, C. G. 1950. New locality for Mt. Lyell salamander. Yosemite Nature Notes, 29(2):18-19.

Davis, D. D. 1936. The distribution of Bidder's organ in the Bufonidae. Zool. Ser. Field Mus. Nat. Hist., 20(15):115-25.

Dethlefsen, E. S. 1948. A subterranean nest of the Pacific giant salamander, *Dicamptodon ensatus* (Eschscholtz). Wasmann Collector, 7(3):81-84.

Dice, L. R. 1923. Notes on the communities of the vertebrates of Riley County, Kansas, with especial reference to amphibians, reptiles, and mammals. Ecology 4(1):40-53.

Dickerson, M. C. 1906. The frog book. (New York: Doubleday), xvii + 253 pp.

———. 1920. The frog book (Garden City, N.Y.: Doubleday), xvii + 253 pp.

Diller, J. S. 1907. A salamander-snake fight. Science, 26:907-08.

Drake, C. J. 1914. The food of *Rana pipiens* Schreber. Ohio Nat., 14(5):257-69.

Duellman, W. E. 1948. An Ambystoma eats a snake. Herpetologica, 4(5):164.

Dunlap, D. G. and R. M. Storm. 1951. The Cascade frog in Oregon. Copeia, 1951(1):81.

Dunn, E. R. 1926. The salamanders of the family Plethodontidae (Northampton, Mass.: Smith Coll. Anniv. Ser.), xii + 441 pp.

———. 1938[1939]. Notes on frogs of the genus Acris. Proc. Acad. Nat. Sci. Phila., 90: 153-54.

———. 1940. The races of *Ambystoma tigrinum*. Copeia, 1940(3):154-62.

———. 1942. An egg cluster of *Aneides ferreus*. Copeia, 1942(1):52.

———. 1944. Notes on the salamanders of the *Ambystoma gracile* group. Copeia, 1944 (3):129-30.

Eaton, T. H. Jr. 1935. Report on amphibians and reptiles of the Navajo Country. Rainbow Bridge–Monument Valley Exped. Berkeley, Calif. (1933) Bull. 3 (June, 1935): 1-18.

Eckert, J. E. 1934. The California toad in relation to the hive bee. Copeia, 1934(2): 92-93.

Eisen, G. 1901. The spermatogenesis of *Batrachoseps*. Jour. Morph., 17(1):1-117.

Ellis, M. M., and J. Henderson. 1913. The Amphibia and Reptilia of Colorado, Part I. Univ. Colo. Studies, 10(2):39-129.

———. 1915. Amphibia and Reptilia of Colorado, Part II. Univ. Colo. Studies, 11(4): 253-63.

Emmel, V. E. 1924. Studies on the non-nucleated elements of the blood. 2. The occurrence and genesis of non-nucleated erythrocytes or erythroplastids in vertebrates other than mammals. Amer. Jour. Anat., 33(2):347-406.

Engelhardt, G. P. 1917. Grand Canyon Notes. Copeia, 1917(39):5-7.

———. 1918. Batrachians from southwestern Utah. Copeia, 1918(60):77-80.

Eschscholtz, F. 1829-33. Zoologischer Atlas, enthaltend Abbildungen und Beschreibungen neuer Thierarten, während des Flottcapitains von Kotzebue zweiter Reise um die Welt, auf der Russisch-Kaiserlichen Kriegsschlupp Predpriaetië in den Jahren 1823-1826 (Berlin, G. Reimer), 5 parts, part 5, 1833 (edited and partly written by Martin Heinrich Rathke), viii + 28 pp.

EVENDEN, F. G. JR. 1946. Notes on the herpetology of Elmore County, Idaho. Copeia, 1946(4):256-57.

———. 1948. Food habits of *Triturus granulosus* in western Oregon. Copeia, 1948(3): 219-20.

EVERMANN, B. W. 1897. U.S. Fish Commission investigations at Crater Lake. Mazama, 1(2):230-38.

FARNER, D. S. 1947. Notes on the food habits of the salamanders of Crater Lake, Oregon. Copeia, 1947(4):259-61.

FITCH, H. S. 1936. Amphibians and reptiles of the Rogue River Basin, Oregon. Amer. Midl. Nat., 17(3):634-52.

FITZINGER, L. J. 1861. Eine neue Batrachier-Gattung aus Neu-Seeland, Verhandl. k. k. zool.-bot. Gesellsch. Wien, 11:217-20. Pl. 6.

FLOWER, S. S. 1925. Contributions to our knowledge of the duration of life in vertebrate animals. II. Batrachians. Proc. Zoöl. Soc. London, 1925:269-89.

FORCE, E. R. 1925. Notes on reptiles and amphibians of Okmulgee County, Oklahoma. Copeia, 1925(141):25-27.

———. 1933. The age of the attainment of sexual maturity of the leopard frog *Rana pipiens* (Schreber) in northern Michigan. Copeia, 1933(3):128-31.

FRANKLIN, D. 1915. Notes on *Amblystoma tigrinum* at Flagstaff, Arizona. Copeia, 1915(21):30-31.

FROST, S. W. 1935. The food of *Rana catesbeiana* Shaw. Copeia, 1935(1):15-18.

GADOW, H. 1905. 2. The distribution of Mexican amphibians and reptiles. Proc. Zoöl. Soc. London, 2(1):191-244.

GAIGE, H. T. 1917. Description of a new salamander from Washington. Occas. Papers Mus. Zoöl. Univ. Mich., 40:1-3.

———. 1920. Observations upon the habits of *Ascaphus truei* Stejneger. Occas. Papers, Mus. Zoöl. Univ. Mich., 84:1-9.

GARMAN, H. 1892. A synopsis of the reptiles and amphibians of Illinois. Bull. Ill. State Lab. Nat. Hist., 3(13):215-385.

GASCO, F. 1881. Les amours des axolotls. Zool. Anzeiger, 4(85):(1)313-16, (2)328-34.

GILMORE, R. J. 1924. Notes on the life history and feeding habits of the spadefoot toad of the western plains. Colo. Coll. Publ. (Sci. Ser.) 13(1):1-12.

GIRARD, C. 1854. A list of the North American bufonids, with diagnoses of new species. Proc. Acad. Nat. Sci. Phila., 7:86-88.

GLOYD, H. K. 1928. The amphibians and reptiles of Franklin County, Kansas. Trans. Kans. Acad. Sci., 31:115-41.

GNAEDINGER, L. M. and C. A. REED. 1948. Contribution to the natural history of the plethodont salamander *Ensatina eschscholtzii*. Copeia, 1948(3):187-96.

GORDON, K. 1939. The Amphibia and Reptilia of Oregon. Oreg. State Monogrs., 1:1-82.

GORMAN, J. 1951. Northward range extension of the salamander *Triturus sierrae*. Copeia, 1951(1):78.

GRAF, W. 1949. Observations on the salamander *Dicamptodon*. Copeia, 1949(1):78-80.

GRAY, J. E. 1850. Catalogue of the specimens of amphibia in the collection of the British Museum. Part II. Batrachia Gradientia, etc. (London, printed by order of the trustees), 72 pp.

GREEN, J. 1825. Description of a new species of salamander. Jour. Acad. Nat. Sci. Phila., 5(1):116-18.

GRINNELL, J. and C. L. CAMP. 1917. A distributional list of the amphibians and reptiles of California. Univ. Calif. Publ. Zoöl., 17(10):127-208.

GRINNELL, J. and T. I. STORER. 1924. Animal life in the Yosemite (Univ. of Calif. Press), xviii + 752 pp.

HALLOWELL, E. 1848[1850]. Description of a new species of salamander from Upper California. Proc. Acad. Nat. Sci. Phila., 4:126.

HAMILTON, R. 1948a. The egg-laying process in the tiger salamander. Copeia, 1948(3): 212-13.

HAMILTON, W. J. JR. 1946. Summer habitat of the yellow-barred tiger salamander. Copeia, 1946(1):51.

———. 1948b. The food and feeding behavior of the green frog, *Rana clamitans* Latreille, in New York State. Copeia, 1948(3):203-7.

HARDY, G. A. 1926. Amphibia of British Columbia. Rep. Prov. Mus. Nat. Hist., Victoria, B. C., for 1925, pp. C21-C24.

HARPER, F. 1931a. Physiographic and faunal areas in the Athabaska and Great Slave lakes region. Ecology, 1931(12):18-32.

———. 1931b. Amphibians and reptiles of the Athabaska and Great Slave lakes region. Canadian Field-Nat. 45:68-70.

———. 1947. A new cricket frog (Acris) from the Middle Western states. Proc. Biol. Soc. Wash., 60:39-40.

HARTMAN, F. A. 1906. Food habits of Kansas lizards and batrachians. Trans. Kans. Acad. Sci., 20(2):225-29.

HECHT, M. K. and B. L. MATALAS. 1946. A review of middle North American toads of the genus *Microhyla*. Amer. Mus. Nov., 1946(1315):1-21.

HENRY, W. V. and V. C. TWITTY. 1940. Contributions to the life histories of *Dicamptodon ensatus* and *Ambystoma gracile*. Copeia, 1940(4):247-50.

HILDEBRAND, H. 1949. Notes on *Rana sylvatica* in the Labrador Peninsula. Copeia, 1949(3):168-72.

HILTON, W. A. 1945. Distribution of the genus Batrachoseps, especially on the coastal islands of southern California. Contribution No. 32 from the Los Angeles Museum Channel Islands Biological Survey. Bull. So. Calif. Acad. Sci., 44(32):101-29.

———. 1948. *Aneides* from Oregon. Herpetologica, 4(3):117-19.

HOLBROOK, J. E. 1836. North American herpetology; or, a description of the reptiles inhabiting the United States. (Philadelphia, J. Dobson), 1:83.

HOLMES, S. J. 1927. The biology of the frog. (New York: Macmillan), ix + 386 pp.

HOWARD, W. E. 1950. Birds as bullfrog food. Copeia, 1950(2):152.

———. 1950. Eggs of the salamander *Ensatina eschscholtzii platensis*. Copeia, 1950(3):236.

HUDSON, G. E. 1942. The amphibians and reptiles of Nebraska. Neb. Conserv. Bull. 24:1-146.

INGRAM, W. M. and E. C. RANEY. 1943. Additional studies on the movement of tagged bullfrogs, *Rana catesbeiana* Shaw. Amer. Midl. Nat., 29(1):239-41.

JACOBS, D. L. 1950. *Pseudacris nigrita triseriata* on the north shore of Lake Superior. Copeia, 1950(2):154.

JAMESON, D. L. 1950. The development of *Eleutherodactylus latrans*. Copeia, 1950(1): 44-46.

JOHNSON, D. H., M. D. BRYANT, and A. H. MILLER. 1948. Vertebrate animals of the Providence Mountains area of California. Univ. Calif. Publ. Zoöl, 48(5):221-376.

JOHNSON, V. O. 1939. A supplementary note on the larvae of *Bufo woodhousii woodhousii*. Herpetologica, 1(6):160-64.

KAUFFELD, C. F. 1943. Field notes on some Arizona reptiles and amphibians. Amer. Midl. Nat. 29(2):342-59.

KELLOGG, R. 1932a. Notes on the spadefoot of the western plains (*Scaphiopus hammondii*). Copeia, 1932(1):36.

———. 1932b. Mexican tailless amphibians in the United States National Museum. U.S. Nat. Mus. Bull., 160:iv + 224 pp.

KESSEL, E. L. and B. B. KESSEL. 1942. An egg cluster of *Aneides lugubris lugubris* (Hallowell). Wasmann Collector 5(2):71-72.

———. 1943a. The rate of growth of the young larvae of the Pacific giant salamander, *Dicamptodon ensatus* (Eschscholtz). Wasmann Collector, 5(3):108-11.

———. 1943b. The rate of growth of the older larvae of the Pacific giant salamander, *Dicamptodon ensatus* (Eschscholtz). Wasmann Collector. 5(4):141-42.

———. 1944. Metamorphosis of the Pacific giant salamander, *Dicamptodon ensatus* (Eschscholtz). Wasmann Collector 6(2):38-48.

KILBY, J. D. 1945. A biological analysis of the food and feeding habits of two frogs. Quart. Jour. Fla. Acad. Sci., 8(1):71-104.

KING, F. W. 1932. Herpetological records and notes from the vicinity of Tucson, Arizona, July and August, 1930. Copeia, 1932(4):175-77.

KIRN, A. J. 1949. Cannibalism among *Rana pipiens berlandieri,* and possibly by *Rana catesbiana,* near Somerset, Texas. Herpetologica, 5(4):84.

KLAUBER, L. M. 1934. Annotated list of the amphibians and reptiles of the southern border of California. Bull. Zoöl. Soc. San Diego, 11:1-28.

KLIMSTRA, W. D. 1949. Early bullfrog transformation. Copeia, 1949(3):231.

KLUGH, A. B. 1922. The economic value of the leopard frog. Copeia, 1922(103):14-15.

KNOWLTON, G. F. 1944. Some insect food of *Rana pipiens*. Copeia, 1944(2):119.

KOSTER, W. J. 1946. The robber frog in New Mexico. Copeia, 1946(3):173.

KUMPF, K. F. 1934. The courtship of *Ambystoma tigrinum*. Copeia, 1934(1):7-10.

LE CONTE, J. 1825. Remarks on the American species of the genera Hyla and Rana. Ann. Lyc. Nat. Hist., New York, 1(2):278-82.

LINSDALE, J. M. 1927. Amphibians and reptiles of Doniphan County, Kansas. Copeia, 1927(164):75-81.

———. 1933. A specimen of *Rana tarahumarae* from New Mexico. Copeia, 1933(4):222.

———. 1938. Environmental responses of vertebrates in the Great Basin. Amer. Midl. Nat., 19(1):1-206.

———. 1940. Amphibians and reptiles in Nevada. Proc. Amer. Acad. Arts and Sci., 73(8):197-257.

LITTLE, E. L. JR. 1940. Amphibians and reptiles of the Roosevelt Reservoir area, Arizona. Copeia, 1940(4):260-65.

Little, E. L. Jr., and J. G. Keller. 1937. Amphibians and reptiles of the Jornada Experimental Range, New Mexico. Copeia, 1937(4):216-22.

Livezey, R. L. 1950. The eggs of *Acris gryllus crepitans* Baird. Herpetologica, 6(5): 139-40.

Livezey, R. L. and A. H. Wright. 1947. A synoptic key to the salientian eggs of the United States. Amer. Midl. Nat., 37(1):179-222.

Lockington, W. N. 1880. List of Californian reptiles and batrachia collected by Mr. Dunn and Mr. W. J. Fisher in 1876. Amer. Nat., 14:295-96.

Logier, E. B. S. 1932. Some account of the amphibians and reptiles of British Columbia. Trans. Royal Canadian Inst., 18(40):311-36.

———. 1937. The amphibians of Ontario. Royal Ontario Mus. Zoöl. Handbook No. 3:1-16.

Lowe, C. H., Jr. 1950. The systematic status of the salamander *Plethodon hardii,* with a discussion of biogeographical problems in *Aneides*. Copeia, 1950(2):92-99.

Marr, J. C. 1943. Range extension for *Rana boylii boylii*. Copeia, 1943(1):56.

———. 1944. Notes on amphibians and reptiles from the central United States. Amer. Midl. Nat., 32(2):478-90.

Maslin, T. P. Jr. 1939. Egg-laying of the slender salamander (*Batrachoseps attenuatus*). Copeia, 1939(4):209-12.

———. 1947. *Rana sylvatica cantabrigensis* Baird in Colorado. Copeia, 1947(3):158-62.

———. 1950. The production of sound in caudate Amphibia. Univ. Colo. Studies (Biol. Ser.) 1:29-45.

McKee, E. D. and C. M. Bogert. 1934. The amphibians and reptiles of Grand Canyon National Park. Copeia, 1934(4):178-80.

Mearns, E. A. 1907. Mammals of the Mexican Boundary of the United States. Bull. U.S. Nat. Mus., 56(1):xv + 530 pp.

Miller, L. H. 1944. Notes on the eggs and larvae of *Aneides lugubris*. Copeia, 1944(4): 224-30.

Miller, L. H. and A. H. Miller. 1936. The northward occurrence of *Bufo californicus* in California. Copeia, 1936(3):176.

Miller, M. A. 1938. Comparative ecological studies on the terrestrial isopod Crustacea of the San Francisco Bay region. Univ. Calif. Publ. Zoöl., 43(7)113-42.

Miller, R. R. 1946. Correlation between fish distribution and Pleistocene hydrography in eastern California and southwestern Nevada, with a map of the Pleistocene waters. Jour. Geol., 54(1):43-53.

Mills, R. C. 1948. A check list of the reptiles and amphibians of Canada. Herpetologica, 4(second suppl., Dec. 10, 1948):1-15.

Minton, J. E. 1949. Coral snake preyed upon by the bullfrog. Copeia, 1949(4):288.

Mittleman, M. B. 1948. American Caudata. II. Geographic variation in *Ambystoma macrodactylum*. Herpetologica, 4(3):81-95.

Mittleman, M. B. and G. S. Myers. 1949. Geographic variation in the ribbed frog, *Ascaphus truei*. Proc. Biol. Soc. Wash., 62:57-68.

Mocquard, M. F. 1899. Reptiles et batraciens recueillis au Mexique par M. Léon Diguet en 1896 et 1897. Bull. Soc. Philom. Paris, 1:154-69.

Moore, G. A. 1937. The spadefoot toad under drought conditions. Copeia, 1937(4):225-26.

MOORE, J. A. 1944. Geographic variation in *Rana pipiens* Schreber of eastern North America, Bull. Amer. Mus. Nat. Hist., 82(8):345-69.

MOSAUER, W. 1932. The amphibians and reptiles of the Guadalupe Mountains of New Mexico and Texas. Occas. Papers Mus. Zoöl. Univ. Mich., 246:1-18.

MUNZ, P. A. 1920. A study of the food habits of the Ithacan species of Anura during transformation. Jour. Ent. and Zoöl. Pomona Coll., 12(2):33-56.

MUSGRAVE, M. E. and D. M. COCHRAN. 1930. *Bufo alvarius,* a poisonous toad. Copeia, 1930(173):96-99.

MYERS, G. S. 1930a. Notes on some amphibians in western North America. Proc. Biol. Soc. Wash., 43:55-64.

———. 1930b. The status of the southern California toad, *Bufo californicus* (Camp). Proc. Biol. Soc. Wash., 43:73-78.

———. 1931. *Ascaphus truei* in Humboldt County, California, with a note on the habits of the tadpole. Copeia, 1931(2):56-57.

———. 1942a. Notes on Pacific Coast *Triturus.* Copeia, 1942(2):77-82.

———. 1942b. The black toad of Deep Springs Valley, Inyo County, California. Occas. Papers Mus. Zoöl. Univ. Mich., 460:1-19.

———. 1943. Notes on *Rhyacotriton olympicus* and *Ascaphus truei* in Humboldt County, California. Copeia, 1943(2):125-26.

MYERS, G. S. and T. P. MASLIN, JR. 1948. The California plethodont salamander, *Aneides flavipunctatus* (Strauch), with description of a new subspecies and notes on other western *Aneides.* Proc. Biol. Soc. Wash., 61:127-38.

NEEDHAM, J. G. 1905. The summer food of the bullfrog (*Rana catesbiana* Shaw) at Saranac Inn. N.Y. State Mus. Bull., 86:9-15.

———. 1924. Observations of the life of the ponds at the head of Laguna Canyon. Jour. Ent. and Zoöl. 16(1):1-12.

NEILL, W. T. 1948. Hibernation of amphibians and reptiles in Richmond County, Georgia. Herpetologica 4(3):107-14.

———. 1950. Taxonomy, nomenclature, and distribution of southeastern cricket frogs, genus *Acris.* Amer. Midl. Nat., 43(1):152-56.

NETTING, M. G. and C. J. GOIN. 1945. The cricket-frog of peninsular Florida. Quarterly Jour. Fla. Acad. Sci. 8(4):304-10.

NOBLE, G. K. 1925. An outline of the relation of ontogeny to phylogeny within the Amphibia. II. Amer. Mus. Nov., 1925(166):1-10.

———. 1927. The value of life history data in the study of the evolution of the Amphibia. Ann. N.Y. Acad. Sci., 30:31-128.

———. 1931. The biology of the Amphibia (New York and London: McGraw-Hill), xiii + 577 pp.

NOBLE, G. K. and L. R. ARONSON. 1942. The sexual behavior of Anura. I. The normal mating pattern of *Rana pipiens.* Bull. Amer. Mus. Nat. Hist., 80(5):127-42.

NOBLE, G. K. and E. J. FARRIS. 1929. The method of sex recognition in the wood-frog, *Rana sylvatica* Le Conte. Amer. Mus. Nov., 1929(363):1-17.

NOBLE, G. K. and P. G. PUTNAM. 1931. Observations on the life history of *Ascaphus truei* Stejneger. Copeia, 1931(3):97-101.

NOBLE, G. K. and L. B. RICHARDS. 1930. The induction of egg-laying in the salamander, *Eurycea bislineata,* by pituitary transplants. Amer. Mus. Nov., 1930(396):1-3.

NOBLE, G. K. and L. B. RICHARDS. 1932. Experiments on egg-laying of salamanders. Amer. Mus. Nov., 1932(513):1-25.

ORTENBURGER, A. I. 1925. VI. Life history notes—Scaphiopus—the spadefoot toad. Proc. Okla. Acad. Sci., 4[1924]:19-20.

ORTENBURGER, A. I. and R. D. ORTENBURGER. 1926(1927). 17. Field observations on some amphibians and reptiles of Pima County, Arizona. Proc. Okla. Acad. Sci. 6(1):101-21.

ORTON, G. L. 1946. Art. XIV. Larval development of the eastern narrow-mouthed frog, *Microhyla carolinensis* (Holbrook), in Louisiana. Annals Carnegie Mus., 30:241-49.

———. 1947. Art. XXI. Notes on some hylid tadpoles in Louisiana. Annals Carnegie Mus., 30:363-83.

———. 1951. Notes on some tadpoles from southwestern Missouri. Copeia, 1951(1):71-72.

PACK, H. J. 1920. Eggs of the swamp tree frog. Copeia, 1920(77):7.

———. 1922. Toads in regulating insect outbreaks. Copeia, 1922(107):46-47.

PARKER, H. W. 1934. A monograph of the frogs of the family Microhylidae (British Museum, London: Printed by order of the trustees), viii + 208 pp.

PATCH, C. L. 1922. Some amphibians and reptiles from British Columbia. Copeia, 1922(111):74-79.

PEABODY, F. E. 1941. Trackways of Pliocene and Recent salamandroids of the Pacific Coast of North America. Master of Arts Thesis in Paleontology, Univ. of Calif., Berkeley, Calif.

PICKWELL, G. 1947. Amphibians and reptiles of the Pacific States. (Stanford Univ., Calif.: Stanford Univ. Press), xiv + 236 pp.

PIERSON, M. A. 1950. Mysterious Mr. Salamander. Yellowstone Nature Notes, 24(2):23-24.

PITELKA, F. A. 1941. Distribution of birds in relation to major biotic communities. Amer. Midl. Nat. 25(1):113-37.

POPE, C. H. 1944. Amphibians and reptiles of the Chicago area (Chicago Nat. Hist. Mus.), 275 pp.

PROSSER, D. T. 1911. Habits of *"Amblystoma tigrinum"* at Tolland, Colorado. Univ. Colo. Studies, 8(4):257-63.

RAHN, H. 1941. The axolotl, or water dog. Wyoming Wild Life, 6(2):12-16.

RANEY, E. C. 1940. Summer movements of the bullfrog, *Rana catesbeiana* Shaw, as determined by the jaw-tag method. Amer. Midl. Nat., 23(3):733-45.

RANEY, E. C. and W. M. INGRAM. 1941. Growth of tagged frogs (*Rana catesbeiana* Shaw and *Rana clamitans* Daudin) under natural conditions. Amer. Midl. Nat. 26(1):201-6.

REED, C. A. 1949. The problem of metamorphosis in the western marbled salamander *Dicamptodon ensatus*. Copeia, 1949(1):81.

———. 1951. Larval ambystomid salamanders from southern Arizona and Sonora. Nat. Hist. Misc., Chicago Acad. Sci., 79:1-3.

RICKER, W. E. and E. B. S. LOGIER. 1935. Notes on the occurrence of the ribbed toad (*Ascaphus truei* Stejneger) in Canada. Copeia, 1935(1) :46.

RIDGWAY, R. 1912. Color standards and color nomenclature. (Washington. D.C., publ. by the author), iv + 44 pp., Pls. I-LIII.

RITTER, W. E. 1897. The life-history and habits of the Pacific Coast newt (*Diemyctylus torosus* Esch.). Proc. Calif. Acad. Sci., Zoöl, 1(2)73-114.

RITTER, W. E. and L. H. MILLER. 1899. A contribution to life history of *Autodax lugubris* Hallow., a Californian salamander. Amer. Nat., 33(393):691-704.

RODGERS, T. L. and W. L. JELLISON. 1942. A collection of amphibians and reptiles from western Montana. Copeia, 1942(1):10-13.

RUTHVEN, A. G. 1907. A collection of reptiles and amphibians from southern New Mexico and Arizona. Amer. Mus. Nat. Hist., 23(23):483-604.

———. 1912. Description of a new salamander from Iowa. Proc. U.S. Nat. Mus., 41:517-19.

RUTHVEN, A. G. and H. T. GAIGE. 1915. The reptiles and amphibians collected in northeastern Nevada by the Walker-Newcomb expedition of the University of Michigan. Occas. Papers Mus. Zoöl. Univ. Mich., 8:1-33.

RUTHVEN, A. G., C. THOMPSON, and H. T. GAIGE. 1928. The herpetology of Michigan (Mich. Handbook Ser., No. 3, Mich. Univ. Mus.) ix + 229 pp.

SAY, T. 1823. *In* Long, Stephen H., Account of an expedition from Pittsburgh to the Rocky Mountains performed in the years 1819 and '20 by order of the Hon. J. C. Calhoun, Sec'y of War; under the command of Major Stephen H. Long from the notes of Major Long, Mr. T. Say, and other gentlemen of the exploring party. Compiled by Edwin James, botanist and geologist for the expedition. (Philadelphia), 2 vols. [+ atlas], 503 + 442.

SCHONBERGER, C. F. 1944. Food of salamanders in the northwestern United States. Copeia, 1944(4):257.

———. 1945. Food of some amphibians and reptiles of Oregon and Washington. Copeia, 1945(2):120-21.

SCHREBER, H. 1782. Der Naturforscher (Halle, Johann Jacob Gebauer), Achtzehntes Stück, 4 + 268 pp. (Beytrag zur Naturgeschichte der Frösche, pp. 182-93).

SETON, E. T. 1918. A list of the turtles, snakes and batrachians of Manitoba. Ottawa Naturalist, 32(5):79-83.

SHANNON, F. A. 1949. A western subspecies of *Bufo woodhousii* hitherto erroneously associated with *Bufo compactilis*. Bull. Chicago Acad. Sci., 8(15):301-12.

SHAW, G. 1802. General zoölogy or systematic natural history (London, G. Kearsley), 3(1):vi + 2 + 312 pp.

SKILTON, A. J. 1849. Description of two reptiles from Oregon. Amer. Jour. Sci. Arts., 2(7):202.

SLATER, J. R. 1931. The mating of *Ascaphus truei* Stejneger. Copeia, 1931(2):62-63.

———. 1934a. Notes on northwestern amphibians. Copeia, 1934(3):140-41.

———. 1934b. *Ambystoma tigrinum* in the state of Washington. Copeia, 1934(4):189-90.

———. 1936. Notes on *Ambystoma gracile* Baird and *Ambystoma macrodactylum* Baird. Copeia, 1936(4):234-36.

———. 1937. Notes on the tiger salamander, *Ambystoma tigrinum* in Washington and Idaho. Herpetologica, 1(3):81-83.

———. 1939a. Some species of amphibians new to the state of Washington. Occas. Papers Dept. Biol. Coll. Puget Sound, 2:4-5.

———. 1939b. *Plethodon dunni* in Oregon and Washington. Herpetologica 1(6):154.

———. 1939c. Description and life-history of a new *Rana* from Washington. Herpetologica, 1(6):145-49.

———. 1941. The distribution of amphibians and reptiles in Idaho. Occas. Papers Dept. Biol. Coll. Puget Sound, 14:78-109.

SLATER, J. R. and J. W. SLIPP. 1940. A new species of *Plethodon* from northern Idaho. Occas. Papers Dept. Biol. Coll. Puget Sound 1940(8):38-43.

SLEVIN, J. R. 1928. The amphibians of western North America. Occas. Papers Calif. Acad. Sci., 16:1-152.

———. 1931. Range extensions of certain western species of reptiles and amphibians. Copeia, 1931(3):140-41.

SMITH, B. G. 1911. Notes on the natural history of *Ambystoma jeffersonianum, A. punctatum,* and *A. tigrinum*. Bull. Wisc. Soc. Nat. Hist., 9(1-2):14-27.

SMITH, H. M. 1934. The amphibians of Kansas. Amer. Midl. Nat., 15(4):377-528.

———. 1946. The tadpoles of *Bufo cognatus* Say. Univ. Kans. Publs. Mus. Nat. Hist., 1(3):93-96.

———. 1947. Subspecies of the Sonoran toad (*Bufo compactilis* Wiegmann). Herpetologica, 4(1):7-13.

———. 1949. Size maxima in terrestrial salamanders. Copeia, 1949(1):71.

SMITH, H. M. and E. H. TAYLOR. 1948. An annotated checklist and key to the Amphibia of Mexico. U.S. Nat. Mus. Bull., 194:iv + 118 pp.

———. 1950. Type localities of Mexican reptiles and amphibians. Univ. Kans. Sci. Bull., 33(8):313-80.

SMITH, R. E. 1940. Mating and oviposition in the Pacific Coast tree toad. Science, 92(2391):379-80.

———. 1941a. Mating behavior in *Triturus torosus* and related newts. Copeia, (4):255-62.

———. 1941b. The spermatophores of *Triturus torosus* and *Triturus rivularis*. Proc. Nat. Acad. Sci. (U.S.A.), 27(6):261-64.

SNYDER, J. O. 1923. Eggs of *Batrachoseps attenuatus*. Copeia, 1923(121):86-88.

SOLER, E. I. 1950. On the status of the family Desmognathidae (Amphibia, Caudata). Univ. Kans. Sci. Bull., 33(12):459-80.

SONNINI, C. S. and P. A. LATREILLE. 1802. La Grenouille criarde, *Rana clamitans*. Histoire naturelle des reptiles, 2:157. In Buffon (G. L. L. de) Count. Histoire Naturelle de Buffon.

STEBBINS, R. C. 1947. Tail and foot action in the locomotion of *Hydromantes platycephalus*. Copeia, 1947(1):1-5.

———. 1949a. Observations on laying, development, and hatching of the eggs of *Batrachoseps wrighti*. Copeia, 1949(3):161-68.

———. 1949b. Courtship of the plethodontid salamander *Ensatina eschscholtzii*. Copeia, 1949(4):274-81.

———. 1949c. Speciation in salamanders of the plethodontid genus *Ensatina*. Univ. Calif. Publ. Zoöl., 48(6):377-526.

STEBBINS, R. C. and C. H. LOWE, JR. 1949. The systematic status of *Plethopsis* with a discussion of speciation in the genus *Batrachoseps*. Copeia, 1949(2):116-29.

STEBBINS, R. C. and H. C. REYNOLDS. 1947. Southern extension of the range of the Del Norte salamander in California. Herpetologica, 4(2):41-42.

STEBBINS, R. C. and W. J. RIEMER. 1950. A new species of plethodontid salamander from the Jamez Mountains of New Mexico. Copeia, 1950(2):73-80.

STEJNEGER, L. 1893. Annotated list of the reptiles and batrachians collected by the Death Valley expedition in 1891, with descriptions of new species. N. Amer. Fauna, 1893(7): 159-228.

STEJNEGER, L. 1899. Description of a new genus and species of discoglossoid toad from North America. Proc. U.S. Nat. Mus., 21(1178):899-901.

STEJNEGER, L. and T. BARBOUR. 1917. A check list of North American amphibians and reptiles (Cambridge, Mass.: Harvard Univ. Press), iv + 5-125 pp.

———. 1943. A check list of North American amphibians and reptiles. Bull. Mus. Comp. Zoöl., 93(1):xix + 260 pp.

STONE, W. and J. A. G. REHN. 1903. On the terrestrial vertebrates of portions of southern New Mexico and western Texas. Proc. Acad. Nat. Sci. Phila., Jan. 1903, 55:16-34.

STORER, T. I. 1925. A synopsis of the Amphibia of California. Univ. Calif. Publ. Zoöl., 27:1-342.

———. 1943. General Zoölogy. (New York and London: McGraw-Hill) v-xii + 798 pp.

STORM, R. M. 1947. Eggs and young of *Aneides ferreus*. Herpetologica, 4(2):60-62.

STORM, R. M. and A. R. ALLER. 1947. Food habits of *Aneides ferreus*. Herpetologica, 4(2):59-60.

STRAUCH, A. 1870. Revision der Salamandriden-Gattungen nebst Beschreibung einiger neuen oder weniger bekannten Arten dieser Familie. Mémoires de l'Acad. Imp. Sci. St.-Pétersbourg, 16(4):1-109 + 1.

STRECKER, J. K. JR. 1908. Notes on the life history of *Scaphiopus couchii* Baird. Proc. Biol. Soc. Wash., 21:199-206.

———. 1910a. Notes on the fauna of a portion of the canyon region of northwestern Texas. Baylor Univ. Bull., 13(4-5):1-31.

———. 1910b. Notes on the robber frog (*Lithodytes latrans* Cope). Trans. Acad. Sci. St. Louis, 19(5):73-82.

———. 1922. Annotated catalogue of the amphibians and reptiles of Bexar County, Texas. Bull. San Antonio Sci. Soc., 4:1-31.

———. 1926. Chapters from the life-histories of Texas reptiles and amphibians. Part I. Contr. Baylor Univ. Mus., 8:1-12.

STROUD, C. P. 1949. A white spade-foot toad from the New Mexico White Sands. Copeia, 1949(3):232.

SVIHLA, A. 1935. Notes on the western spotted frog, *Rana pretiosa pretiosa*. Copeia, 1935(3):119-22.

SVIHLA, A. and R. D. SVIHLA. 1933. Notes on *Ascaphus truei* in Kittitas County, Washington. Copeia, 1933(1):37-38.

TANNER, V. M. 1928. Distributional list of the amphibians and reptiles of Utah. Copeia, 1928(166):23-28.

———. 1931. A synoptical study of Utah Amphibia. Utah Acad. Sci., 8:159-98.

———. 1939. A study of the genus *Scaphiopus*. Great Basin Nat., 1(1):3-20.

TANNER, W. W. 1950. Notes on the habits of *Microhyla carolinensis olivacea* (Hallowell). Herpetologica, 6(2):47-48.

TAYLOR, E. H. 1929. List of reptiles and batrachians of Morton County, Kansas, reporting species new to the state fauna. Univ. Kans. Sci. Bull., 19(6):63-65.

———. 1936a. Notes on the herpetological fauna of the Mexican state of Sonora. Univ. Kans. Sci. Bull., 24(19):475-503.

———. 1936b. Notes on the herpetological fauna of the Mexican State of Sinaloa. Univ. Kans. Sci. Bull., 24(20):505-37. (Bull. Univ. Kans., 37, issued Feb. 16, 1938).

TAYLOR, E. H. 1938. Frogs of the *Hyla eximia* group in Mexico, with descriptions of two new species. Bull. Univ. Kans., 39(11):421-45.

———. 1940. A new frog from the Tarahumara Mountains of Mexico. Copeia, 1940(4):250-53.

———. 1941. A new plethodont salamander from New Mexico. Proc. Biol. Soc. Wash., 54:77-80.

TEVIS, L. JR. 1944. Herpetological notes from Lower California. Copeia, 1944(1):6-18.

THOMPSON, H. B. 1913. Description of a new subspecies of *Rana pretiosa* from Nevada. Proc. Biol. Soc. Wash., 26:53-56.

THORSON, T. and A. SVIHLA. 1943. Correlations of the habitats of amphibians with their ability to survive the loss of body water. Ecology 24(3):374-81.

TING, H. 1951. Du[illegible]on of the tadpole stage of the greenfrog, *Rana clamitans*. Copeia, 1951(1):82.

TWITTY, V. C. 1935. [illegible]o new species of *Triturus* from California. Copeia, 1935(2):73-80.

———. 1941. Data on [illegible] life history of *Ambystoma tigrinum californiense* Gray. Copeia, 1941(1):1-4.

———. 1942. The specie[illegible]f Californian *Triturus*. Copeia, 1942(2):65-76.

VAN DENBURGH, JOHN. 189[illegible] [illegible]otes on the habits and distribution of *Autodax iëcanus*. Proc. Calif. Acad. Sci., 5(1):[illegible]3.

———. 1898. Herpetological [illegible]es. Proc. Amer. Philos. Soc., 37(157):139-41.

———. 1906. Description of a [illegible] species of the genus *Plethodon* (*Plethodon vandykei*) from Mount Rainier, Washin[illegible]n. Proc. Calif. Acad. Sci., 4(4):61-63.

———. 1912. Notes on *Ascaph*[illegible], the discoglossoid toad of North America. Proc. Calif. Acad. Sci., 3:259-64.

———. 1916. Four spe[illegible]es of s[illegible]manders new to the state of California, with a description of *Plethodon* [illegible] [illegible] species, and notes on other salamanders. Proc. Calif. Acad. Sci., 4th [illegible] 6([illegible]

VIOSCA, P. JR. 1923. An ecolo[illegible]cal [illegible]udy of the cold-blooded vertebrates of southeastern Loui[illegible] [illegible]opeia, 1923(115[illegible]

V[illegible] JR. 194[illegible] [illegible]a and flora of the El Segundo sand dunes. 13 Amp[illegible]ian[illegible] [illegible]d reptiles of the [illegible]. Bull. So. Calif. Acad. Sci., 41(1):29-38.

[illegible] G. S. 1938. A ne[illegible]d of *Plethodon vehiculus* (Cooper) from Vancouver, [illegible]itish Columbia. Copeia, [illegible]38[illegible]):89.

——— [illegible]1. Notes on the [illegible]story of *Ambystoma gracile* Baird. Copeia, 1941(1):14-17.

[illegible]EI[illegible]ER[illegible] C. K. 1945. Se[illegible] variation in the mental gland and reproductive organs [illegible]f th[illegible]e *Eurycea bis*[illegible]*ea*[illegible]. Copeia, 1945(2):78-84.

WHIP[illegible] [illegible]. L. 1906. [illegible] naso-labial groove of lungless salamanders. Biol. Bull., 11(1):1[illegible]

WIEGM[illegible]N, [illegible]. Herpetologische Beyträge. 1. Ueber die mexicanischen Kröten nebst Be[illegible]merkungen [illegible]er ihnen verwandte Arten anderer Weltgegenden. Isis von Oken, 1833(7):651-62.

WIGGINS, I. L. 1943. Additional note on the range of *Bufo canorus* Camp. Copeia, 1943(3):197.

WOLTERSTORFF, W. 1935. Über eine eigentümliche Form des kalifornischen Wassermolches, *Tarich torosa* (Rathke). Blätter Aquar. und Terrarienkunde, 46 (8):178-84.

WOOD, J. T. 1948. *Microhyla c. carolinensis* in an ant nest. Herpetologica, 4(6):226.

WOOD, W. F. 1934. Notes on the salamander, *Plethodon elongatus*. Copeia, 1934(4):191.

———. 1935. Encounters with the western spadefoot, *Scaphiopus hammondii*, with a note on a few albino larvae. Copeia, 1935(2):100-102.

———. 1936. *Aneides flavipunctatus* in burnt-over areas. Copeia, 1936(3):171.

WRIGHT, A. A. and A. H. WRIGHT. 1942. Handbook of frogs and toads (Ithaca, N.Y.: Comstock Publ. Co.), xi + 286 pp.

WRIGHT, A. H. 1914. North American Anura. Life-histories of the Anura of Ithaca, New York. Carnegie Inst. Wash., 197:vii + 98 pp.

———. 1929. Synopsis and description of North American tadpoles. Proc. U.S. Nat. Mus., 74(11):1-70.

———. 1932. Life histories of the frogs of Okefinokee Swamp, Georgia. (New York: Macmillan), xvi + 497 pp.

WRIGHT, A. H. and A. A. ALLEN. 1908. Notes on the breeding habits of the swamp cricket frog, *Chorophilus triseriatus* Wied. Amer. Nat., 42(493):39-42.

WRIGHT, A. H. and A. A. WRIGHT. 1949. Handbook of frogs and toads of the United States and Canada. (Ithaca, N.Y.: Comstock Publ. Co.), xii + 640 pp.

YOUNGSTROM, K. A. and H. M. SMITH. 1936. Description of the larvae of *Pseudacris triseriata* and *Bufo woodhousii woodhousii* (Anura). Amer. Midl. Nat., 17(3):629-33.

ZWEIFEL, R. G. 1949. Comparison of food habits of *Ensatina eschscholtzii* and *Aneides lugubris*. Copeia, 1949(4):285-87.

INDEX